D1309790

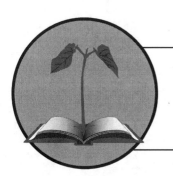

AGRI*books*
The Pearson Custom Publishing Program for **Agriculture**

Introduction to Plant and Soil Sciences

Pearson Learning Solutions

New York   Boston   San Francisco
London   Toronto   Sydney   Tokyo   Singapore   Madrid
Mexico City   Munich   Paris   Cape Town   Hong Kong   Montreal

Senior Vice President, Editorial and Marketing: Patrick F. Boles
Executive Marketing Manager: Nathan L. Wilbur
Senior Acquisition Editor: Debbie Coniglio
Operations Manager: Eric M. Kenney
Development Editor: Christina Martin
Editorial Assistant: Jeanne Martin
Production Manager: Jennifer Berry
Art Director: Renée Sartell
Cover Designer: Jenna Cutruzzula

Cover Art: Courtesy of Digital Vision, Ltd.

Copyright © 2011 by Pearson Learning Solutions
All rights reserved.

Permission in writing must be obtained from the publisher before any part of this work may be reproduced or transmitted in any form or by any means, electronic or mechanical, including photocopying and recording, or by any information storage or retrieval system.

Additional copyright information is included, where applicable, as a footnote at the beginning of each chapter.

This special edition published in cooperation with Pearson Learning Solutions.

Printed in the United States of America.

Please visit our web site at *www.pearsoncustom.com/custom-library/agribooks*.

Attention bookstores: For permission to return any unsold stock, contact us at *pe-uscustomreturns@pearson.com*.

Pearson Learning Solutions, 501 Boylston Street, Suite 900, Boston, MA 02116
A Pearson Education Company
www.pearsoned.com

ISBN 10: 0-558-60644-X
ISBN 13: 978-0-558-60644-2

Contents

I

The Art and Science of Crop Production

1 CROP PRODUCTION AS AN ART

Primitive people lived on wild game, leaves, roots, seeds, berries, and fruits.[1] As the population increased, the food supply was not always sufficiently plentiful or stable to supply their needs. Crop production began at least 9,000 years ago when domestication of plants became essential to supplement natural supplies in certain localities. The art of crop production is older than civilization, and its essential features have remained almost unchanged since the dawn of history. First, people gathered and preserved the seeds of the desired crop plants. In preparing the land, they destroyed other kinds of vegetation growing on the land and stirred the soil to form a seedbed. They planted when the season and weather were right as shown by past experience, destroyed weeds, and protected the crop from natural enemies during the growing season. Finally, they gathered, processed, and stored the products.

The early farmer cultivated a limited number of crops, the cereals being among the first to be grown in most parts of the world.[2] The same crop often was produced continuously on a field until low yields necessitated a shift to new land. This temporary abandonment of seemingly partly worn-out land has been almost universal in the history of agriculture. It is still practiced in some less-developed regions of the world but is rapidly decreasing. Pressure from population growth and dwindling land resources do not allow the abandonment of land today.

The primitive farmer removed by hand the destructive insects in fields and appeased the gods or practiced mystic rites to drive away the evil spirits believed to be the cause of plant diseases. With advancing civilization, materials such as sulfur, brine, ashes, white-wash, soap, and vinegar were applied to plants to suppress diseases or insects.

Cultivated plants are a product of human achievement and discovery that has enabled people to provide food and fiber needs with progressively less labor. The first successful domestication of plants is thought[3] to have occurred in Thailand in Neolithic times. Remnants of rice and broadbeans or soybeans from 10,000 years ago have been discovered. Emmer and barley specimens dating about 6750 BC were recovered at the Jarma site in Iran. Harlan[4] lists both the Middle East and Near East as centers and noncenters of agricultural origin.

Agronomic classification
Agronomy
Bionomial classification
   of plants
Botanical classification
   of plants
Catch crop
Cereal crop
Companion crop
Cover crop
Drug crop
Fabaceae
Fiber crop
Food supply
Forage crop
Genus
Grain crop
Grass
Human population
Legume
Malthusian theory
Oil crop
Plant life cycle
Plant origin
Plant variation
Poaceae
Pulse crop
Root crop
Rubber crop
Scientific name
Silage crop
Soiling crop
Species
Sugar crop
Trap crop
Tuber crop
Vegetable crop

From Chapter 1 of *Principles of Field Crop Production*, Fourth Edition, John H. Martin, Richard P. Waldren, David L. Stamp. Copyright © 2006 by Pearson Education, Inc. Published by Pearson Prentice Hall. All rights reserved.

Much of the record of early agriculture comes from the writings of Greek and Roman scholars such as Herodotus about 500 BC and Pliny about 50 AD. Hieroglyphs of harvest scenes and remains of plants and seeds in ancient tombs show an Egyptian agriculture as early as 5000 to 3400 BC with the cereal grains emmer and barley of major significance. This successful agricultural economy enabled rulers to construct pyramids and beautiful tombs and develop fine arts.

Romans of the first century AD intertilled crops with iron hand knives. In 1639, Wood wrote (New England Prospect) in great detail about the skillful use of "clamme shell hooes" used in maize fields to control weeds. Intertillage with animal power was advocated in England in the seventeenth century.

The value of lime, marl, manures, and green manures for the maintenance of soil productivity was recognized 2,000 years ago. Books on agriculture written by the Romans (Pliny, Varro, and Columella) around the first century AD describe the growing of common crops including wheat, barley, clover, and alfalfa by procedures very similar to those in use today. Much of the work was done with hand labor and the farm implements used were crude.[5] However, in the experimental nursery plots of present-day agronomists, as well as in thousands of home gardens and on the small farms of many lands, one sees crops being grown and harvested using hand methods almost identical with those followed by the slaves in the Nile Valley in the time of the pharaohs 6,000 years ago.

The old art of crop production still predominates in farm practices throughout the world. Plant pathologists and entomologists have found ways to control plant diseases and insect pests more effectively. Chemists and agronomists have found supplements for the manure and ashes formerly used for fertilizers. Rotations perhaps are slightly improved. Many new crop hybrids and varieties (cultivars) have been developed. The control of weeds with herbicides began in the twentieth century.

Improved cultural methods followed observations made by primitive farmers. They found better crops in spots where manure, ashes, or broken limestone had been dropped; where weeds were not allowed to grow; where the soil was dark, deep, or well watered; or where one crop followed certain other crops. Observations or empirical trials quickly revealed roughly the most favorable time, place, and manner of planting and cultivating various crops. These ideas were handed down through the generations. Observation, the only means of acquiring new knowledge until the nineteenth century, continued to enrich the fund of crop lore. Eventually, the exchange of ideas, observations, and experiences, through agricultural societies and rural papers and magazines, spread the knowledge of crop production.

2 CROP PRODUCTION AS A SCIENCE

Agronomy is the branch of agriculture that studies the principles and practice of crop production and field management. The term was derived from two Greek words *agros* (field) and *nomos* (to manage). Scientific research in agronomy may be said to have begun with the establishment of the first experiment station by J. B. Boussingault in Alsace in 1834 and was given further impetus by Gilbert and Lawes who established the famous research facility at Rothamsted, England, in 1843 to study fertilizer use. It was 1870 before such tests were undertaken in the United States at the land grant agricultural colleges. However, long before these landmark efforts were launched, many empirical tests had established numerous facts about crops and soils.

Agronomy has been a distinct and recognized branch of agricultural science only since about 1900. The American Society of Agronomy was organized in 1908. Agronomy had its origins largely in the sciences of botany, chemistry, and physics. Botanical writings describing crop production began with the ancient Greeks.

Theophrastus of Eresus, who lived in about 300 BC, was given the name "Father of Botany." This student of Aristotle listed plant differences that distinguish between monocots and dicots, gymnosperms and angiosperms, and described germination, development, and annual growth rings. He also mentioned "dusting" (pollination) of date palms, which first demonstrated sexuality in plants. Botanical writings continued by herbalists in monasteries and medical practitioners were concerned chiefly with the use of plants for medicinal purposes. It was not until the twelfth century that interest in plants evolved to modern systematic botany and later to other plant sciences. Chemistry had its origin in ancient mystic alchemy and in the work of people who compounded medicines. Lavoisier, often called the father of chemistry, did his work in the second half of the eighteenth century. The application of chemistry to agriculture dates from the publication of the book by Sir Humphry Davy entitled *Essentials of Agricultural Chemistry* in 1813. Physics arose from ancient philosophies. Agricultural engineering is largely applied physics.

The science of agronomy was developed by coordination of knowledge derived from the natural and biological sciences with written records of observations and empirical trials. Later, controlled experiments that dealt with crop production were conducted.

Better crop production results from the use of new knowledge, improved machines, use of pesticides, and the development of superior cultivars. Informed farmers in advanced communities quickly adopt these improvements. This is evident from the worldwide acceptance of hybrid cultivars of corn, sorghum, and sugarbeet, of dwarfed types of rice, wheat, grain sorghum, and sunflower, and of farm mechanization, fertilizers, and chemical pesticides. This results in sharp decreases in the labor expended to produce crops (Figure 1). Improvements in crop production from research and invention often arrive after long and painstaking trials.

Crop production today is rapidly changing from historic times. Farm machines speed up the process or enable the producer to better accomplish tasks. Electronic technology enables the producer to manage fields on a site-specific basis (Figure 2), and biotechnology is changing the very genetic makeup of the plants grown. There has been more advancement in crop science since the start of the twentieth century than in all of recorded history preceding it.

▨ 3 POPULATION AND FOOD SUPPLY

Crop culture will always be an important industry because crop products are essential to the existence of humans. It has been stated that a person who goes without food for 24 hours will quarrel; one who is denied food for 48 hours will steal; and one who is without food for 72 hours will fight. Thus, the difference between peace and anarchy in most countries is a matter of only a few days without food.

Farm Labor Hours In United States

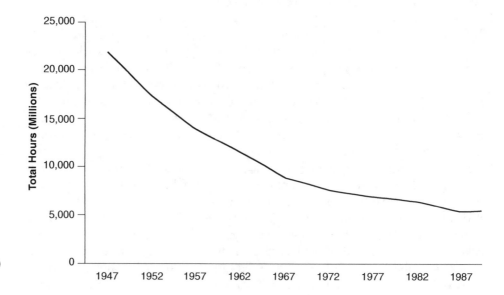

FIGURE 1
Labor used to produce crops has steadily declined as farms become more efficient. [United Nations FAO Statistical Database]

FIGURE 2
Using Global Position System equipment on the farm for precise application of fertilizer, pesticides and herbicides. [Courtesy USDA NRCS]

3.1 Malthusian Theory

Aristotle and Plato agreed that the population of a civilized community should be kept within bounds. Thomas R. Malthus raised the problem of sufficient food for a population that continues to increase in a world of limited land area again in 1798.[6]

He argued that people could increase subsistence only in arithmetic progression, whereas human population tended to increase in geometric progression (i.e.,

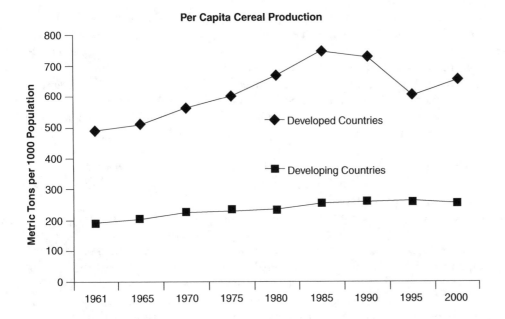

Per Capita Cereal Production

FIGURE 3

Cereal production has increased faster than the population in more developed countries but has barely kept up in lesser developed countries. [United Nations FAO Statistical Database]

by the compound-interest law). So far, Malthus's predictions have not been realized because modern technology has increased production beyond levels predicted even 100 years ago. The basic check on population increase is the maximum limit set by the food supply. Population was formerly contained within that limit by war, famine, pestilence, and premature mortality. This will again occur unless the less-developed populations reduce their birth rate and increase their farm productivity.

The human population at the beginning of the Christian Era has been estimated at roughly 250 million. The aggregate world population doubled to about 500 million by 1650. It doubled again to 1 billion in only 200 years, or by 1850. The United Nations estimate of the world population only 100 years later, in 1950, was 2.4 billion people. It reached 4 billion in 1973 and 6 billion by 2000.

The production of cereal grains that comprise the base of the food supply has exceeded population growth in the United States and other advanced countries (Figure 3). This resulted from increased production and lower birth rates. In recent years, per capita production has declined slightly but developed countries still produce a surplus that is exported to other countries.

The Malthusian Theory has suffered setbacks since 1798.[7] Sometimes food production has outrun population growth in a few countries, following political schemes to inflate farm commodity prices. Despite this, one-third to one-half of the world population suffers at times from malnutrition, hunger, or both and one-sixth is chronically malnourished (United Nations Population Fund, 1999). Areas of the world experiencing the most rapid population increases are Latin America, Asia, Africa, and Oceania. Oceania is the only area of the four capable of excess food production on a relatively predictable basis. FAO reported that in 1998, 62 percent of the world population was in developing countries, where economic growth is slow and large majorities of the people are illiterate and poverty stricken.

Yields of grain crops have increased significantly in the United States since 1900, but there is a limit beyond which increases are impossible. Additional land for increasing production is limited. While the area of potentially arable land is three times the area harvested in any one year (The World Food Problem, White House, May 1967), more than half of this untilled land lies in the tropics. Such land usually requires clearing, drainage, heavy fertilization, new plant varieties, and pest control for successful crop production. Much of it is tropical rain forest and there is increasing concern about the long-term ecological ramifications of clearing those forests, particularly as it affects species extinction and global warming.

In Asia, there is little additional potentially arable land except by irrigation development. It is estimated that in southern Asia over 200 million additional acres (81 million ha) could be irrigated.

Crop yields in Asia are currently being increased by improved short-stem varieties of rice and wheat and by improved maize and sorghum hybrids with expanded geographic adaptation.

Cereal grains are a suitable common denominator for food production, consumption, and trade. On a calorie basis, cereals account for an average of 53 percent of human food in the world by direct consumption. Probably another 20 percent of human food comes indirectly from cereals in the form of meat, dairy products, and eggs.[8] Diets of most of the people in the underdeveloped countries remain appallingly inadequate, primarily due to shortages of animal proteins. The nutritional quality of the diet is usually considered unsatisfactory when more than 80 percent of the calories are derived from cereals, starchy roots, and sugar. For the world as a whole, food supplies for adequate nutrition will need to be greatly expanded.[9, 10]

3.2 Means for Increased Food Production

Agronomists, as well as all other agriculturists, are confronted with the problem of providing food for a world population that continues to grow at an accelerated rate. Underdeveloped countries of Asia, Africa, and Latin America are now in a deficit position with respect to food production for their own populations. World food production can be augmented by expansion of the cultivated land area or by increased yields on present agricultural land (Figure 4). Aside from conventional

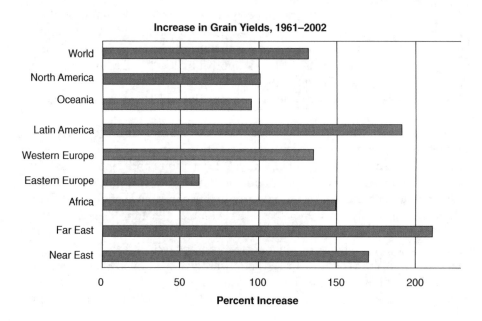

FIGURE 4

Grain yields have more than doubled in most parts of the world since 1961. [United Nations FAO Statistical Database]

agricultural means, food supplies may also be increased by the synthesis of foods and by the culture of certain lower plant forms such as yeast or chorella.

In traditional agriculture, new land was plowed by the peasant or farmer for increased food production. This simple means of expansion of arable land is seldom possible today. Many countries of the world are now essentially fixed-land economies.[5] Roughly 3,400 million acres (1,379 million ha) or about 10 percent of the total world land area is classified as arable land, fallow, and orchards. Another 7,400 million acres (3,000 million ha), or 19 percent of the total, is used for grazing or permanent vegetation. The remainder of the world land area, or about 70 percent, produces little or no food.[8, 11] Potential total arable land has been estimated at about 6,600 million acres (2,700 million ha).

Increased world grain yields (Figures 5 and 6) were achieved by growing more productive varieties and hybrids, greater fertilizer use (Table 1 and Figure 6), and other improvement practices. Increases in Asia, Oceania, and Latin America (Figure 4) are largely a result of new wheat and rice varieties and increased fertilizer use. Increased agricultural production has kept pace with population growth in many less-developed countries (Figure 3). However, these countries are not increasing production enough to provide the increases in food supply necessary to improve their diets.

Higher yields involve technology (applied science) plus capital. Probably 90 percent of the increase in world food production since 1950 has come from higher yields on present agricultural land. Improved crops, fertilizers, irrigation, drainage, pesticides, more effective farm implements, multiple cropping, fallow, improved cultural practices, or some combination of these can increase yields. One of the preconditions for a yield increase usually is literacy of the rural population.[5,12,13] World cereal-grain yields increased about 140 percent between 1961 and 2002 (Figure 4). The area of land irrigated on farms in the United States increased from about 20 million acres (8 million ha) in 1944 to 53 million acres (21 million ha) in 1997, with resulting increases in crop yields.

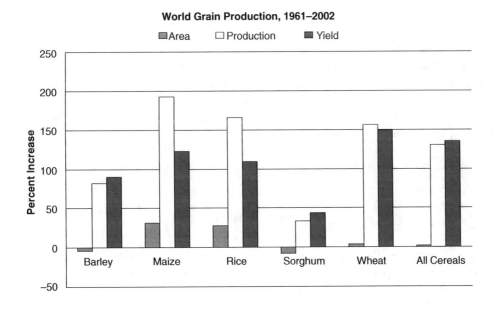

FIGURE 5

Changes in world production and yield of cereal crops from 1961 to 2002. [United Nations FAO Statistical Database]

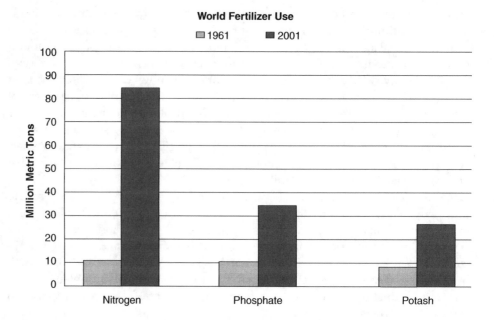

World Fertilizer Use

□ 1961   ■ 2001

FIGURE 6

Comparison of world consumption of N, P_2O_5 and K_2O from 1961 to 2001.
[United Nations FAO Statistical Database]

TABLE 1 Consumption of N, P_2O_5, and K_2O by Geographic Location (100 Metric Tons)

	N			P_2O_5			K_2O		
	1948–49 1952–53	1970–71	2001	1948–49 1952–53	1970–71	2001	1948–49 1952–53	1970–71	2001
World	43,086	316,077	819,696	60,514	206,423	330,495	45,027	165,380	227,106
Europe	18,999	96,748	136,347	25,527	81,456	40,831	25,334	74,846	48,412
North America	12,075	74,765	137,861	21,343	59,100	50,807	13,032	39,929	50,345
Latin America	1,160	14,073	51,960	616	3,464	38,941	549	6,905	35,659
Near East	938	8,003	39,665	178	1,838	13,044	51	371	3,310
Far East	6,172	40,187	428,367	2,500	12,829	159,288	1,626	12,382	78,898
Africa	325	4,752	25,057	1,344	6,856	9,248	277	2,342	5,055
Oceania	174	1,629	13,167	4,691	10,160	16,746	154	1,954	3,897

Source: FAO Statistical Database

World application of major fertilizer nutrients (N, P_2O_5, and K_2O) increased by percentages of 600, 206, and 161, respectively, between 1961 and 2001 (Figure 6). However, there are limits to further increases in yields from conventional inputs such as fertilizers. One possible avenue to further increase production is through the increased utilization of native crops grown in less-developed regions of the world. For example, genetic improvements to pearl millet, a staple grain crop in parts of Africa, are currently where corn improvement was in the 1930s.[14]

■ 4 ORIGIN OF CULTIVATED PLANTS

All basic cultivated plants were probably derived from wild species. However, the exact time and place of origin and the true ancestry of many crops is still as highly speculative as the origin of humans. Most crop species were adapted to the needs of people before the dawn of recorded history. Evidence from archeology and ancient writings support the early origin of most present-day crop plants.[3] The centers of origin of both agriculture and culture were in populated areas favored by a more or less equable climate.[1] Vavilov[15] predicted the center of origin of a crop by finding the region where the greatest diversity of type occurred in each crop plant. However, some plants appear to have originated in two or more centers or over wide zones.[16] DeCandolle[17] concluded that 199 crops originated in the Old World and 45 in the Americas. The crop plants peculiar to the Western Hemisphere include maize, potato, sweet potato, field bean, peanut, sunflower, Jerusalem artichoke, and tobacco. Eurasia yielded wheat, barley, rye, rice, pea, certain millets, soybean, sugarbeet, sugarcane, and most of the cultivated forage grasses and legumes. Sorghum, cowpea, yam, pearl millet, finger millet, and teff were domesticated in Africa. Cotton originated in both American hemispheres.

■ 5 VARIATION IN CULTIVATED PLANTS

Cultivated plants have undergone extensive modifications from their wild prototypes as a result of the continuous efforts of people to improve them. The differences between cultivated and wild forms are largely in their increased usefulness to humans, due to such factors as yield, quality, and reduced shattering of seed. Through the centuries, people selected from many thousands of plant species the few that were most satisfactory to their needs and which, at the same time, were amenable to culture. Primitive people were masters in making these selections, and modern times have added little of basic importance.

All cultivated plants were divided by Vavilov into two groups: (1) those such as rye, oats, and vetch that originated from weeds, and (2) fundamental crops known only in cultivation. Cultivated rye is believed to have originated from wild rye that even today is a troublesome weed in wheat and winter barley fields in certain parts of Asia. Oat is said to have come into culture as a weed found among ancient crops such as emmer and barley. Maize is known only in cultivation.

■ 6 SPREAD OF CULTIVATED PLANTS

In their migrations, people invariably have taken their basic cultivated plants with them to insure a permanent food supply and to support their culture. This occurred in prehistoric as well as in recorded times. People also transported weeds, diseases, and insect pests along with the crops. Pre-Columbian American agriculture was based strictly on plants and animals native to America. None of the many plants involved were known in Europe or Asia prior to 1492, nor were cultivated plants native to Eurasia known in America before that time.[1]

■ 7 CLASSIFICATION OF CROP PLANTS

Crop plants may be classified on the basis of a morphological similarity of plant parts.[16, 18, 19] From an agronomic standpoint, they may be partly classified on the basis of use, but some crops have several different uses.

7.1 Agronomic Classification

Cereal or Grain Crops: Cereals are grasses grown for their edible seeds. The term *cereal* can be applied either to the grain or to the plant itself. They include wheat, oat, barley, rye, rice, maize, grain sorghum, millets, teff, and Job's tears. *Grain* is a collective term applied to cereals. Buckwheat is used like a grain, but it is not a cereal. Quinoa *(Chenopodium quinoa)* is grown for its edible seeds in the Andes highlands of South America.

Legumes for Seed (Pulses): These include peanut, field bean, field pea, cowpea, soybean, lima bean, mung bean, chickpea, pigeonpea, broadbean, and lentil.

Forage Crops: Forage refers to vegetable matter, fresh or preserved, utilized as feed for animals. Forage crops include grasses, legumes, crucifers, and other crops cultivated and used for hay, pasture, fodder, silage, or soilage.

Root Crops: Crops designated in this manner are grown for their enlarged roots. The root crops include sugarbeet, mangel, carrot, turnip, rutabaga, sweet potato, cassava, and yam.

Fiber Crops: The fiber crops include cotton, flax, hemp, ramie, phormium, kenaf, and sunn hemp. Broomcorn is grown for its brush fiber.

Tuber Crops: Tuber crops include the potato and the Jerusalem artichoke. A tuber is not a root; it is a short, thickened, underground stem.

Sugar Crops: Sugarbeet and sugarcane are grown for their sweet juice from which sucrose is extracted and crystallized. Sorghum as well as sugarcane is grown for syrup production. Dextrose (corn sugar) is made from corn and sorghum grain.

Drug Crops: The drug crops include tobacco, mint, wormseed, and pyrethrum.

Oil Crops: The oil crops include flax, soybean, peanut, sunflower, safflower, sesame, castor, mustard, rape and perilla, the seeds which contain useful oils. Cottonseed is an important source of oil, and corn and grain sorghum furnish edible oils.

Rubber Crops: The only field crop grown in the United States that has been used for rubber is guayule, but other plants such as koksagyz (Russian dandelion) have been tested.

Vegetable Crops: Potato, sweet potato, carrot, turnip, rutabaga, cassava, Jerusalem artichoke, field pumpkin, and many of the pulses are utilized chiefly as vegetable crops.

7.2 Special-Purpose Classification

Cover Crops: Cover crops are those seeded to provide a cover for the soil. Such a crop turned under while still green would be a *green manure* crop. Important green manure crops are the clovers, alfalfa, the vetches, soybean, cowpea, rye, and buckwheat.

Catch Crops: Catch crops are substitute crops planted too late for regular crops or after the regular crop has failed. Short-season crops such as millet, sunflower, and buckwheat are often used for this purpose.

Soiling Crops: Crops cut and fed green, such as legumes, grasses, kale, and maize, are soiling crops.

Silage Crops: Silage crops are those preserved in a succulent condition by partial fermentation in a tight receptacle. They include corn, sorghum, forage grasses, and legumes.

Companion Crops: Sometimes called nurse crops, companion crops are grown with a crop such as alfalfa or red clover in order to secure a return from the land in the first year of a new seeding. Grain crops and flax are often used for this purpose.

Trap Crops: Planted to attract certain insect or phanerogamous parasites, trap crops are plowed under or destroyed once they have served their purpose.

■ 8 BOTANICAL CLASSIFICATION OF CROP PLANTS

8.1 Method of Botanical Classification

Botanical classification is based upon similarity of plant parts. Field crops belong to the Spermatophyte division of the plant kingdom, in which seeds carry on reproduction. Within this division, the common crop plants belong to the subdivision of angiosperms, which are characterized by having their ovules enclosed in an ovary wall. The angiosperms are divided into two classes, the monocotyledons and the dicotyledons. All the grasses, which include the cereals and sugarcane, are monocotyledonous plants. The legumes and other crop plants except the grasses are classified as dicotyledonous plants because the seeds have two cotyledons. These classes are subdivided into orders, families, genera, species, subspecies, and varieties (cultivars).

8.2 Families of Crop Plants

Most field crops belong to two botanical families, the grasses *(Poaceae)*, and the legumes *(Fabaceae)*.

THE GRASS FAMILY The grass family includes about three-fourths of the cultivated forage crops and all the cereal crops. They may be annuals, winter annuals, or perennials. Grasses are almost all herbaceous (small, nonwoody) plants, usually with hollow cylindrical stems closed at the nodes.[20,21] The stems are made up of nodes and internodes. The leaves are two-ranked (alternate) and parallel-veined. They consist of two parts—the sheath, which envelops the stem, and the blade. The roots are fibrous. The small, greenish flowers are collected in a compact or open inflorescence, which is terminal on the stem. The flowers are usually perfect, small, and with no distinct perianth. The grain or caryopsis may be free, as in wheat, or permanently enclosed in the floral bracts (lemma and palea), as in oat.

THE LEGUME FAMILY Legumes may be annuals, biennials, or perennials. The leaves are alternate on the stems, pedicillate, with netted veins, and mostly compound. The flowers are almost always arranged in racemes as in the pea, in heads as in the clovers, or in a spike-like raceme as in alfalfa. The flowers of field-crop species of legumes are papilionaceous or butterfly-like. The irregular flowers consist of five petals: a standard, two wings, and a keel that consists of two petals more or less united. The calyx is normally four or five toothed. The fruit is a pod that contains one to several seeds. The seeds are usually without an endosperm, the two cotyledons being thick and full of stored food. Legumes have taproots. Often, the roots have abnormal growths called nodules caused by the activities of a bacterium, *Rhizobium,* which has the ability to fix atmospheric nitrogen and supply it to the host plant. Eventually, surplus nitrogen is left in the plant residues.

The principal genera of legume field crops, all of which belong to the suborder Papilionaceae, are: *Trifolium* (clovers), *Medicago* (alfalfa, burclovers, and black medic), *Glycine* (soybean), *Lespedeza, Phaseolus* (field bean), *Pisum* (field pea), *Melilotus* (sweetclovers), *Vigna* (cowpea), *Vicia* (vetches), *Stizolobium* (velvetbean), *Lupinus* (lupines), *Crotalaria, Lotus* (trefoils), and *Pueraria* (kudzu).

OTHER CROP FAMILIES Among the other botanical families that contain crop plants are: *Cannabaceae* (hops and hemp), *Polygonaceae* (buckwheat), *Chenopodiaceae* (sugarbeet, mangel, and wormseed), *Cruciferae* (mustard, rape, canola, and kale), *Linaceae* (flax), *Malvaceae* (cotton), *Solanaceae* (potato and tobacco), and *Compositae* (sunflower, Jerusalem artichoke, safflower, and pyrethrum).

8.3 Binomial System of Nomenclature

In a botanical classification, each plant species is given a binomial name. Binomial names are sometimes called botanical names or scientific names. This provides two names for a plant: the genus and species. The binomial system of nomenclature is founded upon the 1753 publication of *Species Plantarum* by Swedish botanist Carl Linneaus. A letter or abbreviation indicates the name of the botanist who first proposed the accepted name. For example, the letter *L* following the botanical name of corn or maize (*Zea mays* L.) means that Linneaus named it. Letters and abbreviations associated with binomial names have been omitted to improve readability.

The binomial system provides a practically universal international designation for a plant species, which avoids much confusion. Some crops (e.g., proso millet and roughpea) are known by several different common names in the United States but are immediately identifiable by their botanic names. Corn is called maize in most of the world outside North America.

A species is a group of plants that bear a close resemblance to each other and usually produce fertile progeny when intercrossed within the group. Nearly every crop plant comprises a distinct species or, in some cases, several closely related species of the same genus. Within a species, the plants usually are closely enough related to be interfertile. Interspecies crosses are infrequent in nature, but many of them have been made artificially.

Varietal (cultivar) names are sometimes added to the species name to make them trinomial, but ordinarily crop varieties are given a common name or serial number to designate them. Classifications of agricultural varieties have done much to standardize variety names. The American Society of Agronomy has adopted a rule to use a single short word for a variety (cultivar) name, and the variety is not to be named after a living person. That society also registers properly named improved varieties of several field crops.

8.4 Life Cycles

The life cycles of plants provide us with a simple yet universal means of plant classification. All higher plants can be classified as summer annuals, winter annuals, biennials, or perennials. A summer annual is a short-lived plant that completes its entire life cycle from seed to seed in a single growing season and then dies. A winter annual utilizes parts of two growing seasons in completing its life cycle. Winter annuals are planted in the fall and are vernalized during the fall and winter after which they produce seed and die the following summer. A biennial on the other hand normally utilizes two complete growing seasons to complete its life cycle. Vegetative growth occurs during the first season resulting in a rosette form of growth. This is then followed by flowering and fruiting, a process known as bolting, which occurs in a second growing season. A stalk emerges from the center of the rosette and a flowering inflorescence forms on the terminal end of the stalk. Perennials have an indefinite life period. They do not die after reproduction but continue to grow indefinitely from year to year.

▣ 9 THE LEADING FIELD CROPS

World production of the principle field crops (exclusive of forage crops) is shown in Table 2 and Figure 7. Wheat, rice, corn (maize), soybean, barley, sorghum, and millet occupy the largest areas. These seven crops account for approximately 75 percent of the total. The acreage, yield, and production of the different field crops in the United States and Canada are shown in Tables 2, 3, and 4. Corn, wheat, soybean, alfalfa, and sorghum occupy the largest acreages of specific crops. Soybean, grain sorghum, corn, wheat, and alfalfa production has increased markedly since about 1940. The production of buckwheat, syrup sorghum, cowpea, and broomcorn continues to decline. Former domestic crops that apparently are no longer grown include fiber flax, teasel, hemp, and chicory.

The total land area in the United States is about 2,264 million acres (917 million ha). Less than half of this area, 932 million acres (377 million ha), was in farms in 1997. Of this, 431 million acres (174 million ha) were classed as cropland (Table 5). The total area for grazing was 492 million acres (199 million ha), not counting the harvested cropland in grains and forages that were grazed for part of the season or after harvest. There has been a steady decline in farmland over the years from expansion of urban areas, roadways, and other uses (Table 5). According to the USDA's 1997 National Resources Inventory, an average of 3.2 millions acres (3 million ha) of forest, cropland, and open space were converted annually to urban and other uses from 1992 to 1997. An average of 4 million acres (567,000 ha) was converted from 1982 to 1992. Texas and Pennsylvania had the biggest development rate increases, followed by Georgia, Florida, North Carolina, California, Tennessee, and Michigan.

TABLE 2 Area, Production, and Yield of the Principle Crops, Except Forages, in the World and the United States in 1999 (FAO Statistical Database)

Crop	Area Hectares (Millions)		Production (Million Metric Tons)		Yield (Metric Tons per Hectare)	
	World	USA	World	USA	World	USA
Wheat	213.8	21.9	583.9	62.8	2.7	2.9
Rice	153.1	1.5	588.8	9.6	3.8	6.6
Maize	139.9	28.7	604.4	242.3	4.3	8.4
Barley	57.6	1.9	133.6	6.1	2.3	3.2
Sorghum grain	45.9	3.4	68.1	15.2	1.5	4.4
Millets	37.0	0.1	28.6	0.2	0.8	1.5
Oats	13.8	1.0	26.1	2.1	1.76	2.1
Rye	10.0	0.2	20.3	0.28	2.0	1.8
Buckwheat	2.7	0.04	2.8	0.04	1.0	1.1
Soybeans	71.9	29.5	154.9	72.8	2.1	2.4
Peanuts (in shell)	24.8	0.6	32.8	1.7	0.9	2.9
Dry beans	26.9	0.8	19.4	1.4	0.7	1.9
Dry peas	6.1	0.1	11.3	0.3	1.9	2.1
Cowpeas	7.5	0.0	3.2	0.0	0.4	0.9
Lentils	3.4	0.07	3.0	0.1	0.8	1.5
Vetch	1.1	0.0	1.0	0.0	0.9	
Lupins	1.5	0.0	1.5	0.0	1.1	
Cottonseed	33.9	5.4	54.7	9.3	1.6	1.7
Rapeseed (canola)	27.1	0.4	42.2	0.6	1.5	1.4
Sunflower seed	24.5	1.5	28.8	2.3	1.2	1.6
Linseed	3.5	0.5	2.7	0.2	0.8	1.1
Sesame seed	6.2	0.0	2.4	0.0	0.4	
Castor	1.3	0.0	1.2	0.0	0.9	0.0
Tobacco	4.6	0.3	7.0	0.57	1.5	2.1
Potatoes	17.6	0.6	288.5	21.8	13.3	37.3
Sweet potatoes/yams	9.0	0.03	156.4	0.6	22.9	17.1
Sugarcane	19.6	0.4	1276.9	34.1	65.3	85.3
Sugarbeets	6.8	0.6	259.8	30.3	38.1	49.1

The labor required in 1971 to produce the major field crops, except tobacco, was only ⅙ to ¹⁄₁₉ of that required in the 1910–1914 period. Labor has continued to decrease as farms get larger and more mechanized (Figure 1). Yields of crops have increased tremendously since 1900 as a result of increased fertilizer and pesticide use, more irrigation, more productive cultivars, improved cultural practices, timelier field operations, and shifts of many of the crops to more productive areas or to areas where they could be produced more economically with less labor.

The use of chemical pesticides is not the only method for controlling diseases and insects. Breeding crops for resistance to diseases began after 1890 and is a much expanded and necessarily continuous enterprise today. Selection and breeding for resistance to insects has been in progress for about 80 years. Sex

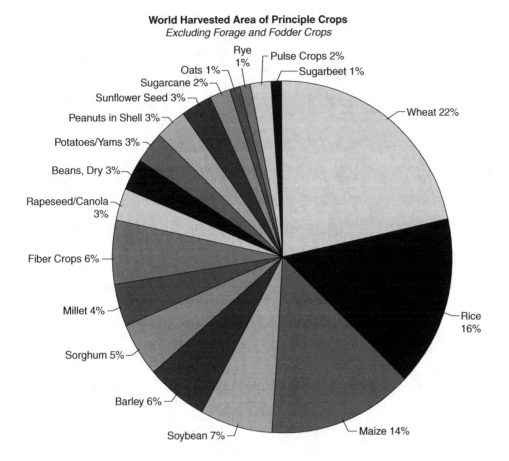

World Harvested Area of Principle Crops
Excluding Forage and Fodder Crops

Rye 1%
Pulse Crops 2%
Oats 1%
Sugarbeet 1%
Sugarcane 2%
Sunflower Seed 3%
Peanuts in Shell 3%
Wheat 22%
Potatoes/Yams 3%
Beans, Dry 3%
Rapeseed/Canola 3%
Fiber Crops 6%
Millet 4%
Rice 16%
Sorghum 5%
Barley 6%
Soybean 7%
Maize 14%

FIGURE 7
Wheat, rice, and maize are grown on over one-half of the cropland in the world. [United Nations FAO Statistical Database]

attractants are being developed to permit sterilization of male insects by radiation. Other attractants are used as baits for trapping insects. Natural enemies of insect pests and disease organisms and viruses may help to control some pests. Natural defenses are being incorporated into existing hybrids and cultivars using biotechnology. It will be many years, if ever, before pesticides can be replaced for protecting all farm crops. Chemicals are not the only hazard to mankind. Sunshine, in excess, can cause sunburn, skin cancer, and sunstroke, but we cannot live without it.

Destructive insects were a problem before the beginning of agriculture in an area. The following item, dated July 19, 1806, appears in the diary of Captain Wm. Clark while in Montana en route east from the Pacific Coast: ". . . emence sworms of grass hoppers have destroyed every sprig of grass for many miles on this side of the [Gallatin] river."[22]

Even as late as 1951 to 1960, losses in various crops ranged from 3 to 28 percent from plant diseases, 3 to 20 percent from insects, and 3 to 17 percent from weed competition. This justified greater pesticide use. Current fertilizer use has not restored the fertility levels of most of the virgin soils. Water pollution has been present since the earth was created, as is evident from the considerable amounts of mercury present deep in the Greenland icecap. Many other countries are modernizing their agriculture along lines similar to those in North America.[9, 10]

TABLE 3 Acreage, Production, Yield, and Principle States of Farm Crops in the United States in 2000–2003

Crop	Harvested Acreage (1,000)	Acre Yield	Production (1,000)	Leading States
Corn				
Grain (bushel)	70,419	137	9,624,576	IA, IL, NE, MN, OH
Silage (ton)	6,469	16	103,000	WI, NY, CA, PA, MN
Sorghum				
Grain (bushel)	807	56	439,129	TX, KS, NE, AR, MO
Silage (ton)	345	10	3,564	TX, KS, SD, NE, AZ
Oat (bushel)	2,130	62	131,855	ND, MN, SD, WI, IA
Barley (bushel)	4,571	58	267,281	ND, ID, MT, WA, MN
Wheat (bushel)				
Winter	33,113	43	1,139,728	KS, OK, WA, TX, OH
Spring	13,953	36	497,000	ND, MN, MT, SD, ID
Durum	2,984	31	92,490	ND, MT, AZ, CA, SD
Rye (bushel)	287	27	7,756	OK, GA, ND, SD
Rice (pound)	3,139	6,500	20,406,475	AR, CA, LA, MS, TX
Soybean (bushel)	72,550	37	2,705,551	IL, IA, MN, IN, NE
Flaxseed (bushel)	595	19	11,119	ND, MT, MN, SD
Peanut (pound)	1,338	2,801	3,751,850	GA, TX, AL, FL, NC
Cotton (pound)	13,058	725	8,747,520	TX, GA, MS, CA, AR
Alfalfa (ton)	23,578	3.2	79,307	CA, SD, IA, MN, WI
Other hay (ton)	39,310	1.9	76,354	TX, MO, KY, TN, OK
Dry bean (pound)	1,489	1,657	2,474,500	ND, NE, MI, MN, CA
Sugarbeet (ton)	1,348	23	30,605	MN, ID, ND, MI, CA
Sugarcane (ton)	998	35	34,503	FL, LA, HI, TX
Sunflower (pound)	2,392	1,255	3,019,915	ND, SD, KS, MN, CO
Canola (pound)	1,324	1,340	1,773,399	ND, MN
Buckwheat (bushel)	161	19	2,985	ND, WA, MN, NY, PA
Potato (100 wt)	1,250	367	459,045	ID, WA, WI, ND, CO
Proso millet (bushel)	463	21	10,460	CO, NE, SD

Source: USDA National Agricultural Stastistics Service

■ 10 FUTURE INCREASES IN PRODUCTIVITY

"Give a man a fish and he can live for a day; teach him to fish and he can live forever!" This philosophy, from an ancient Chinese proverb, is reflected in the growing realization that less-developed countries of the world must have the desire to succeed in modernizing agriculture. Leaders of these nations must make an effort to provide the multiple factors involved in modernizing agriculture with help, where available and necessary, from outside.

Several promising research developments are pointing toward continued future increases in productivity:

1. Collection of plant species and broadening of germplasm bases
2. Improved breeding techniques including the use of biotechnology

TABLE 4 Acreage, Production, and Yield of Crops in Canada in 2002 (FAO Statistical Database)

Crop	Harvested (1,000 Ha)	Production (1,000 Mt)	Yield (Kg/Ha)
Wheat	8,836	16,198	18,332
Barley	3,348	7,489	22,369
Oats	1,379	2,911	21,110
Rye	77	134	17,442
Mixed grains	132	359	27,231
Corn for grain	1,283	8,995	70,111
Corn for forage	220	6,356	289,163
Soybeans	1,024	2,335	22,811
Buckwheat	12	12	10,252
Rapeseed	3,262	4,178	12,810
Mustard seed	255	154	6,056
Sunflower seed	95	157	16,638
Sugarbeets	10	345	341,287
Potatoes	171	4,697	274,816
Linseed	633	679	10,726
Canary seed	214	164	7,645
Beans, dry	215	225	18,930
Chickpeas	154	157	10,182
Lentils	561	354	9,144
Broad beans, dry	5	9	17,500

TABLE 5 Land Utilization on Farms in the United States in 1969 and 1997 (USDA NASS)

Number of Farms	1969 2,858,051	1997 1,911,859
	Million Acres	
Cropland		
Harvested	300	309
Fallow or crop failure	36	21
Crop failure	NA	3
Cover crops or idle	51	33
Pastured	88	65
Total	475	431
Woodland—not grazed	50	42
Farmsteads, roads, waste	25	32
Grazed area		
Grassland pasture	452	397
Woodland pasture	62	30
Conservation or wetlands reserve	NA	30
Total land in farms	1,176	932

3. Crop physiology advances in understanding plant efficiency in utilization of light and nutrients
4. Interactions between plant breeders, geneticists, soil chemists, engineers, etc., are increasingly bringing together the best of many disciplines
5. Extension of areas of adaptation of previously restricted varieties
6. Improved disease and insect control with advances in chemical and biological methods
7. Improved protein quality factors such as high lysine corn
8. Improved medication and breeding principles in livestock
9. Reduced production costs of nitrogen fertilizer
10. Improved winter hardiness of varieties to extend crop production

These are but a few of the areas in which progress is being made. A combination of enhanced agricultural production and population control to achieve subsistence must be a primary goal of all peoples of the world.

REFERENCES

1. Merrill, E. D. "Domesticated plants in relation to the diffusion of culture," *Bot. Rev.* 4 (1938): 1–20.
2. Heiser, C. B., Jr. *Seed to Civilization*, San Francisco: Freeman, 1981.
3. Flannery, K. V. "The Origins of Agriculture." *An. Rev. of Anthropology*. 2: 271–310. An. Reviews Inc., Palo Alto, Cal. 1973.
4. Hitchcock, A. S., and Chase, A. "Manual of the grasses of the United States," *USDA Misc. Pub.* 200, 1950, pp. 1–1051.
5. Brown, L. R. "Increasing world food output," *USDA Foreign Agricultural Economic Rpt.* 25, 1965, pp. 1–140.
6. Malthus, T. R. *An Essay on the Principle of Population, 1798–1803*. Reprint New York: Macmillan, Inc., 1929, pp. 1–134.
7. Borlaug, N. E. *Mankind and Civilization at Another Crossroad*. Madison, Wis.: Wise. Agri-Business Council, Inc., 1971, pp. 1–48.
8. Brown, L. R. "Man, land, and food," *USDA Foreign Agricultural Economic Rpt.* 11, 1963, pp. 1–153.
9. Aldrich, D. C. *Research for the World Food Crisis*. Washington, D.C.: AAAS, 1971, pp. 1–320.
10. *Agricultural Research: Impact on Environment. IA State University Spec. Rpt.* 69, 1972, pp. 1–84.
11. Cook, R. C. "Population and food supply," *Freedom from Hunger Campaign, FAO Basic Study*, 7 (1962): 1–49.
12. Army, Thomas J., Frances A. Greer, and Anthony San Pietro. *Harvesting the Sun; Photosynthesis in Plant Life*. New York: Academic Press, 1967.
13. Columella, L. Junius Moderatus. *Of Husbandry* (translated into English with several illustrations from Pliny, Cato, Varro, Palladius, and other ancient or modern authors), London, 1797, pp. 1–600.
14. National Research Council. *Lost Crops of Africa, Vol. I: Grains*. Washington, D.C.: National Academy Press, 1996.
15. Vavilov, N. I., and D. Love. *Origin and Geography of Cultivated Plants*. London: Cambridge University Press, 1992.

16. Harlan, J. R. "Agricultural origins: Centers and non-centers," *Science* 174, 4008 (1971): 468–74.

17. De Candolle, A. *Origin of Cultivated Plants*, 2nd ed. New York: Hafner, (reprint), 1959, pp. 1–468.

18. Hitchcock, A. S. *A Text Book of Grasses*, New York: Macmillan, Inc., 1914, pp. 1–276.

19. Pawley, W. H. "Possibilities of increasing world food production," *Freedom from Hunger Campaign, FAO Basic Study* (1963): 1–231.

20. Schooley, J. *Introduction to Botany,* Stamford, CT: Delmar, 1997.

21. Theophrastus. *Enquiry into Plants.* Translated by Sir Arthur Hort. New York: Putnam, 1916.

22. Lewis, Merriwether, and William Clark. Edited by Elliott Coues. *The Journals of Lewis and Clark.* New York: F. P. Harper, 1893.

Agricultural Production Systems

PURPOSE

Crops are produced by farmers in various parts of the world according to certain production packages suited to the region and the socioeconomic situation. In this chapter, basic production systems in use around the world are discussed. Organic crop production is also discussed.

EXPECTED OUTCOMES

After studying this chapter, the student should be able to:

1. Define and describe a natural ecosystem.
2. Compare a natural ecosystem with an agroecosystem.
3. Discuss the components of a crop production system.
4. Discuss plant communities in crop production and their response to competition.
5. Discuss the nature, advantages, and disadvantages of crops grown in monocultures and polycultures.
6. Discuss the role of agroforestry practices in crop production.

KEY TERMS

Agroecosystem	Biodiversity	Monoculture
Agroforestry	Crop rotation	Polyculture
Allelopathy	Ecosystem	Relay cropping
Antagonism	Intercropping	

From Chapter 11 of *Principles of Crop Production: Theory, Techniques, and Technology*, Second Edition, George Acquaah.
Copyright © 2005 by Pearson Education, Inc. Published by Pearson Prentice Hall. All rights reserved.

To the Student

Crop production involves managing production resources (e.g., crop cultivars, land, and water) within a given socioeconomic system. Crops are grown as populations of plants. These populations are organized in two basic ways: only one crop at a time on the same land season after season or different crops in one season on the same land. Each approach has pros and cons. As you study this chapter, pay attention to the role of crop diversity and technology in crop production systems. Farmers grow crops as plant stands or populations in various production regions using certain production packages. Plants interact with each other and with the environment during production. Farmers use various technologies along with natural resources to increase crop productivity. Modern crop production depends heavily on agrochemicals to protect plants and to increase soil fertility. Excess agrochemicals find their way into the general environment where they pollute groundwater. Pesticides enter the food chain through animals feeding on contaminated plants and the use of toxic products to protect food crops in the field and the storehouse. As you study this chapter, visualize the farm as a giant organism comprised of biotic components (animals, plants) and abiotic components (soil, environment) that are managed or manipulated by humans (farmers) in an economically sustainable and environmentally sound fashion.

1: What Is a Crop Production System?

A *production system* is a mix of crop(s), natural resources, and socioeconomic factors employed in the production of an agricultural product. Crop production entails the management of (1) inputs, (2) biological processes, and (3) sources of depletion of production resources for productivity. The importance of each of these three basic elements of crop production depends on the farm and the farming system.

1.1 INPUTS

Primary production inputs in crop production are seed (or appropriate propagating material), water, fertilizers, labor, pesticides, and energy. The amount of these external inputs depends on the nature of the operation. Some production systems are labor-intensive; others are mechanized and chemical-intensive.

1.2 BIOLOGICAL PROCESSES

Photosynthesis is the single most important plant physiological process in crop production. Other biological processes that interact in crop production include natural nutrient cycling, biological nitrogen fixation, biological control, and mycorrhizae effects on phosphorus uptake by plants. Cultivars differ in their capacities to conduct these physiological activities. Genetic factors are thus important in crop production. They determine climatic adaptation, resistance to pests, and efficiency in using nutrients and water.

1.3 DEPLETION OF INPUTS

Modern conventional crop production requires repeated inputs for high productivity because the inputs are depleted during production. Natural nutrient cycling, important in sustainable agriculture, is "leaky" and thus experiences losses. Some of the depletion is desirable and planned. Crops are planted to remove soil nutrients and convert them into

---

Terminology: Farming practices, methods, and systems

A *farming practice* is the way a farmer conducts a specific production activity, such as pesticide application or fertilizer application. A *method of farming,* on the other hand, is the systematic way in which the farmer achieves a particular production function, such as crop stand establishment. A *farming system* is an approach to farming that integrates farming methods, practices, technologies, knowledge, and expertise, coupled with the specific goals and values of the producer.

---

products. Other factors, such as leaching, fixation, and erosion, deplete soil of its nutrients in ways that are uneconomical. The producer as a manager should implement practices that eliminate or reduce negative and wasteful activities.

2: Natural Ecosystem Versus Agroecosystem

How is crop production like the operation of an ecosystem? In crop production, living organisms interact with their environment under human supervision. *Ecology* is the study of how living things relate to their environment. In terms of the kinds of groupings of organisms in a given area, there are two terms that need defining. A group of individuals of one species occurring at one location constitutes a *population.* A population may be described based on a simple count (number) of individuals, the number of individuals per unit area (density), and the total mass of individuals (biomass) at the location.

The occurrence of living organisms (biotic factors) and nonliving organisms (abiotic factors) interacting with each other in a specific location constitutes an **ecosystem**. The abiotic factors in an ecosystem are light, temperature, water, soil, and air. These factors determine how plant species are distributed in the ecosystem. Ecosystems are naturally self-sustaining (Figure 1). This is possible through three mechanisms: photosynthesis, energy flow through food chains, and nutrient recycling. Photosynthesis is the process by which plants capture and convert light energy into chemical energy. Plants in the ecosystem are called *producers.* They provide food for the herbivorous animals in the system, which are called *primary consumers.* They are, in turn, preyed on by other organisms such as flies, ticks, and leopards (called *secondary consumers*). When producers and consumers die, their organic matter is broken down by microorganisms (bacteria and fungi) called *decomposers.* They cause the organic minerals to be converted into inorganic forms for recycling for plant use, a process called *mineralization.* In an **agroecosystem**, farmers and ranchers constitute the fourth group of players. They are manipulators (or managers) of the ecosystem for producing agricultural products.

In natural ecosystems, a biological balance is created by a diversity of networks of interacting plants and animals in a dynamic equilibrium. The component species are adapted to the prevailing environment. Further, each is a source of food for others. The species survive or escape their competitors and natural enemies. Each ecological niche in the natural ecosystem is occupied in both time and space. Disease epidemics are uncommon under such conditions where there is environmental stability.

On the other hand, a typical agricultural system (agroecosystem) operates in a manner that is counter to the mechanics of biological balance. In modern crop production, especially in developed economies, farmers frequently grow one crop at a time, a practice

Ecosystem. A living community and all the factors in its nonliving environment.

Agroecosystem. The population of selected plants and/or animals growing at a location and interacting with biotic and abiotic environmental factors under the management and supervision of humans.

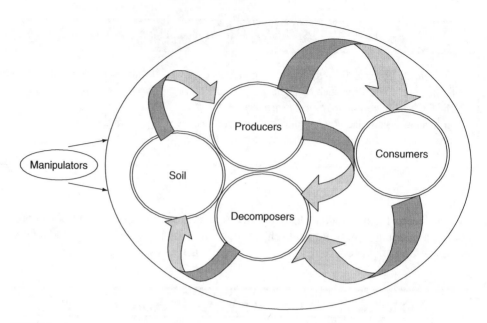

FIGURE 1 A conceptual model of a natural ecosystem. Natural nutrient cycling and other natural cycles sustain the ecosystem. Producers (plants) extract nutrients from the soil to make products. When they die, their organic matter is decomposed and chemicals mineralized into inorganic forms that can be reabsorbed by plants. Some products may be used by consumers who, upon dying, release the nutrients back into the soil through the processes of decomposition. These interactions occur within an environment that involves a hydrologic cycle and various gaseous exchanges between plants and animals and the larger environment. The ultimate source of energy in the ecosystem is sunlight, which is used in making food by producers through photosynthesis. The activities of manipulators (humans) impact both natural ecosystems as well as agroecosystems. The thinning of forests by logging, forest fires, and dam construction impact ecosystems.

called *monoculture*. This severely restricts the advantage of diversity. Further, this single genotype is not adapted to the environment well enough to survive without human intervention. Crop producers have to protect their crops from competitors and supplement the nutrients in the environment as needed.

The use of modern production inputs (pesticides, tillage, etc.) and other production practices creates empty niches, resulting in increased frequency of diseases. Modern agricultural production is filled with shocks (e.g., changes in production practices such as irrigation, seeding rate, and tillage) that can upset the balance in the agroecosystem.

To restore biological balance in an agroecosystem, the crop producer may use adapted and disease-resistant cultivars and practices that increase soil organic matter. Changing planting dates and introducing antagonists of pathogens are helpful strategies.

A critical aspect of an ecosystem is natural cycling and interdependency of all its components. On the contrary, modern production systems either bypass or exclude certain key components of natural ecosystems. The consequence is lack of, or limited cycling of, nutrients (Figure 2). Modern producers are hence compelled to resort to expensive maintenance of soil fertility through the continuous addition of artificial chemicals. The consequence of the intensive use of chemicals is pollution of the environment. In order to limit the inputs into modern agriculture, production practices should encourage natural cycling of nutrients, as advocated by the concept of sustainable agriculture.

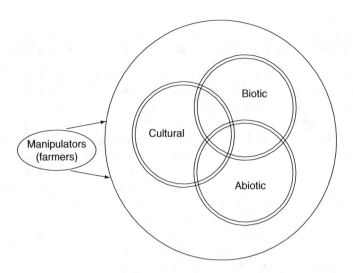

FIGURE 2 A conceptual model of an agroecosystem. There is limited nutrient cycling as the crop is harvested for use elsewhere, and consumers do not recycle the nutrients from where they were extracted. Agroecosystems, hence, depend on humans for additional nutrients and other cultural inputs. Further, participants in an agroecosystem are not selected by nature and hence are not necessarily compatible. Through the use of technology, agro-ecosystems can be designed to overcome natural barriers to growth and development. For example, through irrigation, crops can be produced in arid regions. In crop production, farmers manipulate the production environment through agronomic practices (irrigation, pesticide use, fertilization) to produce crops and raise farm animals.

Like natural ecology, the concept of agroecology (or crop ecology) describes attempts by humans (manipulators) to nudge nature to their advantage, rather than having a balance that favors all components in an ecosystem. Agroecologists utilize technologies to enhance and work with nature to increase productivity of the crop of their choice.

3: CROP FARMS AND FIELDS ARE AGROECOSYSTEMS

An agroecosystem is complex in its structure, embracing many agricultural technologies. Agricultural production started as a largely mechanical-based operation in which machines were developed to replace human labor. This reduced the tedium in field production. Modern crop production depends heavily on the use of agrochemicals to manage weeds, insect pests, and diseases and to improve soil fertility. The next step in the evolutionary trend in agriculture was to emphasize the biological aspects of crop production. The goal of this was to reduce the chemical component of modern crop production, which is the chief source of criticism of modern agriculture.

In terms of a scientific basis, an agroecosystem should have three basic technologies: *mechanical, biological,* and *chemical.* However, for sustainability, an agroecosystem should consider the additional dimensions of social, economic, and environmental factors. A sustainable crop production system should be environmentally responsible, being operable with minimal environmental consequence. It should be socially acceptable.

Ecosystem and the balance of nature

An ecosystem is constituted by living organisms interacting with one another and with factors in their non-living environment. The non-living components of an ecosystem include physical and chemical factors such as light, water, air, soil, and temperature. Plants vary in their requirement for these factors, which consequently affect their distribution in the ecosystem. Plant distribution is also influenced by their interaction with the biotic community. Natural ecosystems are self-sustaining through food manufacture by plants (by photosynthesis), energy flow (by the food chain), and nutrient recycling (through microbial activities in natural cycles).

Light is the ultimate source of energy in the ecosystem. This energy is harnessed by plants (called *primary producers* or *autotrophs*) and converted to energy-storing molecules. Some animals (e.g., cows and sheep) feed directly on plants to obtain this energy. These animals are called *primary consumers* and are food for *secondary consumers* such as lions and other flesh-eaters. Consumers are *heterotrophs* (unable to synthesize their own food and dependent on others). When these three categories of ecosystem components die, the nutrients in their bodies are recycled primarily by the action of bacteria and fungi *(decomposers)* that decompose dead organic matter. Producers and consumers interact to form food chains in which producers are at the bottom. Organisms in the community feed on those below and are in turn preyed on by those above in the chain. The length and complexity of a food chain are variable, since most organisms have multiple sources of food and are in turn food for a number of consumers. Different food chains may link together to produce a *food web*. Energy moves in the ecosystem in the form of a pyramid. The farther away one is from the source (producer), the less energy obtained from the food.

Once an ecosystem has stabilized (attained a natural balance), it becomes self-sustaining. Population explosion is eliminated because every organism has its natural enemy.

Humans are capable of profoundly impacting ecosystems. Their role is both as consumers and manipulators. Through technology and general knowledge of the operation of an ecosystem, humans are able to manipulate the system to their advantage.

Unacceptable social costs associated with modern production include soil erosion and its attendant problems of silting of rivers and reservoirs, deterioration of wildlife habitats, and loss of soil fertility. Silting of water systems is corrected at a cost to society. Municipal water is treated at extra cost if it becomes polluted. Further, changes in crop production practices and farming systems affect farm resource use and eventually farm populations. In this regard, rural communities are most vulnerable.

Production practices and farming systems should be economically viable. Farm profitability is key to a crop production enterprise. Producers will embrace new methods only if they are profitable. Some aspects of profitability stem from government policies and decisions that producers have to comply with in order to benefit from various economic assistance programs. Programs such as the Conservation Compliance Provision and the Conservation Reserve Program of the 1985 Food Security Act were designed to protect U.S. natural resources from deterioration from field production activities.

Crop production is a high-risk operation. Field production is subject to the vagaries of the weather. Profitability is affected by prices of agricultural products, consumption patterns, and global economic patterns. Producers, naturally, make choices that they deem less risky and in their interest. Managerial skill is essential to success in production. Sustainable agriculture does not focus on removing or overcoming natural obstacles to production. Rather, through skillful management, the producer uses innovation to determine the best system to implement, considering the natural resources available. In this regard, no one best system is suitable for all farms.

In effect, an agroecosystem is a purposive (goal-oriented) system. It responds differentially under different environments. However, the producer is able to change goals under a constant environment, or the producer can pursue the same goals in different environments by adopting different behaviors. An agroecosystem is a creation of the knowledge, skills, attitudes, and values of the creator.

A key differentiating factor between the natural ecosystem and an agroecosystem is the human (management) element. An agroecosystem exists because someone willed it into existence. As a purposeful system, it contains human elements (or subsystems) that interact with the other components (physical, biological) within the context of an environment. Physical, biological, socioeconomic, and cultural factors characterize this environment.

Agroecosystems differ also in productivity, stability, and sustainability. Management or manipulators are the key factor in determining the productivity (or yield) of an agroecosystem. Stability (usually of yield of a crop) of an agroecosystem is the amount of variation that occurs around the dynamic equilibrium of this characteristic. There are many factors that cause the variability (e.g., pests, weather factors). A third attribute of an agroecosystem is sustainability. Field crop production is prone to stress in the production environment. Stress may be in the form of, for example, erratic rainfall. The crop producer as a manager of production resources may intervene by providing supplemental moisture (through irrigation). If unseasonable weather brings about excessive moisture, surface runoff or erosion might be a problem. A crop ecosystem in which groundcover occurs would be more resistant to soil erosion forces. The sustainability of a field crop agroecosystem is a measure of the difficulty with which the producer manages production resources to minimize stresses for high crop productivity. A *sustainable system* is one that requires minimal and continuous economical and management inputs to manage productivity constraints.

4: PLANT POPULATIONS (AND MIXTURES) AND COMPETITION

How important is spacing among plants in crop production? Plants growing together in a crowded space compete for growth factors. Crop production entails the planting of crop plant populations, of like or dislike plants, depending on the cropping system. When there is crowding, plants in populations tend to encroach upon each other's demands for growth resources. *Competition,* or *interference,* is a crowding phenomenon of plant populations whereby component plants interact in response to physical growth factors—namely, water, nutrients, light, oxygen, and carbon dioxide. These factors all affect photosynthesis, the key to crop productivity. Space is a factor of competition especially in root crops. Competition arises because the supply of resources at a production site is less than the collective ability of closely spaced plants to use them.

Competition, or interference, among plants may also arise as a result of the phenomenon of **allelopathy**, the release of chemical compounds from a plant or its residue. This interference suppresses the growth of other plants in the immediate vicinity.

Crowding response in plants is mostly indirect and manifested through changes in the crop environment. One plant, for example, may aggressively deplete the soil of water, causing the nearest plant to find insufficient amounts of water for growth. Plant response to competitive stress may be classified into three phenomena: *density-dependent mortality, plastic response,* and *hierarchy of exploitation.* Density-dependent response results in reduction in plant density (number of plants per unit area). Plastic response occurs when plants under competitive stress reduce in size of vegetative parts or number of yield components. This results in decreased crop yield. Hierarchy of exploitation occurs between

Allelopathy. The process by which one plant species affects other plant species through biologically active substances introduced into the soil, either directly by leaching or exudation from the source plant, or as a result of the decay of the plant residues.

Models of agriculture

The primary goal of agriculture is to manage photosynthesis to produce food and fiber for humans. The manipulation of photosynthesis is done according to one of two general models: *industrial* and *sustainable*.

Industrial model

The *industrial model* of agriculture (also called the *conventional model*) considers agriculture as an industrial enterprise in which farms are factories and fields the production plants. The products that are made (production units) may be animals or grain. The producer acquires and uses production inputs to make specific products. Fresh inputs are acquired for each production cycle. The prevailing philosophy is one of a *component approach* to crop production, whereby the producer focuses on individual farming practices and methods. An industrial plant is designed for a specific production practice, where components are assembled to make a product. In the industrial model of crop production, obstacles to production are removed through the use of innovative technologies. The natural environment is modified or controlled (e.g., controlled environment agriculture in a greenhouse). Control also makes it potentially possible for steady progress to occur.

Sustainable ("holistic") model

The philosophy of the *sustainable model* of agriculture is that agricultural production should be viewed from a *whole systems* perspective. It emphasizes the need for producers to conduct their agricultural activities in harmony with the biosphere. This holistic system model promotes *working with* rather than *controlling* or subjugating nature. The natural resource base of agricultural production should be conserved and protected; the environment should also be protected. In effect, the producer, in this approach, focuses more on managing the internal resources (natural resources) of the farm (or agroecosystem) rather than on production inputs that are purchased and introduced into production.

Conventional versus sustainable agriculture

Conventional agriculture is the term for the predominant farming practices, methods, and systems of crop production adopted by producers in a region of production. In technologically advanced regions, these production systems are generally capital-intensive and chemical-dependent. Crop productivity is significantly increased but at a cost to the environment and human health. Agrochemicals build up in the environment and pollute groundwater and the air. Chemical residues in food are health hazards to humans and animals.

Sustainable agriculture seeks to increase crop productivity without the adverse effects to the environment and society as a whole. Since this is a concept that emphasizes a goal rather than a set of practices, producers adopt various farm-based innovations to accomplish the general goal. The innovative aspect of sustainable agriculture comes about because there is no one correct way to arrive at the general goal. This is because each producer's farming situation is different, regarding soils, climate, cropping system, method of production, and market needs.

Sustainable agriculture

The traditional purpose of agriculture is production of food and fiber for society. To this end, traditional agron-

Monoculture. The cropping system in which a single crop is repeatedly cropped on the same piece of land season after season.

Polyculture. The cultivation of more than one crop species on the same piece of land in various temporal and spatial patterns.

unidentical genotypes in competition when one is better able to exploit growth factors than the other(s).

As previously indicated, field crops are cultivated populations of plants. Agronomists manage these populations. There are two basic types of cultivated **monocultures** and *mixed cropping*, or **polycultures**. These types differ in genetic content and structure (in terms of density, spacing pattern, plant size, and stage of development). Agroecosystems are dynamic, being subjected to change from intervention of human managers (farmers) and changes in weather factors. They intensify and change because managers perceive opportunities or simply change their perception of the current status of the crop omy focuses on removing physical and biological constraints to production. The natural environment is modified or controlled so that crop production is orchestrated according to a schedule that theoretically makes unlimited production possible. Agriculture is evolving in a direction that views crop production within an ecological context, as already stated. The trend is not to control but to farm in harmony with the biosphere. There is a holistic approach in which crop production is conducted in an environmentally responsible manner. Production practices are selected to complement and accommodate the factors in the production environment.

This systems approach to production is called *sustainable agriculture*. This has given rise to different kinds of terminology that generally describe the same concept. These include *organic farming, alternative agriculture, biological agriculture, regenerative agriculture, reduced input agriculture, ecological farming,* and *environmentally sound agriculture*. Notwithstanding the name, the concept describes strategies of achieving synergy for production by integrating several practices. These practices are not new; they are combined strategically such that crop production is enhanced while the natural resource base is protected for posterity.

The goals of sustainable agriculture are

1. Increased profitability of crop production
2. Natural resource conservation in crop production
3. Use of environmentally prudent farming systems in crop production.

Sustainable agriculture is a dynamic concept that emphasizes a goal rather than a set of production practices. *Alternative agriculture*, on the other hand, describes the process of on-farm innovation adopted by crop producers toward achieving the goal of sustainable agriculture.

Sustainable agriculture is also called *limited (or low) input sustainable agriculture (LISA)*, a terminology that is sometimes incorrectly thought of as low-technology production. On the contrary, sustainable agriculture calls for the use of the best production technology in a productive, cost-effective, and environmentally responsible manner. Crop producers as managers combine scientific know-how with on-farm resources for highest possible productivity and without adverse environmental consequence or depletion of natural resources. An important objective of sustainable agriculture, however, is to limit the intervention of the crop producer through the use of agrochemicals. Instead, it encourages the production environment to be self-sustaining like an ecosystem. The sustainable agricultural model is founded on the concept of agroecology. Natural processes and production technologies are integrated to develop a particular production system. The sustainable farmer must be knowledgeable to be able to develop a site-specific, integrated, and sustainable system of production.

In conventional crop production, there is intensive crop management and specialization. On the other hand, sustainable agriculture depends on biological interactions and diversification for success. On-farm cycles that are managed in sustainable agriculture include crop rotations, nitrogen fixation, genetic resistance in crops, and several others. This dichotomy is not always as clear cut as presented. There are transitions between these models.

ecosystem. The market dynamics may bring about changing profitability of a production enterprise. The agricultural producer then makes decisions to change production inputs (e.g., fertilizer, cultivars) to respond to prices of products.

Two important attributes of agroecosystems of economic importance to the producer or manager are stability and sustainability of yield. Yield stability is a measure of homeostasis. Sustainability, on the other hand, measures the difficulty the crop producer faces as he or she attempts to manage production resources in response to production constraints. If the management required is not economical or practical, the agroecosystem is deemed unsustainable.

5: MONOCULTURE

Why is monoculture a popular crop production system in industrialized economies? Monoculture is at one extreme of the cropping systems spectrum. Crop production in industrialized societies is primarily monoculture. This method of production is characterized by the planting of only one cultivar on a large acreage (Figure 3). The land is often flat and readily amenable to mechanization, which is used at all stages of crop production. Monocultures are input-intensive, depending on agrochemicals (fertilizers and pesticides) for high productivity. Plants in this system feed at the same level in the soil and draw the same nutrients. Pests associated with the crop tend to build up, necessitating the intensive use of pesticides to manage them.

Monocultures are cultivated populations that consist of only one species. Monocultures may experience interspecific competition. Biomass accumulation in monocultures is exponential in pattern. This pattern is modified by plant density; the lag-phase shortens as density increases. Competition among plants in a population sets in after a certain period of no interaction, when seedlings have adequate growth resources. The onset of interference occurs as plants increase in size. In the early growth, plants have equal mass. The mass then begins to vary according to intensity and duration of interference. Spacing of field crops is selected such that the plants are ideally crowded to maximize the environmental resources. Under this ideal plant density, no plant dies or becomes unproductive. Individual plants experience less than the optimal yield possible if they had unlimited resources. However, as a population, the yield is optimized.

In crop production, plants that have large adult size are widely spaced at planting. This low plant density means initially the ground cover is low, encouraging weed infestation while crop cover develops. Plant competition sometimes has casualties. Where plant spacing is close (high density), as occurs in the seeding of grasses and forage legumes, smaller plants become crowded out of the population. This competition-induced mortality is called *self-thinning*. This phenomenon is useful in nature but undesirable in crop production, since it wastes soil nutrients; plants use some of it, only to die eventually.

FIGURE 3 Monoculture of cotton. (Source: USDA)

Another plant response to competition is *morphological plasticity*. Certain genotypes have the capacity to adjust their size at different plant densities and still be productive. Plants that tiller, like small grains (wheat, barley, oats), are able to attain the same number of heads and final yield over a wide period of planting densities. Modern corn cultivars, on the other hand, have been bred to be single-stalked (uniculmn) or with minimum tillering. As such, corn is unable to maintain final yield over a wide range of planting densities, as opposed to wheat. Corn loses plasticity above a certain maximum seeding rate.

Morphological plasticity is one of the reasons that seeding rates vary widely among crops. The seeding rates, row widths, and plant spatial arrangements are determined based on the degree of plant plasticity. Several patterns of spatial arrangement are used in crop production. The most efficient arrangement (that reduces overshading) depends on plant structure and morphology. Hexagonal arrangement favors plants such as sugar beet that display their foliage in a circle around the axis. Row cropping (rectangular arrangement) suits crops such as corn, cotton, sorghum, and sunflower.

5.1   ADVANTAGES OF MONOCULTURE

The advantages of monoculture include the following:

1. Industrialized nations have the technology and know-how to grow crops in monoculture.
2. Monocultures are responsible for producing very large quantities of food that feed the world.
3. Diversity can be introduced into monoculture by practices such as crop rotations and cover cropping.
4. Monocultures are easier to manage. The producer has to contend with one set of practices, rather than different sets for different crops.

5.2   DISADVANTAGES OF MONOCULTURE

The disadvantages of monoculture include the following:

1. The production activity is susceptible to pests and disaster. Pest outbreak can wipe out the entire enterprise, since all plants are equally susceptible to a particular pest.
2. There is no insurance against adversity (weather-related or pests).
3. Lack of diversity means the presence of a fewer number of natural enemies of the pests that plague the crop. Further, the crop enterprise has less capacity to rebound from a temporary environmental stress.

6: POLYCULTURE

Crop production, especially in developing economies, involves different kinds of crop combinations, simultaneously cultivated on the same site. Growing different kinds of crops on the same piece of land is called *polyculture, mixed cropping,* or simply *mixtures* (Figure 4). Some of these mixtures involve unlike genotypes of the same species or different species.

Polycultures are most common in the tropics (Africa, Asia, and Latin America). Why is this so? Polycultures are associated with small-scale, subsistence agriculture. For example, corn and cowpea are often grown in association. There is diversity in crop cultivars

FIGURE 4 Polyculture involving corn and soybean. (Source: USDA)

planted. Operations are not mechanized, depending on draft and human labor as sources of farm energy. Subsistence agriculture is generally low-input, with minimal or no use of agrochemicals. Natural methods are depended upon for improving soil fertility. Most production under this system is rain-fed.

Planting crop mixtures is common in forage production where legume-grass combinations are frequently grown. Interspecies mixtures experience interspecific competition that is brought about by mechanisms similar to those that prevail in monocultures. The severity of the competition depends upon the differences between the species in the mixture regarding plant size, growth habit, and response of plants to weather factors.

Donald is credited with developing the principles of competition among plants in mixtures. His four basic principles governing plant association in mixtures are

1. Mixtures generally yield less than the higher-yielding pure culture.
2. Mixtures generally yield more than the lower-yielding pure culture.
3. Mixtures generally yield less than the average of the two pure cultures but may yield more.
4. Evidence of cooperation (or mutual benefit) among plants in mixtures is not widespread; there is little evidence that mixtures exploit the environment better than pure cultures.

Exceptions to these general principles exist. Oat-barley mixtures are found to be highly productive. Mixed grain production strategy results in yield stability, especially in a variable land environment.

Three basic interactions occur among unlike plants cohabiting in time on the same plot as the proportions of the species are varied. As one species is progressively introduced into a pure culture of a second species, one of two types of competitive interaction, *complementation* or competition, may develop progressively.

6.1   COMPLEMENTATION

Two or more species planted as mixed cultures are said to complement each other if they perform better in mixtures than in pure stand. This phenomenon may arise by one of two mechanisms. The two species may acquire resources from different spaces in the growing environment. This cohabitation is called *niche differentiation* (different space). Species with different root morphologies may feed at different depths of the soil and have niche differential for water. Legume-cereal mixtures have niche differentiation for nutrients, especially nitrogen. Legumes can utilize atmospheric nitrogen while non-legumes depend on soil nitrogen. Apart from spatial difference, niche differentiation may occur through temporal difference. Producers may maximize the use of production resources through planting practices whereby multiple crops are produced in one growing season. For example, planting cool season and warm season forages together extends the production season.

6.2 COMPETITION

If the total yield of the two species is less than either pure culture, the interaction is described as antagonistic or competitive. Mixtures or blends of cultivars of cereal crops, grain crops, and forage crops have been developed to improve crop yield stability. When genetically very similar lines derive from a series of crosses with disease resistance lines and backcross to a common parent, the product is called *multi-line*. Jenkins proposed the multi-line concept. The product has yield stability derived from different genes for disease resistance introduced from the crosses. Hierarchy of exploitation is the response to competition in which mixtures of two species or two cultivars of the same species display an *aggressor-suppressed* relationship. One component in the mixture, the aggressor, is more successful in exploiting the environment to the detriment of the other component. The aggressor uses up a disproportionate amount of the nutrients, light, water, and other growth factors in the environment. In forage mixtures, the producer can manipulate the hierarchy of exploitation by adopting certain management practices that favor one component of the mixture. For example, the application of nitrogen fertilizers to a legume-grass mixture may enhance the vegetative growth of a non-aggressive grass to the extent that it outcompetes the legume for light.

Polycultures have several distinct advantages:

1. The genetic heterogeneity may slow the dispersal and spread of diseases and insect pests if susceptible host plants are interspersed with resistant plants. One component species may have the capacity to serve as a trap crop for insects.
2. Mixtures have yield stability because of the diversity in genotypes.
3. Multiple cropping systems provide insurance against total crop failure, in case of environmental adversity.
4. For subsistence producers, multiple cropping enables the farmer to plant a variety of crops to provide a good balance in diet.
5. Resource-use efficiency can be maximized. The production is integrated.

The disadvantages of polycultures include

1. The genetic diversity that may provide defense against diseases and insect pests may also increase these problems. The greater diversity in hosts may also mean greater diversity of pests and diseases, especially soil-borne problems.
2. Crop rotations are used to control soil-borne diseases in monocultures. This strategy is not practical in mixtures.
3. Planting and harvesting operations are complicated by the diversity of plants. Mechanization is restrictive.
4. Agronomic management is complex; fertilization, irrigation, and pest control are difficult to implement.

7: TYPES OF POLYCULTURE

There are different ways of combining crops and sequence of planting crops in polyculture. Examples of specific polycultures that are used in crop production include mixtures, **intercropping**, strip cropping, *overlap planting (e.g. relay cropping, double cropping, nurse crop),* and **crop rotation**. **Agroforestry** practices are polycultures that include trees and shrubs.

7.1 MIXTURES

Growers may plant different varieties of crops in mixtures or a mixture of different species. Put another way, crop mixtures range from growing multi-lines (diversity at single genotype level) to agroforestry (diversity at the plant order level). Multi-lines represent a mixture of genotypes that are identical except at a specific trait locus. Diversification is the key characteristic of mixtures. When cultivar mixtures are grown, the population enjoys diversification in desired resistance genes as well as a combination of other mutually complementary traits that are not found in any one genotype. Producers may mix agronomically compatible fodder crop species (e.g., different cereal species or legume-cereal combinations). Mixture components may be selected such that they mature at the same time and can be harvested together (e.g., a combination of winter wheat and winter field beans or spring oats and peas). In a legume plus cereal mixture, the harvested crop can be separated into the components during processing.

Crop monocultures are successful in achieving maximum yield in high-input production at near-optimal environmental conditions. Monocultures are suited for risk-averse, highly profitable, non-sustainable agricultural production systems in which environmental considerations are not a high priority. However, when producing crops under more sustainable conditions that are suboptimal for maximum yield, crop mixtures have proven to be superior to monocultures. Under these less optimal environmental conditions, mixtures are able to better exploit all the resources through enhanced crop plasticity to provide greater yield and quality stability. Crop plasticity enables mixtures to perform appreciably in more marginal and higher-risk environments. The producer with good management can increase profitability and lower the risk of the enterprise by reducing production inputs. Mixtures can also be produced under the high input, near-optimal production environments.

7.2 INTERCROPPING

Intercropping is the crop production practice in which one crop is planted in the open areas of another. The goal of this planting format is to increase *land equivalent ratios* (the amount of monoculture land area needed to produce the same amount of polyculture yield). This simultaneous cropping system may not have any competitive interaction at all. It may be used in the early years of establishing an orchard when the tree cover is low. The open spaces can be cropped to annuals until the tree cover is fully established.

Intercropping systems are common in developing countries, especially in the tropics. There are different versions of intercropping systems. Crops may be planted in organized, alternating rows; grouped in different sections of the field; or planted in haphazard fashion. For best success, the plants to be intercropped must be judiciously selected to reduce interplant competition. It is best if the crops fill different niches so they can better use resources in the production environment (e.g., include annuals and perennials, shallow and deep-rooted plants, legumes and non-legumes). These combinations represent complementary associations.

Intercropping. The crop production system in which one crop is planted in the open space of another.

Relay cropping. The cropping system in which one crop is seeded into another standing crop that is near harvesting.

Crop rotation. A planned sequence of crops growing in a regularly recurring succession on the same piece of land.

Agroforestry. The simultaneous cultivation and management of trees and agricultural crops or livestock in various spatial and temporal patterns to optimize productivity of the land and protect natural resources, among other benefits.

FIGURE 5 Contour strip cropping. (Source: USDA)

7.3 STRIP CROPPING

Strip cropping is used by some farmers in the United States and other regions of the world. This is a practice in which strips of different crops are planted at intervals within the crop in the same field (Figure 5). It is an effective and inexpensive method of controlling soil erosion. Three main types of strip cropping are in use—contour, field, and buffer strip cropping. In *contour strip cropping,* alternative strips of row crops and soil-conserving crops (e.g., sods) are grown on the same slope or elevation perpendicular to the wind direction or water flow. If soil is dislodged from the row crops by erosive forces, some of it becomes trapped in the dense soil-conserving strip. It is applicable to short slopes of up to about 8% steepness. In *field strip cropping,* strips of a uniform width are located across the general slope of the land, while in *buffer strips,* strips of grass or legumes are laid between contour strips of crops in irregular rotations.

7.4 OVERLAP PLANTING SYSTEMS

In *overlap planting systems,* two or more species overlap for portions of their lifecycles. The producer accomplishes this through selecting and planting crops that differ in maturity in strategic temporal sequence. In one growing season, a monoculture may be used to start crop production. This is intercropped with another species at some point in the growing season, the two crops maturing at different times. With careful choice of specific and proper planting times, interspecific competition is minimal under this system. For example, wide-spaced and long-term crops such as cassava may be interplanted with an early crop such as beans or okra.

The period of overlap is variable. When the overlap period is very short such that the seasonal crop is planted just before the first is harvested, the plant culture is called *relay cropping* (e.g., seeding of winter wheat into a standing crop of soybean).

The advantage of relay cropping is that competition is further reduced between two species (e.g., bean-corn relay). In some production areas, producers are able to maximize the growing season by growing two crops in one season, one after the other, without any cohabitation. This is called *double-cropping* and involves no interspecific competition.

FIGURE 6 Double-cropping is possible in some areas in the eastern half of the United States where a longer growing season occurs. In 1997, 67 million acres of soybean were double-cropped. (Source: USDA)

FIGURE 7 Double-cropping soybean into corn. (Source: USDA)

Double-cropping is adopted by some producers in the eastern half of the United States where the growing season is long (Figure 6). An example of double-cropping is cropping soybean after wheat (Figure 7).

7.5 NURSE CROP

The concept of a *nurse crop* is incorporated into the practice of overlap planting. It is implemented in various forms. A nurse crop may be an annual, fast-growing species that is planted with the economic or desired crop to suppress weed growth while the economic crop establishes in the field. The nurse crop may then be controlled with chemicals once the desired crop is established, or it may die out eventually as the desired crop gains dominance in the field. For example, to establish alfalfa without the use of herbicides, a grower may seed it along with oats as a nurse crop. The oat plants compete with the early weeds until the alfalfa crop stand is well established. The term *nurse crop* is sometimes used synonymously with *companion crop*. Onions can be planted as a companion crop with carrots, the role of the former being to mask the smell of carrots from the devastating carrot fly. Similarly, cabbage root fly in Brussels sprouts may be controlled by using clover as companion crops in the production of brassica and other crops.

7.6 CROP ROTATION

Also called *sequence cropping,* crop rotation is the growing of multiple crops on the same piece of land, one after the other (Figure 8). The different crops do not interact

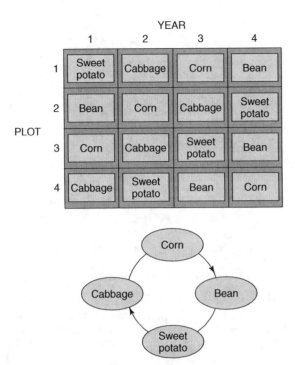

FIGURE 8 Crop rotation involves strategic sequencing of crops in production. Species with similar demands on growth factors should not follow each other directly.

but are separated temporally. Crop rotation strategies differ in design. The land may be divided into sections and the crops assigned to specific sites. The sites are changed in subsequent growing seasons. Alternatively, the entire field is planted with one crop species in one season, followed by a different cultivar of the same species or a different species the next season.

The success of a crop-rotation enterprise depends on careful choice and order of cropping. A legume fixes nitrogen for the next crop. However, sorghum has a high C:N ratio; thus, its residue decomposes slowly. Following sorghum with a crop that requires heavy use of nitrogen will cause yield reduction. Another consideration is disease infestation. Crops attacked by the same pest should not follow each other; otherwise, pest buildup will occur.

Crop rotation is a cropping practice in which a set of crops is cultivated in a predetermined sequence, avoiding the same crop being cultivated continuously at the same location. In organic farming, the importance of crop rotation is in the management of soil fertility, diseases, and pests. Continuous cropping of the same piece of land leads to nutrient deficiency and nutritional imbalance.

Crop rotation promotes a buildup of high natural resistance to soil pests and a high level of biological activity. Beneficial microbes are required for mineralization of organic molecules and for suppression of harmful microbes. Crop rotation is the primary strategy for controlling pests in an organic farming system.

The underlying principle in the use of crop rotation is that of creation and maintenance of **biodiversity** in the agroecosystem as a means of establishing equilibrium in the system. Such an equilibrium would prevent the population explosion of any particular pest in the agroecosystem, thereby creating a natural means of pest management. Organic farmers may use cropping systems such as polycultures (e.g., mixed cropping, intercropping) to create biodiversity. Most field crops are commonly rotated in production (Figure 9).

There are certain principles applied in the design and effective use of crop rotation systems:

Biodiversity. The occurrence of a variety of biological species.

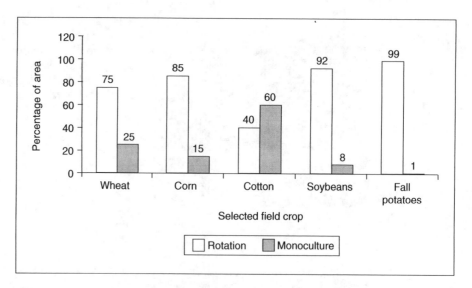

FIGURE 9 Cotton is mainly grown in monoculture, especially in the Delta Region. However, most field crops are commonly rotated in production. Common crop rotation systems include corn—soybean, fallow—wheat, and row crops—small grains. From 1994 to 1995, 99% of all fall potatoes was planted in rotation; 82% (162 million acres) of crops was in some form of rotation in this period. Cotton in 1995 was cultivated primarily in monoculture. (Source: USDA)

1. Follow a deep-rooted crop with a shallow-rooted crop for good soil structure maintenance.
2. Alternate between crops with high root biomass and those with low root biomass. This is because a high root biomass provides food for soil microorganisms.
3. Include green manures and catch crops to protect soil erosion and nutrient loss through leaching and to accumulate nitrogen.
4. Include nitrogen-fixing crops and alternate with crops with high nitrogen demand.

7.7   FERTILITY RESTORATIVE CROPPING

Regardless of the cropping system (monoculture or polyculture), farmers may interrupt their normal production sequence by leaving the land uncropped *(fallow)* or cropping it to a noncash crop *(cover crop)*. In another practice, the farmer abandons an exhausted soil for a fertile one *(shifting cultivation)*. A farmer may grow certain species for the express purpose of incorporating them into the soil (called green manure). Some of these practices were discussed previously in this chapter.

Cover Crop

As previously discussed, cover crops are used to improve soil fertility and protect an uncropped soil from erosion. They may be planted when normal cropping would be uneconomical. The crop can be grazed by livestock or plowed under as a green manure to fertilize the soil for normal cropping. Cover crops are normally legumes (e.g., alfalfa, pea, red clover, crimson clover, cowpea, and pigeon pea). These crops fix nitrogen. Cover crops also suppress weeds and reduce soil compaction. Grasses (e.g., rye) may be

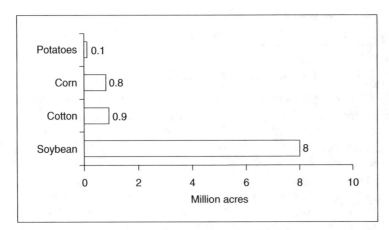

FIGURE 10 Cover crops are used most significantly with soybeans in the southern states for winter soil protection. Eight million acres of soybean crop area were planted to winter cover crops. The cover crop in 1995 was usually winter wheat or rye that was harvested as double-crop.

used as cover crops. Cover crops may be grown in association with cash crops to act as living mulches. They are used to a large extent with soybean production in the southern states (Figure 10).

Green Manures

Green manures are leguminous plants that are planted and plowed under the soil while still green. These crops can be planted as cover crops and then later incorporated into the soil. All cover crops are not usable as green manures because they are not all leguminous species. Examples of green manure species are hairy vetch, crimson clover, alfalfa, cowpea, and peanut. As an organic amendment (a biodegradable material incorporated into the soil), a green manure crop can improve soil structure, increase soil organic matter, and enhance soil fertility. As previously discussed, the utility of a soil amendment as a source of soil nutrients depends on the C:N (carbon to nitrogen) ratio, which impacts the rate of nitrogen released through decomposition and mineralization. Most green manures have a C:N ratio of 20:1 or less and are a good source of organic nitrogen. If incorporated while green, green manure plants have high nitrogen content, accumulated from biological nitrogen fixation.

Fallow

A fallow occurs when normal cropping of the land is suspended for a period of time. Fallow cropping was discussed previously.

Shifting Cultivation

Also called *slash-and-burn agriculture,* shifting cultivation is a cropping system found in many developing countries in the tropics and subtropics. In this cropping system, the land is cleared (by slashing and clearing with various hand-held tools and burning). The land is then immediately cropped, the ashes fertilizing the soil. After several years of repeated cropping of the land, yield decline sets in as the soil becomes exhausted of nutrients. The producer abandons the land and clears a new site. This trend is repeated in subsequent years. The farmer returns to the beginning land after a fallow period of no cropping. One criticism of this system of cropping is that new land is continually cleared, leading to deforestation (or removal of other vegetation cover) and its attendant problems. Population pressure means shifting cultivation is currently not sustainable because competition for land does not allow the long fallow periods necessary for the land to rejuvenate.

8: AGROFORESTRY

8.1 WHAT IS AGROFORESTRY?

As previously mentioned, *agroforestry* is the generic name used to describe the land use system in which trees are intentionally combined spatially and/or temporally with agricultural crops and/or animals. As a farming practice, agroforestry is very old and widely practiced, especially in the tropical and subtropical regions of the world. The concept was introduced to the United States in the early 1900s. It was revived, in its present form as agroforestry, in the 1970s.

A modern definition of agroforestry is the integration of agronomy and forestry conservation and production practices into land use systems that can conserve and develop natural resources while increasing economic diversity at both the farm and community levels. The trees in an agroforestry production enterprise are managed as an independent farm enterprise. Existing cropping land is not converted into a forest but is managed as an agroforestry system by integrating trees into the existing operation. Likewise, crop farms with existing woodland may be managed as agroforestry systems for special forest products. The trees in an agroforestry system provide forest products such as timber, nuts, and firewood, as well as shelter for livestock, control of soil erosion, habitat for wildlife, and improved soil fertility (e.g., through nitrogen fixation when leguminous species are used).

Generally, agroforestry practices tend to be more ecologically complex, compared with lands used only for annual crops. This is largely because of the complex interactions that occur among the components of an integrated system. However, with careful consideration, agroforestry practices can be effectively integrated into sustainable agricultural crop production systems to provide numerous environmental and financial benefits to the producer and the rural community.

An agroforestry system may be classified in several ways, depending on the purpose for which it is intended. Two useful and common ways of classifying agroforestry systems are according to structure and function. *Structure* refers to the composition and arrangement of the components of the agroforestry system that may be separated in time and space. Three basic structural classifications are as follows:

1. *Agrisilviculture*—consists of crops and trees
2. *Silvopastoral*—consists of pasture/animals and trees
3. *Agrosilvopastoral*—consists of crops, animals, and trees

The *function of an agroforestry system* refers to the main output and role of, especially, the woody components. The two generalized functional roles are productive and protective functions:

1. *Productive function.* The woody components of an agroforestry system may be used to provide food, fodder, and fuelwood, among others.
2. *Protective function.* The woody components may be used for crop protection (e.g., acting as windbreaks or shelterbelts) or for soil conservation and fertility management.

8.2 AGROFORESTRY PRACTICES

The design and technologies involved in an agroforestry system are variable. The distribution of agroforestry practices in the United States is presented in Figure 11. There are 5 major types of agroforestry practices: alley cropping, windbreaks or shelterbelts,

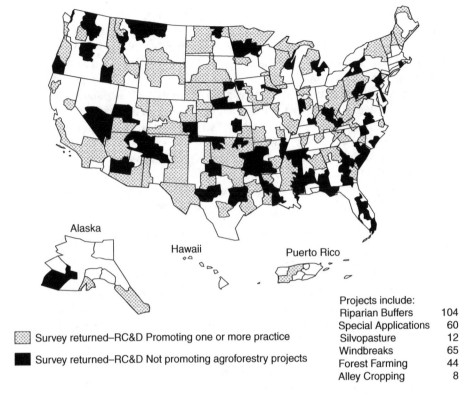

Projects include:
Riparian Buffers	104
Special Applications	60
Silvopasture	12
Windbreaks	65
Forest Farming	44
Alley Cropping	8

Survey returned–RC&D Promoting one or more practice

Survey returned–RC&D Not promoting agroforestry projects

FIGURE 11 Agroforestry practices occur widely throughout the United States, according to a survey conducted in spring 2000 by the National Association of Resource Conservation and Development Councils (NARC&DC). Among the practices, 81% of respondents indicated the observation of riparian buffers, 68% observed the use of windbreaks, and 13% used alley cropping. (Source: USDA—National Agroforestry Center.)

riparian forest buffers, forest farming, and silvopasture. In addition, agroforestry has special applications.

Alley Cropping

Alley cropping is the growing of an annual or perennial crop between rows of high-value trees. The agricultural crop generates annual income, while the longer-term tree crop matures. Examples include growing soybeans between rows of black walnut or hay between rows of fast-growing pine or poplar. The type of annual crop grown varies as the trees grow larger and produce more shade.

Crop producers adopt alley cropping for several reasons.

1. *It improves farm economics.* The farmer can derive income from both the short-term annual as well as the long-term tree crops, thus increasing productivity of the land, instead of leaving the alley unutilized. The farmer also diversifies his or her enterprise for insurance against adversity. Trees may provide fruits, wood, nuts, or foliage for additional income.
2. *It protects soil from erosion and enhances its quality.* Cropping the alleys provides ground cover that protects the soil from erosion. The litter from the trees adds organic matter to the soil to enrich soil fertility. Nitrogen-fixing trees and shrubs add additional nitrogen to the soil.

3. *It modifies the microclimate in the alleys.* The temperature and moisture patterns in the alleys are modified through the shading effect of the tree canopies and the reduction in wind velocities. Evapotranspiration in the intercropped area is reduced. These conditions are conducive to the cultivation of certain crops. The trees and grass strip filter modify the hydrologic cycle by filtering the water flow and enhancing water infiltration. However, the trees that surround the intercropped area sometimes also deplete soil moisture in these areas.

4. *It improves aesthetics.* Combining trees and crops enhances the landscape by adding more biological diversity.

5. *It provides habitat for wildlife.* Rows of trees provide enhanced surroundings in which wildlife species dwell.

6. *It provides for a gradual transition to agroforestry.* This practice initially removes only a small amount of land from crop production.

The limitations of alley cropping include the following:

1. *It requires intensive management.* Alley cropping requires the producer to be familiar with both trees and annual crop plant and to be capable of managing them simultaneously. Some pruning and thinning may be required for better wood production and to enhance the light conditions in the alleys for cropping.

2. *Trees occupy cropland.* Including trees in a cropping system takes up the space of land that could otherwise be cropped to field crops, as well as some of the soil moisture.

3. *It increases marketing needs.* The producer has to seek marketing outlets for multiple crops instead of just one.

In terms of design, the trees are planted first and in rows. Generally, single rows are used, but two- and three-row sets have been successfully installed. Spacing between the row sets is designed to create alleys that can accommodate the mature trees as well as the crops and the farm machinery to be used. The crop may be an annual or a perennial, a row crop or forage crop. As trees grow bigger, they occupy more space and cast wider shadows. Light management is hence critical to the success of alley cropping. Rows are usually oriented east to west to maximize light in the alleys. One practice in light management is to grow sun-loving crops (e.g., corn and soybean) while the trees are young and small, then switch to shade-tolerant crops (e.g., mushroom and forages) after trees grow older and bigger. If such a switch is not desirable, the row spacing should be wide from the start.

Planting trees in a row facilitates other post-planting activities. Single or multiple rows of either softwood or hardwood may be used. Further, a single species or a mixture of species may be used (Figure 12). In certain designs, short rotation species are grown (e.g., Christmas trees), which are then harvested at an appropriate time and replanted. In single-row planting, the trees take up less space but often require pruning to produce high-value wood products. Sometimes, a row of hardwood species is flanked by conifers (called *trainer trees*). If unflanked, hardwood species tend to bend toward light in the alleys, thus reducing the wood quality. If timber or wood is the primary value to the producer, narrower spacing should be used. Nut trees may be widely spaced. Row spacing of 40 feet is desirable for alley cropping cereals, soybean, and corn for 5 to 10 years. If a longer period of cropping is desired, the row spacing should be doubled to 80 feet. Nut trees such as black walnut and pecan are often planted since, in addition to having high-value wood, commercial quantities of nuts can be harvested in as little as 7 to 10 years.

The number-one priority in alley cropping is the proper selection of woody species. Most commonly, the long-term intent is to produce high-quality, knot-free saw timber of

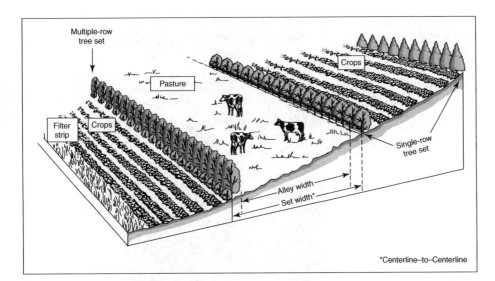

FIGURE 12 Alley cropping involves the use of the vacant space between established crops for additional crop production or other beneficial agricultural use, such as pasture for livestock. (Source: USDA—National Agroforestry Center)

commercially valuable species. Tree species should be adapted to the site, mesh with economic markets, and be compatible with companion crops. If trees are deciduous, early foliage loss would enhance the lighting in the alleys for the production of spring-ripening crops such as wheat and barley. Some species have nitrogen-fixing capacity [e.g., black locust (*Robinia psuedoacacia L.)* and leucaena (*Leucaena lecocephala* Lam)]. However, some desirable species such as black walnut have allelopathic effects on some crops. Other species of high commercial value for alley cropping include pecan, chestnut, oak, ash, and conifers. These trees may be intercropped with companion species such as row crops (e.g., corn, wheat, peas, and potato) and forage crops (e.g., white clover, alfalfa, Kentucky bluegrass, big bluestem, tall fescue, and ryegrass). Horticultural species (specialty crops) such as Christmas trees and small fruits may also be alley cropped. Biomass crops (e.g., poplar and birches) may be alley cropped to produce pulp for the paper industry. An advantage of pulp markets is that there is no need to prune the trees; however, if saw lumber markets exist, the price for pruned saw logs may be three to four times that of pulp.

The adoption of alley cropping is highest in the Midwest, where Missouri, Illinois, Indiana, Iowa, and Ohio have a combined total of more than 7.5 million hectares of alley cropped land. The Plains states (Nebraska and Kansas) have 6.5 million hectares of alley cropped land. The eastern half of the United States has more alley cropped land than the western half. Other states with significant alley cropped land include Oregon, Washington, Texas, and Minnesota.

Windbreaks (or Shelterbelts)

Windbreaks can prevent soil erosion and protect crops, livestock, buildings, work areas, roads, or communities (Figure 13). Living snowfences primarily protect roads but can also harvest snow to replenish soil moisture or fill ponds. The four basic types of windbreaks are farmstead/community, field, livestock, and living snowfences.

Windbreaks may be designed to enhance the general productivity of the crop farm enterprise, enhance wildlife habitat, or enhance the environment of the general community:

1. *Enhancing farm productivity.* The general farm productivity is enhanced through various functional roles of agroforestry practices in a cropping system. In many instances, windbreaks profoundly increase wildlife populations of game birds and

FIGURE 13 Windbreak protects a field crop (Source: USDA)

mammals. Many landowners are able to generate significant revenue from hunting fees for deer and pheasant.

2. *Effect on crop production and produce quality.* It has been well documented that, although windbreak trees do displace some cropland and will compete with adjacent rows of crops for moisture, in areas such as the Central Plains, where hot, dry summer winds prevail, windbreaks almost always increase crop yield on a per-field basis. In essence, the benefits of windbreaks for reducing evapotranspiration in these cropping systems are so pronounced that the farmers can grow the trees for free.

Crops such as cereals, vegetables, and orchard crops are wind-sensitive. Strong winds may cause severe lodging or fruit-drop, resulting in reduced crop yield. Windbreaks modify the microclimate of the cropped area by reducing wind velocity, which in turn modifies soil temperature, evapotranspiration rates, and relative humidities within the cropped area. These climate modifications are caused by the sheltering effects of the canopies of trees. The trees may trap snow that will improve the moisture content of the soil upon thawing. Reducing these meteorological parameters favorably alters the hydrologic cycle to enhance crop growth and development. The reduction in evaporative losses improves irrigation efficiency in sheltered cropping areas.

Windbreaks also protect soils from wind erosion by interrupting the saltation process. In addition to reducing soil fertility depletion, they enhance soil fertility by adding organic matter to the soil through the decomposition of leaves that drop and the effect of tree roots in the soil. In this regard, windbreaks aid in soil nutrient cycling. Trees are deeper feeders than annual crops and hence do not compete for nutrients with the target crop being produced (except when deep-rooted crops such as alfalfa are involved). Another way in which windbreaks enhance farm productivity is through economic diversity. If properly established and managed, the trees in the windbreak may be sources of additional income through the provision of secondary farm products such as wood, nuts, fruits, and foliage. Windbreaks may interrupt the spread of diseases from one section of the field to another, especially where the disease spreads by airborne structures. Several studies have documented the presence of beneficial insects in windbreaks.

3. *General community enhancement.* By reducing wind velocity, windbreaks reduce air infiltration into buildings and consequently reduce heat loss. They also reduce snowdrifts that block roads and pile up in residential areas, necessitating expensive snow removal. Windbreaks increase the biological diversity of the agricultural landscape. They can be designed to screen out unsightly areas on the farm, especially where animal production is involved. Windbreaks also filter the air and improve air quality by capturing airborne particles such as odor, dust, smoke, and drift products from pesticide applications.

The limitations of windbreaks are similar to those of alley cropping:

1. They require a more intensive management system involving annuals and perennials and trees or shrubs.
2. Cropping land is reduced.
3. Reduced farm sizes (because of division) will limit size of farm machinery that can be used.
4. Introduced trees may create an environment that harbors crop pests.
5. Crop performance is reduced in areas adjoining trees because of reduced light and reduced moisture.

Normally, wind speed needs to be at least 20 kilometers per hour, and blowing 30 centimeters above the ground, in order to begin to dislodge soil particles. The design of a windbreak depends on the purpose for which it is intended. For crop production purposes, the key factors the producer needs to consider include the wind direction (especially the direction from which most wind damage results), the crops being cultivated, the tillage practice and conservation measures being implemented, the irrigation practices (if any), the farm machinery and equipment being used, and any specific experiences with wind-related damage (e.g., wind erosion or crop damage). The producer needs to anticipate any future changes in cropping strategies and use of equipment.

The effectiveness of a windbreak depends on its height, density, orientation, number of tree rows, and length. A windbreak must be at least 75 centimeters high to impact wind speed. Height (H) is the most significant determinant of the downward area of protection provided by the windbreak. Windbreaks reduce wind speed for two to five times the height of the windbreak (2 H to 5 H) on the windward side and up to 30 H on the leeward side of the barrier. The area protected is directly proportional to H.

Windbreaks are porous structures. Windbreak density is measured as the ratio of the solid part of the barrier to the total area of the barrier. Barrier density can be adjusted to provide various levels of wind protection and modification of the microclimate. The denser the barrier, the more restrictive the wind flow (Figure 14). Deciduous species are more porous (25 to 35% density), while conifers provide a denser barrier (40 to 60% density).

Winds rarely blow exclusively from one direction. The orientation of a windbreak is critical to its effectiveness. The most effective orientation is at right angles to the direction of the prevailing wind. It may be desirable to establish a windbreak with multiple "legs" to provide more effective protection against uncertain wind direction.

The total amount of area protected by a windbreak depends on the length of the barrier. It is recommended that the length of a windbreak be at least 10 times its height. This recommendation will reduce the effect of end-turbulence on the protected area.

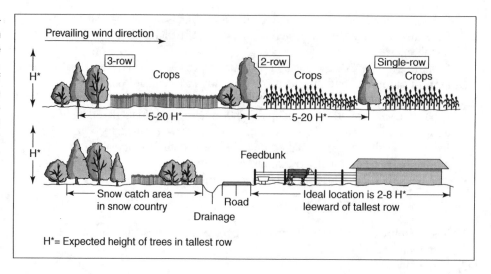

FIGURE 14 Windbreaks reduce wind speeds in cropped land. They are used for other purposes. Single or multiple rows of trees may be used in the design of a windbreak, depending on the purpose of the windbreak. (Source: USDA—National Agroforestry Center)

Designing a windbreak system for crop and soil protection starts with the identification of the structural or physical features on the area. A conservation plan map or photo will help locate the areas needing protection, property lines, roads, wind direction, utilities, and other factors. The recommended goal for crop and soil protection is to establish a primary windbreak of 40 to 60% density. This may be accomplished by using a combination of conifers and deciduous species in multiple rows. Further, a field may have a network of barriers spaced throughout the area. For this layout, a break-to-break interval of 15 H to 20 H is adequate for most field crops.

Certain crops are more sensitive to wind-related damage than others. A break-to-break spacing of 6 H to 10 H is recommended for sensitive crops. The farmer may implement additional conventional buffer practices, such as crosswind trap strips, to supplement the effects of the primary windbreaks.

Like all agroforestry practices, trees and shrubs selected should be adapted to the region and suited to the purpose for which they are being established. Tree seedlings should be planted at appropriate spacing to provide the desired density. The trees may be protected from rodents and other pests during establishment. Replanting of trees may be needed to fill in the spots where initial planting failed. Once established, the trees require pruning of the limbs and stems to maintain the proper density.

Windbreaks are often routinely incorporated into cropping systems in the Great Plains and Central Plains farming regions, where strong winds are common. In other regions, windbreaks are used to protect sensitive crops, such as tomato and apple, from bruising.

Riparian Forest Buffers

Riparian forest buffers are natural or planted woodlands adjacent to streams or water bodies and are comprised of trees, shrubs, and grasses. They provide a buffer against non-point source pollution, such as excess nutrient and pesticide runoff generated from agricultural activities. Riparian forest buffers also reduce stream bank erosion, enhance aquatic environments, augment wildlife habitat, and provide aesthetic value.

Modern crop production converts a variety of natural ecosystems (e.g., native prairie, wetlands, forests) into agroecosystems. In search of productive farmlands, producers sometimes utilize land that is sensitive or unstable and prone to rapid deterioration. Sometimes, stream channels are modified to increase the riparian area for crop production. In a typical watershed in places such as central Iowa, about 50% of the total length of a stream channel may be cultivated to the bank edge, while another 30% may be in pasture. Grazing has significantly changed the riparian zones in the rangelands of the West. Livestock adversely impact the stream channel, the stream banks, and the riparian zone through trampling and increasing of the sediment and nutrient load. In addition to this, general agricultural production is responsible for depositing large amounts of pollutants (sediments, fertilizers, pesticides) from uplands into streams through surface runoff.

It is clear from the foregoing that modern agriculture has placed the agroecosystem at risk through its product-oriented activities. It is imperative, therefore, that measures be implemented to restore the rapidly deteriorating riparian regions and the pollution of groundwater aquifers and streams. One effective strategy is through the installation of *riparian forest buffer strips,* consisting of trees, shrubs, or grasses (or a combination of these species), that are planted along streams or water bodies for the purpose of buffering non-point source pollution and sediments from waterways. These strips stabilize the banks and channels of water bodies and forestall the loss of adjacent cropping land. They also provide habitat for terrestrial wildlife and improve aquatic ecosystems.

A riparian zone by nature is a link between the aquatic ecosystem of the stream and the adjacent terrestrial ecosystem. Thus, it plays a critical role in the hydrology of watersheds. Further, the riparian zone is very productive for cropping and should be managed effectively for sustainable use.

Depending on the location of the riparian zone, a riparian forest buffer may serve one or more of the following purposes:

1. *Filter and retain sediments.* Large amounts of sediments can flow toward the stream from the upland region. This may consist of eroded soil particles carried in floodwaters or agrochemicals (pesticides and fertilizers) from upland agroecosystems. Trees and other plants established in the riparian buffer strip can filter and trap these sediments before they reach the stream, especially when the runoff occurs as sheet flow (as opposed to channelized flow). The standing trees and organic debris on the ground provide frictional surfaces that impede the flow of the runoff, thereby causing sedimentation to occur.

2. *Process nutrients and other chemicals.* Plants in the riparian buffer strip remove some of the dissolved nutrients (e.g., nitrates and phosphates) in the runoff, thereby reducing the amounts that reach the stream. Similarly, the activities of soil microorganisms in the buffer immobilize and transform some of the dissolved chemicals from the upland agricultural activities.

3. *Control stream environments and morphology.* Forest buffers stabilize the banks of streams through the soil-binding effects of plant roots. The canopies of trees modify the microclimate (especially light intensity and temperature) of the stream channel through shading. Further, the plants add organic matter to the stream. These events positively alter the aquatic biology of the stream.

4. *Enhance local hydrology.* Forested regions capture and absorb more rainfall than denudated sites. Riparian forest buffers impede the flow of floodwaters, thereby enhancing infiltration for recharging local groundwater.

5. *Protect cropland from flood damage.* Forested buffer zones can reduce the effect of flooding by reducing the erosive force of the running water and out-of-bank flow, thereby saving cropland and crops.

6. *Provide wildlife habitat.* Riparian buffers provide an enhanced habitat for wildlife. They also serve as travel corridors connecting different upland and aquatic habitats. Riparian buffers are rich in plant species diversity.

7. *Supplement income.* Riparian forests can be managed to provide wood, fruits, nuts, and fiber products.

8. *Create recreational activities.* The community may develop the riparian strip for various recreational uses, such as fishing, hunting, and camping.
9. *Enhance carbon storage.* Their favorable hydraulic position in the landscape means riparian zones often have ample moisture and nutrients, which lead to rapid plant growth. This translates to high rates of carbon accumulation.

The limitations of a riparian buffer include the following:

1. A sizable amount of productive cropland will be taken out of production to install a forested buffer strip.
2. By providing an enhanced wildlife habitat, a buffer strip may encourage some of the animals to become pests of crops being produced in the area.
3. The buffer requires management to keep it effective. For example, the riparian vegetation will continue to be an effective nutrient sink only as long as the plants are accumulating biomass. Likewise, grass strips at the interface of the cropped field and the forest buffer need to be periodically disked and reseeded to incorporate trapped sediments into the soil and maintain the ability of the buffer to trap new sediment.

Design   There are certain basic guidelines to follow in the design and implementation of a forested riparian buffer for agricultural lands:

1. *Problem identification and needs of the farmer.* The first step is to identify the problems at the site for which the intervention is intended. This should be viewed in relation to agricultural activities being conducted by the landowner, those that are endangering the riparian region, and the potential benefits that the agroforestry practice would bring. It is important to know the objective of the farmer in his or her desire to install a forested buffer (e.g., need to check erosion that threatens to reduce cropland).
2. *Plant species selection.* Plant species differ in their effectiveness at correcting various problems associated with the riparian region. For example, trees are effective for stabilizing stream banks and absorbing nutrients but are less effective in filtering sediments, a function better performed by grasses.
3. *Determination of minimum acceptable width.* The minimum acceptable width depends on the problem to be tackled with the buffer, the benefits desired by the landowner, and the cost of the project.
4. *Development of a plan.* The plan should include installation and maintenance strategies.

A General-Purpose Riparian Buffer for a Cropland   The USDA has developed guidelines for a three-zone design concept for riparian forest buffers (Figure 15). Zone 1 begins at the edge of the stream and is designed to provide bank stability and an undisturbed ecosystem. It provides the final filter of materials entering the stream. Logging and grazing are not permitted in this zone. Zone 2 is a managed forest area that provides maximum infiltration of surface runoff and nutrient uptake, as well as organic matter for microbial processing of agrochemicals. Zone 3 is a non-woody (grasses and herbs) strip that converts concentrated flow to sheet flow for enhanced infiltration of agrochemicals.

A general-purpose riparian buffer may be 50 feet wide, with trees occupying the first 20 feet in zone 1, while shrubs and grasses occupy the next 10 feet and 20 feet, respectively. The trees should be spaced 6 to 10 feet apart, while the shrubs are spaced 3 to 6 feet apart.

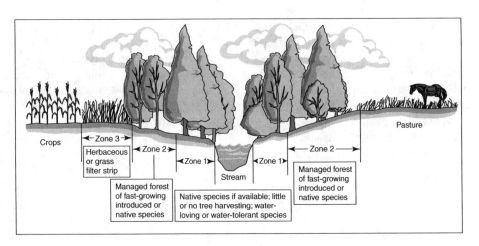

FIGURE 15 Riparian buffer strips are used to protect stream banks to prevent the erosion of adjacent cropland, among other objectives. (Source: USDA—National Agroforestry Center)

This design will utilize 6 acres of land per each mile of stream bank. The composition of plants and space allocations may be modified as needed to meet unique needs.

Forest Farming

Forest farming cultivates high-value specialty crops under a forest canopy that has been modified to provide the correct shade and microenvironment for the crop. These specialty crops usually fall into four categories: foods, botanicals, ornamentals, and handicrafts.

1. Foods—e.g., mushrooms and nuts
2. Botanicals—e.g., herbs and medicinals such as ginseng
3. Ornamental—e.g., floral greenery and dyes
4. Handicrafts—e.g., baskets and wood products

Silvopasture

Silvopasture may be defined as the purposeful integration of trees into pastures for the purpose of making a more productive system and gaining improved financial returns for the producer. As an agroforestry practice, silvopasture is a practice specifically designed and managed for the production of trees, tree products, forage, and livestock. The management of the silvopasture system emphasizes the production of high-value timber component, while providing short-term cash flow from the livestock component. To be successful, the producer should be aware of the environmental requirements in the area.

The trees and forage species to be combined should be selected for compatibility, as well as for adaptation to the soil and climate of the area. The timber component should be of high quality, marketable, fast-growing, and capable of providing desired products and environmental services. The forage component should be a perennial species that is suitable for livestock grazing and tolerant of shade. It should also be adapted to the region and amenable to intensive use and management. Both wildlife and livestock may be included in a silvopastoral system. The selected animals should be compatible with the tree and forage species in terms of grazing habits.

Once established, a variety of management tools are used for the proper management of the system. These include proper tree harvesting and thinning, fertilization of the pasture, introduction of legumes to enhance soil fertility and forage quality, fencing for rotational grazing, and supplemental feeding of the livestock.

Silvopastural operations have several advantages. Marketable products can be obtained while waiting for the forest products to be ready. Such a multiple product system reduces the risk of agricultural production. The land is also well used to produce a variety of products, while protecting the environment from degradation. Trees can benefit from livestock manure, while the shade trees provide can also stabilize the climate for the comfortable use by livestock.

SUMMARY

1. Ecology is the study of how living things relate to their environment and to each other.
2. In an ecosystem, there is natural cycling and interdependency of all components.
3. In an agroecosystem, farmers nudge nature to their advantage instead of allowing a natural balance to occur where all components are favored.
4. Crop production entails the management of inputs and biological processes for productivity, as well as sources of depletion of production resources.
5. In crop production, plants are planted in population, either of like plants (monoculture) or unlike plants (polyculture).
6. Examples of polycultures are intercropping, relay cropping, double-cropping, crop rotation, and alley cropping.
7. Mixtures or polycultures are common in forage production where legume-grass mixtures are planted.
8. Modern crop producers who mechanize their production frequently adopt monocultures.
9. Plants in a population interact in a competitive, complementary, or antagonistic fashion.
10. Crop producers employ a variety of techniques to restore soil fertility on site. These include the use of cover crops, green manures, fallow, and shifting cultivation.
11. Crop producers in various parts of the world have adopted production systems that have evolved over the years. Some of these production systems are low-input and less intensive, while others are high-input and intensive. The level of technology is determined largely by socioeconomic factors.
12. Agroforestry systems involve combining trees spatially and/or temporally with agricultural crops and/or animals.
13. In terms of structure, there are three agroforestry categories: agrisilviculture, silvopastoral, and agrosilvopastoral.
14. Agroforestry systems serve two basic purposes—productive and protective functions.
15. There are six agroforestry practices: alley cropping, windbreaks, riparian forest buffers, forest farming, silvopasture, and special applications.

REFERENCES AND SUGGESTED READING

Altieri, M. A. 1987. *Agroecology, the scientific basis of alternative agriculture.* Boulder, CO: Westview Press.

Beetz, A. 1999. *Agroforestry overview.* Appropriate Technology Transfer for Rural Areas (ATTRA).

Garett, H. E., Rietveld, W. J., and Fisher, R. F. 1999 (eds.). *North American agroforestry: An integrative science and practice.* American Society of Agronomy, Madison, Wisconsin.

Hearn, A. B. and G. P. Fitt. 1992. Cotton cropping systems. In Pearson, C. J. (ed.). *Ecosystems of the world: Field crop ecosystems.* New York: Elsevier.

Johnson, L. A. (ed). 1992. *Sustainable agriculture: Enhancing the environmental quality of the Tennessee Valley region through alternative farming practices.* University of Tennessee Agricultural Extension Service.

Juo, A. S. R. and H. C. Ezumah. 1992. Mixed root-crop systems in wet sub-saharan Africa. In Pearson, C. J. (ed.). *Ecosystems of the world: Field crop ecosystems.* New York: Elsevier.

Kormondy, E. J. 1984. *Concepts of ecology,* 3rd ed. Englewood Cliffs, NJ: Prentice Hall.

National Research Council. 1991. *Sustainable agriculture research and education in the field. A proceedings.* Washington, DC: National Academy Press.

Powers, E. R. and R. McSorley. 2000. *Ecological principles of agriculture.* Albany, NY: Delmar.

Rietveld, B., and Irwin, K. 1996. *Agroforestry in the United States.* Agroforestry notes, USDA Forest Service. Rocky Mountain Station.

Ruark, G. A. 1999. Agroforestry and sustainability: Making a patchwork of quilt. *Journal of Forestry.* August 1999.

Smika, D. E. 1992. Cereal systems of the North American Central Great Plains. In Pearson, C. J. (ed.). *Ecosystems of the world: Field crop ecosystems.* New York: Elsevier.

SELECTED INTERNET SITES FOR FURTHER REVIEW

http://www.nal.usda.gov/afsic/afslinks.htm

Alternative farming system information center; good links.

OUTCOMES ASSESSMENT

PART A

Answer the following questions true or false.

1. T F   In a natural ecosystem, bacteria are producers.
2. T F   An agroecosystem has a socioeconomic component.
3. T F   Plants are producers in an ecosystem.
4. T F   Hexagonal plant arrangement favors plants with foliage that is circular around the axis.
5. T F   Trees can be incorporated into field crop production.

PART B

Answer the following questions.

1. The study of how living things relate to their environment is _____.

2. Cultivated communities consisting of one crop species are called _____.

3. Define relay cropping.

4. Define intercropping.

5. What is allelopathy?

6. What is morphological plasticity?

7. Competition-induced plant mortality is called _____.

8. _____ is the agroforestry practice of growing crops, trees, and pasture with animals simultaneously.

9. Define the term agroforestry.

PART C

Write a brief essay on each of the following topics.

1. Describe a natural ecosystem.

2. Compare and contrast a natural ecosystem with an agroecosystem.

3. Discuss the competition among plants in a monoculture.

4. Discuss the competition among plants in a polyculture.

5. Discuss the advantages of polyculture.

6. Discuss the advantages and disadvantages of monoculture.

7. Discuss the phenomenon of self-thinning in a plant population.

8. What is agroforestry?

PART D

Discuss or explain the following topics in detail.

1. How can biotechnology support organic farming?

2. Will sustainable agriculture ever dominate U.S. crop production?

3. What are the benefits of agroforestry?

Soil and Land

PURPOSE

The purpose of this chapter is to discuss soil physical, chemical, and biological properties and how they influence crop production. The distribution of arable lands and classification of land based on land capability are also discussed. Also, soil fertility and its management are discussed.

EXPECTED OUTCOMES

After studying this chapter, the student should be able to:

1. List and briefly describe the twelve soil orders in relation to crop production.
2. Discuss the role physical characteristics (texture, structure, soil bulk density, porosity, permeability, and aggregation) play in crop production.
3. Define and discuss CEC and its importance.
4. Define and discuss soil pH and its importance.
5. Discuss the distribution of arable land in the world.
6. Describe and discuss soil organisms and their importance.

KEY TERMS

Arable land	Humus	Parent material
Bulk density	Igneous rock	Ped
Cation exchange capacity (CEC)	Liming	Sedimentary rock
	Loess	Soil aggregate
Denitrification	Metamorphic rock	Soil colloid
Expanding clay	Mycorrhizae	Soil horizon
Flocculation	Non-expanding clay	Soil permeability

From Chapter 7 of *Principles of Crop Production: Theory, Techniques, and Technology*, Second Edition, George Acquaah.
Copyright © 2005 by Pearson Education, Inc. Published by Pearson Prentice Hall. All rights reserved.

Soil profile   Soil structure   Topsoil
Soil reaction   Soil texture   Weathering
Soil separates

TO THE STUDENT

"Dirt" is what you sweep off the floor. "Soil" is the medium in which field crop production is carried out. Nutrients, water, and air, key factors that are needed for plant growth and development, are provided through the soil. The soil also provides physical support to plants and serves as a recycling center for nutrients and organic waste. As a natural resource, soil can be degraded and depleted of plant nutrients through natural factors as well as human activities. Certain soils are more suitable for crop production than others. However, provided any weaknesses can be corrected or managed in crop production, most soils can be used to produce certain crops.

1: WHAT IS SOIL?

The Soil Science Society of America defines soil as the unconsolidated mineral or organic material on the immediate surface of the earth that serves as a natural medium for the growth of land plants. It is also defined as the unconsolidated mineral or organic matter on the surface of the earth that has been subjected to and shows the effects of genetic and environmental factors of climate (including water and temperature effects) and macro- and microorganisms, conditioned by relief, acting on parent material over a period of time. Further, a product-soil differs from the material from which it was derived in many physical, chemical, biological, and morphological properties and characteristics.

The society also defines soil science as the science that deals with soils as a natural resource on the surface of the earth, including soil formation; classification and mapping, the physical, chemical, biological, and fertility properties of soils per se; and these properties in relation to the use and management of soils.

2: SOIL FORMATION

How is soil formed? Soil formation is a slow process; for all practical purposes, soil is not a renewable resource. It is important, therefore, that soils be managed properly because it is difficult to reclaim damaged soil. Soil is weathered rock. The process of weathering, by which soil is formed, is slow and sequential, involving physical, chemical, and biological factors. It involves the alteration of rocks and their minerals, resulting in their disintegration, decomposition, and modification. Soil is a dynamic system, changing as it is impacted by environmental factors and by the plant and other organisms that live in it.

The five factors of soil formation are *parent material, climate, organisms* (organic matter), *topography* (relief), and *time*. These factors of soil formation are interrelated, each one affecting and being affected by the others.

2.1 SOIL ORIGINATES FROM MINERAL AND ORGANIC MATERIALS

The starting point in soil formation is the parent material, the rock material on which agents of weathering act. This material is classified into two types, based upon origin. Some parent material is formed in place *(sedentary)*, while some is *transported* by various agents and deposited in certain places. A soil formed from parent material that was transported by ice is called *glacial*, while a soil formed from parent material transported by wind is called **loess**. Most soils in the United States are formed from non-glaciated parent material. Glacial soils occur in the central parts of the United States, especially the midwestern states.

Parent materials are formed from parent rocks (these consist of primary minerals such as augite, feldspar, hornblende, mica, olivine, and quartz), which are of three basic types: **igneous, sedimentary**, and **metamorphic**.

1. Igneous rocks (e.g., granite) are consolidated, hard rocks that consist of minerals, including quartz and feldspar.
2. Sedimentary rocks are unconsolidated and consist of pieces of rock transported by various agents. Upon deposition, various products are formed, such as limestone, sandstone, and shale.
3. Metamorphic rock is produced when other rock types (igneous and sedimentary) are subjected to intense heat and pressure. The resulting products (metamorphic rocks) include slate, gneiss, marble, and schist.

Some soils originate from organic material. Peat and marsh (bog) soils are high in organic matter.

2.2 WEATHERING PROCESSES CAN BE PHYSICAL OR CHEMICAL

Weathering is the process by which parent materials are broken down into the finer particles that form the soil. Agents of weathering act upon parent materials. These agents can be physical or chemical.

Physical Weathering

Physical weathering occurs primarily through disintegration of rock material. This occurs in several ways. Rocks consist of different chemical materials with different rates of expansion and contraction. Under temperature fluctuation, rocks crack and peel off (exfoliation) as the chemical components expand and cool at different rates. Cracks in rocks collect water, which upon freezing expands to further widen the crack. Glacial movement involves grinding and scraping of rocks as the ice moves on the earth's surface. Similarly, moving water carries rocks that crack and crush as they tumble with the currents. Sometimes, plant roots grow into cracks in rocks and widen them, as the roots grow larger.

Chemical Weathering

Chemical weathering occurs by one of several distinct chemical processes. These reactions increase the disintegration rates of minerals.

1. *Carbonation.* Carbon dioxide dissolves in water to form a weak acid [carbonic acid (H_2CO_3)], which then reacts with carbonates and other minerals in rock

Loess. Soil particles, predominantly silt-sized, transported and deposited by wind.

Igneous rock. Rock formed by the cooling and solidification of molten rock (magma).

Sedimentary rock. Rock formed from material originally deposited as a sediment, then physically or chemically changed by compression and hardening.

Metamorphic rock. A rock (igneous or sedimentary) that has been greatly altered from its previous condition by a combination of high temperature and pressure.

Weathering. The processes by which parent material changes in character, disintegrates, decomposes, and synthesizes new compounds and clay minerals.

materials that are easier to decompose, such as calcium bicarbonate. This reaction is called *carbonation:*

$$CaCO_3 + H_2O + CO_2 \rightarrow Ca(HCO_3)$$

2. *Hydration.* Hydration entails adding water molecules to materials to form hydrated products that are easier to break down—for example,

$$CaSO_4 + 2H_2O \rightarrow CaSO_4 \cdot 2H_2O \text{ (hydrated calcium sulfate, or gypsum)}$$

3. *Hydrolysis.* Hydrolysis is a reaction involving water in which ions in parent materials are made more readily available through the formation of more soluble products such as KOH.

$$KAlSi_3O_8 \rightarrow HAlSi_3O_8 + KOH$$

$$2HAlSi_3O_8 + H_2O \rightarrow Al_2O_3 \cdot H_2O + 6H_2SiO_3$$

4. *Oxidation.* Minerals in rocks may react with oxygen (oxidation) to produce less stable materials. This occurs especially where minerals contain iron. The oxides formed are visible as reddish-yellow coloration (rust).

$$4FeO + O_2 \rightarrow 2Fe_2O_3$$

5. *Reduction.* Under conditions of low oxygen, the oxidation reaction may proceed in the reverse direction to produce products that are less oxidized.

6. *Solution.* Certain rock minerals dissolve readily in water, creating weaknesses in the rock material and promoting physical disintegration.

Weathered parent materials produce a large variety of metallic ions that may be recrystallized into new minerals, called *secondary minerals,* such as clay.

2.3 SEVERAL FACTORS ARE RESPONSIBLE FOR SOIL FORMATION

Parent material. The material from which soil is developed by the process of weathering.

Soil development occurs at a rate that is dependent on **parent material**, *time, climate, biota,* and *relief.*

Parent Material

What kinds of materials can be converted to soil? Most soils are formed from unconsolidated materials produced by the action of erosive forces (wind, water, air) or sediments that are glacial in origin. These deposits vary in particle size as well as chemical composition. Whether the parent material will play a dominant role in determining the physical and chemical properties of the soil formed will depend on the extent of weathering of the material. Slightly weathered parent material plays a more dominant role than well-weathered parent material in this regard. Parent materials differ in their rate of weathering, quartz being among the most resistant.

Climate

Climate affects the rate of soil formation and the type of soil that is ultimately formed. The role of climate is both direct and indirect:

1. *Direct.* What are the general differences in soils formed under high rainfall conditions and those formed under drier conditions? High rainfall and temperature provide conditions that promote rapid weathering, high leaching (downward loss of nutrients through the soil profile), and high oxidation. The soils formed tend to have red or yellow colors, which are characteristic of oxidized soil material. Soils formed under drier conditions, on the other hand, experience salt (e.g., calcium and magnesium) accumulation (not leaching). Such soils are thus high in salt and may require leaching *(desalination)* to render them useful for crop production.

2. *Indirect.* The indirect effect of climate is in the type of vegetation it supports. Semiarid climates support shrubs and grasses, while heavy rains encourage trees and forest conditions. Organisms and organic matter affect soil formation as described next.

Biota (Organisms)

Do soils formed under forest vegetation tend to have more organic matter than those formed under grassland? The *biota* (living things) affects soil formation. The vegetation determines the type and amount of organic matter in the soil. Grasses differ from pines in the type of organic matter they produce. Soils developed under grasses have high organic matter. Much of the organic matter in forested regions lies on the soil surface and decomposes slowly. It is not incorporated into the soil as effectively as organic matter from grasses. Further, soils under forested areas are heavily leached, depleting the top horizon of organic matter and clay minerals, which accumulate in the lower horizon. Soils formed under conditions where soil-burrowing organisms (e.g., moles, gophers, earthworms, and termites) abound experience constant mixing of the soil within the profile. This causes fewer but deeper horizons to develop. Soil microbes are also beneficial to soil formation by decomposing organic matter and causing weak acids to form to aid in dissolution of minerals.

Topography

Topography, or *relief,* determines the rate of soil erosion and hence the depth of the soil formed through its effect on water and temperature. Erosion is more pronounced on steep slopes. Rapid soil movement does not allow the soil enough time to develop. The soil profile on gentle slopes is deeper and supports more luxuriant vegetation. The soil profile under such conditions is not well defined. Topography influences soil drainage and thus the amount of moisture available for weathering processes. In low-lying regions, drainage may become a problem, thereby causing anaerobic conditions to occur. Organic matter decomposition is slow and hence it accumulates, leading to the formation of high organic matter soils such as peat and muck.

Time

Soil formation is a continuous process. Rock materials differ in rates of decomposition. Limestone decomposes rapidly, while granite is very resistant to weathering. Profile development is dependent on time. Old soils have more defined profiles, because they have been exposed extensively to weathering agents. This allows decomposition and modification of component chemicals. The rate of soil development depends on the effect of time on soil forming factors. Are older soils necessarily better for crop production?

3: CROP PRODUCTION OCCURS PRIMARILY IN THE TOPSOIL

Soil profile. A vertical cross section of a soil through all of its horizons.

Soil horizon. A layer of soil, approximately parallel to the soil surface, with distinct characteristics produced by soil-forming processes.

Topsoil. The layer of soil that is disturbed during cultivation.

A vertical cross section of the soil reveals its vertical distribution, called the **soil profile**. A profile is characteristic of the soil genesis, or origin. Depending upon the age of the soil, the conditions under which it was formed, and parent material, among other factors, a soil profile will show different and distinguishable layers called the **soil horizon** (Figure 1). Figure 2 presents an actual soil profile. There are six master horizons designated by uppercase letters as O, A, E, B, C, and R. The R horizon is consolidated rock. Lowercase letters may also be added to further distinguish the horizons. For example, a Bt horizon indicates that the layer has clay deposits. Further, there are transitional horizons that are indicated by two uppercase letters—for example, AE. For crop production purposes, a simplified and typical soil profile will have three horizons. In agricultural soils, the O horizon is often absent because of tillage operations that mix it up with the A horizon material.

1. *A horizon.* This is also called the **topsoil** and consists of the uppermost layer of the soil. It has the most organic matter and is the most leached layer of the

FIGURE 1 Soil profile. There are six master horizons in a typical soil profile. There are subdivisions and intermediate layers between the layers. For crop production purposes, a simplified profile has three parts: topsoil, subsoil, and the underlying parent material. Most crop roots occur in the topsoil. (Source: Modified after USDA)

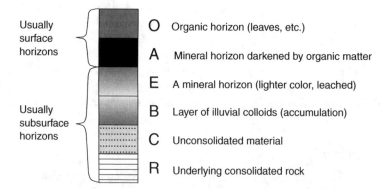

O Organic horizon (leaves, etc.)

A Mineral horizon darkened by organic matter

E A mineral horizon (lighter color, leached)

B Layer of illuvial colloids (accumulation)

C Unconsolidated material

R Underlying consolidated rock

FIGURE 2 (a) A soil profile, showing variation in soil color between the top and low horizons. (b) A technician extracts a soil core using a truck-mounted powered soil auger. (Source: USDA)

(a)   (b)

profile. Thus, it is sometimes referred to as the *zone of leaching (zone of eluviation)*. This is the portion of the soil that is tilled for crop production. Does it mean we should not care about the lower layers?

2. *B horizon*. Materials leached from the A horizon accumulate in the B horizon, also called the *zone of accumulation (zone of illuviation)*. This includes leached salts and clay minerals. The soil in this layer is less weathered. Roots of deep-rooted plants may reach this layer.

3. *C horizon*. This zone consists of unconsolidated material. There is little or no profile development. The underlying consolidated rock material is called the *R horizon*.

The soil profile can be modified by agricultural activity. As previously indicated, plowing mixes soil in the O and A horizons to form the *plow layer*. Further, the use of heavy tillage machinery can create compacted layers, called *hard pans*, that are impermeable to root penetration, and impede drainage.

4: SOIL GROUPS IN U.S. CROP PRODUCTION

The United States may be divided into two broad regions according to soil characteristics by dropping a line from western Minnesota through central Texas (Figure 3). The soils to the east of this line are called *Pedalfers* and are generally leached (low or deficient in basic materials—Na, K, Ca, Mg). The absence of these basic materials makes the soils on the eastern region acidic in reaction. Similarly, the soils of the humid Pacific Northwest are acidic. The soils on the west side of the United States are called *Pedocals*. Contrary to the eastern soils, these soils have an accumulation of soluble salts in the subsurface or subsoil. This accumulation of soluble salts occurs because the rainfall in the region is inadequate to leach the salts out of the soil. These leached soils are naturally fertile. However, low rainfall limits plant growth, making it necessary to irrigate crops in order to realize optimal productivity unless the season is wet.

The soils in most of the humid parts of the drier region of the west were formed under grassland, called *Chernozem soils;* they are black in color and very high in organic matter. They are very fertile and suited to the production of grasses and small grains, such as wheat. Where the climate is drier, the vegetation is sparse and consequently soil organic matter is low, making these soils lighter in color in the A and B horizons. Other soil groups in the west are the *Chestnut soils, Brown soils, Sierozem (Gray) soils,* and *Desert soils*. The Chestnut soils are suited to wheat production but growers should be aware of unseasonable weather. Similarly, the Brown soils are suited to wheat and sorghum (with the same warning of adverse weather) in the moist season, and for grazing in the driest areas. The Sierozem soils of the semidesert regions are generally low in organic matter, high in soluble salts, and relatively shallow. These soils are used for crops only when irrigation is possible; otherwise, they are used for grazing.

The Corn Belt region has soils that are very dark brown in color, high in organic matter, and naturally fertile. Called *Prairie soils,* they are suited to producing grains and a variety of other field crops. The climate of this region is very conducive to crop production. The combination of good natural fertility and good climate makes the Corn Belt one of the most productive soils in the world.

The northern humid regions, including the Great Lakes regions, are also acidic because of the leaching under the prevailing climate. Called *Podzol soils,* they are not naturally fertile and are suited to hay and pastures. Next to these soils to the south lie the Gray-Brown Podzolic soils of the Great Lakes and eastern Corn Belt states. They were

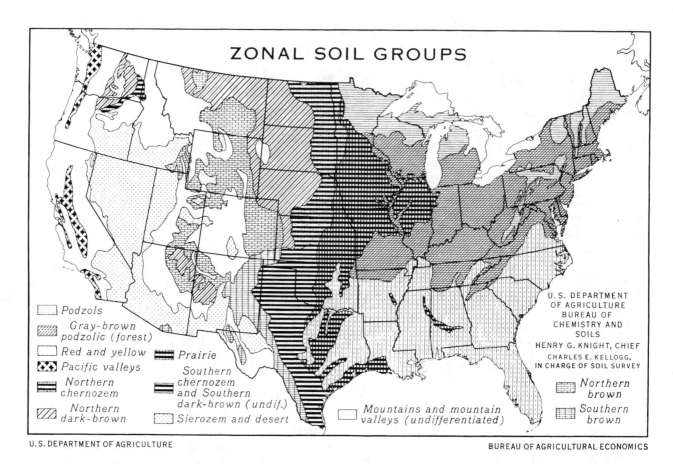

FIGURE 3 The United States is divided into two broad regions of soil groups, the Pedalfers (leached with no accumulation of lime) to the east and the Pedocals (accumulation of calcium carbonates) to the west. (Source: USDA)

developed under deciduous forests and a moist temperate climate. These soils are naturally relatively more fertile than the Podzols (but less fertile than the Prairie soils) and are suited to producing various crop plants. The Gray-Brown Podzolic soils are suited to producing a variety of crops, especially when limed and fertilized.

There are pockets of peat and marsh soils that have unusually high organic matter. Similarly, these are regions with excessive accumulation of bases such that they are unsuitable for cropping until leached by heavy irrigation. These alkaline soils are called *Solonchack soils;* they occur in arid regions.

5: THE USE OF SOIL FOR AGRICULTURAL PRODUCTION DEPENDS ON ITS PROPERTIES

What are the key soil physical properties that impact crop production? To what extent can a producer modify these properties for higher crop productivity? Some soils consist primarily of mineral matter (e.g., sand in the desert areas), whereas others consist predominantly of organic matter (e.g., peat bogs). A good soil for crop production, however, should have a good balance of certain basic components. These are mineral matter, organic matter, air, and water (Figure 4).

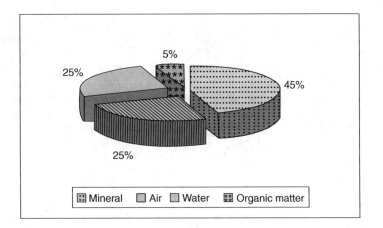

5.1 SOIL CONSISTS OF PARTICLES THAT ARE ARRANGED IN A CERTAIN PATTERN

Understanding soil physical properties is important to crop productivity. These properties impact how soil functions in an ecosystem and how it can be best managed. Soil physical properties affect how soil water and solutes move through and over the soil, as well as the suitability for agricultural use. Two important soil physical properties of mineral soils are its **soil texture** and **soil structure**. They help determine the nutrient-supplying ability of soil solids and the ability of the soil to hold and conduct the water and air required for proper root activity for proper plant growth.

Soil Texture

The soil textural class may be determined in the field by the "feel" method. A moist soil sample is rubbed between the thumb and forefingers and squeezed out to make a "ribbon." A non-cohesive appearance plus a short ribbon indicates a sandy loam, while a smooth appearance plus a crumbly ribbon indicates a silt loam. Clay makes a smooth, shiny appearance plus a flexible ribbon.

Soil may be physically separated into three particle size groups called **soil separates**. These are *sand, silt,* and *clay* (Table 1). Soil texture is defined as the proportions (or percentages) of sand, silt, and clay particles in a soil. Agricultural soils typically consist of a combination of all three particle sizes (called a *loam*). To determine the textural grade or textural class of a soil after mechanical analysis, the USDA textural triangle may be used (Figure 5). Can a soil that is predominantly clay, silt, or sand be successfully used for crop production?

Soil texture is very important in crop production. Fine-textured soils (clay soils) generally have poor drainage and are prone to waterlogging. However, they have high water-holding capacity. Clay soils are further described as heavy soils and are difficult to till. They impede root development and thus are not suitable for root crop production. Texture affects soil porosity. Clay soils have a preponderance of *micropores,* or capillary pores (small pores) that impede drainage. Sandy soils have more *macropores,* or non-capillary pores (large pores). Clay soils are also described as cold soils and tend to require warming (e.g., by drainage) for use in early cropping. Poorly drained soils have low microbial activity, but clay soils have high **cation exchange capacity (CEC)**, the ability of soil to attract and hold cations. Thus, clay soils have high nutritional status, while sandy soils, which are coarse-textured, have low CEC. On the other hand, sandy soils are light soils and are easier to till. They also have greater infiltration rates, drain better, and

Soil texture. The relative proportions of sand, silt, and clay in a soil.

Soil structure. The arrangement of primary soil particles into secondary particles, units, or peds.

Soil separates. The individual particle size groups (sand, silt, and clay) of a mineral soil.

Soil permeability. The amount of water that moves downward through the saturated soil.

Cation exchange capacity (CEC). The sum total of exchangeable cations that a soil can adsorb.

Table 1 Selected General Properties of the Three Soil Separates of Inorganic Soil

Property	Sand	Soil Separate Silt	Clay
Range of particle diameter (mm)	2.0–0.05	0.05–0.002	Smaller than 0.002
Visible with/under	Naked eye	Microscope	Electron microscope
Dominant minerals	Primary	Primary	Secondary
Aeration	Excellent	Good	Poor
Cation exchange capacity	Low	Moderate	High
Permeability by water	Fast	Moderate	Slow
Water-holding capacity	Low	Moderate	High
Drainage	Excellent	Moderate	Poor
Consistency when wet	Loose, gritty	Smooth	Sticky, malleable
Consistency when dry	Very loose and gritty	Powdery with few clods	Hard clods
General ease of tillage	Easy	Moderate	Difficult
General spring temperature	Warms fast	Warms moderately	Warms slowly
General erodibility by water	Easy	Moderate	Difficult

FIGURE 5 The USDA soil textural triangle. To use this guide, first obtain a physical analysis of the soil (i.e., the proportion of sand, silt, and clay, such as 40, 35, and 25). Locate 40% on the axis labeled "sand" and draw a line parallel to the axis labeled "silt." Next, locate either the clay or silt. Locate 25% on the clay axis and draw a line parallel to the sand axis to intersect the previous line from the sand axis. The section of the triangle in which the intersection occurs indicates the soil textural class. (Source: USDA)

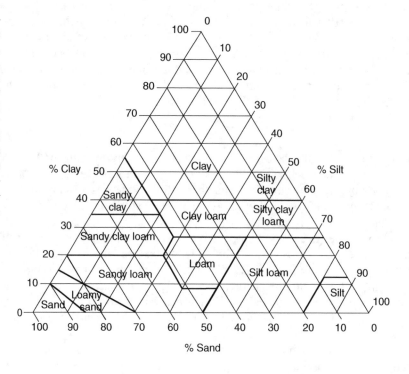

are warm. However, crop production on sandy soil requires frequent irrigation to make up for its poor water-holding capacity. Soil texture has implications in irrigation of field crops. The method and frequency of irrigation depend on soil texture.

Soil Structure

Soil structure is the arrangement of soil primary particles (soil separates) into secondary particles, units, or **peds**.

Soil particles are arranged in different shapes and sizes. The common arrangements are

Ped. A unit of soil structure, such as an aggregate or a crumb, formed by natural processes.

1. *Prismlike.* Particles are arranged in the vertical plane.
2. *Platelike.* Arrangement of particles is in the horizontal plane.
3. *Blocky.* This soil structure consists of rectangular shapes.
4. *Granular-crumb.* For agricultural purposes, the granular-crumb structure is ideal, and occurs in the furrow slice or plow layer. This structure consists of spheroidal units or circular arrangement of peds. However, this desirable structure is influenced by cultural practices and is subject to alteration.

Soil structure can be destroyed through compaction from traffic from farm animals, vehicles, and raindrops. Tilling the soil while it is wet, and applying certain soil amendments (e.g. liming), can destroy soil structure. Poor soil aggregation is partly the cause of poor drainage and poor water-holding capacity. Soil structure can be improved through, for example, the addition of organic matter.

Certain factors force these particles to make contact and to form secondary units called **soil aggregates**. These factors include soil tillage, organic matter, cations, and physical processes. The kind of cations adsorbed by soil colloids affects aggregation. Na^+ ions cause dispersion, while Ca^{2+}, Mg^{2+}, and Al^{3+} ions encourage aggregation by the process of **flocculation**. In crop production, it is important to maintain soil aggregate stability. Soils vary in their resistance to alteration from factors such as rain and tillage implements. Heavy rains can cause crusting of the soil surface, thus impeding seedling emergence and water infiltration. Clay soils are naturally prone to crusting. Artificial soil conditioners such as *synthetic polymers* can aid the stabilizing of soil aggregation.

Soil aggregate. A clump of many primary soil particles.

Flocculation. The aggregation of especially clay particles into clumps.

5.2 SOIL PARTICLES MAY BE LOOSELY OR DENSELY PACKED

How important is the degree of packing of soil particles to crop production? **Bulk density** of soil is defined as the mass (weight) of a unit volume of dry soil. This is the volume of soil as it exists naturally and thus includes air space and organic matter. *Particle density* is the density of the solid soil particles only. Bulk density is calculated as follows:

Bulk density. The mass of dry soil per unit of bulk volume, including the air space.

$$\text{Bulk density} = [\text{oven dry soil mass}]/[\text{soil volume}]$$

Bulk density is useful in estimating the differences in compaction of a given soil. Compaction on the farm is caused by the use of heavy farm machinery and implements. Trampling of soil by humans and farm animals also causes soil compaction. A compacted soil has an increased bulk density. Finely textured soils such as clays are more packed and are called *heavy soils*. They have high bulk densities and are more difficult to till. Heavy soils also drain poorly and have high water-holding capacity. Sandy soils are loose and are called light soils. They have lower bulk densities and are thus much easier to till. Root growth is impeded when bulk density is high. Bulk density is generally higher in the lower layers of the soil profile.

For good plant growth, a clay soil should have a bulk density of less than 1,400 kg/m³. For cultivating sands, a bulk density of less than 1,600 kg/m³ is desirable. Greenhouse soils contain a variety of soilless components such as vermiculite and perlite. These materials make them light and of very low bulk density, about 100 to 400 kg/m³. To improve bulk density, organic matter may be incorporated into the soil. The system of crop and soil management adopted also affects soil bulk density.

A typical mineral soil consists of about 25% pore spaces, or voids. There are two types of pore size: *micropores* and *macropores*. Clay soils have fine particles and a preponderance of micropores (small pores). Sand and coarse-textured soils have more macropores (large pores) than micropores. Total pore spaces in sandy soils may range between 35 and 50%. Cropping of soil tends to reduce soil organic matter and lower total space. Macropores play a role in drainage and aeration. Compaction reduces aeration and drainage. Is soil compaction more of a problem under mechanized farming than non-mechanized farming?

6: Clay and Humus Have Colloidal Properties That Are Critical to Soil Fertility

6.1 SOIL COLLOIDS

Soil colloid. Organic and inorganic matter with very small particle sizes and a correspondingly large surface area per unit of mass that remain in suspension for a long time

Expanding clay. Clay mineral with a 2:1 lattice structure that is subject to significant swelling upon wetting and shrinking upon drying.

Non-expanding clay. Clay mineral with a 1:1 lattice structure that resists swelling upon wetting and shrinking upon drying.

Humus. The usually darker fraction of soil organic matter remaining after the major portion of added residues have decomposed.

How do soils hold and make available the nutrients essential to plants? The chemical properties of soils are determined by **soil colloids**. Colloids are minute particles that remain in suspension for a long time. They have large surface areas that are charged. The predominant soil colloids of importance to crop production are clay and humus.

Clay colloids have a net negative charge and hence attract cations. They are secondary minerals (reformed from other partially dissolved minerals). Most clays are crystalline. A clay particle is called a *micelle* and consists of layers of atoms of oxygen, silicon, and aluminum. The layers may be spread apart to allow access to cation exchange sites on the internal surface. Such clays are called **expanding**, or *swelling, clays*, as opposed to **non-expanding**, or *non-swelling, clays* that have tightly bonding layers. There are several arrangements of the layers in the micelles in crystalline clays, which form a basis of their classification (Table 2).

Humus is an amorphous, largely water-insoluble temporary remainder of the decomposition of organic matter. It is called an *organic colloid* and has a net negative charge arising solely from mineralization of hydrogens from R–OH groups.

6.2 SOIL SOLUTION AND LEACHING

Soil water is not pure (drinking water) but, rather, contains hundreds of dissolved organic and inorganic substances. Consequently, soil water is best described as *soil solution*. This dilute solution supplies dissolved nutrient elements to plant roots. Some of these nutrients are critical to plant growth and development and are called *essential elements*. These elements are discussed later in the chapter. The soil solution has a reaction (acidic or alkaline), depending on the preponderance of certain dissolved ions (H^+, OH^-), a property called soil pH.

Soil nutrients move in the soil solution. The desired effect of soil water movement is to deliver nutrients to the root zone. Under some conditions, the nutrients are moved out of the root zone, a process called leaching. Leaching has consequences: (1) soil nutrients

---

Table 2 Selected Features of Major Categories of Clay Minerals

1. *Noncrystalline (amorphous) clays:* e.g., glass and opal
2. *Crystalline layer silicate clays:*
   a. *Kandite group:* e.g., kaolinite
      Has one sheet of tetrahedral: one octahedral sheet per layer (i.e., 1:1 crystal lattice). It is non-expanding (non-swelling) clay.
   b. *Smectite group:* e.g., talc and montmorillonite
      Has two tetrahedral sheets: one octahedral sheet per layer (i.e., 2:1 crystal lattice). It is expanding (swelling) clay (expands when wet and shrinks and cracks upon drying).
   c. *Hydrous mica group:* e.g., vermiculite (used in horticultural potting soils). It is 2:1 clay.

---

are not accessible to plants, leading to reduced yield and economic loss; (2) leached nutrients may contaminate groundwater and pose a health hazard to humans. A high CEC shows cation leaching because cations are bound to the soil colloids. Coarse soils with more macropores are more susceptible to leaching because of high gravitational water flow. On the other hand, compact soils have poor internal drainage but are susceptible to surface runoff, which also moves dissolved nutrients into surface water. Nitrates are most susceptible to leaching to contaminate groundwater.

Leaching losses are more likely to occur when high rates of fertilizer are applied at a stage in the crop growth cycle when nutrient uptake is slow. Loss of nutrients to leaching is likely to be greater in spring because high rainfall and low evapotranspiration occur at about the same time that mineralization and nitrification are just beginning and plant growth is slow.

6.3 SOILS DIFFER IN THE AMOUNT OF CATIONS THEY CAN HOLD

The cation exchange capacity (CEC) is an index of soil fertility that is based on the base-exchange capacity or measure of the total exchangeable cations a soil can hold. Cations (positively charged ions) useful to plant nutrition include Mg^{2+}, Ca^{2+}, K^+, and Mn^+. These ions are adsorbed by colloids. Adsorbed cations can be replaced (exchanged) by other cations in solution by *mass action* (competition for the negative sites because of a large number of ions present). The strength of adsorption of the ions on the surface depends on the valence of the cation, the charge density, and the strength of the site's negative charge. Protons (H^+) are small and have high charge density. They are very tightly ionic-bonded to clay. Na^+, on the other hand, has a small charge density and hence is weakly adsorbed and highly prone to leaching. Ranking of ions in decreasing charge density (lyotrophic series) and decreasing adsorption to colloids is as follows:

$$H^+ > Al^{3+} > Ca^{2+} > Mg^{2+} > K^+ = NH_4^+ > Na^+$$

The kinds of mineral ions present in the soil depends on the chemical nature of the parent material and the effect of climate. CEC is measured in meq/100 g of soil. A small CEC means the soil can hold small amounts of essential nutrients. It will be dominated by H^+ and Al^{3+} ions, making it acidic and of low fertility. Organic matter is more capable of cation exchange than clay, having 100 to 300 meq/100 g as compared with only 80 to 150 meq/100 g for clay. In terms of CEC, the order for soil colloid is generally humus > vermiculite > montmorillonite > illite > kaolinite > sesquioxides. Since clay and organic matter are the principal colloidal materials in the soil, can it be said that, without some clay and organic matter, a soil is useless for crop production?

6.4 SOIL PH

What makes one soil acidic and another alkaline? How can producers correct soil acidity or reclaim alkaline soils? **Soil reaction**, or *pH*, defines the soil acidity or alkalinity based on the hydrogen ion concentration. On the pH scale, a value of 7.0 indicates a neutral reaction. All values below 7.0 indicate acidity, while all values above 7.0 indicate alkalinity (Figure 6). The pH scale is logarithmic (i.e., $pH = -\log_{10}[H^+]$). This means that a pH of 4.0 is 10 times as acidic as a pH of 5.0.

Total acidity in the soil can be divided into three categories:

1. Active acidity—caused by H^+, Al^{3+} ions in the soil solution
2. Salt-replaceable acidity—due to H^+ and Al^{3+} ions that are easily exchangeable by other cations in the simple, unbuffered soil solution

Soil reaction. The degree of soil acidity or alkalinity, usually expressed as a pH value.

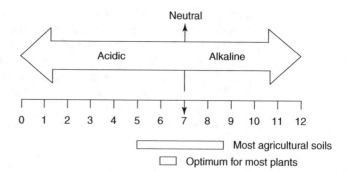

FIGURE 6 The soil pH scale is logarithmic and divided into units ranging from 0 to 14. Car battery acid has a pH of less than 1, while household bleach has a pH of about 12.5. Pure water is neutral; lemon juice has a pH of about 2; coffee has a pH of about 4.2.

FIGURE 7 An illustration of the soil nutrient availability as affected by pH. The range of availability for each nutrient element depends on whether the soil is mineral, organic, or in between.

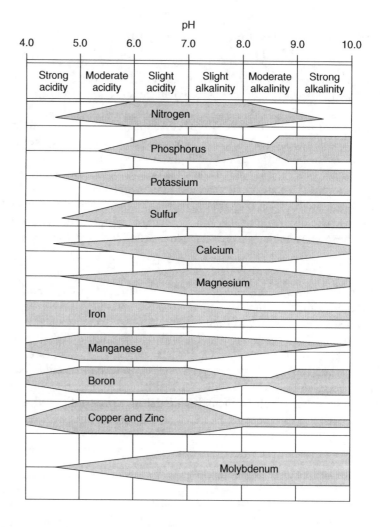

3. Residual acidity—can be neutralized by limestone but not susceptible to salt-replaceable techniques

Even though only a small fraction of the total soil acidity, active acidity is very important because plant roots and soil microorganisms are exposed to the soil solution.

Each nutrient element has a pH range within which it is available to plants (Figure 7). Similarly, plants have pH adaptation, some being sensitive to acidity, while

Table 3 Relative Crop Yields Affected by Soil pH

Crop	Relative Yield at Indicated pH				
	4.7	5.0	5.7	6.8	7.5
Alfalfa	2	9	42	100	100
Barley	0	23	80	95	100
Corn	34	73	83	100	85
Oats	7	93	99	98	100
Red clover	12	21	53	98	100
Soybeans	65	79	80	100	93
Sweet clover	0	2	49	98	100
Wheat	68	76	89	100	99

Source: Ohio Agricultural Experimental Station, Special Circulation number 53, 1938.

others are sensitive to alkalinity (Table 3). The optimum pH range for most plants is 6.5 to 7.0. Most agricultural soils have a pH of between 5.0 and 8.5. Not only is soil pH important for knowing the nutrient availability, but certain pH values cause the release into the soil of toxic amounts of certain elements (e.g., Al^{3+} at highly acidic pH) that are required by the plant in small amounts.

6.5 SALT-AFFECTED SOILS

Most soils in arid and semiarid regions are *alkaline* and *salt-affected* because of the accumulation of high amounts of salts in the soil. Even though most are not used for cropping, these soils cannot be totally ignored in crop production. In the United States, 15% of the cropland is irrigated and accounts for 40% of the total crop value in such dry areas. The high alkalinity results from the lack of adequate precipitation to leach these base-forming cations (Ca^{2+}, Mg^{2+}, K^+, Na^+, etc.) salts out of the plant root zone. These soils have a high base saturation and high pH values, often above 7.0.

High salt concentration usually reduces plant growth by the osmotic effect. As soil salt concentration increases, the force with which water is held in the soil increases, requiring plant roots to expend more energy to extract water from the soil solution. Sometimes, the salt concentration is so high that, instead of roots absorbing water, they lose water by exosmosis into the soil solution. Such a reverse trend in moisture flow can result in the death of some plants, especially young plants.

Salt accumulation in the soil inhibits the germination of seeds, reduces crop growth and development, and decreases crop yield. Salt-loving plants are called *halophytes*. Plants used in crop production vary in salt tolerance (Table 4). Plant breeders have developed salt-tolerant cultivars in certain crops. Barley and cotton are both relatively salt tolerant. Salt-affected soils have reduced permeability to water, encouraging surface erosion.

Soil salinity may be measured by electrical conductivity, whereby an electrode is used to obtain an indirect measurement of the salt content. A soil sample is saturated with distilled water and mixed to a paste (saturation paste extract method). Soils that contain large quantities of soluble salts (Na^+, Ca^{2+}, Mg^{2+}, Cl^-, SO_4^{2-}, etc.) are called *saline (salty) soils*. When the Na^+ saturation of the soil is 15% or higher, the soil pH may rise above 8.5, creating a *sodic soil* that is unproductive and very hard to manage.

Table 4 Relative Salt Tolerance of Selected Crops

Tolerant	Moderately Tolerant	Moderatively Sensitive	Sensitive
Barley (grain)	Barley (forage)	Alfalfa	Strawberry
Cotton	Sugar beet	Corn	Bean
Bermudagrass	Wheat	Peanut	Potato
	Oats	Rice (paddy)	Tomato
	Fescue (tall)	Grape	Pineapple
	Soybean	Sweet clover	Onion
	Sorghum	Broad bean	Raspberry
	Sudangrass	Sweet potato	
	Cowpea	Timothy	
	Rye (hay)	Clover (red, ladino)	

Another measurement of soil alkalinity is the *sodium adsorption ratio (SAR),* calculated as

$$SAR = Na^{2+}/\sqrt{1/2[Ca^{2+}] + Mg^{2+}}$$

SAR is used to evaluate the suitability of water for irrigation.

A saline soil has an electrical conductivity of 4.0 decisiemens/meter (dS/m) or SAR of 13 or less. A sodic soil has SAR of 13 or greater. Salty soils can be reclaimed by (1) establishing an internal drainage in the soil to remove excess water, (2) replacing the excess exchangeable sodium, or (3) leaching out most of the soluble salts by heavy irrigation. Plants may also be planted on the slope of a ridge to avoid the salt that has been drawn up to the top of the ridge.

6.6 CORRECTING SOIL ACIDITY

Liming. The application of agricultural lime or other materials containing the carbonates, oxides, and/or hydroxides of calcium and/or magnesium to neutralize soil acidity.

Low soil acidity can be corrected by **liming**, the procedure of applying limestone ($CaCO_3$) or gypsum ($CaSO_4$) to raise soil pH. On the other hand, to lower soil pH, sulfur may be applied. Certain fertilizers tend to increase soil acidity because they leave acid residues. Liming is beneficial to soil microbial growth and activity, since bacterial activity is reduced under low pH.

7: THE SOIL IS HOME TO ORGANISMS THAT ARE EITHER BENEFICIAL OR HARMFUL TO PLANTS

What role do soil organisms play in plant production? Soil organisms from all of the five kingdoms in both living and dead forms influence soils. Some of the activities of these organisms are beneficial to crop production, while others are detrimental, causing diseases and loss of productivity.

7.1 SOIL ORGANISMS

The soil is teeming with a wide diversity of organisms. The animals (fauna) of the soil range in size from macrofauna (e.g., earthworms, moles), through mesofauna (e.g., springtails, mites), to microfauna (e.g., nematodes). The plants (flora) in the soil include the roots of higher plants (e.g., weeds, crops) and microscopic algae. In addition to these, some of which are visible to the naked eye, there are other microorganisms (e.g., bacteria, fungi, actinomycetes) that are visible under the microscope.

1. *Animalia*
   a. *Burrowing animals.* These include moles, prairie dogs, gophers, mice, badgers, and rabbits. They bore large holes into the soil and incorporate plant materials, thereby improving aeration and soil fertility. Unfortunately, these animals often eat the crop plants of economic interest to the producer. Hence, overall, burrowing animals are destructive to crop production.
   b. *Earthworms.* Earthworms are perhaps the most important macroanimals in the soil. They ingest about 2 to 30 times their weight of both plant and animal residues, as well as soil, each day. They excrete large amounts of partially digested organic and soil material as small granular aggregates called *casts.* Their activities in the soil improve aeration and drainage, stirring the soil for enhanced water infiltration and root penetration, as well as enhancing soil fertility. However, they can also spread diseases. Earthworms work best under moist soil conditions where organic matter is available as a source of food and the pH is about 5.5 to 8.5. The optimum temperature for worms is about 10°C; hence, their peak activities in the temperate regions are in spring and autumn. They function less in compacted soil (from heavy machinery use), sandy soils, salty soils, drought conditions, acidic soils, extreme temperature, and rodent-infested soil.
   c. *Arthropods and gastropods.* The important arthropods (invertebrates with jointed foot) include termites, mites, millipedes, beetles, and ants. Termites (or white ants) are most prominent in the grasslands (savannas) and forests of tropical and subtropical regions. They are known for constructing mounds of varying sizes. They are not as useful as earthworms in positively affecting soil fertility and physical qualities. Their activities are more localized (in termite mounds). Important gastropods (belly-footed organisms) include slugs and snails. They feed on decaying vegetation and can feed on crop plants.
   d. *Nematodes.* Nematodes (eelworms, threadworms) may be omnivorous (living mainly on decaying organic matter), predaceous (preying on soil bacteria, fungi, algae), or parasitic (infecting plant roots). The most common nematodes are omnivorous. Parasitic nematodes are known for the characteristic and conspicuous knots they form on the roots of susceptible plants. Many food crops and vegetables are susceptible to nematodes, but more so are soybean, sugar beet, and corn, in which they cause yield losses exceeding 50%. Nematodes are beneficial on golf courses and sod farms, where they control white grub.
2. *Plantae.* Living roots of plants impact soil physical properties as they push through it. They secrete a variety of compounds into the soil. When plants die or are harvested, a large mass of roots comprising about 10 to 40% of the plant vegetative body is left in the soil, contributing to soil organic matter. The area in the soil immediately around the living roots is called the *rhizosphere.* Some of the root exudates exert growth-regulating effects on other plants and soil microorganisms, a phenomenon called *allelopathy.* Algae growth occurs in production systems that use surface irrigation (e.g., in flood-irrigated rice fields).
3. *Soil fungi.* Fungi may be unicellular (e.g., yeast) or multicellular (e.g., molds, mildews, rusts, mushrooms). They are responsible for most of the economic

diseases of crop plants, as described elsewhere in this book. Some of the toxins (mycotoxins) they produce are deadly to animals (e.g., aflatoxin). Fungi have beneficial roles in the ecosystem. They decompose organic matter and thereby enhance soil fertility. They help some plants absorb soil nutrients through a symbiotic association called **mycorrhiza**.

4. *Protista.* This group includes protozoa and slime molds. They cause a few plant diseases but cause many animal diseases (e.g., malaria, amoebic dysentery, Texas cattle fever).

5. *Monera.* Actinomycetes are known for producing antibiotic compounds (actinomycin, neomycin, streptomycin). They also decompose organic matter. Soil bacteria are important in their symbiotic relationships with plants. They may be autotrophic (self-nutritive, making their own food) or heterotrophic (deriving nutrition from organic substances). Soil bacteria are engaged in several important processes that help soil fertility including biological nitrogen fixatron, nitrification, and mycorrhiza

Mycorrhiza. The association, usually symbiotic, of fungi with roots of some seed plants.

7.2 CULTURAL PRACTICES IN CROP PRODUCTION MAY BE USED TO MANAGE SOIL MICROBES

Since the soil contains both beneficial and harmful microbes, the crop producer should adopt practices that encourage the beneficial microorganisms while controlling harmful ones. Just as a good growth environment favors both weeds and crop plants, good conditions for beneficial organisms may also encourage the growth of harmful ones. Thus, how can a grower selectively promote beneficial organisms while suppressing harmful ones? There are certain practices that can give an advantage to beneficial microbes:

1. *Inoculation.* There are native bacteria in the soil. Since symbiotic activities involve specificity for host bacteria, it is advantageous to inoculate the soil with the *Rhizobium* of interest.
2. *Application of lime.* Acidic soils should be limed to raise the pH to about 6.0. High acidity destroys bacteria.
3. *Reduction of fumigation.* Soil fumigation or sterilization kills both harmful and beneficial microbes and should not be conducted too frequently. In the greenhouse, however, sterilization of soil and other materials is routine and desirable.
4. *Sanitation.* Remove and destroy infected and diseased plants and residue to avoid spreading harmful microbes.
5. *Maintenance of good soil environment.* The soil should be well aerated, should be drained (no waterlogging), should have good moisture (no drought), and should not contain abnormal levels of salts.
6. *Organic matter content.* Soil microbes depend on soil organic matter for energy. A good, healthy soil should have adequate organic matter.

The following strategies are helpful in reducing the populations of harmful microbes:

1. Establish crops by using healthy, disease-free planting material.
2. Observe good sanitation: clean tools after use. Remove and destroy infected plants and their remains.
3. Eliminate vectors: insect vectors are carriers of diseases and can be eliminated to reduce the spreading of a pest.
4. Maintain good microclimate: high humidity, still air, and high temperature encourage growth of fungi and other microbes. Pruning, a horticultural practice

of removing branches and other plant parts, can be used to open the plant canopy for aeration. Irrigation should be done in the morning, so that plant leaves dry during the day. This helps to reduce disease.

5. Maintain soil at a slightly acidic pH: the spread of some pathogens such as fungal rots of sweet potato are reduced when soil pH is slightly acidic. Potato scab is effectively controlled at a pH of below about 5.2.
6. Protect plants from mechanical injury: pathogens enter plants through natural pores and wounds.
7. Do not allow infestations to build up.

7.3 SELECTED ROLES OF SOIL MICROORGANISMS

Soil microbes are involved in activities that enhance soil fertility, one of the basic roles being in decomposition of organic matter to recycle immobilized nutrients. Some additional specific roles of soil microbes are as follows.

Nitrification

Nitrification is the process by which ammonia ions are enzymatically oxidized by autotrophic nitrifying bacteria—*Nitrosomonas* and *Nitrobacter* in the following reactions:

$$2NH_4^+ + 3O_2 \xrightarrow{\text{\textit{Nitrosomonas}}} 2NO_2^- + 4H^+ + 2H_2O + \text{energy}$$

$$2NO_2^- + O_2 \xrightarrow{\text{\textit{Nitrobacter}}} 2NO_3^- + \text{energy}$$

This transformation process is slowed under cold temperature, strong acidity, and waterlogging (anaerobic conditions). NO_3^- ions are most rapidly absorbed by plants.

Denitrification

Denitrification, a biological process involving bacteria, is the source of the most extensive gaseous nitrogen loss. Under anaerobic conditions, bacteria convert NO_3^- into nitrogen gas:

$$2NO_3^- \rightarrow 2NO_2^- \rightarrow 2NO \rightarrow N_2O \rightarrow N_2$$

Consequently, it is undesirable to fertilize crops with nitrate fertilizers if the soil will be flooded in a production practice (e.g., paddy rice production).

Denitrification. The biological reduction of nitrate or nitrite to gaseous nitrogen or nitrogen oxides.

Biological Nitrogen Fixation

There are two kinds of biological nitrogen fixation (BNF) processes—*symbiotic* and *nonsymbiotic*. Nonsymbiotic BNF is undertaken by free-living bacteria and cynobacteria that are not associated with plants. The bacteria involved include *Clostridium* and *Azotobacter*. Symbiotic nitrogen fixation involves bacteria that live mostly in the roots of legumes and non-legumes. Infected plants produce root nodules (root modifications that are the site of nitrogen fixation) by the following general reaction:

$$N_2 + 8H^+ + 6e^- \xrightarrow{\text{\textit{nitrogenase}}} 2NH_3 + H_2$$

$$NH_3 + \text{organic acids} \rightarrow \text{amino acids} \rightarrow \text{protein}$$

The reduction of N_2 involves the enzyme nitrogenase. The best known symbiotic bacteria belong to the genus *Rhizobium*. The amount of nitrogen fixed depends on the species. Symbiotic BNF in alfalfa yields an average of about 200 kg/ha of nitrogen per season versus 45 kg/ha of nitrogen per season under ideal conditions. In the commercial production of legumes, such as peanut and soybean, producers treat seeds with commercial inoculants containing the appropriate bacterium to augment the native bacteria population.

Mycorrhizae

Mycorrhizae (or fungus roots) are of two kinds, based on growth habit—*ectomycorrhiza* and *endomycorrhiza*. Ectomycorrhizae penetrate only the outer cell layers of the root walls, forming a fungus mat on the root surface. Endomycorrhizae penetrate the host cell. Some hyphae (filaments) are from vesicular-arbuscular mycorrhizae (VAM). They form highly branched structures called *arbuscules*. VAM are the most important form of mycorrhizae found on plants and are very helpful in phosphate absorption. In addition to phosphate absorption, they help reduce stress due to drought. Mycorrhizae function best in highly weathered tropical soils that are low in base ions, are acidic, and are low in levels of phosphorus and aluminum. Most agronomic crops (e.g., cotton, potato, soybean, rice, wheat), vegetables, and tree crops benefit from VAM. Mycorrhizae are absent in Cruciferae (e.g., cabbage, canola) and Chenopodiaceae (e.g., sugar beet, spinach).

8: SOIL ORGANIC MATTER AFFECTS BOTH PHYSICAL AND CHEMICAL PROPERTIES OF SOIL

Soil organic matter is the decomposed remains of organisms that have been incorporated into the soil. Soil organic matter consists of about 45 to 50% carbon. The skeletal residue remaining after decomposition of organic matter is called *soil humus*. This is a very complex organic material. Based upon solubilities, there are different classes of soil humic substances. *Humin* is the part of humus that is insoluble in sodium hydroxide. *Fluvic acid* and *humic acid* are soluble in dilute sodium hydroxide solution but the latter precipitates out at acid pH.

Decomposition of organic matter is an enzymatic process. Since organic matter consists of different chemical bonds, there are different enzymes for breaking each of these bonds. The products of decomposition depend on the conditions under which the biological reaction occurred. Under aerobic conditions, products of decomposition include CO_2, NH_4^+, NO_3^-, SO_4^{2-}, $H_2PO_4^-$, and H_2O. When decomposition occurs under anaerobic conditions, some toxic products, such as H_2S and dimethylsulfide, are produced. The characteristic foul odor associated with swamps is caused by the evolution of CH_4 (methane), also called *swamp gas*.

The greater the population of decay microbes, the faster the decomposition. However, the rate of decomposition of organic matter usually depends on the amount of nitrogen present. Soil microbes use nitrogen and carbon for growth and reproduction. The nitrogen content of an organic matter is measured by its *carbon to nitrogen ratio (C:N)*. Straw has a C:N of 80:1, while sawdust has a C:N of 400 to 800:1 (Table 5). Alfalfa crop residue has a C:N of only 13:1. The lower the C:N ratio the faster the crop residue de-

---

Let it rot! Decomposition of organic matter

Nutrient cycling is critical to the success of organic farming. Inorganic nutrients are absorbed by plants and then metabolized and converted into organic matter (cells and tissues). Upon dying, organic matter is subject to decomposition, which results in the conversion of the organic form of nutrients into inorganic components. De-composition is simply the breakdown of organic matter. Either way, the processes of decomposition involve chemical or biochemical events that often require oxygen.

There are two categories of decomposition. *Abiotic decomposition* (without living organisms) occurs primarily through burning in which oxygen reacts with the organic matter to produce carbon dioxide and other substances in the ash. The ash provides nutrients for cropping in a slash-and-burn production system. However, most of the carbon is lost as carbon dioxide.

Biotic decomposition (with living organisms, especially bacteria and fungi) may involve aerobic or anaerobic microbes. These microbes utilize organic matter as a source of energy. Unlike abiotic decomposition, biotic decomposition takes place in a series of steps in which organic matter is sequentially broken down into inorganic compounds through a series of intermediate organic compounds.

The decomposition of importance to cropping occurs in the soil or the soil surface. *Litter* consists of fragments of the source of organic matter that makes it easy to identify the organism. This may be leaves, stems, and other parts of the plant. When litter is broken down into smaller unrecognizable organic material, the product is called *detritus*. The next stage of decomposition is *humus,* a dark brown mixture of various compounds and substances. Inorganic compounds are freed from the organic compounds by the process of *mineralization.*

Mineralization: setting minerals free

Inorganic nitrogen (e.g., NH_4^+, NO_3^-, NO_2^-, and N_2 gas) is used by plants and soil bacteria and converted into organic nitrogen compounds in the tissues and other structures. The nitrogen in this organic form is said to be immobilized and the process is called *immobilization.* The organic form of nitrogen is unavailable to plants. Upon dying, the organic matter undergoes decomposition. A stage in the process of decomposition called *mineralization* releases the immobilized nitrogen in inorganic form for use by plants and other organisms.

Mineralization is an enzymatic process that may be summarized as follows

$$\longrightarrow \textbf{Mineralization}$$

$$\underset{-H_2O^+}{\overset{+H_2O^+}{RNH_2 \rightleftharpoons ROH + NH_4^+}} \underset{+O_2}{\overset{+O_2}{\rightleftharpoons NO_2^- + 4H^+}} \underset{+[O]}{\overset{+[O]}{\rightleftharpoons NO_3^-}}$$

$$\textbf{Immobilization} \longleftarrow$$

Through hydrolysis, the hydrogen in the amine group (NH_2) is removed in the form of ammonia (NH_3), which reacts with water or acids in the soil solution to produce the ammonium ion (NH_4^+). Plants can utilize this form of nitrogen. However, it may also be further transformed by enzymatic oxidation by the process of *nitrification* to produce nitrates. Nitrification is a two-step process involving two different kinds of microorganisms called *nitrifying bacteria:*

Step 1: $2NH_4^+ + 3O_2^- \rightarrow 2NO_2^- + 2H_2O + 4H^+ + energy$

This step is undertaken by bacteria called *Nitrosomonas.*

Step 2: $2NO_2^- + O_2 \rightarrow 2NO_3^- + energy$

This step is carried out by bacteria called *Nitrobacter.*

Nitrates are highly soluble in water and hence prone to leaching. Further, nitrogen may be lost through *denitrification,* which occurs under conditions of poor drainage and aeration.

---

composes. Sawdust, therefore, is highly resistant to decomposition. The C:N ratio narrows as decomposition progresses and carbon is released as carbon dioxide.

The conditions required for decomposition are warm temperature and good moisture. Waterlogged soils (anaerobic conditions) slow decomposition. Similarly, dry soils inhibit microbial action. Rate of decomposition is most rapid during the first 2 weeks. A

Symbiotic nitrogen fixation: organic fertilizer manufacturing

Biological nitrogen fixation is the process by which elemental nitrogen is combined into organic forms. An estimated 175 million metric tons of nitrogen is fixed by bacteria either independently or in association with plants, the latter being called *symbiotic nitrogen fixation*. Symbiosis is the cohabitation between two organisms for mutual benefit. Certain bacteria, especially those of the genus *Rhizobium*, invade the roots of legumes, causing the production of swellings called *nodules*. The legume host provides the bacteria with carbohydrates for energy, and in return the bacteria fix elemental nitrogen in organic form directly into the plant roots. This legume-bacterial symbiosis has significant specificity—that is, one *Rhizobium* species will effectively inoculate a certain legume species but not others. Based on symbiotic associations, legumes may be classified into seven cross-inoculation groups:

Group	Rhizobium *Species*	Legumes
Alfalfa	*R. meliloti*	Alfalfa (*Medicago*), certain clovers (*Melilotus*)
Clover	*R. trifolii*	Clovers (*Trifolium* spp.)
Soybean	*R. japonicum*	Soybean (*Glycine* max).
Lupine	*R. lupini*	Lupines (*Lupinus*), serradella (*Ornithopus* spp.)
Bean	*R. phaseoli*	Dry bean (*Phaseolus vulgaris*), runner bean (*P. coccineus*)
Peas and vetch	*R. leguminosarum*	Pea (*Pisum*), vetch (*Vicia*), sweet pea (*Lathyrus*), lentil (*Lens* spp.)
Cowpea miscellany	Various species	Cowpea (*Vigna*), lespedeza (*Lespedeza*), peanut (*Arachis*), pigeon pea (*Cajanus*), crotalaria (*Crotolaria*), kudzu (*Pueraria*), stylo (*Stylosanthes*), Acacia, desmodium (*Desmodium*)

The general mechanism by which biological nitrogen fixation occurs is the reduction of nitrogen gas to ammonia, a reaction that is catalyzed by *nitrogenase* and involves iron and molybdenum. The ammonia is subsequently combined with other organic acids to form amino acids and eventually proteins.

Table 5 Carbon–Nitrogen (C:N) Ratios of Selected Organic Materials

Material	*C:N ratio*
Wheat straw	80:1
Corn stover	57:1
Alfalfa (mature)	25:1
Alfalfa (young)	13:1
Sawdust	400:1 or more

crop residue with a narrow C:N ratio will make nitrogen available sooner than one with a wide C:N ratio (Figure 8). The producer can plant immediately after plowing under a crop such as alfalfa. On the other hand, after plowing under a material such as straw, a waiting period of about 6 weeks is required before planting. The effect of soil organic matter is summarized in Table 6.

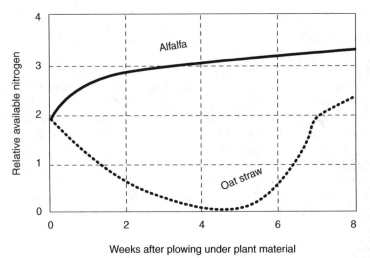

FIGURE 8 The carbon–nitrogen ratio (C:N) for alfalfa is lower than that for oat straw. When plowed under, alfalfa decomposes rapidly to release nitrogen into the soil. However, oat has a high C:N ratio and decomposes slowly. Initially, it causes a decrease in available nitrogen until after about 4 weeks, when microbial population decreases; then more nitrogen becomes available for plant use.

Table 6	Effects of Soil Organic Matter

Benefits

1. Provides 90 to 95% of all the nitrogen in unfertilized soils (acts as a "slow-release" fertilizer)
2. Supplies soil-binding factors (polysaccharides) for soil aggregation
3. Has colloidal properties and accounts for about 30 to 70% of cation exchange in the soil
4. Increases soil water content at field capacity
5. Improves soil aeration and water flow in fine-textured soils
6. Acts as chelate
7. Provides carbon for microorganism in the soil
8. Can be used as mulch to reduce soil surface erosion and conserve moisture
9. Can modify soil temperature (insulation), increasing it in cold weather and cooling it in hot weather
10. Acts as a soil buffer against rapid pH alteration and other changes in soil chemistry

Adverse Effects

Organic plants may release plant toxins (phytotoxins) upon decomposition. This effect is called allelopathy. Known allelochemicals include alkaloids, benzoxainones, coumrins, cyanogenic compounds, quinines, flavanoids, and terpenes. Crops with such properties include sorghum, johnsongrass, black walnut, and peach.

Crop residues contain chemicals that may be toxic *(phytotoxins)*. *Allelopathy* is the term used to describe the effect of harmful or beneficial chemicals *(allelochemicals)* produced by one plant on another plant. These chemicals are leached out of crop residues. Many perennial weeds such as johnsongrass, quackgrass, and nutsedge are suspected to have allelopathic effects.

9: SOIL COMPACTION

Soil compaction is a form of soil degradation that is characterized by an increase in soil density by the packing of soil particles when pressure is applied to it. The packing of the primary soil particles (sand, silt, clay) and soil aggregates closer together dramatically changes the balance between soil solids and voids (pore spaces) (Figure 9). The degradation starts with the collapse and elimination of macropores (large pores), thereby severely restricting water movement (especially gravitational water), root penetration, and air movement. Soils of uniform texture (e.g., sandy soil) are less susceptible to compaction than are those with a wide range of textures (e.g., fine sandy loam). Under pressure, the finer particles readily fill the larger pores created by the coarse components of the textural class, increasing soil density.

9.1 CAUSES OF SOIL COMPACTION

The causes of soil compaction occurring on cropping land may be categorized according to farm activities, location of the problem, or origin.

1. *Farm activities.* According to farm activities, compaction may be tillage-induced or traffic-induced.

   Tillage operations exert pressure on the soil from the tractor or the implements it draws. Primary tillage implements (e.g., disc plows) tend to compact the soil at the plow depth, creating an impervious layer over time if the plow depth is not varied periodically. Secondary tillage also affects soil structure by destroying soil aggregation and increasing soil density. The tillage-induced compaction is worsened when soils are tilled under wet conditions. Also, this compaction type affects mainly the plow layer (about 6–12 inches) through contact pressure with implements.

   Traffic-induced compaction is caused mainly by the wheels of farm vehicles and, in pastures, by the trampling of livestock. This compaction affects the subsoil layers in proportion to the axle load of the vehicles. Modern mechanized crop production predisposes the field to compaction because of the use of machinery at all stages of production (seeding, chemical treatment, harvesting).

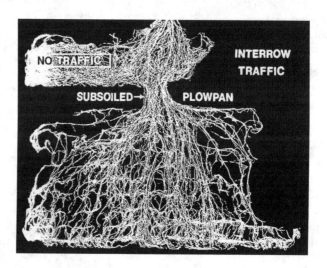

FIGURE 9 Soil compaction hinders normal root growth in the soil. Areas in the field where there has been no traffic shows more root development, whereas interrow traffic and plowpans severely restrict the penetration of the roots into the soil. Roots that find cracks in compacted layers are able to penetrate into the subsoil. (Source: Drawn from USDA photo)

2. *Location of Problem.* Compaction may also be classified, according to the location, as surface or subsoil compaction. The classification essentially corresponds to that based on farm activities, the surface being equivalent to tillage-induced compaction, and the subsoil being equivalent to traffic-induced compaction. Surface compaction is caused mainly by the contact pressure from vehicle tires, while compaction from below the plow layer is related to the total axle load of the vehicles.

3. *Origin.* Compaction may also be classified as being human-induced (e.g., from farming activities) or as originating from natural causes (e.g., the splashing of rain drops).

9.2 DIAGNOSING COMPACTION IN THE FIELD

A producer may suspect that a field is compacted when he or she observes the presence of tell-tale signs in the soil or plants or when he or she has made some investigations.

Soil Observations

The major soil changes that suggest compaction include the following:

1. *Ponding of water on the soil surface.* When water collects in a pool in relatively level parts of the field, it may suggest drainage problems.

2. *Presence of dark streaks on the soil surface.* As a result of the prolonged ponding of water on the field in tire tracks, the soil in those spots becomes blackened as the water dries up.

3. *Increased power needed for tillage.* When the operator notices that more machine power than usual is needed for a tillage operation, the soil may be more dense than normal.

4. *Increased runoff.* When gently sloping land has excessive surface runoff following a moderate amount of rain or irrigation, there may be soil compaction.

5. *Surface soil crusts.* Crusting of the surface soil can be the result of surface compaction.

Plant Observations

Soil compaction is manifested in plant-related symptoms:

1. *Incomplete crop stand.* Crusting and other compaction-related structures may hinder seed germination, leading to an incomplete stand.

2. *Uneven crop stand.* Plants may germinate but, because of compaction in various parts of the field plant growth may be uneven. Plants in compacted sections may be stunted, while those in normal soil grow properly, leading to variation in height and plant size.

3. *Changes in plant color.* Compacted areas of the field may be waterlogged, causing moisture stress to plants that may manifest as chlorosis (yellowing) or purpling of the stem in early growth.

4. *Restricted root development.* Instead of plant roots growing deep into the soil, an obstruction may promote more horizontal root growth or balling of the roots.

5. *Unexpected wilting.* Compaction may limit plants' roots to the top, preventing the extraction of moisture from lower depths and causing earlier than normal wilting.

6. *Reduced yields.* Soil compaction reduces plant roots and hence nutrient and water absorption, consequently reducing crop yield.

Soil Investigations

The soil's resistance to penetration by an object indicates the soil density. Various instruments and tools (e.g., soil probe, penetrometer, small-diameter soil sampling tube) may be used to physically test the penetrability of the soil. A soil probe or shovel is pushed through the soil to determine resistance to penetration. A penetrometer provides electronic readings to indicate soil strength and resistance to root penetration. However, it is very sensitive to soil moisture; hence, the reading should be interpreted with caution. One may also dig a small pit to expose the root zone of the plant to examine the growth pattern.

9.3   EFFECTS OF SOIL COMPACTION

Soil compaction may have desirable effects in crop production, depending on the degree of compaction, the season of occurrence, and the crop species.

Desirable Effects

Light soil compaction is needed at seeding for good contact between seed and soil for seed germination. Some planters are designed to cover seeds and press down the soil for those purposes. Sometimes, special implements (soil packers) are mounted on tractors and used at seeding times to compact the soil over the seed. Studies have shown that a medium soil texture of bulk density of 1.2 gm per cubic centimeter (74 lb/cubic foot) is favorable for root growth. Where this bulk density is less, moderate amount of compaction may be beneficial for optimal root development. This will bring the roots into more effective contact with the soil to absorb more nutrients, especially those that are immobile (e.g., phosphorus).

Undesirable Effects

As previously indicated, excessive soil compaction hinders proper root growth and consequently reduces the amount of soil moisture and nutrients that can be absorbed. In the dry season, moderate compaction is desirable, increasing yields because the roots are in better contact with the soil to extract whatever moisture is available. As compaction increases, yield decreases as other factors come into play. However, in the wet season, increasing compaction reduces soil aeration, promoting denitrification and reduced root metabolism, leading to decreased yield.

9.4   MANAGING SOIL COMPACTION

Soil compaction is largely caused by the activities of producers through the use of machinery. Because mechanization in crop production is here to stay and likely to increase, and because some compaction is desirable, the producer should find ways of minimizing its adverse effects in production. The approaches used in managing soil compaction include prevention and correction.

It is best to prevent soil compaction because, once it occurs, it is usually very expensive to correct.

1. *Proper timing of field operations.* Tillage and other field operations should not be undertaken when the soil is wet. This may not always be prudent because delaying an operation (e.g., planting, harvesting) may have serious economic consequences.
2. *Proper choice of machinery.* Use vehicles with larger-diameter tires, reduced tire pressure, and reduced axle loads. Use all-wheel-drive vehicles when possible. Also, use only enough ballast to reduce slippage.

3. *Traffic patterns.* Reduce the number of passes over the field with equipment. Use larger-capacity equipment with wider working width for fewer passes. Fewer passes means that a smaller portion of the field actually comes into contact with the wheels of farm machinery and equipment.
4. *Drainage.* Improve drainage of the field to reduce soil wetness.
5. *Crop rotation.* Plant the field to crops with different root depths, including deep-rooted species, such as alfalfa.
6. *Tillage depth.* Instead of tilling the field to the same depth season after season, it is best to vary the depth regularly (e.g., reduce the depth in a wet year and increase it in a dry year to break the compacted layer).

When compaction has occurred, it may be corrected by one of several means. Some of these measures may also be used as preventive measures.

1. Subsoiling is the practice of tilling the soil to a very low depth to break compaction at the subsoil level. This is a very expensive activity that is done when the soil is dry. It should be followed with preventive measures.
2. Variation in the tillage depth may be used to alleviate light to moderate compaction caused by tillage operations.

10: SOIL EROSION

Even though modern advances in science enable some crop production to occur in soilless (lacking natural rock mineral materials) media (e.g., in greenhouses), most crops are produced in the soil in the field. *Soil erosion* is the removal of soil by water and wind. Soil is a non-renewable resource and hence should be properly managed, so that it is able to sustain crop production indefinitely. Most crop roots occur in the topsoil, the part that is most prone to erosion. The displaced soil must be deposited elsewhere, often with adverse consequences. Soil erosion may also be defined as a process that transforms soil into sediment. There are two main processes of soil erosion—by *water* and by *wind*. The Great Plains region and the Corn Belt have significant amounts of soil erosion (Figure 10). Excessive cropland erosion occurs on farms, especially in these regions of the United States.

10.1 WATER EROSION

Water erosion occurs in three basic steps—detachment of soil particles, transportation of the dislodged particles downhill, and deposition at a lower elevation (Figure 11). The direct impact of raindrops may disintegrate aggregated soils by the splashing effect. The particles are transported by runoff water. The soil surface may be depleted in more or less a uniform manner as water flows gently over the surface. This soil removal is called *sheet erosion.* When the sheet flow concentrates into tiny channels, soil removal is concentrated in those channels (called *rill erosion*), as commonly occurs on bare land, newly planted land, and fallows. When the volume of runoff is further concentrated, it moves with more turbulence and cuts deeper as it rushes through the field, creating larger channels (called *gulley erosion*).

The amount of soil loss by water erosion by rill and sheet can be estimated by the Universal Soil Loss Equation (USLE) or by the more recent computerized version, the Revised Universal Soil Loss Equation (RUSLE) as follows:

$$A = RKLSCP$$

FIGURE 10 The heavily farmed crop-lands of the Great Plains and the Midwest are susceptible to soil erosion. (Source: USDA)

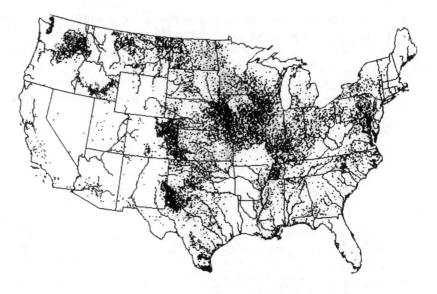

FIGURE 11 Water erosion starts as gentle and light soil removal, as in rill erosion (left), and soon develops into massive soil removal, as in gulley erosion (right), if it is unchecked. (Source: USDA)

where A = erosion (soil loss in tons/acre/year)
R = rainfall factor
K = soil erodibility factor (ranges from 1 = most easily eroded to 0.01 = least easily eroded)
LS = field length and slope factor
C = vegetative cover and management factor
P = practice used for erosion control

R and K are rain-related factors; K and LS are soil-related factors; C and P are management-related factors.

Water erosion can be controlled by controlling sediment detachment or sediment transport:

1. Sediment detachment is controlled by maintaining a vegetative cover on the soil (e.g., planting cover crops, stubble mulching, or keeping crop residues on the soil). These and other preventive practices are discussed in detail under conservation tillage.
2. Controlling sediment transport is achieved by slowing the speed of water flow (e.g., by the reduction of the slope in the land, with terraces, or by contour strip cropping). These practices are also discussed under conservation tillage.

10.2 WIND EROSION

Wind erosion entails the removal, transport, and deposition of fine soil particles by winds (Figure 12). The mechanics are similar to those of water erosion. The damage is greatest when the wind is strong, and the soil is dry, bare, or weakly aggregated. One of the ecological devastations on record is the Dust Bowl of the 1930s, during which wind erosion precipitated by drought devastated the agriculture of the Great Plains region (see boxed reading). Wind erosion occurs in three ways. *Suspension* is the movement of small soil particles over long distances in dust clouds. *Saltation* is the mode of transport of soil particles by short successions of bounces. Coarser soil particles are too heavy to be airborne and, instead, are moved by rolling along the soil surface, called surface creep. The wind erosion equation (WEQ) and the revised equation (RWEQ) are as follows:

$$E = f(ICKLV)$$

where erosion is a function (f) of

I = soil erodibility factor
C = climate factor
K = soil-ridge-roughness factor
L = width of field factor
V = vegetation cover factor

Wind erosion can be controlled by:

1. Maintaining good soil moisture with irrigation
2. Using windbreaks to slow down wind speed

FIGURE 12 An unprotected and recently plowed field shows a cloud of dust as the wind blows, whereas the cropped field in the foreground is unaffected (left). A roadside ditch adjoining a farm is gradually becoming clogged with wind-deposited soil (right).

The Great Plains and dryland farming

Dryland farming is crop production without irrigation (i.e., rainfed production) in semiarid regions. Although some dryland farming occurs in parts of the Pacific Northwest and the Pacific Southwest, this production system is concentrated in the Great Plains region, an expansive semi-arid region that includes parts of 10 states in the U.S. (Montana, North Dakota, South Dakota, Wyoming, Nebraska, Colorado, Kansas, New Mexico, Oklahoma, and Texas) and the prairie dryland region of Canada. It is the largest dryland farming region in the U.S.

Once called the "Great American Desert," the history of the Great Plains is dominated by two weather-related events. The "Dust Bowl" of the 1930s was, without a doubt, one of the most devastating ecological disasters the world had ever experienced. Nevertheless, in the 1950s, the region experienced the driest years on record. The Great Plains region generally experiences scarce precipitation that severely hampers crop production. However, the region is no stranger to drought. In fact, severe droughts occur about every 20 years, and minor ones occur every 3–4 years. However, there is no other historical account similar to the peculiar winds and the erosion that accompanied the drought of the 1930s, which are often referred to as if they were a single event. In actuality, there were at least 4 distinct drought events during that period—1930–1931, 1934, 1936, and 1939–1940. During this period, numerous dust storms were recorded (e.g., 14 storms in 1932, 38 in 1933, 22 in 1934, etc.).

Drought is often cited as the cause of the Dust Bowl, but it also points out that the poor land management practices of that period's farmers made the Great Plains totally vulnerable to, and exacerbated the consequences of, the drought. The period between 1925–1930 is described as the boom years of the Great Plains. The region was first settled in 1875–1876. These settlers had some success with agricultural production in the wet cycles, which encouraged them to remain in the region in spite of the periodic drought episodes. Proponents of dryland agriculture encouraged the rapid population of the Great Plains through misleading information about the region's agricultural potential. The Great Depression (economic decline), which occurred during that period, and the economic over-expansion contributed to

---

3. Tillage to provide clods on the surface of the soil, vegetative materials on the soil, and adoption of conservation practices such as strip cropping, cropping perpendicular to the wind direction, and stubble mulching.

10.3 IMPORTANCE OF RESIDUE MANAGEMENT IN EROSION CONTROL

Residue management through conservation tillage is one of the most effective and least expensive methods of reducing soil erosion. Maintaining a 20% residue cover can reduce soil erosion by 50%. No-till planting systems leaves the most residue on the soil surface. In such cases, soil erosion can be reduced by 90 to 95% of what occurs in conventional tillage.

Farmhouse in a dust storm.

the adverse effects of the drought that followed. New crop production technologies were introduced, including new varieties, machinery, row-cropping, and disc plowing. Most of the newly plowed land was cultivated to wheat, increasing the production of the crop by 300 percent and creating a glut in the process in 1931. In the early 20s, the expansion was necessary to pay for the new farming equipment and to offset the low crop prices that occurred after World War I. Farmers were compelled to cultivate more land to meet their financial obligations, resulting in the cultivation of submarginal lands. Soil conservation practices were abandoned to reduce production costs. Livestock was introduced into the agriculture of the regions, adding to the soil's de-

struction through the pulverizing impact of their trampling on the soil exposed by cultivation.

When the drought hit in the early 30s, the conditions were ideal for massive wind erosion to occur. Dust storms characterized the events of this period. The more dramatic dust storms called "black blizzards," rose to heights of 7,000–8,000 feet. Crops and property were destroyed. One of the storms in 1935 was recorded to have lasted 908 hours. The Soil Conservation Service estimated the Dust Bowl to have covered about 100 million acres in 1935, declined to 22 million acres by 1940, and disappeared in the late 40s.

The most visible impact of the 30s drought was the devastation to agricultural production in the Great Plains. The most severely affected areas were west Texas, eastern New Mexico, the Oklahoma Panhandle, western Kansas, and east Colorado. The Federal Government intervened to provide economic relief assistance to the affected states. About 68 percent of the relief went to farmers. In 1934 alone, the Federal Government provided assistance to the tune of $525 million. The Natural Resources Conservation Service (NRCS), formed from the Soil Conservation Service, developed proactive programs to prevent the recurrence of the catastrophe of the 1930s. Currently, the NRCS continues to emphasize the implementation of soil conservation measures. Other practical measures developed after the Dust Bowl included increased irrigation, crop diversification, federal crop insurance, regional economic diversification, and removal of sensitive agricultural lands from production.

11: Soil Drainage

Drainage is the removal of excess gravitational water from soils by natural or artificial methods. Artificial drainage is used on over 10% of all cropland in the world and on about 30% of the cropland in North America. Poor soil drainage has adverse consequences, including the following:

1. Reduced soil aeration, leading to reduced root respiration and growth
2. Reduced absorption of nutrients, especially phosphorus and potassium
3. The formation and accumulation of toxic substances

11.1 BENEFITS

The benefits of drainage include the following:

1. Wet soils are naturally fertile because of high clay and organic matter. Drainage makes them suitable for cropping.
2. Drainage improves soil aeration for quick warming in spring.
3. Wet spots are eliminated to give a uniform field soil moisture.
4. Microbial activity is promoted for more efficient decomposition of organic matter.
5. Denitrification that occurs under anaerobic conditions is reduced.
6. Root growth and development are promoted for more effective exploitation of the soil for improved crop productivity.
7. A drained soil is adaptable to the production of a wider variety of crops, not just those that tolerate excessive soil moisture.

11.2 CAUSES

The factors that cause poor soil drainage include the following:

1. High water table
2. Shallow depth of the bedrock
3. Presence of a low permeable clay layer
4. Accumulation of water at a rate faster than natural drainage occurs

11.3 METHODS

Soil drainage systems are of two main types—*surface* and *subsurface*.

Surface Drainage

Surface drainage systems are used for removing excess irrigation water from the field, lowering the water table, and removing water trapped in surface depressions. Drainage is accomplished with open ditches, ridge-tillage, and the grading or smoothing of a field to remove minor depressions that collect water (Figure 13).

FIGURE 13 Excess water from a field can be drained through grassed open ditches.

FIGURE 14 Engineers install a perforated tube for subsurface drainage (left); drained water from the subsurface is discharged into an open drainage line (right).

Subsurface Drainage

Subsurface drainage systems consist of submerged units that include tiles and porous plastic tubes (Figure 14). An advantage of this system is that the area above the drainage units can still be cultivated, unlike surface systems that take significant amounts of land out of agricultural production. Subirrigation systems are more expensive to install, those using tiles being more so than those using plastic tubes.

12: LAND SUITABLE FOR CROP PRODUCTION

Land varies in its use for agricultural production. Certain pieces of land are naturally fertile and most preferred for crop farming. Others need various levels of management to become usable for cropping. What soil orders tend to have natural fertility for crop production? The USDA-NRCS has developed certain criteria for classifying lands according to the level of soil management needed. This is called the *land capability classification.* There are eight classes identified in this system (Table 7). A Class I land is one that can be used continuously for intensive crop production with good farming practice. This land also has few limitations. Prime farmlands have good average temperature that favors most crops. They are deep, are well-drained, have a desirable pH (4.5 to 8.4), and have a reliable source of water for crop production (either from rain or irrigation). Class VIII land, on the other hand, has severe limitations (e.g., wet land, rocks, and steep slopes) and is usually unfit for crop production (Figure 15).

A *unique farmland* has characteristics that favor the production of specific crops. This type of land is used for producing specific high-value food and fiber crops with unique soil and/or climatic requirements (e.g., citrus, tree nuts, and vegetables).

By definition, *prime farmland* is the best land available for a specific enterprise. Prime farmland is land whose soils are best suited to producing food, feed, fiber, and oilseed crops. These lands produce the highest yields with minimal production inputs and least damage to the environment.

Table 7 Land Capability Classes and Their General Properties

Class	Properties
Class I	The land has few limitations on its use. It is nearly level and has deep and well-drained soils. It can be used continuously for cropping under normal management. The land is suitable for cultivation of row crops and others.
Class II	The land has significant limitations to its use for intensive crop production. It usually has a gentle slope (2 to 5%) and requires the implementation of some conservation practices as part of the management practice. Minimum tillage is desirable. Row crops can be cultivated with proper management.
Class III	The land has severe limitations on its use for intensive cropping. The slope is more pronounced (6 to 10%). Special conservation and management practices (e.g., drainage) are necessary prior to use. Crops that protect the soil from erosion (grasses and legumes) may be cultivated.
Class IV	The land has more severe limitations than Class III. Row crops are not suited to this land (unless they are grasses and densely populated species that protect the soil from erosion). It is best to grow perennial species such as pastures. No-till cropping systems, terracing, or other special conservation practices should be implemented.
Class V	The land has very severe limitations that are impractical to rectify by conventional conservation practices. It is prone to excessive moisture from flooding and is too rocky to be tilled. The land can be developed into a pastureland but is unsuited for row cropping.
Class VI	The limitations of this land are extremely severe. The slopes are very steep. It is best left as a woodland or wildlife reserve. Pasture may also be developed on this land.
Class VII	The land has extreme limitations. Pasture production is not practical. It is best developed as a woodland or wildlife reserve.
Class VIII	The land is so severely limited that the only recommended uses are for wild-life, recreation, esthetic purposes, and watershed protection. The land has steep slopes and is rocky, is swampy, or has very sensitive vegetative cover.

12.1 DISTRIBUTION OF ARABLE LAND IS NOT EQUITABLE

Arable land. Land suitable for production of crops.

Arable land, or *cropland,* is land that can be utilized for crop production. Whether a piece of land can be utilized for crop production or not depends on the climate (temperature, rainfall) and soil type. Of the over 13 billion hectares of land in the world, about 50% is completely unusable for crop production. Only about 11% of the total land area of the world is arable. About 24% of the land is in pasture, while another 31% is in forests. Most of the arable land is located in the United States, Europe, Russia, India, China, and Southeast Asia. Most productive soils were formed under grassland (e.g., the prairies of the midwestern United States) or hardwood forests (e.g., Europe and India).

There are twelve soil orders in the United States (Figure 16). The most dominant soil orders in the world are aridisols (19%) and alfisols (13%); the least dominant include histosols (1%) and vertisols (2%). Of the 9% of oxisols and 6% of ultisols in the world, about 90% and 45%, respectively, are located in Latin America and Africa. The characteristics

FIGURE 15 An expanse of land in San Mateo County, California, is used to demonstrate a variety of soil capability classes. (Source: USDA)

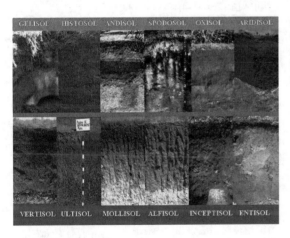

FIGURE 16 The 12 common soil orders recognized by the Natural Resources Conservation Service, with the typical soil profile of each order. (Source: USDA)

of these soil orders are summarized in Table 8. What are the challenges of crop production in tropical regions such as Latin American and Africa? The soils in these regions are highly leached, acidic, and low in nutrients. However, they can be made productive through the application of soil amendments and fertilizer. Unfortunately, producers in these regions can ill-afford these production inputs. The practice of slash-and-burn agriculture and shifting cultivation are prevalent in these regions. Whereas the slash-and-burn agriculture has the short-term benefit of providing nutrients from the ashes for crop use, the high rainfall in these regions quickly leaches out nutrients. The exposed soil is also prone to soil erosion, increased temperature, and rapid organic matter decay. The consequences are that

Table 8 A Summary of the Characteristics of the 12 Common Soil Orders Recognized by the NRCS

Histosols

Histosols are organic soils. They occur in wet, cold areas. Organic soils have high water retention, high CEC, low bulk densities, and usually deficiencies in nutrients, especially nitrogen, potassium, and copper. Properly drained, the organic matter can decompose rapidly. The soil is used for vegetable production.

Entisols

Entisols are slightly developed soils that lack defined horizons. They may derive from recent alluvial deposits or recent volcanic ash deposits. They occur in floodplains and rocky mountain regions. Those in floodplains are very good agricultural soils.

Inceptisols

Inceptisols are more weathered than entisols. Many soils used for paddy rice production are of this soil order. Some are too wet or exist in cold regions.

Andisols

Andisols are generally weakly developed soils. They are high in organic matter and have high amounts of amorphous aluminum and iron clays. Andisols are among the most productive soils in the world when well managed. They include the volcanic soils of Hawaii.

Aridisols

Aridisols occur in regions dominated by long dry periods. They have low organic matter content and high basic cation saturation of 100%. They are among the most productive soils under irrigation and fertilization.

Mollisols

Mollisols are dark-colored soils formed mainly under grasslands but also under some hardwood forests. They have deep, dark color and more than 50% base saturation. They are very fertile soils, with high nitrogen and humus.

Vertisols

Vertisols have more than 30% swelling clays (montmorillonite) and go through swelling and shrinking cycles with moisture and drying. They are very sticky when wet and very hard when dry with cracks. They have high CEC and relatively high humus content.

Alfisols

Alfisols are characterized by the translocation of clay downward to accumulate in the Bt layer. They are the most naturally productive soils without fertilization or irrigation. The top soil may be moderately acidic. Application of fertilizers usually produces high yield.

Spodsols

Spodsols have high salt content. They usually occur in cold, wet climates under acidic conifer forests or other vegetation. They have a white leached E horizon and a very low basic cation saturation percentage.

Ultisols

Ultisols are warm and low in basic cation saturation (acidic), occurring in humid regions. Without fertilization, they become worn out with time. However, with high-level management (fertilizers, liming, etc.), ultisols can be among the world's most productive soils.

Oxisols

Oxisols are the most widely weathered soils. They occur on old landforms in humid, tropical, and subtropical climates. They usually have bright yellowish to red colors. They are rich in residual irons and aluminum hydrous oxide residues. Oxisols are very low in nutrients. They are used for producing carbohydrate and oil crops. With adequate nitrogen phosphorus potassium, they are productive for bananas, sugarcane, coffee, rice, and pineapple.

Gelisols

Gelisols have permafrost (perennially frozen soil horizon under the upper soil) within the upper 1 to 2 meters. They are young soils with little profile development. Gelisols mainly support tundra vegetation of lichens, grasses, and low shrubs during the brief summers. Very few areas of Gelisols are used for agriculture.

the deterioration of the soil is accelerated. It is estimated that about 5 to 7 million acres of land are lost to degradation from various sources.

Even though most of the land in semiarid regions consists of alfisols that are less leached than ultisols and oxisols, production in these regions is constrained by erratic rainfall. Periodic drought devastates crop production and causes famines. Mollisols are base-rich and very productive. Unfortunately, the distribution of this soil order in the world is not widespread.

Aridisols occur in areas where sunlight is abundant. They are productive soils if supplemental irrigation and fertilizers are provided. This is the case in Pakistan, India, and the Middle East, where crop production is very successful with high inputs.

The rate of cropping of potentially arable land varies from one region to another and is influenced by socioeconomic factors, among other factors. Europe and Asia have cropped most (80% and 65%, respectively) of their potentially arable land. This is partly due to intense and prolonged population pressures in these places. On the other hand, only about 20 to 30% of the arable land in Africa, South America, and Oceania is in crop production. Whereas the European countries and some in Asia can afford to import additional food, many economically poor countries are being overwhelmed by population growth and the inability to increase food production.

To increase crop production, there are three strategies countries may adopt:

1. Clear new (virgin) arable land for cropping.
2. Increase cropping intensity (number of crops per year).
3. Intensify the use of existing cropped arable lands.

The third strategy is applicable to regions such as Europe where arable land is scarce and population is high but resources are available to increase productivity on existing cropped land. The situation is much different in regions of poor economies such as Africa and South America. Much of the unutilized arable land is not readily accessible. The management of these new lands for sustainable production is yet to be determined. Clearing of virgin forests and steep slopes only results in degradation of the land. Watersheds are destroyed, while rivers and streams are polluted. Also, the domestic water supply is adversely impacted while biodiversity is jeopardized.

12.2 THE DECISION TO USE LAND FOR A PARTICULAR PURPOSE IS INFLUENCED BY SEVERAL FACTORS

How does a producer decide the kind of production enterprise to carry out on a piece of land? Land is the most basic requirement for crop production. The decision to use land for a particular purpose is influenced by several factors, including the following:

1. *Location.* This pertains to the climatic zone as well as the distance from major transportation links, distance from urban center, and distance from parks and recreational facilities. Land located near the city center is attractive and valuable for residential construction and for commercial development. The potential use of land and its location determine its economic value.
2. *Topography.* Not only are steep slopes difficult to farm, but they also predispose the soil to erosion. Undulating land may require some leveling to make it amenable to certain practices such as irrigation.
3. *Productivity.* Prime farmlands and unique farmlands are preferred for crop production. Unproductive lands are utilized for construction (industrial, residential, etc.).
4. *Erodibility.* Highly erodible land is not suitable for crop production. Certain government programs are implemented to prevent the cultivation of erodible lands.

What is the exact location of your farm?

Properties in urban areas have exact addresses that permit them to be located without much difficulty. The system used to show the exact location of property in rural areas is called the *legal description*. This system dates back to 1784, when a congressional committee was charged with preparing a survey ordinance to address the boundary litigations arising from indiscriminant settlement. Since many of the old states had been well settled prior to the survey ordinance, they were left to continue their system of property demarcation—the *metes and bounds system*. Most states west of the Mississippi (excluding parts of Texas) and many east of the Mississippi use the product of the 1784 ordinance called the *rectangular survey system*.

The rectangular survey system begins with the establishment of a *principal meridian* and a *base line*. The principal meridian runs in a true north and south direction, while the base line runs east and west at right angles to the principal meridian. The point of intersection of these lines is the *initial point, or starting point*. Beginning at the initial point, surveyors mark out lines in the north-south direction and on either side of the meridian, every 6 miles. Similarly, lines spaced 6 miles apart are marked parallel to the base line. The

A township is divided into 36 smaller areas measuring 1×1 miles square. Each smaller area is called a "section"; sections are numbered from the north right towards the left and down in a serpentine fashion.

lines parallel to the base line are called *township lines*, and those parallel to the principal meridian *range lines*. The result is a grid of squares.

Each of these 6-square-mile areas constitutes a *congressional township* (not to be confused with *civil township*). Each congressional township is further divided into 36 squares, each square called a *section*. The sections are numbered from the top right-hand corner to the bottom right corner in a serpentine fashion. A section is assumed to be 640 acres. This size is not constant for all sections, due to the curvature of the earth's surface, which causes range lines to converge. Surveyors correct for convergence at specific intervals by measuring from the principal meridian. This explains why jogs occur in the north-south section line roads at regular intervals. Consequently, sections on the north (1-6) and those on the west side (6-31) are not full sections. A section may be subdivided into quarters. The partial sections on the north and west sides will yield parcels of land that are less than 40 acres and are called *correction lots*. These lots also occur along rivers *(river lots)*.

The description of land is based on a quarter section as the basic unit, while using the north pole as ref-

Each square is called a "township" and has an area of 6×6 miles square. Area "X" is located in "Township 2 North Range 3 East" while area "Y" is called "Township 2 South Range 4 East."

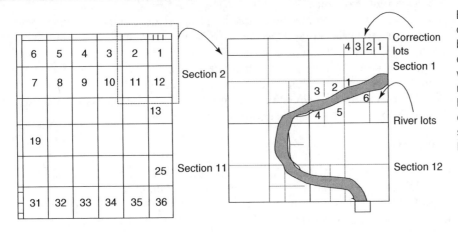

Each section is divided into quarters. Some tracts may be less than a quarter and called correction lots or, when they border a river, river lots. River lots are numbered downstream in a sequence until they reach a section line, then the numbering continues upstream.

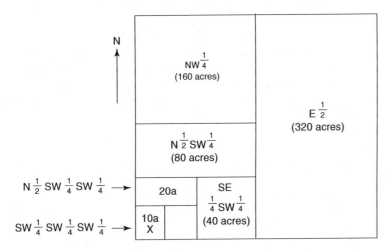

Each section measures 640 acres in area. A 40-acre tract of land is called a lot or correction lot. Correction lots are less than 40 acres.

erence. A tract of land that is smaller than a quarter is described as part of the quarter in which it occurs. Uppercase letters and fractions are used in writing the legal description of a tract of land (backwards—starting from the right to the left). The plot labeled "X" occurs in the $SW\frac{1}{4}$ section. Further, it occurs in the southwest corner of the southwest sections (i.e., $SW\frac{1}{4} SW\frac{1}{4}$). Again, it occurs in the southwest corner of the $SW\frac{1}{4} SW\frac{1}{4}$ subsection (thus $SW\frac{1}{4} SW\frac{1}{4} SW\frac{1}{4}$). The area represented by this description is 10 acres. The legal description is completed by tagging on the section number (e.g., $SW\frac{1}{4} SW\frac{1}{4} SW\frac{1}{4}$ section 10). A clue to this nomenclature is that, when two letters appear together (e.g., SW), it always means $\frac{1}{4}$ of what follows (e.g., SW section 5 means $\frac{1}{4}$ of section 5). Similarly, when a letter appears by itself, it indicates $\frac{1}{2}$ of whatever follows (e.g., N sec-

tion 10 means $\frac{1}{2}$ of section 10). If a tract to be described consists of more than one parcel (40 acres), it is described in more than one part. For example, a land of area 120 acres consists of 80 + 40 acres tracts. The two are described separately and linked (e.g., $N\frac{1}{2} SW\frac{1}{4}$ and $SE\frac{1}{4} SW\frac{1}{4}$). Half of a section (e.g., $N\frac{1}{2}$) may also be designated as N^2. Since a section consists of 640 acres of land, one can determine the acreage of a tract of land from the legal description. For example, $SE\frac{1}{4} SE\frac{1}{4} = 40$ acres, while $S\frac{1}{2} SE = 80$ acres.

To get to an address by reading a legal land description, one needs to have the general highway map for the county in which the property is located. The townships are also designated with reference to the starting point (e.g., *T 16N R 14W* indicates township 16 north and range 14 west).

5. *Government policies and programs.* The government intervenes to protect lands and soil from devastation through the creation and implementation of conservation programs.
6. *Management skills.* Prime and unique farmlands require minimal management for use in crop production. Marginal lands require more challenging management operations to make them productive.
7. *Age of landowner.* Older people tend to be more conservative, while younger ones may be more adventurous and have longer-term goals.
8. *Landowner's expectations.* When all is said and done, the landowner will use the land for whatever he or she deems profitable or rewarding.

SUMMARY

1. Mineral soil is weathered rock. Some soils are derived from organic material.
2. Weathering agents may be physical, chemical, or biological.
3. Soil formation depends on parent material, climate, biota, topography, and time.
4. As soils form, they develop a vertical cross section called a profile, consisting of layers called horizons. The profile is dependent upon the age of the soil and conditions under which formation occurs, among others.
5. In soil taxonomy, soils are classified into 13 orders in the United States.
6. A typical mineral soil has some mineral matter, air, water, and organic matter.
7. Soil texture is dependent on the proportions of soil separates—sand, silt, and clay. It affects drainage, water-holding capacity, tillage, and other factors.
8. Soil structure depends on the arrangement of soil particles. It can be destroyed by compaction from farm machinery, animals, and others.
9. Bulk density and soil porosity are important soil physical properties in crop production. They affect drainage, tillage, and other production activities.
10. Soil colloids (clay and humus) are able to attract cations, the source of fertility for crop production.
11. Soil reaction (pH) determines the availability of nutrients.
12. The soil has organisms, some of which are beneficial, while others are pests.
13. The soil can be managed to control the population of harmful microbes.
14. When organisms die, they decompose and the minerals are recycled.
15. Only about 11% of the total land area of the world is arable.
16. Certain lands are suited for farming of a specific crop (unique farmlands), while others are suited for general food, feed, and fiber production (prime farmland).
17. The use to which land can be put depends on certain factors, including topography, zoning restrictions, land capability, management skills, and age of the operator.

REFERENCES AND SUGGESTED READING

Brady, C. N., and R. R. Weil. 1999. *The nature and properties of soils.* 12th ed. Upper Saddle River, NJ: Prentice Hall.

Burns, R. C., and R. W. F. Hardy. 1975. *Nitrogen fixation in bacteria and higher plants.* Berlin: Springer-Verlag.

Hauck, R. D., ed. 1984. *Nitrogen in crop production.* Madison, WI: American Society of Agronomy.

Kletke, D. (no date). *Legal land descriptions in Oklahoma.* Oklahoma State University, Extension facts, No. 9407.

Mengel, K., and E. A. Kirby. 1987. *Principles of plant nutrition.* 4th ed. Bern, Switzerland: International Potash Institute.

Miller, W. R., and D. T. Gardner. 1999. *Soils in our environment.* 9th ed. Upper Saddle River, NJ: Prentice Hall.

Natural Resources Conservation Service. 2000. Soil Taxonomy USDA, Washington, DC.

Penny, D. C., S. C. Nolan, R. C. McKenzie, T. W. Goddard, and L. Kryzanowski. 1996. Yield and nutrient mapping for site specific fertilizer managment. *Communications in Soil Science and Plant Science Analysis* 27:1265–79.

Stevenson, F. J. 1986. *Cycles of soil carbon, nitrogen, phosphorus, sulfur, and macronutrients.* New York: Wiley.

Usery, E. L., S. Pocknee, and B. Boydell. 1995. Precision farming data managment using geographic information systems. *Photogrammetric Engineering and Remote Sensing* 61:1383–91.

SELECTED INTERNET SITES FOR FURTHER REVIEW

http://www.nhq.nrcs.usda.gov/land/index/soils.html

Soils and soil types.

http://www.statlab.iastate.edu/soils/photogal/orders/soiord.htm

Photos of soil orders.

http://www.nhq.nrcs.usda.gov/land/index/lcc.html

Land capability classification.

http://www.statlab.iastate.edu/survey/SQI/sqiinfo.html

Soil quality factors—available water, erosion, leaching, pesticide, compaction, organic matter.

http://www.fertilizer.org/PUBLISH/PUBMAN/introdc.htm

OUTCOMES ASSESSMENT

PART A

Answer the following questions true or false.

1. T F Soil is weathered rock.
2. T F A pH of 7.8 is acidic.
3. T F Clay soils have a finer texture than sandy soils.
4. T F Incorporating organic matter into the soil increases its bulk density.
5. T F Kaolinite clays have 1:1 clay lattice structure.
6. T F Hydrogen ions are more tightly bound to soil colloids than potassium ions.

PART B

Answer the following questions.

1. Give the five major factors of soil formation.

   _____

   _____

   _____

   _____

   _____

2. Give the three basic types of rocks. _____

   _____ _____

3. What is weathering? _____

   _____

4. Give 5 of the 12 soil orders in the United States.

   _____

   _____

   _____

   _____

   _____

5. The porter's clay is a silicate clay and is also called _____.

6. What does the acronym CEC stand for? _____

   _____

PART C

Write a brief essay on each of the following topics.

1. Discuss physical weathering.
2. Discuss the role of climate in soil formation.
3. Describe the composition of a typical mineral soil.
4. Discuss the role of soil texture in crop production.
5. Discuss the role of soil structure in crop production.
6. Discuss the nature and role of humus in soil structure.
7. Discuss the role of soil organisms in crop productivity.
8. Discuss the distribution of arable land in the world.

PART D

Discuss or explain the following topics in detail.

1. Discuss the impact of leached fertilizer on the environment.

2. Discuss the role of fertilizers in boosting crop productivity in the United States.

3. Is soil a renewable resource? Explain.

Tillage Practices

■ 1 HISTORY OF TILLAGE OPERATIONS

Tillage began before the earliest written records of mankind. The first implements were hand tools to chop or dig the soil, usually made of wood, bone, or stone. They were used to subdue or destroy the native vegetation, make openings in the soil to receive seeds or plants, and reduce competition from native plants and weeds growing among the crops. The next stage of tillage, the use of domestic animals,[1] occurred in parts of the world before the dawn of history. This made possible development of implements that moved forward at a steady pace. Among these were the crooked-stick plow to stir the soil and the brush drag to pulverize the surface. Little further progress was made for many centuries except that eventually some plows were fitted with iron shares despite a common misunderstanding that iron poisoned the soil. The development of steel in 1833 resulted in a plow with sharp edges that cut the soil layer and a curved polished surface that permitted the plow to scour. That straight-line movement of the plow has since been improved with the development of the disk plow, harrow, rotary hoe, and other pulverizing and stirring tools.

Very little was known about the effects of cultural operations in the Middle Ages.[2] In 1733, Jethro Tull published *The Horse-Hoeing Husbandry* in England. He believed that plants took up the minute soil particles. In other words, the more finely the soil was divided, the more particles would be absorbed by the roots.

During the nineteenth century, it became evident that nutrition of plants depended on certain chemical elements from the soil minerals, organic matter, water, and air. The foundation for this concept was proposed by Justus von Liebig and others. The idea became widespread that tillage, by increasing the aeration in the soil, increased the oxidation of chemical compounds in the soil and made them more soluble.

Early American writers believed that tillage allowed the roots to penetrate more deeply or refined the soil to make a greater surface to hold nutrients while others recognized the importance of tillage in weed control. The idea that harmful effects might result from excessive tillage, particularly from greater oxidation of organic matter or from increased erosion, was also pointed out by early writers in this country. Not until after 1890 did experimental evidence begin to show the basic reasons for tillage.

From Chapter 5 of *Principles of Field Crop Production*, Fourth Edition, John H. Martin, Richard P. Waldren, David L. Stamp. Copyright © 2006 by Pearson Education, Inc. Published by Pearson Prentice Hall. All rights reserved.

KEY TERMS

Artificial mulch
Conservation tillage
Cultivator
Disk plow
Fallow
Harrow
Intertillage
Lister
Moldboard plow
No-tillage
Residue cover
Soil mulch
Soil nitrate
Subsoiling
Subtillage implement
Summer fallow
Sweep implement
Terrace
Water erosion
Wind erosion
Zero tillage

TABLE 1 Average Amount of Residue Incorporated by Different Tillage Implements

Tillage	Residue Incorporated (%)
Moldboard plow	100
Oneway disk	40
Tandem or Offset disk	
18–22 inch disks	40
24–26 inch disks	50
Anhydrous applicator	20
Chisel plow	25
Mulch treader	20–25
Sweep plow, 30" or wider blades	10–15
Rod weeder	5–10
Grain drill, double disk openers	20
Planter, double disk openers	10
Slot planter	0
Till planter	20

2 PURPOSES OF TILLAGE

The fundamental purposes of tillage[1] are: (1) to prepare a suitable seedbed, (2) to eliminate competition from weed growth, and (3) to improve the physical condition of the soil. This may involve destruction of native vegetation, weeds, or the sod of another crop. Tillage can further involve removal, burial, or incorporation in the soil of manure or crop residue. In other cases, the tillage operation may be solely to loosen, compact, or pulverize the soil. The best system of tillage is, then, the one that accomplishes these objectives with the least expenditure of labor and power.

The incorporation of plant residues and its subsequent effect on soil erosion must also be considered in planning all tillage operations (Table 1). The kind of tillage for seedbed preparation on dry lands is governed almost entirely by the effects of tillage upon the conservation of soil moisture and the prevention of surface runoff and wind erosion. It may be necessary to till the soil surface to protect the soil from wind erosion after crops that leave little residue such as cotton and soybean.[3]

Under most conditions, a desirable seedbed is one that allows close contact between the seed and the soil particles. Seeding equipment must cut through any residues present. The seedbed should contain sufficient moisture to germinate the seed when planted and support subsequent growth. In irrigated regions, it is occasionally necessary to plant the crop and then irrigate the field in order to supply sufficient moisture for germination, but this practice is avoided whenever possible because of frequent irregular stands. Irrigation before planting is preferable.

3 IMPLEMENTS FOR SEEDBED PREPARATION

Originally, an acre of land was the area tilled by one ox-drawn plow in one day. Tractor-drawn implements cover 0.3 to 0.6 acre per hour per foot of width (0.4 to 0.8 ha/hr/m width).

FIGURE 1
A moldboard plow.
[Courtesy Case IH]

3.1 Moldboard Plows

The moldboard plow breaks loose or shears off the furrow slice by forcing a triple wedge through the soil. This action inverts the soil and breaks it into lumps. Some pulverization takes place (Figure 1). Several different shapes of moldboard plow bottoms are used. At one extreme is the breaker type with a long moldboard adapted to virgin or tough sod for completely inverting the furrow slice without pulverization. At the other extreme is the stubble bottom with a short, abrupt moldboard that pulverizes the furrow slice while turning the soil in order to mix the residue with the soil. The general purpose, or mellow-soil, plow is intermediate between these two types in length, slope, and action. The two-way plow is adapted to steep hillsides because it throws the soil downhill when drawn across the slope in either direction. It is often used on irrigated land to avoid dead furrows. Better incorporation of residue is facilitated on all plows by the use of attachments such as coulters, jointers, rods, and chains. The majority of moldboard plows range in size from 7 to 18 inches (18 to 46 cm) in width of furrow cut.[4] The 14 inch (36 cm) width is common.

3.2 Disk Plows

Disk plows (Figure 2) are important for use in loose soils but also in those soils too dry and hard for easy penetration of moldboard plows. In some sticky soils, neither type of plow will scour when the soil is wet. In this case, scrapers help keep the disks clean. The disks vary in size from 20 to 30 inches (51 to 76 cm), while the depth of plowing may vary from 4 to 10 inches (10 to 25 cm). The one-way disk plow (Figure 3) has been widely used in stubble fields of the wheat belt. The one-way should be avoided for bare summer fallow land, or dry fields

FIGURE 2
Disk plow. [Courtesy Case IH]

FIGURE 3
The one-way disk plow leaves about one-third of the crop residue on the soil surface. [Courtesy John Deere & Co.]

sparsely covered with stubble or weeds where it tends to pulverize the soil so that the soil blows easily.

3.3 Subtillage Implements

Blade or subtillage implements, that leave crop residues on the surface of the soil, are used in semiarid areas.[5] Wide-sweep blades with staggered mountings undercut the stubble and weeds but do not pulverize the soil surface (Figure 4). This

FIGURE 4
Stubble mulch after the use of sweep blades. [Courtesy Richard Waldren]

so-called stubble mulch reduces soil erosion as well as runoff, but it may not increase soil moisture storage. Special seeding equipment is needed to cut through residue and open seed furrows on land covered with heavy crop residue unless a disc cutter is used to chop up the straw.

3.4 Lister

The lister (middlebuster) resembles a double plow with a right-hand and a left-hand bottom mounted back to back. In some of the southern humid sections, it is used to raise beds on which to plant cotton, potato, or other row crops. In the semiarid regions, the lister was widely used to furrow the land. It replaced the moldboard plow in seedbed preparation because it covered the field in half the time. The ridges also checked wind erosion, snow drifting, and runoff when the furrows ran on the contour or across the slope. Row crops are planted in the moist soil at the bottom of the lister furrows. For drilled crops such as small grains, the lister ridges or middles are broken down or leveled with ridge busters. The lister has been largely replaced by sweep blade implements or the one-way plow for the initial seedbed preparation in the semiarid areas.

■ 4 SURFACE IMPLEMENTS IN FINAL SEEDBED PREPARATION

Tillage can prepare a seedbed after the land has been plowed by using harrows, field cultivators, or other machines equipped with disks, shovels, teeth, spikes, sweeps, knives, corrugated rolls, or packer wheels. Under most conditions, a smooth, finely pulverized seedbed should not be prepared until just before a crop is to be planted.

4.1 Harrows

Harrows, that smooth and pulverize plowed soil, compact it, and destroy weeds, require less power than do plows or listers. The disk harrow cuts, moves, pulverizes the soil, and destroys weeds. The spike-tooth harrow breaks clods, levels the land, and kills small weeds. Both disk and spike-tooth harrows are detrimental when soil is subject to blowing. The spring-tooth harrow consists of flexible spring-steel teeth about 2 inches (5 cm) wide that penetrate sufficiently to tear up deep clods or bring them to the surface while destroying weeds. The corrugated roller is used to crush clods as well as to compact the seedbed.[6] It is used particularly for small seeds to improve the chances of germination.

4.2 Cultivators

Several types of cultivators, mainly the duckfoot (field cultivator) and the rod weeder, are used in fallow and seedbed preparation. The field cultivator has sweeps or shovels on the ends of stiff or spring bars. The bars are staggered in two rows, so that the weeds are cut off by the overlapping sweeps. This implement leaves the soil surface rough and cloddy, a condition necessary to prevent wind erosion. The principal feature of the rod weeder is a rotating horizontal square rod at right angles to the direction of travel at a depth of 3 to 6 inches (8 to 15 cm) below the soil surface. This rod pulls out the weeds. The rod is driven by gears or sprocket chains from one of the support wheels, so that it revolves in a direction opposite the direction of travel, which keeps the rod in the ground (Figure 5). The rotation of the rod keeps it from clogging, while weeds, straw, and clods are lifted toward the surface, where they check soil erosion.

■ 5 TILLAGE IN SEEDBED PREPARATION

Tillage buries green or dried material, loosens the soil, removes or delays competition with weeds, and roughens the soil surface to reduce runoff of rain water.[7] Other effects of tillage are control of certain insects and diseases and promotion of nitrification.

FIGURE 5
Rotary rod weeder
cultivating summer fallow.
[Courtesy John Deere & Co.]

5.1 Time for Tillage

Fall-tilled land is warmer in the spring because bare soil, which usually is darker than the plant vegetation, absorbs more solar heat and thus hastens corn emergence and growth.[8]

Land to be summer fallowed is usually not disturbed until the spring following harvest except when it is very weedy. Weeds and stubble are left to hold snow and reduce wind and water erosion. Early spring tillage for fallow is very important[6] to stop weed and volunteer growth and thus conserve moisture and permit accumulation of nitrates. In the more humid regions, early seedbed preparation may be inadvisable because of water erosion.[9, 10]

Land tilled in spring may be higher in nitrates than that left untilled due to rapid mineralization, but the increase is not always evident immediately after tillage.[11] The difference becomes pronounced during the summer season but almost disappears during the winter when nitrates are leached downward.

5.2 Depth of Tillage

At the Pennsylvania Experiment Station, deep 12-inch (30-cm) plowing was compared with ordinary 7.5-inch (19-cm) plowing for corn, wheat, oat, barley, alfalfa, clover, and timothy.[12] The average yields failed to show any advantage from the deeper plowing.

The effect of depth of tillage on soil erosion was studied in Missouri.[13, 14] On land where no crop was grown, the annual erosion from tilled soil was greater than from soil that was not stirred and there was no advantage to deeper tillage.

For 100 years, advocates of deeper plowing recommended that the depth of plowing be increased gradually so as not to turn up too much raw subsoil in any one year. The reasoning behind such a practice seems logical, but there is no research that would either prove or disprove the soundness of this recommendation. Varying the plowing depth from year to year may avoid establishing a compact "plow-sole" or "tillage-pan" in heavy soils, but heavy soils commonly have compact subsurface layers. The more friable and muck soils do not form plow soles.

Plows with very large moldboards that penetrate 1 to 4 feet (30 to 122 cm) deep are used for land reclamation operations such as turning under brush or turning up topsoil that has been buried under water-borne sand.

■ 6 SUBSOILING

Tillage below the depth reached by the ordinary plow was once advocated widely. There was a popular belief that plants utilize only the soil moved by tillage, and deeper tillage provides a greater opportunity for root development and moisture storage. Another belief was that to merely loosen, stir, pulverize, or invert the deeper soil layers permits more effective plant growth. Great Plains research that covered ten states showed no general increase in yields from subsoiling or other methods of deep tillage.[15]

The same general results were obtained under other conditions.[12, 16, 17] Increased water infiltration and better crop yields have sometimes followed the deep tillage of land that had a dense hard subsurface layer or a tillage pan that tended to be rather impervious to water. Such benefits may be evident for only one or two years, but the cost of the operation may offset any gain in yield.[18] Deep tillage is ineffective unless the tillage pan is dry enough to be shattered.[19]

The reasons why deep tillage is often ineffective are rather obvious. Heavy soils shrink and leave wide cracks when they dry out, thus providing natural openings for periodical water absorption and aeration. When such soils are wetted, they swell tightly and the cracks close up so that any effect of deep tillage is only temporary. Light soils do not shrink and swell much, and they are always open. Since roots of crop plants ordinarily penetrate several feet below any tilled layer, deep tillage is not essential to deep rooting. The chisel, an implement with a series of points that break up the soil to a depth of 10 to 18 inches (25 to 46 cm) without turning it, is sometimes used on heavy soils. As a substitute for plowing, the chisel opens and roughens the soil so that heavy rains can be absorbed quickly without danger of wind or water erosion. Such deep tillage may favor the growth of sugarbeet because of its large taproot.

■ 7 CONSERVATION TILLAGE

Conservation tillage is a collective term used for any tillage system whose primary goal is maintenance of plant residue on the soil surface.[20] Other more specific terms used include no-tillage, direct-seeding or drilling, and residue farming. With strip-tillage, a narrow strip is tilled over the seeded row. With ridge-till (ridge-plant), ridges are formed and seed is placed in the ridge. Two early proponents of reducing tillage were Faulkner and Scarseth.[21, 22]

Implements with large sweeps or blades leave the residue on the soil surface to form a partial mulch (Figure 6). This process must be repeated during the season

FIGURE 6
Wheat that was planted into stubble mulch fallow.
[Courtesy Richard Waldren]

to control weeds, because the straw and stubble from a single crop are insufficient to smother all the weeds.[7, 23, 24] However, this partial mulch checks soil blowing, stops runoff, and increases the surface infiltration of rainfall. Soils are cooler under residue mulch in summer. However, heavy residues may keep the soil too cool in the spring for favorable germination of early planted corn, sorghum, or soybean. It also fails to control certain weeds and grasses, especially cheatgrass (*Bromus tectorum*), where herbicides are not fully applicable, unless a machine such as the skew treader or rotary tiller is used to chop through the mulch and cut out the weeds. Damage to the crop from mice, slugs, and birds can increase in heavy mulches. Special equipment such as coulters, chisels, or scalpers to push residue aside are used on planters for mulch tillage fields. Heavy nitrogen applications are necessary to maintain crop yields and hasten the ultimate decay of the residues.[13, 25, 26, 27]

Zero tillage of sod land requires killing the grass plants with chemicals and using a modified planter that cuts through the sod while planting the crop. The dead sod mulch conserves some soil moisture, and the yield of corn may equal that following 8-inch (20 cm) plowing and discing.[28] Zero tillage also reduces water runoff and soil erosion.

The practice of conservation tillage has rapidly increased in recent years (Figures 7, 8, 9). Conservation tillage was used on 41 percent of the corn acreage, 55 percent of the soybean acreage, and 22 percent of the wheat acreage in ten midwest states during the 1995 crop year (USDA NASS). Conservation tillage in northwest Ohio increased from essentially zero in the mid-1980s to about 50 percent of all corn and soybean fields in the mid-1990s and has remained at that level.[29] In 2000, no-tillage was used on more than 51 million acres (21 million ha) in the United States. That is 17.5 percent of total planted acres and is a three-fold increase since 1990.[30] No-tillage is increasing rapidly in other countries as well (Table 2).[31]

A minimum of 30 percent residue cover is the common standard used to signify conservation tillage. A 30 percent residue cover reduces erosion by 80 percent.[3] Although there are different methods for estimating residue cover, the line-transect

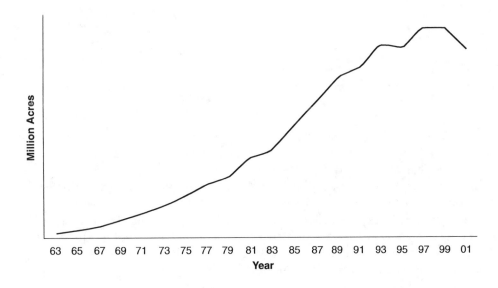

FIGURE 7
Conservation tillage trends in the U.S.

FIGURE 8

Soybean seedings that were planted without tillage into wheat stubble. [Courtesy USDA NRCS]

TABLE 2 Total Area of No-Tillage in Various Countries, 1998–1999

Country	Area	
	Hectares	Acres
United States	19,347,000	47,787,000
Brazil	11,200,000	27,664,000
Argentina	7,270,000	17,000,000
Canada	4,080,000	10,000,000
Australia	1,000,000	2,470,000
Paraguay	790,000	1,950,000
Mexico	500,000	1,235,000
Bolivia	200,000	500,000
Chile	96,000	240,000
Uruguay	50,000	125,000
Others	1,000,000	2,470,000
Total	45,533,000	111,441,000

method is an easy and practical way to estimate residue cover using a 100-foot tape.[32] Residue cover can also be estimated by calculating the amount of residue left after tillage operations.[33]

The amount of residue after harvest depends on the type and yield of the crop.[33] As shown in Table 3, most crops leave sufficient residue to provide adequate cover; in some cases, incorporation of some residue can be beneficial. The amount of residue remaining after tillage operations depends on the type of residue and the type of tillage implement. Residue can be classified as non-fragile when it is resistant to destruction during tillage and fragile when it will easily break up during

FIGURE 9
No-till row crop planter
seeding on the contour.
[Courtesy USDA NRCS]

TABLE 3 Crop Residue Classification and Typical Percent Residue Cover After Harvest of Various Crops

Non–Fragile Residue		Fragile Residue	
Crop	% Cover	Crop	% Cover
Alfalfa	85	Canola/rapeseed	70
Corn for grain, 60–120 bu/ac	80	Dry edible beans	15
Barley*	85	Dry peas	20
Corn for grain, 120–200 bu/ac	95	Potatoes	15
Corn for silage	10	Soybeans	70
Forage silage	15	Sugarbeet	15
Grain sorghum	75	Sunflower	40
Hay crops	85	Vegetables	30
Millet	70		
Oat*	80		
Pasture	85		
Popcorn	70		
Rye*	85		
Wheat,* 30–60 bu/ac	50		
Wheat,* 60–100 bu/ac	85		

*For small grains, if a rotary combine or a combine with a straw chopper is used, or if the straw is otherwise cut into small pieces, consider the residue to be fragile.

tillage. Table 3 lists types of residues and their fragility. Table 4 shows the amount of residue remaining after various tillage operations.

Residue reduces water erosion by forming ponds that reduce runoff velocity and delay runoff and by obstructing and diverting runoff, which increases the length of the down slope flow path (Figure 10). Residue also keeps smaller flows

TABLE 4 Estimated Percentage of Residue Remaining on the Soil Surface After Specific Implements and Field Operations

Implement	Residue Remaining (%)	
	Non-Fragile Residue	Fragile Residue
Moldboard plow	0–10	0–5
Disk, primary tillage	30–60	20–40
Disk, secondary tillage	40–70	25–40
V-ripper/subsoiler	60–80	40–60
Chisel-subsoiler	50–70	40–50
Disk-subsoiler	30–50	10–20
Chisel-sweep	70–85	50–60
Disk-chisel-sweep	60–70	30–50
Sweep, >30 inches	75–95	60–80
Sweep, <30 inches	70–90	50–75
Sweep-mulch treader	60–90	45–80
One-way disk	40–50	20–40
Spring tooth harrow	60–80	50–70
Rotary rod w/ shovels	70–80	60–70

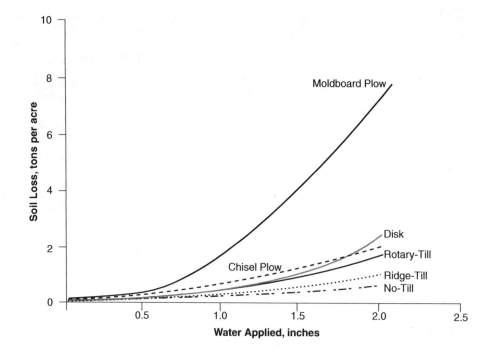

FIGURE 10

Soil loss from a silt loam soil on a 10 percent slope with water applied at a rate of 2.5 inches per hour [From Wortman, 2003].

from combining into larger flows that have the capacity to carry more soil parti-cles.[1] Wind erosion is reduced by protecting fragile soil particles and providing mi-crobarriers to the force of the wind. Residues can increase resistance of surface aggregates to the destructive effects of freeze-thaw cycles.[34, 35]

Tillage alters the albedo (reflectivity) of the soil, the surface area exposed to the atmosphere, and the penetration of wind into the soil. Evaporation from a non-tilled soil will be higher initially than a tilled soil, but, as a dry layer develops at the surface of a non-tilled soil, rate of evaporation will be reduced to less than that of a tilled soil. The time and rate depend on soil factors. There are more benefits from non-tillage on fine-textured soils than on coarser-textured soils.[36]

Residues at seeding reduce early season evaporation and conserve water for increased transpiration later in the season.[37, 38] A study of five locations from east-central United States to the Great Plains showed that the water-filled pore space in the top 6 inches (15 cm) was higher in no-tilled soils than in tilled soils.[39] Moisture loss from the surface foot of both irrigated and dryland soils in Utah[40] was retarded by a residue mulch.

Leaving residues on the soil surface affects soil organic matter concentrations and soil microbial populations. Some studies show that soil organic matter is highest near the soil surface, but lower soil horizons are unaffected.[41] In long-term studies of tillage management of winter wheat-fallow systems in Nebraska, leaving residues on the soil surface decreased soil organic matter content in the topsoil. But that decline is partly offset by increased dry matter production due to higher yields and reduced fallow times.[42] Nonsymbiotic nitrogen fixation was two times higher in no-till soils than plowed soils due primarily to higher soil water content which favors microbial development.[43]

When residue is left on soil surface there is increased immobilization of soluble N, especially when residues have a high C/N ratio. Also, mineralization is decreased when residues are not incorporated.[44] Not incorporating residues decreases nitrification and increases denitrification.[45] A depressive effect on nitrate accumulation in soils may occur where straw mulches are heavy enough to suppress weed growth.[10]

There is an increased risk of bacterial and fungal diseases when residues are left on the soil surface that might, in some cases, preclude the use of conservation tillage. There is also an increased risk of phytotoxins when residues are left on the surface. However, these effects are short-lived and should not be overshadowed by the increased erosion protection that the residues provide.[44]

When tillage is reduced or eliminated, weed control is accomplished almost exclusively with herbicides. As shown in Tables 5 and 6, weed species may change when tillage is reduced.[46] When perennial noxious weeds are present, it may be necessary to combine tillage with herbicides to obtain complete control.

Figure 11 shows the short-term and long-term changes that may occur with the adoption of conservation tillage.[34] Earthworm numbers are likely to increase and soil structure will likely improve over the long term. Pest protection, fertilizer requirements, and crop yield will likely remain the same over the long term. Total cost of production and labor will likely decline over the long term. And, although machinery costs will be higher in the short term as new equipment is purchased, machinery costs will be less in the long term as less tillage equipment will be needed.

Conservation tillage has the potential to conserve soil, time, energy, and labor. However, there are restrictions to conservation tillage: (1) soils high in nonexpanding clay minerals, silt, and fine sand may need tillage periodically to reduce soil compaction and improve structure; (2) excess precipitation on poorly drained soils can cause problems when using conservation tillage; and (3) there can be an increase of water-soluble toxins in the residue and toxins from microbial decomposition of residue.[34]

TABLE 5 Densities of Annual Weeds in Conservation Tillage Systems Compared to Conventional Tillage Systems (from Moyer, 1994)	
Lower Densities	**Greater Densities**
Velvetleaf (*Abutilon theophrastis*)	Parsley piert (*Alchemilla arvensis*)
Fools parsley (*Aethusa cynapium*)	Blackgrass (*Alopecurus myosuroides*)
Scarlet pimpernel (*Anagallis arvensis*)	*Amaranthus* spp.
Spreading orach (*Atriplex patula*)	Prairie threeawn (*Aristida oligantha*)
Wild oat (*Avena fatua*)	Wild oat (*Avena fatua*)
Wild mustard (*Brassica kaber*)	Browntop millet (*Brachiaria ramose*)
Shepherd's purse (*Capsella bursa-pastoris*)	*Bromus* spp.
Common lambsquarter (*Chenopodium album*)	Shepherd's purse (*Capsella bursa-pastoris*)
Fumitory (*Fumaria officinalis*)	Field sanbbur (*Chenchrus incertus*)
Matricaria spp.	Common lambsquarter (*Chenopodium album*)
Corn poppy (*Papaver rhoeas*)	Horseweed (*Conyza Canadensis*)
Polygonum spp.	Texas croton (*Croton texensis*)
Wild radish (*Raphanus raphanistrum*)	*Descurainia* spp.
Green foxtail (*Seteria viridis*)	*Digitaria* spp.
Common chickweed (*Stellaria media*)	Barnyard grass (*Echinochloa humistrata*)
Field pennycress (*Thalaspi arvense*)	Goose grass (*Eleusine indica*)
Field violet (*Viola arvensis*)	Prostrate spurge (*Euphorbia humistrate*)
Common cocklebur (*Xanthium strumarium*)	Common sunflower (*Helianthus annuus*)
	Kochia (*Kochia scoparia*)
	Prickly lettuce (*Lactuca serriola*)
	Rigid ryegrass (*Lolium rigidum*)
	Matricaria spp.
	Carpetweed (*Mollugo verticillata*)
	Fall panicum (*Panicum dichotomiflorum*)
	Annual bluegrass (*Poa annua*)
	Prostrate knotweed (*Polygonum aviculare*)
	Erect knotweed (*Polygonum erectum*)
	Common purslane (*Portulaca oleracea*)
	Tumblegrass (*Schedonnardus paniculatus*)
	Common groundsel (*Senecio vulgaris*)
	Setaria spp.
	Prickly sida (*Sida spinosa*)
	Cutleaf nightshade (*Solanum triflorum*)
	Shattercane (*Sorghum bicolor*)
	Common chickweed (*Stellaria media*)
	Puncturevine (*Tribulus terrestris*)

■ 8 FALLOW

Land that is uncropped and kept cultivated throughout a growing season is known as fallow. Under humid conditions, however, land that merely lies idle for a year or two is often referred to as fallow. The most important function of fallow is storage of moisture in the soil, but fallowing also promotes nitrification and is a means

TABLE 6 Densities of Biennial and Perennial Weeds in Conservation Tillage Systems Compared to Conventional Tillage Systems (from Moyer, 1994)

Biennial Weeds with Greater Densities	Perennial Weeds with Greater Densities
Chervil (*Anthriscus cerefolium*)	Russian knapweed (*Acroptilon repens*)
Biennial wormwood (*Artemisia biennis*)	Woolyleaf bursage (*Ambrosia grayi*)
Plumeless thistle (*Carduus acanthoides*)	Broomsedge (*Andropogon virginicus*)
Musk thistle (*Carduus nutans*)	Hemp dogbane (*Apocynum cannabinum*)
Water hemlock (*Cicuta* spp.)	Common milkweed (*Asclepias syriaca*)
Bull thistle (*Cirsium vulgare*)	Hedge bindweed (*Calystegia sepium*)
Prickly lettuce (*Lactuca serriola*)	Trumpet creeper (*Campsis radicans*)
Sweetclover (*Melilotus* spp.)	Hoary cress (*Cardaria draba*)
Western salsify (*Tragopogon dubius*)	Tumble windmill grass (*Chloris verticillata*)
	Canada thistle (*Cirsium arvense*)
	Field bindweed (*Convolvulus arvensis*)
	Bermuda grass (*Cynodon dactylon*)
	Cyperus spp.
	Quackgrass (*Elytrigia repens*)
	Leafy spurge (*Euphorbia esula*)
	Jerusalem artichoke (*Helianthus tuberosus*)
	Foxtail barley (*Hordeum jubatum*)
	Skeleton weed (*Lygodesmia juncea*)
	Wirestem muhly (*Muhlenbergia frondosa*)
	Dallis grass (*Paspalum dilatatum*)
	Plysalis spp.
	Swamp smartweed (*Polygonum coccineum*)
	Rosa spp.
	Rubus spp.
	Rumex spp.
	Sassafras (*Sassafras albidum*)
	Horsenettle (*Solanum carolinense*)
	Perennial sowthistle (*Sonchus arvensis*)
	Johnsongrass (*Sorghum halepense*)
	Sand dropseed (*Sporobolus cryptandrus*)
	Dandelion (*Taraxacum officinale*)

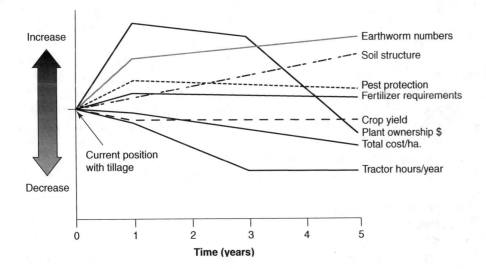

FIGURE 11

Short- and long-term trends likely to occur when converting from conventional tillage to conservation tillage. [Copyright CRC Press, Used with permission]

TABLE 7 Minimum Amounts of Plant Residue Needed at Wheat Seeding for Erosion Control

Soil Texture	Minimum Residue (pounds per acre)
Sandy to sandy loam	1,700
Very fine sandy loam to silt loam	1,200
Silty clay loam	1,000
Clay loam	750

of controlling weeds. Fallowing is a common practice in semiarid sections where annual precipitation of less than 20 inches (500 mm) is insufficient to produce a satisfactory crop every year. Averages of 15 to 31 percent of the precipitation that fell during the fallow period were stored in the soil at different locations in the dry farming regions.[9, 47] Moisture conservation by fallow is most effective in winter rainfall areas and where summer evaporation is low. Fallow conserves little moisture in coarse sandy soils or in high rainfall areas.

For successful fallow, certain principles must be observed: (1) the surface of the soil must be protected with residues (Table 7) or kept sufficiently rough to absorb rains and prevent wind erosion, (2) weed growth must be suppressed to conserve soil moisture, and (3) the operations must be accomplished at a low cost. Fallow tillage should be early in the spring,[5] worked as little as necessary to control weeds, and, when not seeded to winter grains, also ridged in the fall at right angles to the prevailing winds where soil blowing is likely to occur. Sweep plows, field cultivators, or rod weeders are best for fallow tillage because they cut off the weeds and leave the surface rough and cloddy.

In semiarid regions, fallow has been widely used in alternation with small grains (Figure 12). In southwestern Kansas, consistently higher yields of winter wheat were obtained on fallow than on land continuously cropped.[48] Fallow was the best preparation for winter wheat at the Central Great Plains Field Station near Akron, Colorado, where the rainfall is about 18 inches (450 mm) per year.[15, 49] In South Dakota, where the mean annual rainfall averaged 16 inches (406 mm), yields of spring wheat increased 74 percent on fallowed land and 46 percent on disked corn land, compared to land continuously cropped to wheat.[50] The respective increases were 109 percent and 48 percent for winter wheat. The relative yields of barley and oat after fallow were much the same as those of spring wheat. Similar results were obtained at Havre, Montana, where the annual precipitation averaged 11 inches (280 mm).[51] In comparison with small grains grown continuously, fallow gives a better distribution of yields between years, with much less frequent failures. At Mandan, North Dakota, fallowing a light soil showed little advantage for spring-wheat production.[52] Fallow may be replaced entirely by cultivated crops under such conditions. The most common is wheat alternated with corn.

In the Great Basin region, where most of the precipitation occurs in the winter months, fallowing has been standard practice for wheat production since the nineteenth century. Yields of winter wheat after fallow are nearly double that from continuous cropping. Continuous cropping is impractical in the driest ar-

FIGURE 12

A wheat-summer fallow system in Kansas. [Courtesy Richard Waldren]

eas. Fallow operations seldom conflict with the seeding or harvesting of wheat, which enables a farmer to grow as large an acreage of wheat each year as with continuous cropping. Fallowing often involves only one to three additional rapid tillage operations. The higher yields from fallowing, as compared with continuous cropping, more than compensate for the investment in double the acreage of tillable land.[53]

Stubble mulch fallow is an excellent method for erosion control but excessive amounts of straw can cause seeding problems that can be detrimental to wheat yields. Nitrogen fertilizers applied to the soil avoid yield decreases from medium amounts of straw. The practice of continuous stubble mulch increases infestation of weeds such as cheatgrass (*Bromus tectorum*). Tillage or herbicides must be used to control it. Special seeding equipment must also be used to cut through heavy residues (Figure 13). Stubble much fallow involves tillage with a field cultivator or sweep-blade implement that leaves crop residues on the surface.[9, 23, 24] Subsequent tillage is done with a rod weeder or a blade implement.[5] In the central High Plains, stubble mulch fallow has resulted in better moisture retention and higher yields[54] (Table 8).

As better seeding equipment has become available for seeding into residues and more effective herbicides for weed control, the practice of stubble mulch fallow has increased. In some areas, particularly in the Northern Plains, no-tillage practices have increased efficiency of precipitation absorption sufficiently to eliminate fallow altogether. U.S. farmers reduced fallow acreage by 43 percent from 1964 to 1997, with the largest reductions in the Great Plains (USDA-NASS). However, in the Pacific Northwest, adoption of reduced tillage practices in wheat-fallow systems has been slow due to increased economic risks and reduced profit.[55]

FIGURE 13

No-till wheat. [Courtesy Richard Waldren]

TABLE 8 Progress in Fallow Systems at Akron, Colorado (adapted from Greb, 1979)

Years	Tillage	Water Storage in Fallow			Wheat Yield	
		(inches)	(mm)	(% of total)	(bu/ac)	(kg/ha)
1916–1930	Maximum tillage (plow, harrow, dust mulch)	4.02	102	19	16	1,070
1931–1945	Conventional tillage (shallow disc, rod weeder)	4.65	118	24	17	1,160
1945–1960	Improved conventional tillage, began stubble mulch in 1957	5.39	137	27	26	1,730
1961–1975	Stubble mulch, began minimum tillage with herbicides in 1969	6.18	157	33	32	2,160
1976–1979	Minimum tillage	7.20	183	40	40	2,690

■ 9 SOIL MULCHES FOR MOISTURE CONSERVATION

Soil mulches are created by stirring the surface soil until it is loose and open. Although research in the early twentieth century advocated shallow tillage to conserve soil water,[56] later studies do not support this theory.[36] Soil mulch reduces evaporation from the soil surface when free water is present only a few feet below the surface of the soil.[57] Although capillary water can move upward 15 to 120 inches (38 to 300 cm) during a season,[58] capillary movement to appreciable heights is very slow,[59] and movement decreases as the soil moisture decreases. Water in sufficient quantities to support crop plants can be raised only a few inches from a moist subsoil.[60] Most of this movement takes place at moisture contents well above the wilting point. Capillarity and gravity combined may move moisture downward for greater distances and with about twice the quantity that occurs in the upward movement against gravity.

Evaporation from a bare soil surface is a three-stage process. The initial stage is energy-limited with a steady rate of evaporation. In the second stage, the surface dries and the rate begins to decline as the water flow to the surface is limited. The third stage consists of a slow, nearly constant rate of evaporation.[38]

In eastern Kansas, plots with soil mulches actually lost more water than did bare, undisturbed plots where the weeds were kept down with a hoe.[7] In experiments in California where the water table was from 18 to 40 feet (5 to 12 m) below the surface, mulching by thorough cultivation failed to save moisture.[61] On upland soils in Pennsylvania where there was no water table in the soil mantle, frequent cultivation did not decrease the evaporation loss materially.[62]

In Nebraska,[63] in soils partly dry and away from a source of free water, capillary movement was so slow that it could barely be detected. In the northern Great Plains, no water moved up appreciable distances to replace that removed by roots. Water was supplied to wheat roots only by the soil they occupied and only that part of the soil suffered exhaustion or reduction of its water content.[64] Once water is in soil deep enough to escape rapid drying at the surface, it mostly remains until it is reached and removed by plant roots.[63]

In semiarid regions, the rainfall is sufficient to wet the soil to a depth of only a few feet.[64] This is usually exhausted each year by growth of native vegetation or crops. The lower layers are dry except in the wettest of seasons. The water table may be more than 20 feet (6 m) below the surface. Formerly, dust mulch was advocated to prevent moisture loss by capillary rise. After some disastrous experiences with soil blowing, the dust mulch theory was abandoned and a clod mulch was advocated. Soon thereafter, the effectiveness of any soil mulch to check moisture loss under dryland field conditions was refuted.

Thus, a soil mulch can reduce surface evaporation where the water table is so shallow that drainage rather than moisture conservation is desirable. In fields, the mulch formed by tillage is merely incidental to weed control.

■ 10 CULTIVATION IN RELATION TO SOIL NITRATES

Cultivation, by drying and aerating the soil, which promotes nitrification, is a benefit to a heavy water-logged soil. Controlling weeds by cultivation permits nitrates to accumulate, since nitrates are used up when a crop or weeds occupy the land. Weed control by cultivation also saves soil moisture and thus favors nitrification, which does not operate in dry soil. Cultivation, otherwise, has not produced a regular increase in the accumulation of nitrates, especially in light soils. Greater nitrification occurred in a compacted Kansas soil as compared to an uncompacted soil, up to the point where the moisture content reached two-thirds saturation. In Arkansas, varied depths of cultivation had little effect on accumulation of nitrate nitrogen in a soil of rather open structure.[65] In Pennsylvania research, scraped soil and soil cultivated three to eight times contained almost equal quantities of nitrate nitrogen.[62] Natural processes promote sufficient aeration to admit needed oxygen in the soil. Excessive cultivation reduced the nitrates in Missouri soil where the cultivation kept so much surface soil continually dry that nitrate production apparently was retarded in the upper 7 inches (18 cm).

Other experiments have shown either slight or distinct increases in nitrate accumulation from surface cultivation as compared with soil that was merely scraped.[11, 66, 67, 68, 69] The higher nitrate content in these cultivated soils may have been due to increased aeration.[64] When weed growth was prevented, Kansas research showed that sufficient accumulation of nitrates took place in uncultivated soil to insure an excellent growth of wheat, despite the lower nitrate content.[70] Nitrates leach downward so rapidly after rains that their measurement in the surface foot is of little significance.[67]

11 OTHER EFFECTS OF CULTIVATION

Cultivation can conserve soil moisture by prevention of runoff. Under semiarid conditions, up to 88 percent of the water in a dashing rain can be lost by runoff. A cultivated surface retains more water from a rain than does an uncultivated surface.[63] The faster the rain falls, the greater the difference in the amount of water held between a cultivated and uncultivated surface. On the other hand, excessive pulverization of the surface soil is likely to result in a quickly puddled condition with great runoff losses. Under subhumid conditions, there is little or no relation between the type of tillage treatment for a given crop and amount of soil moisture. Fallow areas merely scraped to control weeds have proved to be slightly less effective in moisture conservation than those that received normal cultivations, probably as a result of increased runoff on the scraped plots.[67]

A loosened soil surface acts as an insulator, so a cultivated soil is slightly cooler than uncultivated soil.[62] Many soils naturally have sufficient aeration for optimum bacterial and chemical activity without cultivation.[2]

12 INTERTILLAGE OR CULTIVATION

The primitive farmer hoed or pulled out the weeds that grew among crops planted at random in small clearings. In ancient and medieval field husbandry, field crops were planted at random or in close rows with the seed dropped in plow furrows. These crops were later weeded by hand or with crude hoes or knives. Jethro Tull introduced intertillage into English agriculture in 1733 when he applied it to crops like turnips that were planted in rows.

12.1 Purposes of Intertillage

The primary purpose of intertillage is weed control. Intertillage also breaks a crust that otherwise might retard seedling development, and in some cases roughens the soil sufficiently to increase water infiltration. Some have claimed, without substantial proof, that intertillage brings about aeration of the soil, with the result that plant foods are more readily available because of increased bacterial and chemical action in the soil.

Crops that generally require planting in rows with sufficient space between them to permit cultivation during their growth include corn, cotton, grain sorghum, sugarbeet, sugarcane, tobacco, potato, and field bean. Intertillage controls weeds that grow in the open spaces before the crop can shade the ground.

Crops with relatively slender stems, such as small grains, hay crops, and flax thrive under close plant spacing and cover the land rather uniformly. Without cultivation, these crops tend to suppress weeds by root competition and shading. Yields of these crops are usually low when they are planted in cultivated rows because they do not fully utilize the land.[71] The leaf canopy never closes, resulting in poor utilization of sunlight. Where conditions are so severe that small grain and hay crops succeed only in cultivated rows, they are generally unprofitable.

12.2 Intertillage Implements

Many different types of implements are used for intertillage. They come equipped with shovels, disks, teeth, sweeps, or knives.

ORDINARY CULTIVATORS Shovel or sweep cultivators are the types most used for intertillage because they are suited to practically all soil conditions. Cultivator width should correspond with planter width so that it operates over a group of rows that were planted simultaneously (Figure 14). Shovels or sweeps are sometimes replaced or supplemented by disks or disk hillers when considerable soil is to be moved or where a considerable amount of residue or roots is to be cut. Shovel cultivators are likely to clog under such conditions.

FIGURE 14
Cultivating soybeans.
[Courtesy Case IH]

ROTARY HOE The rotary hoe consists of a series of 18-inch (46 cm) hoe wheels each of which is fitted with teeth shaped like fingers. As the wheels rotate, these teeth penetrate and stir the soil. This hoe is useful for uprooting small weeds by *blind* cultivation before the crop emerges, as well as for early cultivations of young corn and other row crops. Its success depends on its use before weeds have made as much growth as the crop; otherwise, the crop plants would also be uprooted.[4] The rotary hoe is also effective in breaking soil crust that results from hot sunshine after a torrential rain.

OTHER CULTIVATION IMPLEMENTS The ordinary spike-tooth harrow is used with little injury to corn to kill small weeds when the corn plants are small and when the field is comparatively free of residue. Special cultivators for listed crops planted in furrows are necessary for following the furrows and turning the soil along their sides. The lister cultivator is equipped with disks or knives or both and sometimes with disks and shovels. For the first cultivation, the disks are set to cut the weeds on the sides of the furrow with the soil thrown away from the crop row. The shovels can be set to stir the soil near the plants. Hooded shields prevent the soil from rolling in on the young plants. For the second and usually final cultivation, the disks are set to roll the soil into the trench around the plants. This buries the weeds in the row while the rows are being leveled. Knife cultivators (go-devils or knife sleds) cut off the weeds below the surface while slicing the lister ridges.

12.3 Cultivation for Weed Control

Today, most weed control is accomplished by the application of herbicides. However, cultivation can be an economical alternative in some cases, especially in organic or sustainable systems when producers want to limit or eliminate the use of chemicals.

In the Corn Belt, about four cultivations are required for surface-planted corn. Experiments at the Illinois Agricultural Experiment Station[72] as early as 1888–1893 showed that corn yielded as well when the weeds were merely cut off with a hoe as when it received four or five deep cultivations.

These results were not taken seriously because of the widespread belief that cultivation was necessary for reasons other than weed control.[73] Later, results were summarized[74] for 125 experiments with corn carried on for 6 years in twenty-eight states, in which regular cultivation was compared with scraping with a hoe to destroy weeds. The average of all the tests showed that the scraped plots produced 95.1 percent as much fodder and 99.1 percent as much grain as did the cultivated plots. Cultivation was not beneficial to the corn except in destruction of weeds. These results were confirmed by additional experiments.[17, 62, 67] Other crops responded in a similar manner.[62] Competition for soil moisture is not the only reason for the low yield of corn in weedy fields, because irrigation of such fields increases the corn yield only slightly.[17]

12.4 Cultivation of Drilled Crops

Small grain fields sometimes have been harrowed in the spring, but in general this has been of no benefit to yield, nor has it eliminated all the weeds.[6] Cultivation of alfalfa sod with the toothed renovator or disk harrow to destroy grassy weeds, which formerly was widely advocated, was discontinued after it was found that the resulting injury to the alfalfa crowns permitted entrance of the bacterial wilt organism.

■ 13 ARTIFICIAL MULCHES

Plastic mulches, as well as asphalt-coated paper mulches, increase the mean temperature but also decrease the temperature range of the soil. This may hasten germination and reduce deflocculation of the soil due to freezing and thawing. These mulches reduce soil moisture loss and stop weed growth but may fail to increase yields.[57, 75] The cost of these mulches limits their use for most field crops.

■ 14 TILLAGE IN RELATION TO WATER EROSION

Seventy-five percent of the cultivated land in the United States probably has a slope greater than 2 percent on which the wasteful processes of accelerated soil erosion and runoff occur when the land isn't managed properly.[23, 49, 76] There are three types of water erosion: sheet, rill, and gully. Gully erosion causes deep channels in the field that interfere with cultivation; rill erosion produces small channels; sheet erosion is the nearly uniform removal of the topsoil from the entire slope. Severe sheet erosion on cultivated fields leads to gully formation.

Erosion is greatest in the southeastern states where heavy rainfall, rolling topography, unfrozen soil, and predominance of intertilled crops combine to cause excessive soil loss. Widely spaced crops, such as corn, cotton, tobacco, and soybean, are most generally associated with erosion.[77, 78, 79, 80] The numerous fibrous roots of sorghum and its more complete drying of the soil may account for the lower erosion on sorghum land than is observed on the land devoted to the taprooted cotton plant.[78] The greatest losses are on bare land,[78] being about twice those on corn land.[59] However, on continuously fallowed land the soil is nearly saturated with moisture.[81] Consequently, excess water is lost by runoff. Land in small-grain crops erodes very little except during periods when the soil is bare or nearly so.[23] Pasture and grass crops are very efficient in soil conservation[2] unless they are overgrazed and trampled. Erosion from continuously ungrazed, untrampled sod or meadow is almost negligible. Heavily grazed pasture may have more than three times the runoff of a moderately grazed pasture.[81] A three-year corn, wheat, clover-timothy rotation showed only twice as much runoff as did a moderately grazed pasture.

Natural vegetative cover usually prevents or greatly retards erosion.[82] Davis[83] stated: "A field abandoned because of erosion soon shows these efforts of nature to prevent devastation."

The chief methods of retarding soil erosion[84] are (1) reversion of steep slopes and abandoned cropland to pastures and woodlands, (2) contour tillage and planting, (3) strip cropping, (4) terracing, (5) cover crops, (6) damming of gullies, and (7) minimum tillage as previously described.

Strip cropping has been practiced in Pennsylvania for generations.[80] The alternate strips of thick-growing crops catch the soil water shed from the areas occupied by cultivated row crops. The sloping land is tilled and crops are planted on the contour. A regular rotation can be followed when the strips are of approximately equal width.

FIGURE 15

Contour terraces and grass waterways help reduce erosion. [Courtesy USDA NRCS]

The bench terrace, long used in Europe, Asia, and the Philippine Islands, is not feasible in the United States because of its excessive costs. Terracing became a common practice in the Southeast after the Mangum terrace was devised by P. H. Mangum of Wake Forest, N.C., in 1885. Later, many of the terraces were abandoned because of frequent failures of the terraces, high costs of maintenance, and questionable benefits from terracing. Many of these early terraces were poorly built or the land was managed improperly.[85] When a terrace breaks, erosion losses exceed those on unterraced land. Broadbase terraces permit farm machines to pass over them. The Nichols terrace, a broad-channel type, is constructed with less labor. This broadbase terrace is 15 to 25 feet (5 to 8 m) wide at the base and 15 to 24 inches (48 to 61 cm) high. The runoff water is carried away in a gradually sloping broad shallow channel at a low velocity (Figure 5). Level terraces are advised where the rainfall is less than 30 inches (760 mm) per year, so all the water is held on the field until it is absorbed.[78] The conservation bench terrace is even more effective because the water above the levee spreads back over a wide bed. The terracing of steep slopes (more than 8 percent) is no longer recommended because of the expense, because all the topsoil may be scraped up to build the terraces,[77] and because steep terrace banks erode badly. As fields and tillage equipment continue to grow larger, many terraces have been abandoned because it is not economical to till the smaller fields that result from terraces. However, if good conservation tillage is practiced, water erosion is less of a problem and may even be eliminated.

Nitrogen, phosphorus, calcium, and sulfur in soil that has been eroded from corn or wheat land can equal or exceed the amounts taken off in the crops.[13] Much of the soil carried by streams comes from stream or gully banks, deserts, and similar areas that have been eroding since the beginning of time. Most important of all, it comes from badlands and breaks. Most of this eroded soil is not topsoil. A combination of computed estimates of the quantity of suspended soil carried into the sea by rivers of the United States[49, 83] indicates that the total is about 1,450 pounds per acre (1,620 kg/ha) per year. Should half of this be topsoil, the equivalent of the total topsoil is washed to the sea every 2,759 years. Thus, only a small part of the erosion losses reported[76, 77] represent soil washed from the continent. Estimates of soil losses can exceed losses actually measured experimentally under the same conditions.[24] Estimates for 1971 suggest that 12 tons of soil per acre (27 MT/ha) were lost by water erosion on farms.[86]

■ 15 TILLAGE IN RELATION TO WIND EROSION

Soil blowing has been going on at times in various parts of the Great Plains for at least 25,000 years. It also occurs elsewhere in the United States when a wind 20 miles per hour (30 km/hr) or more strikes a bare, smooth, loose, deflocculated soil.[87, 88] The organic matter and fine soil particles in the topsoil contain much of the nitrogen.[76, 89] They can be carried great distances and then deposited in some humid area where the additional fertility is needed. When accumulated drifts are stirred and allowed to blow back onto eroded cultivated fields where the soil is caught by vegetation, the aggraded soil that results can be very productive.[90] Uniform sand moves readily with wind where the surface is unprotected. Peat land is subject to serious wind damage. Heavy soils are also subject to movement under certain conditions. The ideal structural condition to prevent erosion is coarse aggregates (clods and crumbs) too large to blow, and yet not so large as to interfere with cultivation and plant growth. There is no advantage in further pulverization.

Summer fallowed land, except when protected by alternate strips of crops, is particularly vulnerable to high winds unless adequate residues are maintained on the soil surface. Land can be ranked as follows for decreasing vulnerability to blowing: (1) bean fields, (2) corn and sorghum stubble, (3) cornstalks, (4) fallow seeded to winter rye or winter wheat, and (5) small-grain or hay stubble.[91] Small grain stubble land rarely blows unless the organic debris is very scanty or has been turned under.

Tillage that furrows the ground or protects the surface soil with small clods and residue is especially desirable in wind erosion control. Furrows should be at right angles to the prevailing wind direction.[87, 92, 93] Among the useful implements are the rod weeder, lister, field cultivator, shovel cultivator, and spring-tooth harrow. The one-way disk plow is satisfactory only on land with heavy stubble because it leaves the residues mixed with and protruding from the surface soil. Cultivation stops wind erosion only temporarily[87] but may delay destructive action until rains start a vegetative cover. Then blowing ceases to be a serious problem.

A permanent vegetative cover is the best protection against soil blowing.[92, 93] The soil is too dry for grass seedlings to become established when soil blowing conditions prevail. When rainfall is ample, weeds cover the land and protect it from erosion without seeding. During severe drought, Russian thistle (*Salsola kali*) and kochia (*Kochia scoparia*) are the predominating weed covers in the Great Plains. These break off and blow away during the winter. In moist seasons, weeds such as wild sunflower (*Helianthus annuus*) and pigweed (*Amaranthus retroflexus*) take root and protect the soil while perennial weeds and grasses become established.

Strips of sorghum planted perpendicular to the prevailing wind direction check soil blowing.[92, 94] Tree belts check soil blowing and accumulate drifted soil. They are, however, of little economic benefit to field crops under semiarid conditions because they preclude crop growth for 4 rods (20 m) on each side and seldom grow more than 20 feet (6 m) high. Tree belts protect farmsteads, gardens, and livestock because they check the wind and catch drifting snow.

REFERENCES

1. Cole, J. S., and O. R. Mathews. "Tillage," in *Soils and Men,* USDA Yearbook, 1938, pp. 321–328.

2. Sewell, M. C. "Tillage: A review of the literature," *J. Am. Soc. Agron.* 11(1919):269–290.

3. Fryrear, D. W., and J. D. Bilbro. "Wind erosion control with residues and related practices," in *Managing Agricultural Residues,* edited by P. W. Unger. Boca Raton, FL: Lewis, 1994, pp. 7–18.

4. Gray, R. B. "Tillage machinery," in *Soils and Men,* USDA Yearbook, 1938, pp. 329–346.

5. Zingg, A. W., and C. J. Whitefield. "A summary of research experience with stubble-mulch farming in the western States," *USDA Tech. Bull.* 1166, 1957, pp. 1–56.

6. Oveson, M. M., and W. E. Hall. "Longtime tillage experiments on Eastern Oregon wheat land," *OR Agr. Exp. Sta. Tech. Bull.* 39, 1957.

7. Call, L. E., and M. C. Sewell. "The soil mulch," *J. Am. Soc. Agron.* 9(1917):49–61.

8. Allmaras, R. R., and others. "Fall versus spring plowing and related heat balance in the western Corn Belt," *MN Agr. Exp. Sta. Tech. Bull. 283,* 1972, pp. 1–22.

9. Duley, F. L. "Yields in different cropping systems and fertilizer tests under stubble mulching and plowing in eastern Nebraska," *NE Agr. Exp. Sta. Res. Bull.* 190, 1960.

10. Evans, C. E., and E. R. Lemon. "Conserving soil moisture," in *Soil,* USDA Yearbook, 1957, pp. 340–359.

11. Albrecht, W. A. "Nitrate accumulation in soil as influenced by tillage and straw mulch," *J. Am. Soc. Agron.* 18(1926):841–853.

12. Noll, C. F. "Deep versus ordinary plowing," *PA Agr. Exp. Sta. Ann. Rpt.* 1912–1913, pp. 39–47.

13. Duley, F. L., and O. E. Hays. "The effect of the degree of slope on runoff and soil erosion," *J. Agr. Res.* 45(1932):349–360.

14. Miller, M. F., and H. H. Krusekopf. "The influence of systems of cropping and methods of culture on surface run-off and soil erosion," *MO Agr. Exp. Sta. Res. Bull.* 177, 1932.

15. Chilcott, E. C., and J. S. Cole. "Subsoiling, deep tilling, and soil dynamiting in the Great Plains," *J. Agr. Res.* 14(1918):481–521.

16. Bracken, A. F., and George Stewart. "A quarter century of dry farming experiments at Nephi, Utah," *J. Am. Soc. Agron.* 23(1931):271–279.

17. Mosier, J. G., and A. F. Gustafson. "Soil moisture and tillage for corn," *IL Agr. Exp. Sta. Bull. 181,* 1915, pp. 563–586.

18. Hobbs, J. A., and others. "Deep tillage effects on soils and crops," *Agron. J.* 53, 5(1961):313–316.

19. Haney, W. A., and A. W. Zingg. "Principles of tillage," in *Soil,* USDA Yearbook, 1957, pp. 277–281.

20. Baker, C. J., K. E. Saxton, and W. R. Ritchie. *No-tillage Seeding: Science and Practice.* Wallingford, UK: CAB International, 1996.

21. Faulkner, E. H. *Plowman's Folly.* Grosset and Dunlap, 1943.

22. Scarseth, G. Ames, IA: Iowa State Univ. Press, *Man and His Earth,* 1962.

23. Duley, F. L., and C. R. Fenster. "Stubble-mulch farming methods for fallow areas," *NE Agr. Ext. Circ.* 54-100 (rev.), 1961, pp. 1–19.

24. Horning, T. R., and M. M. Oveson. "Stubble Mulching in the Northwest," *USDA Inf. Bull.* 253, 1962.

25. Fenster, C. R., and T. M. McCalla. "Tillage practices in western Nebraska with a wheat-sorghum-fallow rotation," *NE Agr. Exp. Sta. SB 515*, 1971, pp. 1–23.

26. Hayes, W. A. "Mulch tillage in modern farming." *USDA Leaflet 554*, 1971, pp. 1–7.

27. Mannering, J. V., and R. E. Burwell. "Tillage methods to reduce runoff and erosion in the corn belt," *USDA Inf. Bull. 330*, 1968, pp. 1–14.

28. Blevins, R. L., and Cook, D. "No-tillage, its influence on soil moisture and soil temperature," *KY Agr. Exp. Sta. Prog. Rpt. 187*, 1970, 1–15.

29. Myers, D. N., K. D. Metzker, and S. Davis. "Status and trends in suspended-sediment discharges, soil erosion, and conservation tillage in the Maumee River Basin-Ohio, Michigan, and Indiana." *U.S. Geol. Surv. Water-Resources Investigations Report 00-4091*, 2000.

30. Köller, K. "Techniques of soil tillage," in *Soil Tillage in Agroecosystems*, edited by Adel El Titi. Boca Raton, FL: CRC Press, 2003, pp. 1–26.

31. Derpsch, R. "Conservation tillage, no-tillage and related technologies," in *Proc. 1st World Congr. Conserv. Agric.* Madrid, Oct. 1–5, 2001. Vols. I and II. 2001.

32. Shelton, D. P., P. J. Jasa, J. A. Smith, and R. Kanable. "Estimating percent residue cover," *NE Coop. Ext. Serv. Nebguide* G95-1132-A. 1995.

33. Shelton, D. P., P. J. Jasa, J. A. Smith, and R. Kanable. "Estimating percent residue cover using the calculation method," *NE Coop. Ext. Serv. Nebguide* G95-1135-A. 1996.

34. Carter, M. R., ed. *Conservation Tillage in Temperate Agroecosystems*. Boca Raton, FL: Lewis, 1994.

35. Slater, C. S. "Winter aspects of soil structure," *J. Soil and Water Conservation 6*, 1(1951):38–41.

36. Jalota, S. K., and S. S. Prihar. *Reducing Soil Water Levels with Tillage and Straw Mulching*. Ames, IA: Iowa Univ. Press, 1998.

37. Duley, F. L., and J. C. Russel. "The use of crop residues for soil and moisture conservation," *J. Am. Soc. Agron. 31*(1939):703.

38. Steiner, J. L. "Crop residue effects on water conservation," in *Managing Agricultural Residues*, edited by P. W. Unger. Boca Raton, FL: Lewis, 1994, pp. 41–76.

39. Mielke, L. N., J. W. Doran, and K. A. Richard. "Physical environment near the surface of plowed and no-till soils," *Soil Till. Res. 7*(1986):355–366.

40. Fenster, C. R., and T. M. McCalla. "Tillage practices in western Nebraska with a wheat-fallow rotation," *NE Agr. Exp. Sta. SB 507*, 1970, pp. 1–20.

41. McCallister, D. L., and W. L. Chien. "Organic carbon quality and forms as influenced by tillage and cropping sequence," *Commun. Soil Sci. Plant Anal. 31*(2000):465–479.

42. Doran, J. W., E. T. Elliott, and K. Paustian. "Soil microbial activity, nitrogen cycling, and long-term changes in organic carbon pools as related to fallow tillage management," *Soil & Till. Res 49*(1998):3–18.

43. Lamb, J. A., J. W. Doran, and G. A. Peterson. "Nonsymbiotic dinitrogen fixation in no-till and conventional wheat-fallow systems," *Soil Sci. Soc. Amer. J 51*(1987):356–361.

44. Doran, J. W., and D. M. Linn. "Microbial ecology of conservation management systems," in *Soil Biology: Effects on Soil Quality*, edited by J. L. Hatfield and B. A. Steward. Lewis, Boca Raton, FL: Lewis, 1994, pp. 1–27.

45. Doran, J. W. "Tillage changes soil," *Crops and Soils Magazine*, Aug-Sep, American Society of Agronomy, Madison, WI. 1982.

46. Lindwall, C. W., F. J. Larney, A. M. Johnston, and J. R. Moyer. "Crop management in conservation tillage systems," in *Managing Agricultural Residues*, edited by P. W. Unger. Boca Raton, FL: Lewis, 1994, pp. 185–210.

47. Thysell, J. C. "Conservation and use of soil moisture at Mandan, N. Dak.," *USDA Tech. Bull. 617*, 1938, pp. 1–40.

48. Von Trebra, R. L., and F. A. Wagner. "Tillage practices for southwestern Kansas," *KS Agr. Exp. Sta. Bull. 262*, 1932, pp. 1–11.

49. Bennett, H. H., and W. C. Lowdermilk. "General aspects of the soil-erosion problem," in *Soils and Men,* USDA Yearbook, 1938, pp. 581–608.

50. Mathews, O. R., and V. I. Clark. "Summer fallow at Ardmore (South Dakota)," *USDA Circ.* 213, 1932.

51. Morgan, G. W. "Experiments with fallow in north-central Montana," *USDA Bull.* 1310, 1925.

52. Sarvis, J. T., and J. C. Thysell. "Crop rotation and tillage experiments of the northern Great Plains Field Station," *USDA Tech. Bull.* 536, 1936, pp. 1–75.

53. Harris, F. S., A. F. Bracken, and I. J. Jensen. "Sixteen years' dry farm experiments in Utah," *UT Agr. Expt. Sta. Bull.* 175, 1920, p. 43.

54. Greb, B. W. "Reducing drought effects on croplands in the west central Great Plains." *USDA Info. Bull.* 420. 1979, pp. 1–31.

55. Juergens, L. A., D. L. Young, H. R. Hinman, and W. F. Schillinger. "An economic comparison of no-till spring wheat and oilseed rotations to conventional winter wheat-fallow in Adams County, WA. *WA State Coop. Ext.* EB 1956E. 2002.

56. King, F. H. *Physics of Agriculture,* 5th ed. Madison, WI: F. H. King, 1910, pp. 158–203.

57. Shaw, C. F. "When the soil mulch conserves soil moisture," *J. Am. Soc. Agron.* 21(1929): 1165–1171.

58. Shaw, C. F., and A. Smith. "Maximum height of capillary rise starting with soil at capillary saturation," *Hilgardia* 2(1927):399–409.

59. McLaughlin, W. W. "Capillary movement of soil moisture," *USDA Bull.* 835, 1920.

60. Lewis, M. R. "Rate of flow of capillary moisture," *USDA Tech. Bull.* 579, 1937.

61. Veihmeyer, F. J. "Some factors affecting the irrigation requirements of deciduous orchards," *Hilgardia* 2(1927):125–284.

62. Merkle, F. G., and C. J. Irwin. "Some effects of inter-tillage on crops and soils," *PN Agr. Exp. Sta. Bull.* 272, 1931.

63. Burr, W. W. "Storage and use of soil moisture," *NE Agr. Exp Sta. Res. Bull.* 5, 1914.

64. Mathews, O. R., and E. C. Chilcott. "Storage of water by spring wheat," *USDA Bull.* 1139, 1923.

65. Sachs, W. H. "Effect of cultivation on moisture and nitrate of field soil," *AR Agr. Exp. Sta. Bull.* 205, 1926.

66. Call, L. E. "The relation of weed growth in nitric nitrogen accumulation in the soil," *J. Am. Soc. Agron.* 10(1918):35–44.

67. Kiesselbach, T. A., A. Anderson, and W. E. Lyness. "Tillage practices in relation to corn production," *NE Agr. Exp. Sta. Bull.* 232, 1928.

68. Lyon, T. L. "Inter-tillage of crops and formation of nitrates in the soil," *J. Am. Soc. Agron.* 14(1922):97–109.

69. Sewell, M. C., and P. L. Gainey. "Nitrate accumulation under various cultural treatments," *J. Am. Soc. Agron.* 24(1932): 283–289.

70. Shaw, C. F. "The effect of a paper mulch on soil temperature," *Hilgardia* 1(1926): 341–364.

71. Sheppard, J. H., and J. A. Jeffrey. "A study of methods of cultivation," *ND Agr. Exp. Sta. Bull.* 29, 1897.

72. Wimer, D. C., and M. B. Harland. "The cultivation of corn," *IL Agr. Exp. Sta. Bull.* 259, 1925.

73. Williams, C. G. "The corn crop," *OH Agr. Exp. Sta. Bull.* 140, 1903.

74. Cates, J. S., and H. R. Cox. "The weed factor in the cultivation of corn," *USDA B.P.I. Bull.* 257, 1912.

75. Magruder, Roy. "Paper mulch for the vegetable garden," *OH Agr. Exp. Sta. Bull.* 447, 1930.

76. Bennett, H. H. "Cultural changes in soils from the standpoint of erosion," *J. Am. Soc. Agron.* 23(1931):434–454.

77. Clark, M., and J. C. Wooley. "Terracing, an important step in erosion control," *MO Agr. Exp. Sta. Bull.* 400, 1938.

78. Dickson, R. E. "Results and significance of the Spur (Texas) run-off and erosion experiments," *J. Am. Soc. Agron.* 21(1929):415–422.

79. Duley, F. L. "Soil erosion of soybean land," *J. Am. Soc. Agron.* 17(1923): 800–803.

80. Miller, M. F. "Cropping systems in relation to erosion control," *MO Agr. Exp Sta. Bull.* 366, 1936.

81. Smith, D. D., and others. "Investigations in erosion control and reclamation of eroded Shelby and related soils at the Conservation Experiment Station, Bethany, Mo., 1930–42," *USDA Tech. Bull.* 883, 1945, pp. 1–175.

82. Jacks, G. V., and R. O. Whyte. "Erosion and soil conservation," in *Imperial Bur. Pastures and Forage Crops Bull. 25*, Aberwystwyth, England, 1938, pp. 1–206.

83. Davis, R. O. E. "Economic waste from soil erosion." *USDA Yearbook*, 1913, pp. 207–220.

84. Brill, G. D., C. S. Slater, and V. D. Broach. "Conservation methods for soils of the northern Coastal Plain," *USDA Inf. Bull.* 271, 1963.

85. Ramser, C. E. "Farm terracing," *USDA Farmers Bull.* 1669, 1931.

86. Hargrove, T. R. "Agricultural research impact on environment," *IA Agr. Exp. Sta. Special Rpt. 69*, 1972, pp. 1–64.

87. Call, L. E. "Cultural methods of controlling wind erosion," *J. Am. Soc. Agron.* 28(1936):193–201.

88. Kellogg, C. E. "Soil blowing and dust storms," *USDA Misc. Pub. 221*, 1935.

89. Daniel, H. A., and W. H. Langham. "The effect of wind erosion and cultivation on the total nitrogen and organic matter content of soils in the southern High Plains," *J. Am. Soc. Agron.* 28(1936):587–596.

90. Whitfield, C. J., and J. A. Perrin. "Sand-dune reclamation in the southern Great Plains," *USDA Farmers Bull.* 1825, 1939, pp. 1–13.

91. Brandon, J. F., and A. Kezer. "Soil blowing and its control in Colorado," *CO Agr. Exp. Sta. Bull.* 419, 1936.

92. Chilcott, E. F. "Preventing soil blowing on the southern Great Plains," *USDA Farmers Bull.* 1771, 1937.

93. Cole, J. S., and G. W. Morgan. "Implements and methods of tillage to control soil blowing on the northern Great Plains," *USDA Farmers Bull.* 1797, 1938.

94. Jardine, W. M. "Management of soils to prevent blowing," *J. Am. Soc. Agron.* 5(1913):213–217.

Seeds and Seeding

From Chapter 7 of *Principles of Field Crop Production*, Fourth Edition, John H. Martin, Richard P. Waldren, David L. Stamp. Copyright © 2006 by Pearson Education, Inc. Published by Pearson Prentice Hall. All rights reserved.

Seeds and Seeding

1 IMPORTANCE OF GOOD SEEDS

Reasonably good seed is essential to successful crop production, whereas poor seed is a serious hazard for farmers.[1] The variety and the approximate germination and purity of seed should be known before it is planted.[1] Introduction of weeds in the seed often increases the labor for production of the crop, reduces crop yields,[2] and contaminates the current product as well as the seed and soil in future seasons.

2 CHEMICAL COMPOSITION OF SEEDS

Table 1 shows the chemical composition of some common crop seeds. Ether extract is fat and oil content, ash is mineral content, and nitrogen free extract is carbohydrate content. Seeds store food supply for germination and emergence as fat and oil, or as carbohydrate. Grasses store most of their food supply as carbohydrate while legumes store most of their food supply as fat and oil. Also, seeds that are higher in fat and oil will usually be higher in protein. Oat seed is higher in fiber because the glumes are still attached.

3 SEED GERMINATION

3.1 Environmental Requirements for Germination

The most important external conditions necessary for germination of matured seeds are: (1) ample supplies of moisture and oxygen, (2) a suitable temperature, and, (3) for some seeds, certain light conditions. A deficiency in any factor can prevent germination.

Good seed shows a germination of 90 to 100 percent in the laboratory. Some sound crop seeds, particularly small grains, show a seedling emergence of as high as 90 percent of the seed when sown under good field conditions. Even corn, which is a rather sensitive seed, often produces stands of 90 percent or more in the field. Sorghum and cotton give a lower percentage of emergence

128

TABLE 1 Chemical Composition of Seeds

	Dry Matter (%)	Crude Protein (%)	Ether Extract (%)	Crude Fiber (%)	Ash (%)	Nitrogen Free Extract (%)
Barley	90.7	14.2	2.1	6.2	3.3	74.2
Corn	89.3	10.9	4.6	2.6	1.5	80.4
Oat	90.3	14.4	4.7	11.8	3.8	65.3
Peanut	—	30.4	47.7	2.5	2.3	11.7
Rice	88.6	9.2	1.4	2.7	1.8	84.9
Rye	—	14.7	1.8	2.5	2.0	79.0
Sorghum	88.7	12.9	3.6	2.5	2.0	79.0
Soybean	—	37.9	18.0	5.0	1.6	24.5
Wheat	88.9	14.2	1.7	2.3	2.0	79.8

Source: *Composition of Cereal Grains and Forages.* National Academy of Sciences, National Research Council, Publ. 505

because they are more susceptible to attack from seed-rotting fungi. Treated sorghum seed may give a field emergence of 75 percent, but 50 percent emergence is all that is normally expected from untreated seed with a 95 percent laboratory germination, even in a good seedbed. However, when the seed germinates only 60 to 70 percent in the laboratory, many of the sprouts will be so weakened that a field emergence of 20 to 25 percent is all that can reasonably be expected. In a poor seedbed, the emergence may be much less. Seeds that germinate slowly may produce weak seedlings. However, the strong seeds in a low-germinating sample may give good yields, provided enough seed is planted.[3]

Small-seeded legumes and grasses are sown at higher rates to compensate for poor germination, low-seedling survival resulting from the necessary shallow seeding, and the failure of hard seeds to germinate when sown.

With aerial seeding, legume seeds are sometimes pelleted to maintain the viability of the *Rhizobia* inoculant on the seed and to repel pests. When sowing in acid soils, the pellet material should be mostly lime or dolomite. Phosphates are helpful for promoting seedling growth. *Rhizobia* to be added to the seed are most frequently carried in peat. These materials, combined with gum arabic or methyl cellulose, are mixed with the seed in a revolving drum to make the pellets.[4]

In seeded grass-pasture mixtures, the species with the most viable seeds often predominates in the immediate stand.[5] Small-seeded grasses are sown at rates in excess of the rates that would be required if all of the seeds were to produce seedlings because the mortality of the seeds and seedlings is likely to be high. Thus, in a bluegrass pasture, a seeding rate of 25 pounds per acre (38 kg/ha) provides more than 1,000 seeds per square foot (11,000/m^2), whereas 100 plants per square foot (1,000/m^2) would soon provide dense turf.

Commercial seed of Kentucky bluegrass and that of certain other grasses may not germinate over 70 percent. This low germination is due to harvesting when many of the panicles are immature and due to inadequate drying. Any dicotyledonous plant with an indeterminate flowering habit, or a grass that sends up new tillers and panicles over a considerable period, will not mature its seed uniformly. With such crops, immature seed is gathered even though harvesting is delayed until the ripest seeds have already been lost by shattering.

MOISTURE Abundant water is necessary for rapid germination. This is readily supplied by damp blotters or paper towels in a germinator or by soil that contains about 50 to 70 percent of its water holding capacity. Field crop seeds start to germinate when their moisture content (on a dry basis) reaches 26 to 75 percent (e.g., 26 percent in sorghum, millet, and sudangrass; 45 to 50 percent in small grains;[6] and as high as 75 percent for soybean). The minimum moisture for germination of corn is approximately 35 percent in the whole grain and 60 percent in the embryo.[7]

Water usually enters the seed through the micropyle or hilum, or it may penetrate the seedcoat directly. Water enters certain seeds, such as castor and sweetclover, through the strophiole or caruncle, an appendage of the hilum.[8] Water inside the seedcoat is imbibed by the embryo, scutellum, and endosperm. The imbibed water causes the colloidal proteins and starch of the seed to swell. The enormous imbibitional power of certain seeds enables them to draw water from soil that is even below the wilting point, but not in sufficient amounts to complete germination because the adjacent soil particles become dehydrated. Seeds sown in dry soil therefore may fail to germinate, or they may absorb sufficient moisture to swell and partly germinate. Wheat, barley, oat, corn, and pea have been sprouted, allowed to dry, and resprouted three to seven times before germination was fully destroyed.[9] However, germination was lower with each repeated sprouting. Wheat seeds can absorb water from a saturated atmosphere until they reach a moisture content exceeding 30 percent on a wet basis, but this is not high enough to start germination.[10]

OXYGEN Many dry seeds, particularly pea and bean, are impervious to gases, including oxygen. Absorption of moisture may render the seed permeable to oxygen. Seeds planted too deeply or in a saturated soil may be prevented from germinating due to an oxygen deficiency. Rice needs less oxygen than most seeds since it will germinate on the soil surface under 6 inches (15 cm) of water. However, an atmosphere of pure oxygen is as harmful to seeds as it is to humans.

TEMPERATURE The extreme temperature range for the germination of field crop seeds is from 32 to 120°F (0 to 49°C). In general, cool season crops germinate at lower temperatures than warm season crops.

Wheat, oat, barley, and rye may germinate slowly at the temperature of melting ice.[11] Buckwheat, flax, red clover, alfalfa, field pea, soybean, and perennial ryegrass germinate at 41°F (5°C) or less. The minimum temperature for germination of corn is about 50°F (10°C). Tobacco seeds[12] germinate slowly below 57°F (14°C). Of the commonly grown crops, seeds of alfalfa and the clovers will germinate more readily at low temperatures than any others. Since starchy seeds appear to be more easily destroyed by rots, they are less likely to produce sprouts at low temperatures than are oily or corneous seeds of the same species.[13, 14] Smooth, hard, hybrid seed corn gives better stands than do rough, softer types.

A temperature of 59°F (15°C) is about optimum for wheat, with progressively decreasing germination at higher temperatures.[15] Mold increases directly with increased temperatures. Soybean of good quality may germinate equally well at all temperatures from 50 to 86°F (10 to 30°C), but seeds of low vitality germinate best at 77°F (25°C).

The most favorable temperature for germination of tobacco seed is about 88°F (31°C).[12] The optimum laboratory germination for seeds of most cool weather crops is about 68°F (20°C), but certain fescues and other grasses require a somewhat lower temperature. Warm weather crops, particularly the southern legumes and grasses such as crotalaria and bermudagrass, germinate best at 86 to 97°F (30 to 36°C).

Maximum temperatures at which seeds will germinate are approximately 104°F (40°C) or less for the small grains, flax,[16] and tobacco,[12] 111°F (44°C) or less for buckwheat, bean, alfalfa, red clover, crimson clover, and sunflower, and 115 to 122°F (46 to 50°C) for corn, sorghum, and millets. At temperatures too high for germination, the seeds may be killed or be merely forced into secondary dormancy. The killing has been ascribed to destruction of enzymes and coagulation of cell proteins. These reactions as a rule are not observed at temperatures as low as 122°F (50°C), but might occur over the 24 to 28 hours or more necessary to start germination. Secondary dormancy induced by heat may be an oxygen relationship.

LIGHT Light requirement for germination involves the phytochrome system found in most plants. Phytochrome absorbs red light (660 nm) and far red light (730 nm) depending on its configuration. Red light initiates germination, but far red light inhibits germination.[17] Even a flash of light may induce germination in seeds that are wet and swollen.

Light requirement is found mostly in small seeds that need to be close to the soil surface when germinating. If small seeds germinate too deeply in the soil they will exhaust their food supply before reaching the surface. Most weed seeds require light for germination. The absence of light enables such seeds to remain dormant when buried deeply in the soil. Phytochrome is also involved in photoperiodism in plants.

Most field crop seeds germinate in either light or darkness. Many of the grasses germinate more promptly in the presence of, or after exposure to light, especially when the seeds are fresh. Among these are bentgrass, bermudagrass, Kentucky bluegrass, Canada bluegrass, and slender wheatgrass. Light is necessary for germination of some types of tobacco, except at low temperatures of about 57°F (14°C). Most standard American varieties will germinate in its absence, although the rate and percentage of germination may be considerably retarded. The light requirement in all cases is small.[12]

3.2 Process of Germination

When placed under the proper conditions, seeds capable of immediate germination gradually absorb water, until, after approximately three days, their moisture content may be 60 to 100 percent of the dry weight. Meanwhile, the seedcoats have become softened and the seeds swollen. Soluble nutrients, particularly sugars, go into solution. The soluble glucose is transported to the growing sprout by diffusion from cell to cell. It is then synthesized into cellulose, nonreducing sugars, and starch. Proteins are broken down by proteolytic enzymes into amides, such as asparagin, or into amino acids. These are then moved to new tissue and used to rebuild proteins. Fats, which occur mostly in the cotyledons of certain oil-bearing seeds and in the embryos of cereal seeds, are split by enzymes called lipases into fatty acids and glycerol. These, in turn, undergo chemical changes to form sugars, which are used to build up the carbohydrates and fats in the seedlings. Energy for the chemical and biological processes of germination and growth is supplied by respiration or the biological oxidation of carbon and hydrogen into carbon dioxide and water.[17] During germination, respiration proceeds rapidly at a rate hundreds of times faster than in dry seeds.

The energy consumed during germination may amount to one-half the dry weight of the seed.[18] The germination of a bushel of wheat utilizes the equivalent of all the oxygen in 900 cubic feet (25 m^3) of air and requires energy equivalent to that expended in plowing an acre of land. Emerging seedlings exposed to light begin photosynthesis early, but even then their dry weight may not equal the dry weight of the seed until seven to fourteen days or more after the seedling appears above the soil surface.

In seeds that germinate promptly, the growing embryo ruptures the seedcoat within one or two days after the seeds are wetted. The radicle, or embryonic root, is the first organ to emerge in nearly all seeds. At this time the seed has absorbed all the available water in its vicinity. The seedling needs additional water to continue growth that is furnished by the radicle. The radicle is soon followed by the plumule or young shoot (Figures 1 and 2). In many dicotyledonous plants such as the bean and flax, the cotyledons emerge from the soil and function as the first leaves. The plumule emerges in a bent or curved position (Figure 3). The arch thus formed serves to protect the cotyledons as they are brought above the surface of the soil by the elongating hypocotyl. This is called *epigeal germination.*

In grasses (monocotyledonous plants), and also in a few legumes such as pea and vetch, the cotyledons remain in the soil. The plumule grows or is pushed upward by the elongation of an epicotyl or a subcrown internode. This is called *hypogeal germination.* The subcrown internode of different grasses has been called a mesocotyl, epicotyl, or hypocotyl, depending upon the seedling node from which it arises.

The coleoptile of grasses emerges from the soil as a pale tube-like structure that encloses the first true leaf. A slit develops at the tip of the coleoptile, and the leaf emerges through it. Then photosynthesis begins and the seedling gradually establishes independent metabolism as the stored food of the seed nears exhaustion. The roots are well developed by that time.

FIGURE 1

Six successive stages in the germination of the sugarcane seed.

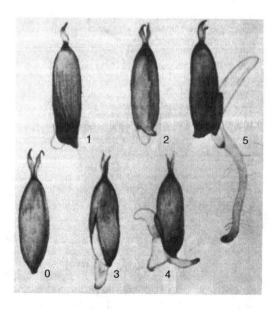

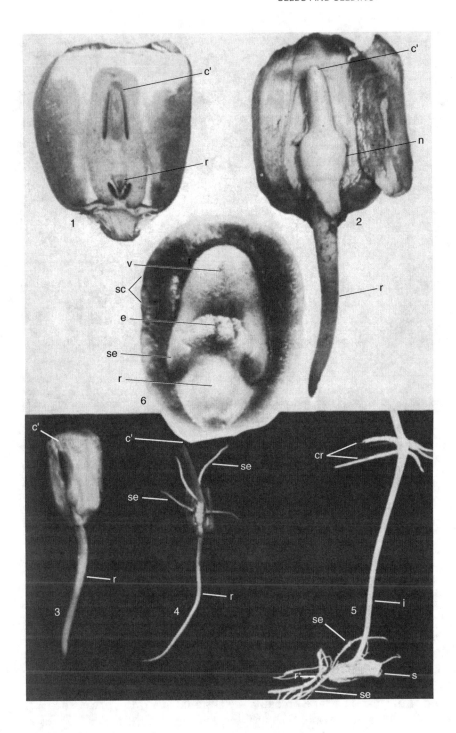

FIGURE 2

Stages in corn germination: *(1)* Before germination; *(2)* germinated 36 hours, *(3)* 48 hours, *(4)* 4 days, and *(5)* 8 days. In the two upper views the seedcoat has been removed to expose the embryo. In germinating the radicle or first seminal root *(r)* pushes out quickly; the nodal region *(n)* swells; the coleoptile, which encloses the first leaves and has a vent at the tip *(c')*, grows upward; additional seminal roots *(se)* arise, usually in pairs above the radicle, after three days. Finally the coronal or crown roots *(cr)* develop and the food substance in the seed *(s)* is practically exhausted. At *(6)* a wheat germ enlarged about 25 times, shows the scutellum *(sc)*, vent in coleoptile *(v)* epiblast *(e)*, seminal root swellings *(se)*, and radicle *(r)*, which is enclosed in the coleorhiza. [Courtesy T. A. Kiesselbach]

3.3 Qualities in Seeds for Germination

WHOLE VERSUS BROKEN SEEDS A marked decrease in germination of mutilated wheat, corn, and alfalfa seeds occurs when the germ is injured.[19] Broken seeds that contain the embryo germinate less, have a higher seedling mortality, and produce smaller plants than whole seeds.[20, 21] Breaks in the seedcoat of cereals are harmful

FIGURE 3

Seedlings of *(1)* bean, *(2)* pea, *(3)* rye, *(4)* sorghum, and *(5)* oat. During germination, the cotyledons *(co)* of the bean are pushed up by the elongating hypocotyl *(hy);* then the cotyledons separate and the plumule of true leaves *(p)* emerges. In the germinating pea, the epicotyl *(ep)* grows upward from the cotyledons *(co)* and the plumule *(p)* grows out from the tip of the epicotyl. In the cereals, the coleoptile grows or is pushed to the soil surface and then the plumule *(p)* grows out through a slit *(c')* at the tip of the coleoptile. In the rye, as in wheat and barley, the coleoptile base *(c)* arises at the seed *(s)* and the crown node lies somewhere within the coleoptile. If sorghum, as in corn, the coleoptile base *(c)* is at the crown node which is carried upward from the seed *(s)* by the elongating subcrown internode *(i)*. In oats, as in rice, the node at the coleoptile base *(c)* stands just below the crown node and also is carried upward from the seed *(s)* by the elongating subcrown internode. Occasionally adventitious roots *(a)* arise from the subcrown internode *(i)* in oats and other cereals. (The irregular direction of roots resulted from germination between blotters instead of in the soil.)

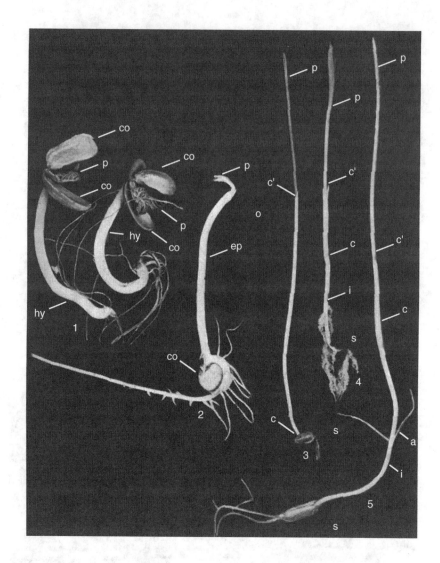

to germination, with injury at the embryo end the most serious.[22] Broken or cracked seeds are more susceptible to mold more than whole seeds.[14] Mechanical injury resulting in broken seedcoats and splitting frequently occurs in field pea. Seeds that consist of the embryo and a single cotyledon, or a part of one, may fail to germinate.[23]

The viability of seeds may be quickly destroyed by mold or heat as a result of the growth of fungi and bacteria on damp seeds stored in a warm place. These organisms break down and absorb the constituents of the seed. The fats are broken down into fatty acids, and germination drops as fatty acids accumulate. After planting, the seeds are exposed to organisms in the soil as well as to those on the seed. The organisms utilize the food materials in the seed, thus starving the young sprout, and certain organisms even invade and kill the young sprouts. Seed-borne and soil-inhabiting organisms often prevent seedling emergence. Sowing healthy seeds at the optimum temperature for germination helps to retard seed rot and seedling blight. Thus, small grains and field pea should be sown when the soil is cool, and planting of corn, sorghum, cotton, peanut, soybean, and millet should be delayed until the soil is warm. The best protection against seed rots and seedling blights is treatment of the seed with approved disinfectants containing a chemical that is toxic to fungi and bacteria.[24] The fungi commonly associated with seed mold or rot and seedling blight are the species of *Pythium, Fusarium, Rhizopus, Penicillium, Aspergillus, Gibberella, Diplodia, Helminthosporium, Cladysporium, Basisporium,* and *Collectotrichum.*[14, 25]

SEED MATURITY Mature seed is preferable to immature seed, but occasionally growers are obliged to plant seeds that have failed to reach full maturity. Prematurely harvested barley kernels have germinated and produced small seedlings when the seeds had attained only one-seventh of their normal weight.[26, 27] Corn seeds grew when gathered as early as twenty days after fertilization of the silks, provided they were carefully dried.[28] Such poorly developed seeds obviously are unsatisfactory for field planting. Table 2 shows that corn gathered as early as the denting stage is suitable for seed.[28]

Mature corn produces heavier sprouts than that harvested at immature stages.[29] Immature corn shows more disease infection and yields slightly less than mature corn.[30]

Immature seed,[31] because of its small size, has a low reserve food supply and usually produces poor plants when conditions are adverse at planting time. Immature seeds, high in moisture, are vulnerable to frost injury.

SEED SIZE Small seeds invariably produce small seedlings. The logarithms of seedling and seed weights are directly proportional (Figure 4).

In Nebraska research,[32] small seeds of winter wheat, spring wheat, and oat yielded 18 percent less than large seeds when equal *numbers* of seeds were sown per acre at an optimum rate for the large seed, but only 5 percent less when equal *weights* of seed were sown, also at an optimum rate for the large seed. Grain drills sow about equal volumes of large or small seeds of any particular grain, so the latter comparison is the most valid. When unselected seed was used, it yielded 4 percent less than large seed when equal numbers were sown per acre, but only 1 percent less when equal weights of seed were sown.

In comparisons of fanning-mill grades of winter wheat over a seventeen-year period, the heaviest quarter yielded 0.3 percent more, and the lightest quarter yielded 2.0 percent less than unselected seed. Similar results were obtained with oat.

TABLE 2 Effect of Maturity of Seed upon the Grain Yield of Dent Corn (Five-Year Average)

Weeks Before Mature	Date Seed Harvested	Days Since Fertilization	Condition of Grain	Field Germination (%)	Yield of Shelled Corn per Acre (bushels)
Mature	September 28	51	Mature	94	55.8
1	September 21	44	Glazing	94	54.4
2	September 14	37	Denting	93	54.9

FIGURE 4

The seedling weight (10 to 12 days after planting) shows a direct logarithmic relation to seed weight: *(A)* relation between weight per seed and weight per stalk 10 days after planting of corn, sorghum, and prove; *(B)* relation between logarithms of the seed weights and of the stalk weights taken at intervals up to 20 days after planting.

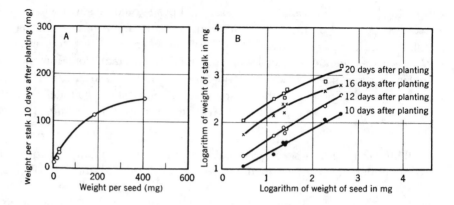

There is no practical gain in grain yield from grading normally developed small-grain seed that is reasonably free of foreign material. Large seeds produce more vigorous seedlings, which better survive adverse conditions, but this advantage within certain limits is largely offset by the greater number of plants obtained from an equal weight of smaller seeds.

The germination and seedling size of shrunken and plump spring wheat, with test weights that ranged from 39.5 to 60.8 pounds per bushel (500 to 780 g/l), was determined.[33] Test weight shows little relation to viability, but shrunken seeds produce such small, weak seedlings that sowing of wheat testing less than 50 pounds per bushel (640 g/l) is not recommended. Kernels of wheat testing 60 pounds per bushel (770 g/l) are about twice as heavy as those testing 50 pounds (640 g/l). A reduction in test weight of one-third (i.e., from 60 down to 40 pounds per bushel [770 to 515 g/l]) reduces the weight of an individual kernel nearly two-thirds,[15] and seedling weights are reduced nearly as much. In general, matured seeds that are less than one-half the normal size are unsuitable for sowing.

Kernel placement on the ear has no effect on corn seed quality. Extensive experiments showed that the average yield of butt seed was 103 percent of that from the middle of the ear, while the yield from tip kernels was 105 percent.[34] In a similar comparison, seeds from the tips, butts, and middles of corn ears yielded comparably.[35] Corn seed will be metered more accurately with plate-type planters if the seed is uniform in size and shape. Modern planters are able to accurately meter mixtures of different sizes and shapes of corn seed.

3.4 Seed Dormancy

Seeds of some crop species exhibit dormancy.[36] These seeds fail to grow immediately after maturity, even though external conditions favor germination, until they have passed through an after-ripening period. This is more common in wild plants, but varieties of cultivated plants differ considerably in dormant tendencies. Dormancy in cereal seeds is indicated by the inability to germinate at higher temperatures when they germinate well at 36 to 50°F (2 to 10°C).

CAUSES OF DORMANCY Dormancy may result from seed characteristics or environmental conditions as follows:[31, 37]

1. Thick or hard seedcoats prevent intake of water and probably also of oxygen. The *hard seeds* in many legumes are an example.
2. Seedcoats interfere with the absorption of oxygen. Examples are cocklebur, oat, and barley.
3. In some species, the embryo is still immature and has not yet reached its full development at harvest.
4. The embryos in some seeds appear to be mature but must undergo certain changes before they will germinate. Immature wheat and barley seeds harvested 12 to 24 days after flowering, and dried quickly, may retain their green color but will germinate poorly and produce weak seedlings. Such green seeds also are found in wheat that has been frosted before maturity. Dormant varieties of winter barley apparently become dormant during ripening or drying because seeds of such varieties sprouted in the head before maturity when the seedcoats were kept wet by artificial watering.[38]
5. Germination inhibitors that must undergo natural or applied chemical changes to permit germination.
6. High temperatures during seed maturity may induce dormancy.

HARD SEEDS IN LEGUMES Hard or impermeable seeds prevent penetration of water and cause an apparent enforced dormancy period. Such seeds are common in alfalfa but are also found in most small-seeded legumes.[39] Hard seeds in alfalfa are due to the inability of the palisade cells to absorb water.[40] Apparently, the cuticle does not restrict the intake of water. The percentage of hard seeds varies among different branches of the same plant. Probably as a result of some scarification, machine-threshed seed contains fewer hard seeds than that which is hand-threshed. Plump seed is more likely to be dormant than is shriveled or immature seed.

AFTER-RIPENING Seeds of peanut, alfalfa, clover, and lupin planted soon after maturity under conditions nearly optimum for germination frequently exhibit dormancy ranging up to two years. The rest period appears to be one of after-ripening in peanut.[41]

Seeds of many small-grain varieties require a short period of dry storage after harvest in order to after-ripen and give good germination at temperatures as high as 68°F (20°C). Seeds are usually stored several months before germination tests are made, but in winter cereals it may be necessary to test the seeds soon after threshing to determine their viability for fall planting. Storage of oat at 104°F (40°C) for three months largely eliminated dormancy[42] and also destroyed most of the molds on the seed.

The embryos of cereals are essentially never dormant, the dormancy being imposed by the seedcoat. Artificial dry heating, opening of the coat structures over the embryo, and cutting off the brush ends admit oxygen which induces germination of non-after-ripened or partially after-ripened seeds of wheat, oat, or barley. A temperature considerably below 68°F (20°C) is most satisfactory for germination of freshly harvested seed of these crops.[43]

Immature, poorly cured wheat has a higher percentage of dormancy.[19] Dormancy may decrease to a minimum after four to twelve weeks of storage and can be broken immediately by placing the seeds in cold storage at 40 to 43°F (4 to 6°C) for five days, and then transferring them to alternating temperatures of 68 to 86°F (20 to 30°C) for three days. Some wheat grown under high altitude conditions may be dormant as long as sixty days after harvest.[44] Seedsmen have repeatedly encountered difficulty in getting satisfactory germination in laboratory tests of sound, plump durum wheat, especially in the fall and early winter. After-ripening is completed during warm spring weather. Good stands are obtained when field planting in cool soil even though durum wheat germinates slowly in laboratory tests until spring.[45] After-ripening of mature corn is coincident with loss of moisture.[7] It may be necessary to reduce the moisture content of immature seeds to approximately 25 percent before normal germination occurs. The mechanism that inhibits normal germination of such seeds is believed to occur in the scutellum rather than in the endosperm or pericarp.

Slow germination of freshly harvested seeds is extremely desirable in a wet harvest season when heavy losses occur from grain sprouting in the field.

Dormant varieties do not sprout appreciably.[46, 47] All degrees of prompt, slow, and delayed germination occur in freshly harvested common oat, but cultivated red oat regularly shows slow or delayed germination.[11] Dormancy disappears in most oat varieties after thirty days. Grain sorghums often sprout in the head in the field during rainy periods before harvest.

The usual dormancy in buffalograss seed can be broken by soaking the seed in a 0.5 percent solution of potassium nitrate for twenty-four hours, then chilling it at 41°F (5°C) for six weeks in a cold-storage room and drying it.[48] However, hulling of the seed is fully as effective, and the treatment is more simple and economical.

SECONDARY DORMANCY High temperatures in storage or in the germinator or seedbed may throw seeds of cereals or grasses into a secondary dormancy. Such seeds usually germinate later at normal temperatures after they have been subjected to cold treatment.

Very dry cotton seeds may fail to germinate as promptly or as vigorously as those with a moisture content of approximately 12 percent when planted. A marked increase of hard seeds occurs when they are dried down to 5 or 6 percent moisture.[49] Excessively dry seed gives satisfactory germination when moistened at planting time with about 2 gallons of water per 100 pounds of seed (8 liters per 64 kg). Certain Texas samples entered into a secondary dormancy and failed to produce a crop when the proper seedbed conditions were not present.

3.5 Scarification of Hard Seeds

Germination of impermeable seeds in legumes such as alfalfa, sweetclover, and the true clovers may be brought about in several ways.[50]

In a mechanical scarifier, the seed is thrown against a roughened surface to scratch the seedcoats. The scarified seeds imbibe water and germinate in a normal manner. However, mechanical scarification is used less today. In tests in Utah,[51] scarification of alfalfa seed increased germination about 30 percent, but there were more weak and moldy seedlings from the scarified seed. Scarification injured about as much good seed as it made hard seeds germinable. Mechanically scarified seed has been found to deteriorate rapidly in storage. When scarified, seed should be planted immediately.

In New York, fall-sown sweetclover seeds softened and grew the next spring, with 50 to 75 percent of the seeds producing plants. This is about as high a percentage as is ordinarily obtained in field seeding. In fact, 90 to 100 percent of fall-sown hard sweetclover seeds will yield better results under such conditions than scarified seeds sown at any time of the year.

3.6 Other Hard-Seed Treatments

Aging brings about slow natural deterioration of the seedcoat in dry storage. In certain experiments, one-third to two-thirds of the hard seeds in red clover were still impermeable after four years, but a majority of the impermeable seeds of alfalfa and hairy vetch became permeable before they were two years old.[52] In another experiment, one-half of the impermeable seeds in alfalfa germinated after 1½ years, while all germinated after eleven years in storage.[44] The percentage of hard seeds in Korean lespedeza is high when the seeds are tested for germination immediately after harvest, but most of them become permeable during the winter.[53] The average percentages of hard seeds in tests made in November, January, and March were 47.25, 12.25, and 11.05, respectively.

Alternate freezing and thawing sometimes stimulates germination of hard seeds of alfalfa and sweetclover but may also destroy some seeds that germinate normally.[54] The breaking of dormancy while in the soil may be due to a period of cold.

The germination of hard seeds of alfalfa or clover also can be achieved by exposure for 1 to 1.5 seconds or less to infrared rays of 1,180 nm wavelength[55] or by exposure for a few seconds to high-frequency electric energy.

3.7 Vernalization of Seeds

Temperatures affect the flowering time of many plants. Winter annuals, biennials, and some perennials must be exposed to a period of cool or cold temperatures before they will flower. This process is called *vernalization.* Vernalization assures that flowering will not be induced in the fall resulting in severe damage or death when winter occurs.

Winter wheat sown in the spring fails to produce heads unless the sprouting seeds or growing plants are subjected to cold or cool conditions. Winter wheat generally needs about forty days when the temperature drops below 40°F (4.5°C).

Spring-planted winter varieties of cereal crops will flower normally if the seeds are first soaked for twelve to twenty-four hours, and then stored for four to nine weeks at a temperature of about 36°F (2°C). This process vernalizes the embryos, and the plants will behave like spring varieties. The degree of sprouting during the cold treatment can be restricted by maintaining the moisture content of the grain at approximately 50 percent (on a dry-weight basis). Winter annual legumes and grasses may respond to similar treatments. Vernalization is so laborious and complicated that it is useful only in certain experiments. The sprouted seeds are difficult to store and sow; germination is often damaged by the treatment.[56] Drying and storing the vernalized seed at warm temperatures often causes the seeds to become devernalized and lose much of the effect of the cold treatment.

Vernalized, spring-sown, winter grain yields much less than when sown in the autumn and about the same or somewhat less than adapted spring varieties sown at the same time as the vernalized grain. Certain spring varieties of cereals that have a partial or intermediate winter growth habit usually respond to vernalization treatment when sown late in the spring,[57] but true spring varieties are not affected. Russian workers reported that special vernalization of corn, sorghum, millet, and other warm-temperature crops is effective in hastening flowering. This treatment consists of germinating the seeds in the dark at normal temperature while restricting the sprouting by adding only limited quantities of water, largely in the form of dilute salt solutions. Extensive experiments in other countries failed to substantiate claims for this type of vernalization.[25] The seeds often mold and lose their viability during treatment.

3.8 Longevity of Seeds

Most crop seeds are probably dead after twenty-five years or less, even under favorable storage conditions. The alleged germination of seeds after prolonged storage in ancient tombs is known to be a myth, although fresh seeds that have been placed in tombs shortly before the visits of gullible travelers often germinate very well. Authentic seeds from the ancient tombs are highly carbonized and have lost much of their original substance.

SEEDS IN DRY STORAGE The optimum conditions for storing seeds that will endure drying are a 5 to 7 percent moisture content, sealed storage in the absence of oxygen, and a temperature of 23 to 41°F (–5 to 5°C).[58, 59] In moist, hot climates, seeds can be kept viable between seasons only by storing them, well dried, in airtight containers.[60] It has been suggested that seed life is doubled for each drop of 1 percent in moisture content and for each drop of 9°F (5°C) in temperature.[61] Under cool, semiarid conditions in Colorado, wheat, oat, and barley germinated about 10 percent lower when ten years old than when one year old.[62] The germination of soybean decreased about 10 percent in five years, but sorgo sorghum germinated about 97 percent after seventeen years. Yellow Dent corn germinated well for five years, but declined to 32 percent after twenty years. After fifteen years of storage[63] other approximate germination percentages were rye, 8; corn, 36; naked barley, 74; wheat, 80; and unhulled barley, 96. After twenty years, the germination percentages of wheat, barley, and oat were 15, 46, and 50, respectively.[54]

In semiarid eastern Washington, certain varieties of barley, oat, and wheat germinated from 84 to 96 percent after thirty-two years of storage. Corn germinated 70 percent, but rye had lost its viability.[5]

Under Nebraska conditions, corn four years old was satisfactory for seed.[64] Kafir sorghum seed retained its germination well for ten years in western Texas but deteriorated almost completely during the next seven years.[41]

Flaxseed of good quality stored under favorable conditions may be expected to maintain its viability for six to eight years. Seeds nine, twelve, fifteen, and eighteen years old germinated 99, 89, 56, and 58 percent, respectively.[16] Tobacco seed usually retains ability to germinate over many years. One lot of seed germinated 25 percent after twenty years.[23] However, there was a marked retardation in rate of germination in seed more than ten years old.

While many seeds in ordinary storage in drier climates may have a life span of fifteen years, they might live fifty or even one-hundred years in sealed storage at low temperatures in the absence of oxygen and after proper desiccation.[36] Seeds of *Albizzia* germinated after one hundred forty nine years in storage in a British herbarium.

BURIED SEEDS Seeds of some species of wild plants retain their vitality in moist soil for fifty years or more. In research begun in 1902 by the United States Department of Agriculture a total of 107 species of seed were mixed with sterilized soil and buried in pots. None of the cereals or legumes whose seeds are used for food germinated when dug up after twenty years. The seeds of wild plants grew better than those of cultivated plants. Several persistent weeds showed high germination after twenty years in the soil, including dock, lambsquarter, plantain, purslane, jimsonweed, and ragweed. Seeds still alive when finally dug up thirty-nine years after they were buried included Kentucky bluegrass, red clover, tobacco, ramie, and some twenty-five species of weeds.[65] After being buried thirty years, wild morning glory seed germinated within two days after it was dug up.

Another classical experiment with buried seeds was started in 1879 by Dr. W. J. Beal of Michigan State College. Seeds of twenty species were placed in bottles filled with sand and buried under 18 inches (46 cm) of soil. Chess and white clover seeds were dead after five years, while common mallow survived for twenty-five years. Curled dock and mullein germinated seventy years after burial.[65]

Dry arctic lupine seeds found buried in lemming burrows beneath 10 to 20 feet (3 to 6 m) of frozen soil in Yukon Territory, Canada, were able to germinate. Their assumed age was about 14,000 years.[66]

■ 4 GERMINATION AND PURITY TESTS

The real value of a seed lot depends upon its purity and the proportion of pure seed in it that will grow. Seeds after threshing usually contain foreign materials such as chaff, dirt, weed seeds, and seeds of other crop plants. These can be removed to a large extent, but not entirely, by cleaning machinery.[24, 61]

The object of laboratory seed testing is to determine the percentages of germination, pure seed, other crop seed, inert matter, the presence and kinds of weed seeds, and, if possible, the kind and variety of the seed sample (Figure 5). This serves as an aid in selecting suitable seed, adjusting seeding rates to germination percentages, giving warning of impending weed problems, and reducing dissemination of serious weeds. Seed testing should be done by well-trained seed analysts. Then the label is an accurate guide to the value of the seed.

Germination tests should include 400 seeds counted from the sample indiscriminately and divided into four or more separate tests (Figure 6).[67] Purity tests should be made by hand separation of a sample that contains approximately 3,000 seeds. The size of the sample specified for purity tests is indicated in Table 3. Most crop seeds are germinated at alternating night and day temperatures of 68 and 86°F (20 to 30°C) in laboratory tests. The alternation of temperatures, which simulates field conditions, favors better germination.

If partly sprouted seeds are present in the sample, the final germination count for legumes with hard seeds is extended for five days. Fresh seeds may require

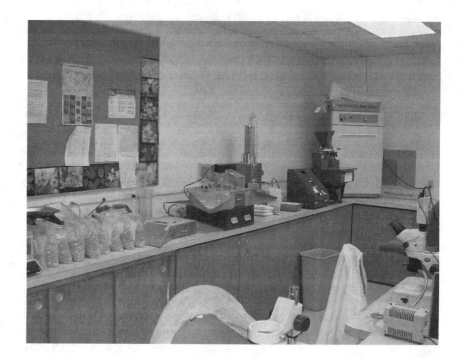

FIGURE 5
A typical seed testing laboratory with equipment to analyze seeds for quality and freedom from weed seeds, insect damage, and seed-borne diseases.
[Courtesy Richard Waldren]

FIGURE 6
A seed germinator for determining seed viability and vigor. [Courtesy Richard Waldren]

prechilling, treatment with 0.1 percent or 0.2 percent potassium nitrate, or scarifying. Different seeds are germinated between blotters, on top of blotters, in paper toweling, in rolled towels, in sand, or in soil.

TABLE 3 Methods for Testing Typical Seeds

Crop Seed	Seeds per Gram	Minimum Weight for Noxious Weed Examination (grams)	Minimum Weight for Purity Analysis (grams)	Germination Test			Special Treatments
				Temperature (°C)	First Count (days)	Final Count (days)	
Alfalfa	500	50	5	20	3	7–12	—
Alsike clover	1,500	50	2	20	3	7–12	—
Bahiagrass	366	50	10	30–35	3	21	Light; hulling
Barley	30	500	100	20	3	7	—
Bean (field)	4	500	500	20–30	5	8–13	—
Buckwheat	60	300	50	20–30	3	6	—
Crimson clover	330	50	10	20	3	7–12	—
Kentucky bluegrass	4,800	25	1	20–30	7	28	Light
Meadow fescue	500	50	5	20–30	5	14	—

4.1 Stress Tests

Stress tests are designed to determine seed vigor under minimum conditions for germination. Usually the seeds are germinated in moist soil at the minimum temperature for germination to simulate field conditions. The seed is placed in soil in containers or wrapped in moist paper towels with soil. Since spring-seeded crops should be planted as early in the season as possible to maximize the growing season, stress tests provide valuable information about how well a particular sample of seeds will perform under these conditions.

The cold test for corn uses soil in containers. The seed is placed in the soil and the soil is moistened to field capacity. The containers are placed in an environment of 50°F (10°C) for seven days. The temperature is then raised to 77°F (25°C) for four days and seedling counts are made.[68]

The cool germination test for cotton is conducted in a different manner. Seeds are placed on moist germination towels as in the standard germination test. The test consists of four replications of fifty seeds each. Rolled towels are placed in a germinator set at a constant 64°F (18°C) for seven days. This temperature is a critical breakpoint for cotton seedling development, and very little variation from this temperature is acceptable. For example, 2°C below (61°F) may result in a greatly reduced number of normal seedlings, while 2°C above (68°F) may result in almost as many normal seedlings as the standard germination test.[69] The cool germination test is also used for sorghum.

4.2 Special Tests

In many cases, tests other than germination, purity, and vigor may be needed. These special tests include: the absence or presence of fungicides, diploidy, or tetraploidy; X rays to detect "hollow seeds"; and any other factors that may be of help to a seed buyer or seller.

The viability and vigor of the embryos of many seeds can be quickly evaluated by a staining (tetrazolium) test.[67] A fluorescence test is useful to identify or separate seeds of certain species or varieties that are indistinguishable otherwise.[70]

■ 5 SEED LAWS AND REGULATIONS

5.1 Federal Seed Act

For many years, low-grade, foul, and adulterated seeds were sold. The Federal Seed Act was passed in 1912 to protect the American farmer from such seed.[59] The act was amended in 1916 to include a minimum requirement of live pure seed. Another amendment was passed in 1926 to provide for staining imported red clover and alfalfa seed so as to indicate its origin. Investigations have shown that many foreign importations are unadapted to certain regions in this country. Red clover seed from Italy is not adaptable for general use in this country, nor is alfalfa seed from Turkestan or South Africa. The Federal Seed Act of 1939 was much more drastic and inclusive than the original act. The 1939 act required correct labeling as to variety as well as purity and germination, established heavier penalties, and permitted penalties for mislabeling without the government having to prove fraudulent intent. False advertising is prohibited. There have been only minor revisions since 1939. Penalties for violation of the act include fines up to $2,000, seizure of the seed, and orders to "cease and desist" violations of the act.

The act prohibits importation of seed that is adulterated or unfit for seeding purposes. Adulterated seed can contain no more than a 5 percent mixture of other kinds of seed, except for mixtures that are not detrimental. Seed specified as unfit for seeding purposes is that with more than one noxious seed in 10 grams of small-seeded grasses and legumes; one in 25 grams of medium-sized seeds such as sudangrass, sorghum, and buckwheat; and one in 100 grams of grains and other large seeds. The act also prohibits importation of seed that contains more than 2 percent weed seed or (with several exceptions) less than 75 percent pure live seed. Seeds that are allowed to have germination percentages lower than 75 percent are bahiagrass, 50; bluegrass, 65; carrots, 55; chicory, 70; dallisgrass, 35; guineagrass, 10; molassesgrass, 25; and rhodesgrass, 35 percent.

Specified noxious weeds are: whitetop (*Lepidium draba*, *L. repens*, and *Hymenophysa pubescens*), Canada thistle (*Cirsium arvense*), dodder (*Cuscuta species*), quackgrass (*Agropyron repens*), johnsongrass (*Sorghum halepense*), bindweed (*Convolvulus arvensis*), Russian knapweed (*Centaurea picris*), perennial sowthistle (*Sonchus arvensis*), and leafy spurge (*Euphorbia esula*). There can also be other kinds of seeds or bulblets that, after investigation, the Secretary of Agriculture finds should be included in the list.

The act also prohibits shipment in interstate commerce of agricultural seeds that contain noxious weeds in excess of quantities allowed by the laws of the state to which the seed is shipped, or as established by the Secretary of Agriculture. The seeds must be labeled to include: variety or type, lot number, origin (of certain kinds), percentage of weed seeds including noxious weeds, kinds and rate of occurrence of noxious weeds, percentages of mixtures of other seeds, germination, hard-seed percentage, month and year of germination test, and the name and address of the shipper and consignee. The Federal Seed Act specifies variations in tolerances when determining germination and purity.

It is now possible for an individual or organizations to obtain a federal plant patent on a new, distinct variety or hybrid of any crop they have originated. This protects the plant breeder or employer from unlawful use of unique cultivars. Patents have become increasingly important as biotechnology is used for developing new strains and cultivars.

5.2 State Seed Laws

All states have seed laws designed to regulate the quality of agricultural seeds sold within their borders. These laws have done much to reduce the spread of weed seeds, especially noxious weeds. Most of the laws were patterned after the Uniform State Seed Law drawn up by the Association of Official Seed Analysts in 1917, and later were revised to conform more closely with the present Federal Seed Act.[71] There is considerable variation in the details of the laws adopted by the various states, but all require seeds in commerce to be labeled. The specifications embodied in these laws are reflected in the information required on the labels: (1) the commonly accepted name of the agricultural seeds, (2) the approximate total percentage by weight of purity (i.e., the freedom of the seeds from inert matter and from other seeds), (3) the approximate total percentage of weight of weed seeds, (4) the name and approximate number per pound of each of the kinds of noxious weed seeds and bulblets, (5) the approximate percentage of germination of such agricultural seed, together with the month and year that the seed was tested.

The weed seeds regarded as noxious by ten or more states include dodders, Canada thistle, quackgrass, wild mustards, buckhorn plantain, corn cockle, wild oat, wild onion, narrow-leaved plantain, wild carrot, ox-eye daisy, leafy spurge, Russian knapweed, bindweed, perennial sowthistle, and curled dock.

The seed laws are usually enforced by designated state officials. Field inspectors draw samples from seeds offered for sale. These are tested in official laboratories. Penalties are inflicted on dealers who sell seeds in violation of the state law.

6 SEED ASSOCIATIONS

Most states have seed or crop improvement associations of growers who produce quality agricultural seeds under strict regulations. These associations usually cooperate closely with their state agricultural colleges to bring superior crop varieties into widespread use at a reasonable cost.[18]

6.1 Registered or Certified Seed

The seed associations, whose rules and regulations differ somewhat among the states, supervise the growing of seeds by their members for certification and registration. The International Crop Improvement Association defines the classes of seed as follows:

1. *Breeder seed* is seed or vegetatively propagated material directly controlled by the originator, or, in certain cases, by the sponsoring plant breeder or

institution that provides the source for the initial and recurring increase of foundation seed.

2. *Foundation seed,* which includes elite seed in Canada, is seed that is handled to most nearly maintain specific genetic identity and purity and that may be designated or distributed by an agricultural experiment station. Production must be carefully supervised or approved by representatives of an agricultural experiment station. Foundation seed shall be the source of all other certified seed classes, either directly or through registered seed.

3. *Registered seed* is the progeny of foundation or registered seed that is so handled as to maintain satisfactory genetic identity and purity and that has been approved and certified by the certifying agency. This class of seed should be of a quality suitable for production of certified seed.

4. *Certified seed* is the progeny of foundation, registered, or certified seed that is so handled as to maintain satisfactory genetic identity and purity and that has been approved and certified by the certifying agency.

6.2 Requirements for Registration or Certification

The majority of seed associations require a grower to start with registered seed or foundation seed from an experiment station or equally reliable source.[2] The seed field is inspected before harvest for varietal purity, freedom from disease, and freedom from noxious weeds. An inspector either takes a bin sample after the crop is threshed, or the grower is instructed to send in a representative sample for purity and germination tests. The seed that comes up to the standard set by the association for the particular crop is registered or certified. This seed is sound, plump, and of good color, has high germination, and is free from noxious weeds. It is usually well cleaned and graded. Registered or certified seed is sold under specific tag labels that carry the necessary pedigree as well as other information required under the state seed law.

■ 7 SOURCES OF FARM SEEDS

A farmer who desires a new variety or a fresh seed supply may secure high-quality pure seed of the standard varieties of most field crops from members of a crop improvement association at reasonable prices. These certified seeds are often available in the community. Seed lists issued each year give the name and address of the grower, the crop and variety grown, the amount of seed available, and the price. In general, certified seed is the highest quality of seed available for field crop production. However, the yields obtained from certified seed are not measurably higher than those from uncertified good seed of quality of the same variety with only a small admixture of other varieties. For commercial crop production, an appreciably higher price for certified seed may not be justified when good uncertified seed is available, unless the grower wishes to obtain a new, improved variety or to be assured of seed relatively free from disease.

Good seed of most adapted crops can be grown on the farm with care to prevent admixtures and weed contamination. The seed can be cleaned with an ordinary fanning mill unless it contains weed seeds that can be removed only with special equipment. Consequently, a farmer's home-grown seed often contains many weed seeds.

The farmer usually finds it necessary to purchase hybrid seeds and small seeds such as clover, alfalfa, and forage grasses. Most commercial seed dealers endeavor to sell correctly labeled seeds but use a disclaimer clause for their protection because the crop produced by the farmer is entirely beyond the control of the seed seller. The disclaimer is usually stated as follows:

The _____ Company gives no warranty, express or implied, as to the productiveness of any seeds or bulbs it sells and will not in any way be responsible for the crop.

This statement on letterheads and seed tags may not exempt dealers from legal redress when the seed is misbranded or fraudulently represented.

◼ 8 SEEDING CROPS

8.1 Implements Used in Seeding

GRAIN DRILLS Combination grain and fertilizer drills are often used. Row spacing is usually from 7 to 14 inches (18 to 36 cm). The single-disk furrow opener is best for penetrating a hard seedbed or cutting through trash (Figure 7). Double-disk and shoe openers are best for mellow seedbeds that are firm below. The hoe-type opener is best in loose soil or where soil blowing is likely to occur. The hoe drill turns up clods and trash and does not pulverize the soil to any extent. The surface drill is used in humid regions, while the furrow and semi-furrow drills are widely used for winter wheat, particularly in the Great Plains under dryland conditions.[72] The furrow drill places the seed deep in moist soil. The ridges and furrows hold snow, reduce winter killing, and tend to protect the young plants from wind erosion.

FIGURE 7
Grain drill. [Courtesy John Deere]

FIGURE 8
No-till row crop planter.
[Courtesy USDA]

Modern grain drills are designed to plant in the heavy residues found in no-till and conservation tillage systems. They usually have a rolling coulter ahead of the opener to cut through residue and either single- or double-disk openers to move residue aside and place the seed in moist soil.

ROW CROP PLANTERS Row planters are widely used for planting intertilled crops. The rows are spaced 20 to 48 inches (50 to 300 cm) apart. By proper selection of drill plates, a plate-type planter can be used to plant corn, sorghum, bean, and other large-seed row crops. The lister planter is a combination tillage machine and planter that has been used under semiarid conditions to plant sorghum, corn, cotton, and other row crops in the bottom of furrows.[72] No-till planting (Figure 8) is growing in popularity. Eliminating tillage before planting reduces soil compaction and labor.

Planters can be equipped with rolling coulters that are 18 inches (46 cm) in diameter or larger. Whether the coulters are fluted, rippled, notched, or smooth, they must be sharp, weighted, or spring pressured and set deep enough to cut cleanly through the residue without punching it into the furrow. Residue mixed into the soil above the seed may cause corkscrewing of the seedlings. Smooth coulters give the best performance for stubble cutting. Fluted coulters provide more loose soil for better seed coverage. However, they do not scour properly when the soil is wet, and they do not cut residue adequately if it is damp. Wide fluted coulters throw residue away from the row better than narrow fluted coulters but require more weight for penetration. They also disturb the herbicide barrier more than the other types. By removing straw from the row, soil warms up faster, which is an advantage when soils are cold.[73, 74]

Modern planters have individual seed boxes on each row unit, or they use air to move seed from a central bin to the planter units. Seed metering devices on each row unit allow accurate seeding of a wide variety of crops at faster speeds than were previously possible. Most row crop planters are equipped to apply fertilizer and herbicides in bands while seeding the crop (Figure 9).

FIGURE 9
Planting row crops and applying fertilizer and herbicides in bands are accomplished in one operation. [Courtesy Case IH]

8.2 Method of Seeding

Modern row crop planters and grain drills are designed to place seeds at a uniform depth and space seeds at regular intervals in the row. They are designed to move sufficient soil away from the row to place seeds into moist soil and provide good seed-soil contact. In some cases, planters and drills are equipped with rolling coulters to cut through residues as described previously.

Most crops are planted into level soil with minimum disturbance of the soil. In some cases, crops are planted in the bottom of lister furrows. However, lister planted corn and sorghum start growth slower, and flower and mature later, than level and furrow planted seed.[75, 76] Crop stands are frequently destroyed by heavy rains that wash soil into the bottoms of lister furrows. The soil buries the seedling or covers the ungerminated seeds too deep for emergence. Most of the advantages of lister planting without its disadvantages can be achieved with a surface planter equipped with disk furrow openers.

In high rainfall areas, seeds are planted in raised beds that are formed prior to seeding. Raised beds help prevent flooding of seed rows and help soil warm up faster in the spring. There are some planters that will form the beds and plant the crop in one pass through the field.

Ridge-plant or ridge-till is a commonly used system in the Midwest. During seeding, existing ridges are removed and the seed is placed in the same location as the original ridge (Figure 10). During the operation, residues and weed seeds are removed from the seed row and thrown into the old furrow. After the crop has grown to a safe height, soil is thrown over the base of the plant to form the ridges

FIGURE 10
Soybean seedlings
emerging in the old corn
ridges from last year.
[Courtesy USDA NRCS]

again.[77] Sometimes shallow tillage of the ridges is performed prior to seeding. Since crops are planted into the same rows every year, machinery following the same tracks can reduce soil compaction except in the track between the rows. Although compaction may be severe in the tracks, crop roots can easily avoid compacted soil since the soil on the other side of the row is not compacted.

8.3 Time of Seeding

The time to seed field crops is governed not only by the environmental requirements for the crop but also by the necessity of evading the ravages of diseases and insect pests.

Spring-planted small grains, like other cool season crops, generally are seeded early in the season to permit maximum growth and development toward maturity before the advent of hot weather, drought, and diseases. Nineteen hundred years ago, Columella wrote, "If the conditions of the lands and of the weather will allow it, the sooner we sow, the better it will grow, and the more increase we shall have."

For winter wheat in the western states,[78] the optimum date of seeding occurs when the mean daily temperature lies between 50 and 62°F (10 and 17°C). Higher temperatures prevail in the South and lower temperatures in the North. In the cold semiarid regions, sowing winter wheat early enough in the fall to allow the seedlings to become established before the soil freezes gives maximum protection against cold.

In humid regions, it is essential that wheat plants be well rooted in order to avoid winter injury from heaving. Columella recommended seeding between October 24 and December 7 in temperate regions; for colder regions, he advised seeding October 1, "so the roots of the [wheat grains] grow strong before they be infested with winter showers, frost or hoar frosts." Soil may heave when it freezes. Plants subjected to soil heaving have many of their roots broken and then are killed by desiccation.[79] Losses from heaving are a common occurrence in late-sown small grains in the eastern half of the United States. Seeding late enough to escape severe injury from Hessian fly is important for winter wheat where that pest is prevalent. In the case of cereal crops, practices that lead to maximum average yields are also satisfactory from the standpoint of crop quality.[80]

Early-sown crops mature earlier than those sown later, but they require a longer growing period. Consequently the difference in harvest date is less than the difference in planting date. Planting summer annual crops as early in the spring as possible increases the total amount of photosynthesis during the season, resulting in higher yields. This reaction in corn, which is typical of both long-day and short-day spring-planted crops, is shown in Figure 11. Later planted crops are not able to fully utilize the growing season.

Corn is a warm-weather crop that generally utilizes the full season. In Nebraska, early planting of corn in a normal season resulted in earlier maturity, lower grain moisture content, and higher grain viability when the crop was exposed to low temperatures.[80] Under Colorado conditions[81] corn has better yield and quality when planted early, and light frosts do less damage than delayed planting.

In North Carolina, cotton planted after the first week of May declines in yield. Drastic yield declines occurred in cotton planted the last week of May and later.[82] On the Texas High Plains, cotton planted on June 1, June 10, and June 20 yielded 7.6, 23.6, and 48.9 percent less, respectively, than cotton planted on May 15.[83] In California, cotton planted on April 15, April 25, and May 10 yielded 4.0, 8.0, and 17.0%, respectively, less than that planted on April 1.[84] Similar planting date–yield relationships have been established for other production regions in the U.S. Cotton Belt.[85]

In Texas experiments, early-planted cotton had a longer period of development before being attacked by root rot (*Phymatotrichum omnivorum*), but development of the disease was more rapid in early than in late plantings. The greatest losses were sustained by early plantings.[86]

Perennial legumes may be seeded either in spring or fall. When sown in fall, they should be seeded early enough to permit satisfactory root development before the ground freezes or else so late that the seeds do not germinate until spring.

With many crops, it is a safe practice to seed at higher than normal rates when seeding has been delayed materially beyond the optimum time determined for the

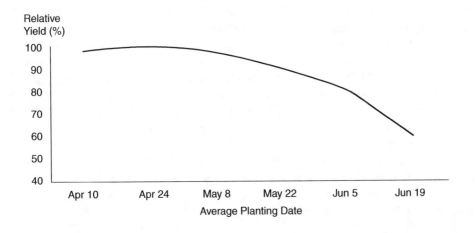

FIGURE 11
Effect of planting date on corn grain yield response in Iowa, 1997–2000. [From Farnham, 2001]

region. The plants will use less moisture and the higher seeding rates help maximize light interception in the leaf canopy.

8.4 Rate of Seeding

The goal of seeding rate is to match leaf area to expected water supply. Irrigated crops are planted at higher rates than dryland crops. Crops with larger plants are planted at lower rates than smaller plants. Varieties and hybrids that tiller or branch more are planted at lower rates than ones that tiller or branch little. Seeding rate is usually higher in narrow row spacing than in wider.

The objective in spacing crop plants is to obtain the maximum yield on a unit area without sacrificing quality. The rate of seeding is determined by the ultimate stand desired. Small short-season varieties of corn require thicker planting than long-season varieties.[87]

Since not all seeds will germinate and develop into a normal healthy plant that will contribute to yield, seeding rates must be greater than harvest population goals. The percentage of good quality seeds expected to emerge for most crops will be from 85 to 90. An expected field emergence of 85 percent is used for good quality seed with a germination rate of 90 percent or better. To predict expected field emergence of poor quality seed with a germination rate of less than 90 percent, multiply germination rate by 0.85.[29] Adjusted seeding rate is calculated by dividing the desired harvest plant population by the expected field emergence, expressed as a decimal (85% = 0.85).

If plant population is too high, plants will be tall, spindly, and more susceptible to lodging. Yields may decrease because not only does lodging make harvest difficult, resulting in greater harvest losses, but it also disrupts the leaf canopy, often limiting grain development and yield. If plant population is too low, there are fewer plants to contribute to yield and weeds will be a greater risk.

In southeastern Saskatchewan, a planting rate of 18 to 36 pounds per acre (20 to 40 kg/ha) was adequate where wheat yields were less than 20 bushels per acre (1,350 kg/ha).[88] In Alberta, where yield levels range from 38 to 51 bushels per acre (2,550 to 3,425 kg/ha), a planting rate of 90 pounds per acre (100 kg/ha) gives optimum wheat yields.[89] In Utah, where irrigated wheat yields ranged from 60 to 80 bushels per acre (4,000 to 5,475 kg/ha), a rate of 50 to 60 pounds per acre (56 to 67 kg/ha) was adequate except when planted late.[90] In western North Dakota, wheat yields were optimized at a stand rate of one million plants per acre at yield levels of 30 to 35 bushels per acre (2,000 to 2,350 kg/ha).[91]

In Nebraska,[92] seeding soybean at about 150,000 seeds per acre (415,000 seeds/ha) will optimize yield. This planting rate with normal plant losses during emergence and the remaining growing season will result in 100,000 or more harvestable plants (247,000 plants/ha). Soybean seeding rate in Missouri ranges from 130,000 seeds per acre (321,000 seed/ha) in 38- to 40-inch (97 to 102 cm) rows, to 200,000 seeds per acre (494,000 seeds/ha) in 6- to 8-inch (15 to 20 cm) rows.[93]

Soybean fields with harvest population of fewer than 100,000 plants per acre (247,000 plants/ha) will be short, have thick stems, be heavily branched at the lower nodes, and will have many pods close to the ground, making harvest difficult. Furthermore, weed control is more difficult with poor soybean stands. Plants in fields with seeding rates above 150,000 seeds per acre (370,000 seeds/ha) will be tall, spindly, and more susceptible to lodging.

Seeding rates in corn continue to increase as new hybrids are released with excellent stalk strength and increased yield potential. Optimum corn seeding rates in the eastern Corn Belt are about 31,000 to 35,500 seeds per acre (76,600 to 87,700 seeds/ha).[94]

INFLUENCE ON CROP QUALITY Grain quality is only slightly affected by usual variations in seeding rate. Most crop plants have a tremendous ability to alter yield components. Within normal populations, fewer plants will result in more production per plant, and more plants will result in less production per plant. At higher populations, corn will produce fewer kernels per ear, soybean will produce fewer pods and seeds per pod, small grains will tiller less, and cotton will produce fewer bolls. Seed size, however, will be about the same because the main objective of a seed plant is to produce healthy, fully developed seed.

In flax, differences in plant spacing show no consistent influence on the oil content of the seed.[95] Since the fineness of stems adds to the palatability of forage crops, it is desirable to seed them more thickly. Ordinarily, the forage will be finer and leafier without reduction in yield. Corn used for silage will be planted at 2,000 to 4,000 plants per acre (5,000 to 10,000 plants/ha) higher than corn planted for grain.[91] In cotton, higher population may contribute to decreased size of boll.[96]

8.5 Depth of Seeding

Seeds will emerge from greater depths in sandy soil than in clay soil and in warm soil than in cold soil. It is customary to plant deep in dry soil in order to place the seeds in contact with moisture. Pea will emerge from a greater depth than will bean when the seeds are the same size because the bean seedling has epigeal emergence and must push the cotyledons up above the soil surface, whereas pea has hypogeal emergence and the cotyledons remain where planted.

Larger seeds have more stored food reserves for germination and emergence. Therefore, in general, the larger the seed, the deeper it can be planted and still emerge from an arable soil (Figure 12). Approximately ¼ inch (6 mm) in heavy soil or ½ inch (13 mm) in sandy soil is the most satisfactory depth for seeding small-seeded legumes and grasses under optimum conditions.[97, 98] These include alfalfa,

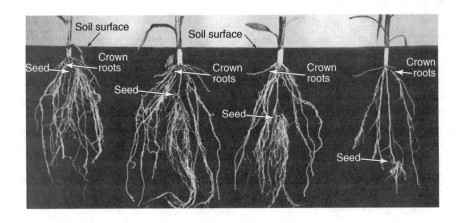

FIGURE 12

Corn planted at 2, 4, 6, and 10 inches deep. The crown formed at nearly the same depth regardless of planting depth.

TABLE 4 Seeding Depths for Seeds of Different Sizes

Normal Depth of Seeding (inches)	Usual Maximum Depth for Emergence (inches)	Seed Size (no. per lb)	Representative Crops
0.25 to 0.50	1 to 2	300,000 to 5,000,000	Redtop, carpetgrass, timothy, bluegrass, fescues, white clover, alsike clover, and tobacco
0.50 to 0.75	2 to 3	150,000 to 300,000	Alfalfa, red clover, sweetclover, lespedeza, crimson clover, ryegrass, foxtail millet, and turnip
0.75 to 1.50	3 to 4	50,000 to 150,000	Flax, sudangrass, crotalaria, proso, beet (ball of several seeds), broomcorn, and Bromegrass
1.50 to 2	3 to 5	10,000 to 50,000	Wheat, oats, barley, rye, rice, sorghum, buckwheat, hemp, vetch, and mungbean
2 to 3	4 to 8	400 to 10,000	Corn, pea, and cotton
4 to 5		4 to 20 (tubers or pieces)	Potato and Jerusalem artichoke

sweetclover, red clover, alsike clover, white clover, timothy, bromegrass, crested wheatgrass, reed canarygrass, and Kentucky bluegrass. Satisfactory emergence of reed canarygrass was obtained from a 1-inch (25 mm) depth and bromegrass from a 2-inch (50 mm) depth on all soil types. A reduction in the stand of soybean followed seeding deeper than 2 inches (50 mm) in fine sandy loam and 1 inch (25 mm) in a clay soil.[99] However, satisfactory stands were secured at depths up to 4 inches (100 mm) in loam and 2 inches (50 mm) in clay soil. Depth of planting may be an important factor in determining the seedling emergence of many grasses and small-seeded legumes.[98]

The seeding depths for seeds of different sizes under field conditions are shown in Table 4. The logarithms of seed size and typical planting depth of most seeds are directly proportional.

REFERENCES

1. Martin, J. H., and S. H. Yarnell. "Problems and rewards in improving shells," in *Seeds,* USDA Yearbook, 1961, pp. 113–118.

2. Parsons, F. G., C. S. Garrison, and K. E. Beeson. "Seed certification in the United States," in *Seeds,* USDA Yearbook, 1961, pp. 394–401.

3. Kiesselbach, T. A., and R. M. Weihing. "Effect of stand irregularities upon the acre yield and plant variability of corn," *J. Agr. Res.* 47(1933):399–416.

4. Plucknett, D. L. "Use of pelleted seed in crop and pasture establishment," *HI Univ. Ext. Circ.* 446, 1971, pp. 1–15.

5. Haferkamp, M. E., E. L. Smith, and R. A. Nilan. "Studies on aged seeds. 1. Relation of age of seed to germination and longevity," *Agron. J.* 45(1953):434–437.

6. McKinney, H. H., and W. J. Sando. "Russian methods for accelerating sexual reproduction in wheat: Further information regarding iarovization," *J. Hered.* 24(1933):165–166.

7. Sprague, G. F. "The relation of moisture content and time of harvest to germination of immature corn," *J. Am. Soc. Agron.* 28(1936):472–478.

8. Martin, J. N., and J. H. Watt. "The strophiole and other seed structures associated with hardness in *Melilotus alba L.* and *M. of officinalis* Willd.," *IA State College Jour Sci.* 18, 4(1944):457–469.

9. Widstoe, J. A. "Dry burning." New York: Macmillan, Inc., 1911, pp. 1–445.

10. Dillman, A. C. "Hygroscopic moisture of flax seed and wheat and its relation to combine harvesting," *J. Am. Soc. Agron.* 22(1930):51–74.

11. Coffman, F. A. "The minimum temperature of germination of seeds," *J. Am. Soc. Agron.* 15(1923):257–270.

12. Johnson, J., H. F. Murwin, and W. B. Ogden. "The germination of tobacco seed," *WI Agr. Exp, Sta. Res. Bull.* 104, 1930.

13. Dungan, G. H. "Some factors affecting the water absorption and germination of seed corn," *J. Am. Soc. Agron.* 16(1924):473–781.

14. Leukel, R. W., and J. H. Martin. "Seed rot and seedling blight of sorghum," *USDA Tech. Bull.* 839, 1943, pp. 1–36.

15. Stoa, T. E., W. E. Brentzel, and E. C. Higgins. "Shriveled lightweight wheat: Is it suitable for cells?" *ND Agr. Exp. Sta. Cir.* 59, 1936, pp. 1–11.

16. Dillman, A. C., and E. H. Toole. "Effect of age, condition, and temperature on the germination of flax seed," *J. Am. Soc. Agron.* 29(1937):23–29.

17. Stanley, R. G., and W. L. Butler. "Life processes of the living seed," in *Seeds,* USDA Yearbook, 1961, pp. 88–94.

18. Palladin, W. *Plant Physiology,* Philadelphia: Blakiston, 1918. pp. 1–320.

19. Whitcomb, W. O. "Dormancy of newly threshed grain," *Proc. Assn. Off. Seed Analysts* 16(1924):28–33.

20. Brown, E. B. "Relative yields from broken and entire kernels of seed corn," *J. Am. Soc. Agron.* (1920):196–197.

21. Sandy, W. J. "Effect of mutilation of wheat seeds on growth and productivity," *J. Am. Sac. Agron.* 31, 6(1939):558–565.

22. Lute, A. M. "Some notes on the behavior of broken seeds of cereals and sorghums," *Proc Assn. Off. Seed Analysts* 17(1925):33–35.

23. Hulbert, H. W., and G. M. Whitney. "Effect of seed injury upon the germination of *Pisum sativum,*" *J. Am. Soc. Agron.* 26(1934):876–884.

24. Gregg, B. R., and others. *Seed Processing.* New Delhi, India: Miss. State Univ. Nat'l Seeds Corp. and USAID, Avion Printers, 1970, pp. 1–396.

25. Anderson, A. M. *Handbook on Seed-borne Diseases,* Assn. Off. Seed corn, *J. Am. Soc. Agron.,* 196–197. 1920.

26. Harlan, H. V., and M. N. Pope. "The germination of barley seeds harvested at different stages of growth," *J. Hered.* 8, 2(1922):72–75.

27. Harlan, H. V., and M. N. Pope. "Development in immature barley kernels removed from the plant," *J. Agr. Res.* 32, 7(1926):669–678.

28. Kiesselbach, T. A. "Corn investigations," *NE Agr. Exp.* Sta. Res. Bull. 20, 1922.

29. Waldren, R. P. *Introductory Crop Science,* 5th ed. Boston: Pearson, 2003, pp. 335.

30. Koehler, B., G. H. Dungan, and W. L. Burlison. "Maturity of seed corn in relation to yielding ability and disease infection," *J. Am. Soc. Agron.* 26(1934):262–274.

31. Bartel, A. T. "Green seeds in immature small grains and their relation to germination," *J. Am. Soc. Agron.* 33, 8(1941):732–738.

32. Kiesselbach, T. A. "Relation of seed size to the yield of small grains," *J. Am. Soc. Agron.,* 16(1924):670–682.

33. Leukel, R. W. "Germination and emergence in spring wheats of the 1935 crop," *USDA B.P.I. Div,. Cereal Crops and Diseases,* Feb. 1936 (processed).

34. Lacy, M. G. "Seed value of maize kernels: Butts, tips, and middles." *J. Am. Soc. Agron.* 7(1915):159–171.

35. Kiesselbach, T. A., and W. E. Lyness. "Furrow vs. surface planting winter wheat," *J. Am. Soc. Agron.* 26(1934):489–493.

36. Crocker, W., and L. V. Barton. *Physiology of Seeds.* Waltham, MA: Chronica Botanica Co., 1953, pp. 1–267.

37. Barton, L. "Seed dormancy," *Encyclopedia Plant Phys.*, 15(1965):699–727.

38. Pope, M. N., and E. Brown. "Induced vivipary in three varieties of barley possessing extreme dormancy," *J. Am. Soc. Agron.* 35, 2(1943):161–163.

39. Stevenson, T. M. "Sweet clover studies on habit of growth, seed pigmentation and permeability of the seed coat," *Sci. Agr.* 17(1937):627–654.

40. Lute, A. M. "Impermeable seed in alfalfa," *CO Agr. Exp. Sta. Bull.* 326, 1928.

41. Lull, F. H. "Inheritance of rest periods of seeds and certain other characters in the peanuts," *FL Agr. Exp. Sta. Bull.* 314, 1937.

42. Brandon, J. F. "The spacing of corn in the West Central Great Plains," *J. Am. Soc. Agron.* 29(1937):584–599.

43. Harrington, G. T. "Forcing the germination of freshly harvested w heat and other cereals," *J. Agr. Res.* 23(1923):79–100.

44. Lute, A. M. "A special form of delayed germination," *Proc Assn. Off. Seed Analysts* 16(1924): 23–29, 1924.

45. Waldron, L. R. "Delayed germination in durum wheat," *J. Am. Soc. Agron.* 1(1908):135–144.

46. Deming, G. W., and D. W. Robertson. "Dormancy in seeds," *CO Agr. Exp. Sta. Tech. Bull.* 5, 1933, pp. 1–12.

47. Harrington, J. B. "The comparative resistance of wheat varieties to sprouting," *Sci. Agr.* 12(1932):635–645.

48. Wenger, L. E. "Buffalo grass," *KS Agr. Exp. Sta. Bull.* 321, 1943, pp. 1–78.

49. Toole, E. H., and P. I. Drummond. "The germination of cottonseed," *J. Agr. Res.*, 28(1924):285–292.

50. Love, H. H., and C. E. Leighty. "Germination of seed as affected by sulfuric acid treatments," *Cornell Agr. Exp. Sta. Bull.* 312, 1912, pp. 294–336.

51. Stewart, G. "Effect of color of seed, of scarification, and of dry heat on the germination of alfalfa seed and some of its imparities," *J. Am. Soc. Agron.* 18(1926):743–760.

52. Harrington, G. T. "Agricultural value of impermeable seeds," *J. Agr. Res.* 6(1916):761–796.

53. Middleton, G. K. "Hard seeds in Korean lespedeza," *J. Am. Soc. Agron.* 25(1933):119–122.

54. Rodriguez, G. "Study of influence of heat and cold on the germination of hard seeds in alfalfa and sweetclover," *Proc. Assn. of. Seed Analysts* 16(1924):75–76.

55. Works, D. W., and L. C. Erickson. "Infrared radiation, an effective treatment of hard seeds in small seeded legumes," *ID Agr. Exp. Sta. Rsh. Bull.* 57, 1963, pp. 1–22.

56. Martin, J. H. "The practical application of iarovization," *J. Am. Soc. Agron.* (note), 26, 3(1934):251.

57. Taylor, J. W., and F. A. Coffman. "Effects of vernalization on certain varieties of oats," *J. Am. Soc. Agron.* 30(1938):1010–1018.

58. Bartel, A. T., and J. H. Martin. "The growth curve of sorghum," *J. Agr. Res.* 57, 11(1938):843–847.

59. Owen, E. B. "The storage of seeds for maintenance of viability," *Commonwealth Bureau Pastures and Field Crops Bull.* 43, 1956, pp. 1–81.

60. Duvel, J. W. T. "The vitality and germination of seeds," *USDA Bur. Plant Industry Bull.* 58, 1904.

61. Harmond, J. E., and others. "Mechanical seed cleaning and handling," *USDA Handbook* 354, 1968, pp. 1–56.

62. Robertson, D. W., and A. M. Lute. "Germination of seed of farm crops in Colorado after storage for various periods of years," *J. Am. Soc. Agron.* 29(1937):822–834.

63. Robertson, D. W., A. M. Lute, and H. Krooger. "Germination of 20-year-old wheat, oats, barley, corn, rye, sorghum, and soybeans," *J. Am. Soc. Agron.* 35(1943):786–795.

64. Kiesselbach, T. A. "Effects of age, size, and source of seed on the corn crop," *NE Agr. Exp. Sta. Bull.* 305, 1937.

65. Quick, C. R. "How long can seed remain alive?" in *Seeds*, USDA Yearbook, 1961, pp. 94–99.

66. Anonymous. "10,000 year old seeds germinate." *Crops and Soils* 23, 8(1971):30–31.

67. Colbry, V. L., and others. "Tests for germination in the laboratory," in *Seeds*, USDA Yearbook, 1961, pp. 433–441.

68. Association of Official Seed Analysts. *Seed Vigor Testing Handbook*. AOSA, 2002.

69. McCarty, W. H., and C. Baskin. "Understanding and using results of cottonseed germination tests." *MS St. U. Ext. Serv. IS* 1364, 2003.

70. Musil, A. F. "Testing seeds for purity and origin," in *Seeds*, USDA Yearbook, 1961, pp. 417–432.

71. Rollin, S. F., and F. A. Johnston. "Our laws that pertain to seeds," in *Seeds*, USDA Yearbook, 1961, pp. 482–492.

72. Hudspeth, E. B., Jr., R. F. Dudley, and H. J. Retzer. "Planting and fertilizing," in *Power to Produce*, USDA Yearbook, 1960, pp. 147–153.

73. Dickey, E. C., and P. Jasa. "Row crop planters: Equipment adjustments and performance in conservation tillage." *NE Coop. Ext. Serv. NebGuide* G83–684, 1989.

74. Wicks, G. A., and N. L. Klocke. "Ecofarming: Spring row crop planting and weed control in winter wheat stubble." *NE Coop. Ext. Serv. NebGuide* G81-551-A, 1989.

75. Jenkins, M. T. "A comparison of the surface, furrow, and listed methods of planting corn," *J. Am. Soc. Agron.* 26(1934):734–737.

76. Salmon, S. C. "Seeding small grain in furrows," *KS Agr. Exp. Stu. Tech. Bull.* 13, 1924, pp. 1–55.

77. Dickey, E. C., and others. "Ridge plant systems: Equipment." *NE Coop. Ext. Serv. NebGuide* G88-876-A, 1988.

78. Martin, J. H. "Factors influencing results from rate and date of seeding experiments with winter wheat in the western United States," *J. Am. Soc. Agron.* 18(1926):193–225.

79. Janssen, G. "Effect of date of seeding of winter wheat on plant development and its relationship to winterhardiness," *J. Am. Soc. Agron.* 21(1929):444–466.

80. Kiesselbach, T. A. "The relation of seeding practices to crop quality," *J. Am. Soc. Agron.* 18(1926):661–684.

81. Robertson, D. W., and G. W. Deming. "Date to plant corn in Colorado," *CO Agr. Exp. Sta. Bull.* 238, 1930.

82. Edmisten, K. "Late planted cotton." *Carolina Cotton Notes.* CCN-97–5a. 1997.

83. Bilbro, J. D., and L. L. Ray. "Differential effect of planting date on performance of cotton varieties on the High Plains of Texas, 1960–65." *TX Agr. Exp. Sta.* MP-934, 1969.

84. Kerby, T. A., S. Johnson, and K. Hake. "When to replant." *California Cotton Review. Univ. of CA Coop. Ext.* 9(1989):7–8.

85. Silvertooth, J. C., J. E. Mulcuit, D. R. Howell, and P. Else. "Effects of date of planting on the lint yield of several cotton varieties planted at four locations in Arizona." *Cotton, A College of Agriculture Report. Series P-77.* Univ. of Arizona. 1989, pp. 69–72.

86. Dana, B. F., H. E. Rea, and H. Dunlavy, "The influence of date of planting cotton on the development of root rot," *J. Am. Soc. Agron.* 24(1932):367–377.

87. Mooers, C. A. "planting rates and spacing for corn under southern conditions, " *J. Am. Soc. Agron.* 12(1920):1–22.

88. Pelton, W. L. "Influence of low seeding on wheat in southwestern Saskatchewan," *Can. J. Plant Sci.* 74(1969):33–36.

89. Guitard, A. A., J. A. Newman, and P. B. Hoyt. "The influence of seeding rate on the yield components on wheat, oats, and barley," *Can. J. Plant Sci.* 41(1961):751–758.

90. Woodard, R. W. "The effect of rate and date of seeding of small grains," *Agron. J.* 48(1956): 160–162.

91. Riveland, N. R., E. W. French, B. K. Hoag, and T. J. Conlon. "The effect of seeding rate on spring wheat yield in western North Dakota-an update," *ND Farm Res.* 37, 2(1979):15–20.

92. Elmore, R. W., and J. E. Specht. "Soybean seeding rates." *NE Coop. Ext. Serv. NebGuide* G99-1395-A, 1999.

93. Helsel, Z. R., and H. C. Minor. "Soybean Production in Missouri." *U. of MO Ag. Pub.G4410.* 1993.

94. Nafziger, E. D. "Corn planting date and plant population." *J. Prod. Ag.* 7(1994):59–62.

95. Klages, K. H. "Spacing in relation to the development of the flax plant," *J. Am. Soc. Agron.* 24(1932):1–17.

96. Tisdale, H. B. "Effect of spacing on yield and size of cotton bolls," *J. Am. Soc. Agron.* 20(1928):298–301.

97. Ahlgren, H. L. "The establishment and early management of sown pastures," *Imperial Bur. Pastures and Forage Crops Bull.* 34, 1945, pp. 139–160.

98. Murphy, R. P., and A. C. Arny. "The emergence of grass and legume seedlings planted at different depths in five soil types," *J. Am. Soc. Agron.* 31(1939):17–28.

99. Stitt, R. E. "The effect of depth of planting on the germination of soybean varieties," *J. Am. Soc. Agron.* 26(1934):1001–1004.

Plant Growth and Development

PURPOSE

The purpose of this chapter is to discuss the concepts of growth and development of plants.

EXPECTED OUTCOMES

After studying this chapter, the student should be able to:

1. Distinguish between growth and development.
2. Describe the general pattern of growth.
3. Define yield and the types of yield.
4. Discuss the concept of yield components.
5. Discuss harvest index and factors affecting it.
6. Discuss photoperiod and its effect on plant growth.
7. Discuss the concept and application of growing degree days.
8. Discuss the growth and development–related management practices in crop production.

KEY TERMS

Biological yield	Growth	Vernalization
Biomass	Phenology	Yield
Economic yield		

From Chapter 4 of *Principles of Crop Production: Theory, Techniques, and Technology*, Second Edition, George Acquaah.
Copyright © 2005 by Pearson Education, Inc. Published by Pearson Prentice Hall. All rights reserved.

TO THE STUDENT

Producers often target a certain part, or component, of the crop in a production enterprise as the commercial product. This part produces the economic yield for which a crop is cultivated. If a crop grows luxuriantly but the economic part is not enhanced satisfactorily, it is to no avail that the producer invested time and resources. For example, if grain is the goal, it is of little use to have good, healthy-looking corn with tiny ears. Thus, the goal of the crop producer is to maximize economic yield. Just like animals in which some are poor converters of feed, some plant cultivars are similarly less efficient in converting photosynthates into economic yield. Apart from choosing an efficient, high-yielding cultivar, the crop producer should provide the proper cultural environment in which plants can optimize their metabolic activities. By studying plant growth, scientists are able to redesign plant types (through plant breeding procedures) that best utilize production resources and efficiently convert them to economic yield. They can also advise producers on how to produce these crops (e.g., spacing, nutritional management) for best results.

1: WHAT IS GROWTH?

Growth. An irreversible increase in cell size or cell number.

How does growth of a crystal or snowball differ from growth of a plant? **Growth** is a progressive and irreversible process that involves three activities—*cellular division, enlargement,* and *differentiation.* Cell division occurs by the process of mitosis followed by cytoplasmic division. Cells enlarge when they take in water by *osmosis* (the diffusion of water or other solvents through a differentially permeable membrane from a region of higher concentration to one of a lower concentration). Water status of a plant is thus critical to its growth and development. Differentiation entails the development and modification of cells to perform specific functions in the plant.

Growth produces an increase in dry matter when the plant is actively photosynthesizing. The rate of growth follows a certain general pattern described by a sigmoid curve (Figure 1). The *s*-shaped curve has four distinct parts:

1. *Lag growth phase.* This phase includes activities in preparation for growth. Dormant cells become active; dry tissue imbibes moisoure; cells divide and increase in size; the embryo differentiates.

FIGURE 1 A typical sigmoid growth curve (a) lag phase (b) log phase, (c) decreasing phase, (d) steady phase.

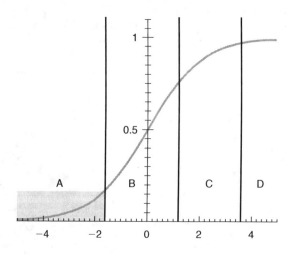

2. *Logarithmic growth phase.* During this phase, the plant experiences an ever-increasing rate of growth. Events that occur in this phase include germination and vegetative growth.
3. *Decreasing growth phase.* The decreasing growth phase is characterized by a slowing down of the rate of growth. The plant activities during this period include flowering, fruiting, and seed filing.
4. *Steady growth phase.* The growth rate either declines or stops during this phase. Plant activities in this phase include maturation.

2: VARIATIONS IN GROWTH PATTERN

The specific shape of the curve varies according to, for example, growth cycle and the part of the plant measured. The shoot growth pattern varies among annuals, biennials, and perennials. The growth pattern for plant height and dry weight differ for the same growth cycle. A rapidly growing species has a growth pattern different from that of a slowly growing species. Biennials require two growing seasons to complete their growth cycle. They go dormant in winter and resume growth in spring. The roots of a herbaceous perennial may remain alive indefinitely, but the shoot may be killed each cold winter.

3: NOT ALL DRY MATTER ACCUMULATION IS ECONOMIC

Crop productivity or production is the rate at which a crop accumulates organic matter per unit area per unit time. It depends primarily on the rate of photosynthesis, the conversion of light energy to chemical energy by green plants.

Yield is the generic term used by crop producers to describe the amount of the part of a crop plant of interest that is harvested from a given area at the end of the cropping season or within a given period. The plant part of interest is that for which the crop producer grows the crop. This could be grain, seed, leaf, stem, root, flower, or any other morphological part. It could also be the chemical content of the plant, such as oil or sugar. In certain industrial crops, such as cotton, the part of economic interest to the producer is the fiber while, for the producer of tea or tobacco, the part of interest is the leaf. A producer may harvest multiple parts of a plant for use or sale.

Biomass is a measure of yield used by scientists such as ecologists to describe the quantity or mass of live organic matter (total individuals present) in a prescribed area at a given point in time. This definition includes both above- and below-ground parts of plants in the area. Crop producers do not use this measure of yield.

Weighing or measuring a product volume quantifies yield, as is the case in liquid products. The weight of the morphological part harvested depends on its moisture content. The moisture content is an important factor in yield measurements, especially in the case of crops that are harvested dry (e.g., grains). The weight of a specified amount of corn taken at 10% moisture content will be higher than one taken at 5% moisture content. For uniformity and fair pricing, industries associated with these kinds of crops observe certain standards with regard to grain or seed moisture content at the time of sale.

Yield. The product of metabolism that may be economic or non-economic.

Biomass. The quantity of live organic matter in a given area at a given point in time.

Scientists sometimes use a more stable basis for yield measurements that eliminates the moisture factor. Yield is then defined as the amount of dry matter produced per unit area of land. To obtain this value, the plant part is dried in an oven to a stable weight before weighing.

4: TYPES OF YIELD

Yield may be divided into two types: biological and economic.

4.1 *BIOLOGICAL YIELD*

Biological yield. The amount of dry matter produced per unit area.

Biological yield is the total dry matter produced per plant or per unit area. This measurement takes into account all plant parts, above and below ground levels. Researchers use this measurement of yield in agronomic, physiological, and plant breeding studies to indicate dry matter accumulation.

4.2 *ECONOMIC YIELD*

Economic yield. The amount (volume or weight per unit area) of the part(s) of the plant of usable or marketable value.

Also called *agricultural yield,* **economic yield** represents the total weight per unit area of a specified plant material that is of marketable value or other use to the producer. The particular valuable plant part or product differs from one crop to another and may be located above ground (as in cereal crops, forage crops, cotton, and soybean) or below-ground (as in root and tuber crops such as sugar beet and Irish potato). The producer determines the part of the plant that is of economic value. The part may be used for food, feed, or industrial purposes. A producer of corn for grain is interested in the grain; a producer of corn for silage is interested in the young, fresh stem and leaves.

All economic yield is biological yield. However, not all biological yield is necessarily economic yield. For example, whereas the above ground part of corn (grain, stalk, leaves) may be used for a variety of economic purposes (e.g., food or feed), the roots have no economic value and are not harvested. On the other hand, root crops such as sugar beet produce roots that are harvested for sugar extraction, while the top leaves may be sold to livestock producers for feed. Thus, in the latter case, the total plant (biological yield) is of economic value.

5: PHOTOSYNTHETIC PRODUCTS ARE DIFFERENTIALLY PARTITIONED IN THE PLANT

Partitioning describes the pattern of carbon use in a plant. The effect of partitioning of assimilates is manifested as changes in plant morphology (e.g., changes in size, shape, and number of plant organs) during the growing season. Unlike animals, in which growth occurs throughout the organism, growth in plants occurs in specific regions called meristems. There are different locations of these growing points that are named accordingly as apical, intercallary, or axillary meristems. These centers of active cell division continue activity throughout most of the lifetime of the plant. Plasticity occurs in plants because of the presence of a variety of meristematic centers. It is important that these competitive centers of activity be coordinated so that plant resources are properly utilized. Certain centers may need to have accelerated activity, while others need to be slowed down at certain periods in the plant growth cycle.

How does the plant decide where to allocate photosynthates? Partitioning is controlled primarily by the capacity of the meristem to grow. This capacity is influenced by intrinsic and extrinsic factors. It has been proposed that growth susbstances (growth hormones), nutritional substrates, and environment are particularly responsible for controlling partitioning. The control by growth substances is especially manifested through apical dominance. Apical meristems produce auxin, a growth hormone that suppresses axillary meristem activity (i.e., branching). When the shoot apex is removed, this apical dominance is abolished, allowing branching to occur. Certain organs have the capacity to act as sinks (importers of substrates), while others are sources (exporters of substrates). However, an organ may be a source for one substrate at one point and then a sink at another time. For example, leaves are sinks for nutrients (e.g., nitrates) absorbed from the soil, while they serve as sources for newly formed amino acids.

Can crop producers influence the way plants allocate photosynthates? Genotypes differ in patterns of partitioning of dry matter. For example, in legumes, bush or erect cultivars differ from pole or prostrate cultivars. In cereals, tall cultivars differ from dwarf types in dry matter partitioning. Plant breeders strive to breed for cultivars that have a larger harvest index. C. M. Donald developed the *ideotype* concept to describe a model of an ideal plant phenotype that represents optimum partitioning of dry matter. An ideotype is developed for a specific cultural condition—e.g., monoculture, high-density mechanized production, irrigated production, or production under high input (fertilizers, pest control).

6: HARVEST INDEX

6.1 WHAT IS HARVEST INDEX?

Harvest index is defined as the proportion of the crop that is of economic importance. In early literature, the term used to describe this proportion was *coefficient of effectiveness*. This may have been because one of the uses of this measurement in plant breeding research is as an indicator of the efficiency with which photosynthates are partitioned or distributed to the plant parts that have a bearing on economic yield. Harvest index is calculated as a ratio as follows:

Harvest index = (economic yield/total yield)

Its value theoretically ranges from 0.0 to 1.0. The higher the value, the more efficient the plant is in directing assimilates to the part of the plant of economic use.

Harvest index is influenced by several factors. In some instances, the researcher deliberately or inadvertently excludes certain plant parts from the estimate. For example, even though assimilates are partitioned to roots, this part of the plant is difficult to harvest (except where roots are the economic parts) and hence is routinely excluded from estimations of harvest index. Also, plants may shed some leaves when they reach maturity. These fallen leaves are not usually picked up and included in the measurement of total yield (biomass). Consequently, harvest index is overestimated on such occasions.

The economic parts of certain plants are very small. There are some crop plants that are nearly completely useful in the sense that nearly all parts have known economic value. This notwithstanding, the producer may choose to emphasize only one component in a crop production enterprise. When this happens, the harvest index values may be very small. A classic example is sugar cane, a versatile crop that may be grown for sugar, syrup, or cane. Harvest index values based only on sugar content may be about 0.2. When sugar and syrup are combined, the value is about 0.6. However, if economic

Plant hormones

Plant *hormones* are organic molecules that are produced in small amounts in one or several parts of the plant and then transported to other parts called *target sites,* where they regulate plant growth and development. Because of this physiological role, plant hormones are also called *plant growth regulators,* a broad terminology that includes and is often associated with synthetic chemicals that have a similar effect as hormones. The way of classifying plant hormones is on the basis of their origin—*natural* or *synthetic.* Unlike animal hormones that have specificity in site of production and target site, plant hormones tend to be more general with respect to both source and target.

There are five basic groups of natural plant hormones:

1. *Auxins.* Auxins are produced in meristematic tissue such as root tips, shoot tips, apical buds, young leaves, and flowers. Their major functions include regulation of cell division and expansion, stem elongation, leaf expansion and abscission, fruit development, and branching. An example of a natural hormone is indole-3-acetic acid (IAA). Synthetic hormones that are auxins include 2,4-dichlorophenoxyacetic acid (2,4-D), which is actually a herbicide for controlling broadleaf weeds such as dandelion in lawns, α-naphthaleneacetic acid (NAA), and indole-3-butyric acid (IBA). Other uses of auxins in horticulture are
   a. As rooting hormones to induce rooting (adventitious) in cuttings
   b. To prevent fruit drop in fruits trees shortly before harvest
   c. To increase blossom and fruit set in tomatoes
   d. For fruit thinning to reduce excessive fruiting for larger fruits
   e. For defoliation prior to harvesting
   f. To prevent sprouting of stored produce, for example, in potatoes; when applied to certain tree trunks, basal sprouts are suppressed

   The concentration of auxin in plants can be manipulated in horticultural plants in cultivation. Auxins are produced in relatively higher concentrations in the terminal buds than in other parts. This localized high concentration suppresses the growth of lateral buds located below the terminal bud. When terminal buds are removed (for example, by a horticultural operation such as pruning or pinching), lateral buds are induced to grow. This makes a plant fuller in shape and more attractive.

2. *Gibberellins.* Gibberellins are produced in the shoot apex and occur in embryos and cotyledons of immature seeds as well as roots. They occur in seed, flowers, germinating seed, and developing flowers. This class of hormones promotes cell division, stem elongation, seed germination (by breaking dormancy), flowering, and fruit development. Fruit size of seedless grapes is increased through the application of this hormone. An example is gibberellic acid (GA_1).

3. *Cytokinins.* These hormones stimulate cell division and lateral bud development. They occur in embryonic or meristematic organs. Examples of natural cytokinins are isopentenyl adenine (IPA) and zeatin (Z). Synthetic cytokinins included kinetin (K) and benzyl adenine (BA). Cytokinins interact with auxins to affect various plant

value is based on fresh cane delivered to the processor or buyer, the harvest index may be above 0.90

The developmental pathway followed by the plant part or chemical component of economic value affects harvest index. In cereal crops such as corn and wheat, the economic part, the grain, fills in a linear fashion up to a definite point and then ceases. Harvest index in these crops depends on the relative duration of vegetative and reproductive phases of plant lifecycle. In root and tuber crops, such as sugar beet and Irish potato, the economic part follows a protracted developmental pathway. In these crops, harvest index depends more on genetics and environmental factors.

functions. A high cytokinin-auxin ratio (that is, low amounts of auxin, especially IAA) promotes lateral bud development because of reduced apical dominance. The principal role of cytokinins in plant physiology is the promotion of cell division.

4. *Ethylene.* Ethylene is a gas that is found in tissues of ripening fruits and nodes of stems. It promotes fruit ripening and leaf abscision. In the horticultural industry, ethylene is used to aid ripening of apples, pineapples, and bananas and to change the rind color of fruits (as in oranges and grapefruits from green to yellow and tomatoes from green to uniform red). On the other hand, ripening of apples produces this gas in large quantities, which tends to lower storage life of fruits. Ethaphon is commercially used for this purpose. This can be reversed by removing the gas with, for example, activated charcoal. Ethylene in the growing environment may cause accelerated senescence of flowers and leaf abscision. Carnation flowers close while rose buds open prematurely in the presence of ethylene. In cucumbers and pumpkins, ethaphon spray can increase female flowers (disproportionately) and thereby increase fruit set.

5. *Abscisic acid.* Abscisic acid (ABA) is a natural hormone that acts as an inhibitor of growth, promotes fruit and leaf abscision, counteracts the breaking of dormancy, and causes the stomata of leaves to close under moisture stress. ABA has an antagonistic relationship with gibberellins and other growth-stimulating hormones. For example, ABA-induced seed dormancy may be reversed by applying gibberellins. Commercial application of ABA is limited partly because of the high cost of the chemical and scarcity of the substance.

Plant hormones may also be classified based on their effect on plant growth as *stimulants* or *retardants*. Cytokinins and gibberellins have a stimulating effect on growth and development, while ABA is a growth inhibitor. Alfalfa is known to produce the alcohol *triacontanol,* which stimulates growth. Naturally occurring inhibitors include benzoic acid, coumarin, and cinamic acid. A number of synthetic growth retardants are in use in producing certain horticultural plants. Their effect is mainly to slow down cell division and elongation. As such, instead of a plant growing tall with long internodes, it becomes short (dwarf), compact, fuller, and aesthetically more pleasing. Examples of these commercial growth retardants are

1. Daminozide (marketed under such trade names as Alar and B-nine; plants affected include poinsettia, azalea, petunia, and chrysanthemum
2. Chlormequat (CCC, cycocel), which retards plant height in poinsettia, azalea, and geranium
3. Ancymidol (A-Rest), which is effective in reducing height in such bulbs as Easter lilies and tulips, as well as chrysanthemums and poinsettias
4. Paclobutrazol (Bonzi), which is used to reduce plant height in bedding plants, including impatiens, pansy, petunia, and snapdragon

Plant maturity plays a role in harvest index, the values increasing with early maturity in crops such as rice. Increasing plant population density in crops such as corn decreases harvest index. Drought (water stress) and fertilization (e.g., nitrogen application) tend to lower harvest index values.

6.2 MANIPULATING HARVEST INDEX

Harvest index in certain crops has been successfully increased through plant breeding. In wheat, this has been generally accomplished by increasing the efficiency with which the plant partitions photosynthates to the grain, while keeping the biomass virtually unchanged. Increase in harvest index in small grain cereals and other species has been achieved by reducing plant height through selection or the use of dwarfing genes (such as the *Rht* genes in wheat breeding). Decreasing plant height in modern cultivars is partially responsible for increased harvest index in certain species. The reduction in the size of plant organs is compensated for in modern production through the application of agronomic inputs such as fertilizers. Such a practice appears to reduce the need for plants to remobilize accumulated reserves in leaves to the grain. This trend, however, is not conclusive in all cases.

The use of early-flowering cultivars, coupled with good crop management (e.g., fertilization, pest control, irrigation) allows the plant to allocate assimilates to seed sooner, thereby leading to reduced accumulation of reserves in the leaves. Early-flowering cultivars in species such as rice may benefit from a high harvest index through this process.

7: The Biological Pathway to Economic Yield Is Variable

7.1 YIELD COMPONENTS

In an effort to manipulate crop yield, researchers attempt to construct the path by which the reproductive, developmental, and morphological features of plants in a crop stand contribute to yield of a specified plant product. There are many such pathways to high yield *(yield components)*. For grain yield, a model is as follows:

Yield/unit area = (plants/unit area) $\times$ (heads/plant) $\times$ (mean number of seeds/head) $\times$ (mean weight/seed)

where the plant species produces tillers, the model may be presented as follows:

Yield/unit area = (plants/unit area) $\times$ (mean number of tillers with ears/plant) $\times$ (mean number of grains/ear) $\times$ (mean grain weight)

These plant features describe yield. They all depend on energy in a fixed pool that is furnished through photosynthesis. Plant breeders and agronomists seeking to influence yield manipulate the components to positively affect photosynthesis.

In interpreting correlation between yield and its components, one should not evaluate the components in terms of relative importance. Seasonal sequence of environmental conditions that affect plant development should be considered. Growing conditions may be ideal in the early growth and development of the crop, leading to good initiation of reproductive features. However, if there is an onset of drought, few pods may complete their development and be filled with seed, leading to low correlation between yield and the number of seeds per pod.

Yield components vary from one species to another in terms of optimum value relative to other components. Further, yield components affect each other to varying degrees. For example, if increasing plant density drastically reduces the number of pods per plant, the number of seeds per pod may only be moderately affected, while seed size remains unchanged or only slightly affected.

Whereas a balance among yield components has great adaptive advantage for the crop, the components are environmentally labile. High yield usually results from one component with extreme value. Further, yield components are determined sequentially. As such, they tend to exhibit *yield compensation,* the phenomenon whereby deficiency or low value for the first component in the sequence of developmental events is made up with high values for the subsequent components. The net effect is that yield is maintained at a certain level. However, yield compensation is not a perfect phenomenon. For example, it may occur over a wide range of plant densities in certain species. In beans, reduction in pod number can be compensated for by an increase in seed number per pod and weight per seed.

7.2 YIELD POTENTIAL

What determines how much a crop can produce? Crop yield is a complex trait (quantitative trait). A given crop cultivar has an inherent optimum capacity to perform under a given environment. This capacity is described as its *yield potential.* When this potential is attained, attempts to improve yield or crop performance will be difficult even if levels of production inputs are increased. At this point, the genetic potential needs to be increased by genetic manipulation through a plant breeding program.

8: PLANT DEVELOPMENT CONCEPTS

Development is the term used to describe the continuing change in plant form and function as the plant responds to environmental factors. It involves the coordination, growth, and longevity of new vegetative and reproductive parts. Newly produced cells from the division of meristematic cells undergo change and specialization through differentiation, a process called *morphogenesis.* The activities of the various meristems produce change in the plant. The shoot meristem supported by intercalary meristems in the internodes produces elongation in the plant. Also, axillary meristems in leaf axils produce branches, while lateral meristems (mainly in the cambium) produce increases in girth.

Since the fruit and seed are commonly the economic yield of most crop plants, crop producers are especially interested in reproductive development. Flowering plants have two phases of development—vegetative and reproductive. At a certain stage in the development, the shoot apices change from the vegetative phase to the reproductive phase. The environment induces this conversion. The yield of the crop depends on the extent to which this conversion occurs, thus making it critical for a crop to complete its reproductive phase during the growing season and without stress. For high productivity, there has to be a good balance between the two phases. A protracted vegetative phase reduces reproductive functions. However, good vegetative development is needed to support good reproductive development.

8.1 DEVELOPMENTAL PHASES

Scientists recognize certain distinctive developmental stages, or *phenostages* (phenological stages), in the course of a plant's development. The lifecycle of a seed-producing crop plant may be divided into five general developmental stages as follows:

1. *Seed germination to emergence.* This is the first critical stage in crop production. The success of the crop starts with a good establishment.
2. *Emergence to floral initiation.* This is the most prolonged phase in the development of the plant. It is the vegetative period of development, during

which the plant roots, stems, and leaves grow and accumulate food for the transition from vegetative to flowering, developing flower buds.

3. *Floral initiation to anthesis.* Anthesis is the opening of the flower buds, called the reproductive stage. The plant needs to sustain an adequate number of flowers for producing the economic product.

4. *Anthesis to physiological maturity.* This critical stage includes the filling of the grain. The grain fills to a stage where additional agronomic inputs do not further enhance its size.

5. *Physiological maturity to cessation of growth.* This cessation of growth may be terminal (such as death in annuals) or temporary (such as dormancy in perennials).

Most of these phenostages can be readily recognized by observation only. Others, such as floral initiation, require dissection and microscopic examination of the tissues. The rate of advance within the intervening *phenophases* is called the *developmental rate.* **Phenology** is the study of the progress of crop development in relation to environmental factors. Individual plants in a crop stand vary in developmental rate. This is caused by the prevalence of different microclimates and some genotypic factors. Crop cultivars of narrow genetic base (e.g., purelines) provide opportunity for synchronized development that enables the producer to administer certain management operations (e.g., fertilizer or pesticide application) as close to the best time as possible.

Normally, vegetative growth ceases when the apical meristem converts from vegetative growth to a reproductive structure. In certain crops, flowering occurs within a limited period of a few days. These are called *determinate crops;* examples include cereal crops. In other crops, vegetative growth and reproductive growth overlap. The apical meristem continues to produce new leaves while flowering continues progressively from axillary meristems. These crops are called *indeterminate crops;* examples include certain legumes, such as soybeans. Some crops have both determinate and indeterminate cultivars in use in crop production.

Phenology. The study of the timing of periodic phenomena such as flowering, growth initiation, or growth cessation, especially as related to seasonal changes in temperature or photoperiod.

8.2 GROWTH STAGING IN CEREAL GRAINS

As previously discussed, plants have distinct developmental stages in their lifecycles. Over the years, a number of systems (staging systems) have been developed by researchers to quantify development for scientific and crop management purposes. The staging systems for cereal grains have been some of the most widely studied and applied. These systems are applied in the crop production industry for proper identification of the best times to apply various production inputs, as well as other management practices.

Of the staging scales in existence, the most widely used are the Feekes, Haun, and Zadoks scales. The characteristics and strengths of these scales are briefly discussed in this section.

The Major Growth Stages of Cereal Grains

Researchers have identified 10 major growth stages that all cereal grain plants go through during a normal lifecycle. These stages are important to producers because they base many of their agronomic practices on stages of plant growth and development. The stages are

1. Germination—the emergence of the radicle and coleoptile from the seed
2. Seedling—the young, newly emerged plant
3. Tillering—the formation of lateral branches that originate from below-ground nodes on the stem
4. Stem elongation (jointing)—stem nodes appear above the ground level

5. Booting—The inflorescence expands inside the upper leaf sheath.
6. Heading—cluster of florets form.
7. Flowering (anthesis)—Anthers extend from the glumes
8. Milk—early development of kernel; kernel has watery and whitish consistency
9. Dough—kernel has semi-solid consistency
10. Ripening—kernel loses moisture and is more solid

Common Staging Scales

Table 1 compares the three major staging scales in terms of physical changes they describe and the various numerical codes used to refer to various growth and development stages.

Feekes Scale This scale is one of the earliest and perhaps the best known and most widely used. The scale describes 11 major developmental stages, starting with the first leaf stage to the grain ripening. The stages in the vegetative phase are assigned numeric values ranging from 0 to 10. The stages in reproductive phase are characterized in more detail, starting from 10.1 (first spikelet of the inflorescence is visible) to 11.4 (hard kernel). A major agronomic application of the Feekes scale is the timing of pesticide application.

Haun Staging System The Haun staging system focuses mainly on leaf production stages of development. The length of an emerging leaf is expressed as a fraction of the length of the preceding fully emerged leaf. A Haun numeric value of 3.2, for example, means that three leaves are fully emerged, the fourth leaf having only emerged to about two-tenths of the length of the third leaf. The scale is less useful when developmental indicators other than leaf numbers are used in decision making.

Zadoks Staging System This two-digit code system is very detailed and more precise than the others. It provides more information during the early developmental stages than the Feekes scale. The Zadoks scale recognizes 10 developmental stages, beginning from germination (0) to ripening of kernels (9). The first of the two digits represents the principal stage of development. Each major developmental stage is subdivided into secondary stages (the second digits). A leaf has to be 50% unfolded or emerged to be counted. A code of 3, for example, is interpreted as a plant seedling with 3 leaves that are at least 50% extended. A second digit of 5 usually indicates that the midpoint of the primary stage has occurred.

8.3 GROWTH STAGING IN LEGUMES

Developmental stages of legumes are usually divided into two: vegetative and reproductive. The following example is of growth staging in soybean.

Vegetative Stages (Vn)

VE—Cotyledons emerge.
VC—Cotyledon emerges and the unifoliate leaf unfolds.
V1—First node has leaves.
V2—Second node has leaves.
V3—Third node has leaves.
Vn—*n*th node has leaves.

Table 1 A comparison of three cereal growth staging scales.

Zadoks	Feekes	Haun	Description
Germination			
00	–	–	Dry Seed
01	–	–	Start of imbibition
03	–	–	Imbibition complete
05	–	–	Radicle emerged from seed
07	–	–	Coleoptile emerged from seed
09	–	0.0	Leaf just at coleoptile tip
Seedling Growth			
10	1	–	First leaf through coleoptile
11	–	1.0	First leaf extended
12	–	1.+	Second leaf extending
13	–	2.+	Third leaf extending
14	–	3.+	Fourth leaf extending
15	–	4.+	Fifth leaf extending
16	–	5.+	Sixth leaf extending
17	–	6.+	Seventh leaf extending
18	–	7.+	Eighth leaf extending
19	–	–	Nine or more leaves extended
Tillering			
20	–	–	Main shoot only
21	2	–	Main shoot and one tiller
22	–	–	Main shoot and two tillers
23	–	–	Main shoot and three tillers
24	–	–	Main shoot and four tillers
25	–	–	Main shoot and five tillers
26	3	–	Main shoot and six tillers
27	–	–	Main shoot and seven tillers
28	–	–	Main shoot and eight tillers
29	–	–	Main shoot and nine tillers
Stem Elongation			
30	4-5	–	Psuedo stem erection
31	6	–	First node detectable
32	7	–	Second node detectable
33	–	–	Third node detectable
34	–	–	Fourth node detectable
35	–	–	Fifth node detectable
36	–	–	Sixth node detectable
37	8	–	Flag leaf just visible
39	9	–	Flag leaf ligule/collar just visible
Booting			
40	–	–	—
41	–	8-9	Flag leaf sheath extending
45	10	9.2	Boot just swollen
47	–	–	Flag leaf sheath opening
49	–	10.1	First awns visible

Zadoks	Feekes	Haun	Description
Inflorescence Emergence			
50	10.1	10.2	First spikelet of inflorescence visible
53	10.2	–	1/4 of inflorescence emerged
55	10.3	10.5	1/2 of inflorescence emerged
57	10.4	10.7	3/4 of inflorescence emerged
59	10.5	11.0	Emergence of inflorescence completed
Anthesis			
60	10.51	11.4	Beginning of anthesis
65	–	11.5	Anthesis 1/2 completed
69	–	11.6	Anthesis completed
Milk Development			
70	–	–	—
71	10.54	12.1	Kernel watery-ripe
73	–	13.0	Early milk
75	11.1	–	Medium milk
77	–	–	Late milk
Dough Development			
80	–	–	—
83	–	14.0	Early dough
85	11.2	–	Soft dough
87	–	15.0	Hard dough
Ripening			
90	–	–	—
91	11.3	–	Kernel hard (difficult to divide by thumbnail)
92	11.4	16.0	Kernel hard (can not be dented by thumbnail)
93	–	–	Kernel loosening in daytime
94	–	–	Overripe, straw dead and collapsing
95	–	–	Seed dormant
96	–	–	Viable seed giving 50% germination
97	–	–	Seed not dormant
98	–	–	Secondary dormancy induced
99	–	–	Secondary dormancy lost

Reproductive Stages (R)

R1—Beginning bloom
R2—Full bloom
R3—Beginning pod
R4—Full pod
R5—Beginning seed
R6—Full pod
R7—Beginning maturity
R8—Full maturity

Because all plants will not be at the same developmental stage at the same time, staging is sometimes generalized as follows:

Late vegetative—stem is about 12 inches tall but no buds or flowers are visible
Early bud—about 1% of plants in the field have flower buds
Mid bud—about 50% of all plants have at least one flower bud
Late bud—about 75% of all plants have at least one flower bud

These stages can be applied to blooming (i.e., first bloom, one-tenth bloom, midbloom, full bloom).

8.4 PHOTOPERIODISM

What makes plants switch from one developmental phase to another? There are several significant developmental switches from the initiation of leaves (vegetative) to flowering (reproductive) that are determined by environmental factors. Some crops are facultative in response to temperature or daylength, in that flowering is not promoted by desirable conditions but occurs nonetheless. In obligate crops, the plants will not flower if the temperature or daylength is above or below a certain critical value. Two developmental switches are *photoperiodism* and *vernalization*.

Duration of length of day is called its *photoperiod* (Figure 2). It affects developmental switches, as from vegetative phase to flowering phase. Based upon plant response to light duration, crop plants may be classified into three general groups: long-day, short-day, and day-neutral.

1. *Long-day* (short night) plants. Long-day plants require a light period longer than a certain critical length in order to flower. These plants will flower in continuous light. The response is common among cool-season plants such as wheat, barley, alfalfa, oat, and sugar beet.
2. *Short-day* (long night) plants. Short-day plants will not flower under continuous light. They require a photoperiod of less than a certain critical value within a 24-hour daily cycle. This response is common among warm-season crop plants, including corn, rice, soybean, peanut, and sugarcane.
3. *Day-neutral* (photoperiod insensitive) plants. These plants will flower under any condition of photoperiod. Examples are tomato, cucumber, buckwheat, cotton, and sunflower.

Effects of photoperiod on crop production are time of flowering of plants and time of maturity. This is critical to the production of crops whose economic part is the grain or seed.

Photoperiodism is photomorphogenic response in plants to day length. Photoperiodic plants actually track or measure the duration of darkness or dark period rather than the duration of light. Thus, short-day plants (or long-night plants) flower only if they receive continuous darkness for equal to or more than a critical value

(Figure 3). If the dark period is interrupted by light of sufficient intensity for even a minute, flowering will not be induced. Similarly, a long-day plant (or short-night plant) will not flower if the critical duration of darkness is exceeded. However, if a long-night period is interrupted by light, flowering will be induced. Interrupting the long night with such a short period of lighting is called flash lighting, a technique that

FIGURE 2 The average day length varies with the seasons. In the northern latitudes (20° to 50° above the equator), day lengths range between 8 hours in winter and 15.5 hours in summer. The day length at the equator remains at about 12 hours all year long.

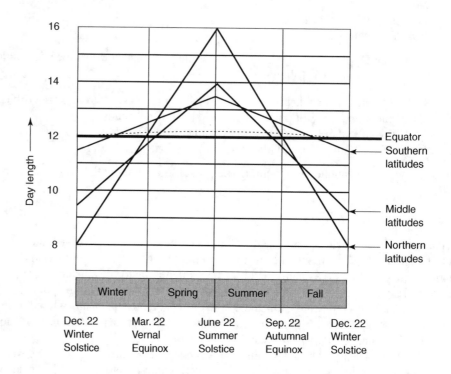

FIGURE 3 Photoperiodic response in flowering species. Light interruption of darkness affects short- and long-day plants differently.

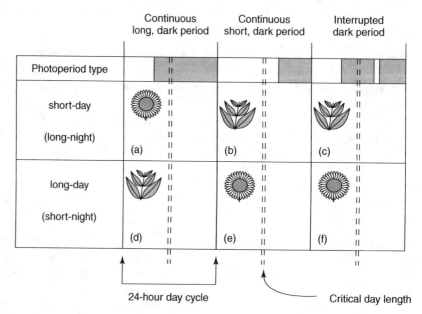

Photoperiodism: What do plants really measure?

Plants respond to the duration and timing of day and night. This seasonal response of plants to the environment is critical to the successful production of certain flowering plants. Work by plant physiologists Karl Hamner and James Bonner revealed that the length of light period is unimportant; rather, plants track or measure the *duration of darkness*, or dark period. The duration of uninterrupted darkness is critical, not the duration of uninterrupted light.

Photoperiod-sensitive plants will flower not according to a certain absolute length of photoperiod but, rather, based on whether the photoperiod is longer or shorter than a certain critical length required by the species. This critical length can be exacting in certain species such that a deviation of even 30 minutes can spell disaster. For example, in the henbane, the critical photoperiod is 10 hours and 20 minutes; 10 hours is ineffective. The environment (e.g., temperature) can modify this critical period. Further, the most sensitive part of the dark period is the middle of the period of exposure, the effect diminishing before or after the mid-period. Some species require only one exposure to the appropriate photoperiod to be induced to flower, whereas others require several days or even weeks (as in spinach).

Certain light-sensitive plant pigments called *phytochromes* are involved in photoperiod response. Phytochromes exist in two photoreversible forms. The *Pr* form absorbs red light, while the other form, *Pfr*, absorbs far-red light. A molecule of Pr is converted to Pfr when it absorbs a photon of 660 nanometer light. Similarly, when Pfr absorbs a photon of 730 nanometer light, it reconverts to Pr instantaneously. The ratio of Pfr to Pr (or P730 to P660) decreases during the growing season as the days become shorter and nights longer. At a critical level, flowering is induced in short-day plants. In the case of long-day plants, as the day length increases and the nights become shorter during the early growing season, the P730 to P660 ratio increases. Flowering is initiated when a critical level is reached.

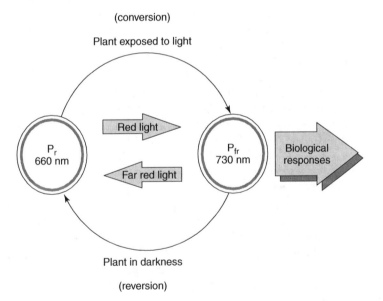

(conversion)

Plant exposed to light

P_r 660 nm — Red light → P_{fr} 730 nm → Biological responses

← Far red light

Plant in darkness

(reversion)

The role of phytochromes in the photoperiodic response in plants. Dark reversion of far red phytochrome to red phytochrome has so far been detected in dicots but not monocots.

is used by producers of ornamental flowering plants to manage the timing of flowering of plants and readiness for the market. Growers also manipulate the photoperiod of certain seasonal and high-income greenhouse plants (e.g., poinsettia) to produce plants in a timely fashion. To do this, growers start the plants under long-day conditions and then finish them under appropriate photoperiods. The required photoperiod is provided by covering the plants with a black cloth between 5 P.M. and 8 A.M. Conversely, the photoperiod may be prolonged during the natural short days by artificial lighting to keep the plants vegetative.

Photoperiod and temperature appear to compensate in their effect to some degree. Most cool-season crops tend to have a long-day response, while most warm-season crops are short-day in their response to photoperiod. The photoperiodic response of some crop plants may be modified by temperature. For example, early-maturing sorghum varieties may grow larger under long photoperiods of the north than they do in the south, where temperatures are more conducive to sorghum production. The time of seeding of crops affects the periods required to reach maturity because of the interaction of temperature and photoperiod.

8.5 VERNALIZATION

Vernalization. The process by which floral induction in some plants is promoted by exposing the plants to chilling for a certain length of time.

Vernalization is the cold-temperature induction of flowering that is required in a broad variety of plants. The degree of coldness and duration of exposure required to induce flowering vary from species to species, but temperature requirements usually lie between 0° and 10°C (32° and 50°F). While plants such as sugar beet and kohlrabi can be cold-sensitized as seed, most plants respond to the cold treatment after attaining a certain amount of vegetative growth. Some plants that need it are not treated because they are cultivated not for flower or seed but for other parts, such as roots (in carrot and sugar beet), buds (Brussels sprouts), stems (celery), and leaves (cabbage). Apple, cherry, and pear require vernalization as do winter annuals, such as wheat, barley, oat, and rye. Flowers such as foxglove (*Digitalis* spp.), tulip, crocus (*Crocus* spp.), narcissus (*Narcissus* spp.), and hyacinth (*Hyacinthus* spp.) need the treatment that may be applied to the bulbs, thereby making them flower in warmer climates, at least for that growing season. However, they must be vernalized in order to flower in subsequent years. In some of these bulbs, the cold treatment is needed to promote flower development after induction, but not for induction. Sometimes, vernalization helps plants such as pea and spinach to flower early but not as a requirement for flowering.

In onion, the bulbs are the commercial products harvested in production. Cold storage (near freezing) is used to preserve onion sets during the winter. This condition vernalizes the sets; if planted in spring, they will flower and produce seed. To obtain bulbs (no flowering), the sets should not be vernalized. Fortunately for growers, a phenomenon of *devernalization* occurs, in which exposure to warm temperatures of above 27°C (80°F) for two to three weeks prior to planting will reverse the effect of vernalization. Onion producers are therefore able to store their sets and devernalize them for bulb production during the planting season.

Flowering in certain species is affected by a phenomenon called *thermal periodicity,* in which the degree of flowering is affected by an alternation of warm and cool temperatures during production. For example, tomatoes in the greenhouse can be manipulated for higher productivity by providing a certain cycle of temperature. Plants are exposed to a warm temperature of 27°C (80°F) during the day and cooler night temperatures of about 17° to 20°C (63° to 68°F). This treatment causes increased fruit production over and above what occurs at either temperature alone.

9: GROWING DEGREE DAYS

As an organism develops, its development is closely related to the daily accumulation of heat. Organisms have specific growth stages. In order to move from one stage of development to the next, a certain amount of heat is needed to provide adequate energy for the process (e.g., the emergence of a new leaf in corn or the hatching of insect eggs). Even though the amount of heat required to move from one stage to the next is constant from one year to the next, the amount of time within which the specific developmental transition occurs is dependent on the environment and hence is variable. Researchers have determined through experimentation the minimum base (threshold) temperature below which development in various organisms would not occur. As temperature rises above this minimum temperature, the growth rate increases up to a certain maximum and then declines.

9.1 CALCULATING DEGREE DAYS

Growing degree days (GDD) (sometimes called *heat units*) are obtained by calculating the heat accumulations above a minimum threshold temperature. Several methods of calculating degree days accumulations are available, the common ones including the averaging methods, Baskerville-Emin (BE) method, and the electronic real time data collection method. The variety in methodologies is due in part to the fact that these base temperatures are affected by photoperiod. The BE method uses a technique that fits a sine curve. It is advantageous over the averaging method when the minimum daily temperature is below the base temperature. The electronic method uses devices (heat unit accumulators) that record temperatures every few minutes, thus giving the most accurate results of all the methods.

9.2 APPLICATIONS

Degree days estimates have many useful applications in crop management. Growing degree days may be used to track the development of many crops and insect pests of interest. For example, in the Central Corn Belt, 2,100–3,200 GDD are needed (depending on the hybrid) to grow corn successfully. In this region, 200 GDD are needed for corn to reach the two-leaf stage, 1,400 to reach silk emergence, and 2,700 to reach physiological maturity (for a 2,700 GDD hybrid). Some alfalfa producers use GDD to determine the best time to cut the crop. GDD is also useful in integrated pest management for scouting. Scouting is more efficient when one knows the number of GDD required for a pest to reach a destructive stage. For example, if a study shows that it takes 300 heat units for alfalfa weevil eggs to hatch, then scouting for the pest may begin once the producer's calculations have accumulated 300 heat units beginning at a certain critical date in the growing season (e.g., from January 1, using 48°F as the developmental threshold). The grower may then use economic thresholds to determine the most appropriate management practices to implement.

9.3 CROP HEAT UNITS

Crop heat units (CHU) are based on a similar principle as GDD, but the calculations are different. The maximum and minimum temperatures are calculated by separate formulas. The CHU for a site is calculated as follows:

Daily CHU $= (Y_{max} + Y_{min})/2$
where $Y_{max} = (3.33 \times (T_{max} - 50°F)) - (0.084 \times (T_{max} - 50°F))^2$
$Y_{min} = (1.8 \times (T_{min} - 4.4)$

Crop varieties are rated according to CHU accumulated between seeding time to physiological maturity. Corn hybrids are rated according to the CHU required to reach 32% kernel moisture, while soybean varieties are rated according to the CHU required to have 95% of the pods turn brown. CHU are accurate to within approximately 100 heat units. To avoid risk, a producer may select a hybrid or cultivar with less CHU rating than the prescribed.

10: GROWTH AND DEVELOPMENT–RELATED CROP MANAGEMENT PRACTICES

The various stages in the lifecycle of flowering plants may be summarized as follows: Seed—seedling—early vegetative—late vegetative—early flowering—late flowering—early seed maturity—late seed maturity. The duration of each of these stages is variable and can be influenced to some degree by manipulating the growth environment. Various agronomic practices are conducted at these stages for optimal plant growth and productivity. Some of these activities are for protection (e.g., seed dressing, pesticide spraying), while others promote vegetative growth (e.g., application of fertilizers, growth regulators). Other practices regulate fruit set and maturity.

The principal plant morphological features are roots, stems, leaves, and flowers. Crop production management practices for each of these organs have been discussed in the corresponding sections.

SUMMARY

1. Crop productivity depends on how dry matter is partitioned.
2. Plant cultivars differ in patterns of partitioning of dry matter. Plants with a larger harvest index are more efficient at partitioning dry matter for higher productivity.
3. Growth is a progressive and irreversible process that involves cellular division, enlargement, and differentiation.
4. The rate of growth follows a general sigmoid curve pattern.
5. Growth may be measured on the basis of individual plants or a community of plants.
6. Yield may be biological or economic. The choice of economic part depends on the crop producer.
7. Harvest index is the proportion of the crop that is of economic importance. It is affected by genetic and environmental factors.
8. The concept of yield components is an attempt by scientists to construct the path by which the reproductive, developmental, and morpohological features of plants in a crop stand contribute to the yield of a specified plant product.
9. Certain developmental switches occur in plants, including photoperiodism and vernalization, that affect the onset of flowering.

REFERENCES AND SUGGESTED READING

Acquaah, G. 2002. *Horticulture: principles and practices,* 2nd ed. Upper Saddle River, NJ: Prentice Hall.

Foskett, D. E. 1994. *Plant growth and development: A molecular approach.* San Diego: Academic Press.

SELECTED INTERNET SITES FOR FURTHER REVIEW

http://www.ag.iastate.edu/departments/agronomy/corngrows.htm #how

Growth of corn; informative.

http://www.plant-hormones.bbsrc.ac.uk/education/kenhp.htm

Great discussion of plant growth hormones.

OUTCOMES ASSESSMENT

PART A

Answer the following questions true or false.

1. T F   All yield is biological.
2. T F   Photoperiod measures the duration of darkness.
3. T F   Photoperiodism is temperature-induced response in plants.
4. T F   Yield components are determined sequentially.
5. T F   Growth is an irreversible process.

PART B

Answer the following questions.

1. Crop yield may be biological or _____.

2. Provide a model for grain yield based on yield components.

   _____.

3. What is phenology? _____.

4. What are growing degree days? _____.

PART C

Write a brief essay on each of these topics.

1. Discuss the sigmoid growth curve.

2. Discuss the concept of yield components.

3. Discuss the concept of yield component compensation.

4. Discuss the occurrence of developmental switches in plants.

5. Discuss the application of growing degree days in crop production.

PART D

Discuss or explain the following topics in detail.

1. Discuss how crop producers can manipulate developmental switches in plants for increased crop productivity.

2. Can the yield potential of crops be raised indefinitely?

3. Discuss the role of growth regulators in plant growth and development.

Plant Morphology

PURPOSE

The purpose of this chapter is to discuss the science of plant taxonomy and how plants are identified. The discussion focuses on plant morphological attributes used in plant identification. Anatomical structure and function of plant parts are also discussed.

EXPECTED OUTCOMES

After studying this chapter, the student should be able to:

1. Define the term *plant taxonomy.*
2. Discuss the rules pertaining to taxonomy.
3. Classify plants on an operational basis, including agronomic use, adaptation, growth form, stem type, and growth cycle.
4. List and give examples of important crop plant families.
5. Describe how plants are identified using morphological features of the leaf, stem, flower, and seed in dicots and monocots.
6. List the major cellular organelles and describe their functions.
7. List the different types of plant tissues.
8. Discuss the structure and functions of simple and complex tissues.
9. Describe the structure and function of the leaf.
10. Describe the structure and function of the stem.
11. Describe the structure and function of the root.
12. Describe the structure and function of the flower.

KEY TERMS

Adventitious roots	Annual plant	Caryopsis
Androecium	Biennial plant	Cell

From Chapter 2 of *Principles of Crop Production: Theory, Techniques, and Technology*, Second Edition, George Acquaah.
Copyright © 2005 by Pearson Education, Inc. Published by Pearson Prentice Hall. All rights reserved.

Chlorophyll	Mitochondria	Rhizome
Cool season plant	Monocarp	Stolon
Dicot	Monocot	Taxon
Dioecious plant	Monoecious plant	Testa
Epidermis	Perennial plant	Tissue
Gynoecium	Phloem	Warm season plant
Meristem	Plant taxonomy	Xylem

TO THE STUDENT

There is enormous biological diversity in nature. Some crop plants are distributed over a wide range of environments in the world. A particular crop has different culture-based nomenclature. There is a need for consensus in classifying and naming plants. Classifying and naming plants facilitates their use by researchers and consumers. A unifying system of classifying and naming plants is especially critical to international collaboration in research and plant use. Whereas a particular plant is called corn in the United States and maize in the United Kingdom, the scientific name *Zea mays* identifies the same plant in all parts of the world. Classification is a work in progress. As new information becomes available, scientists review and reassign plants to more appropriate groups. You will therefore find that older textbooks sometimes have different classes and names assigned to certain organisms. The crop producer may not appreciate the scientific names of plants, which sometimes are rather difficult to pronounce, much less memorize. In this chapter, you will also learn some of the common operational ways of classifying plants that make more sense to the ordinary producer. Plant anatomy is the science of cataloging, describing, and understanding the function of plant structures. It involves the study of the structure of cells, tissues, and tissue systems. An understanding of the anatomy of crop plants helps producers properly allocate and distribute plants in the field. The plant breeder needs to understand plant anatomy to more effectively manipulate plant structure for higher productivity. Your goal in studying this chapter should not be to memorize botanical terminologies and jargon of plant structures. Try to link structure to function. Crop production involves applying basic scientific information to producing crops.

1: WHAT IS PLANT TAXONOMY?

Plant taxonomy. The science of identifying, naming, and classifying plants.

Plant taxonomy is the science of identifying, classifying, and naming plants. This task is accomplished by using data from a variety of sources, including morphological, anatomical, ultrastructural, physiological, phytochemical, cytological, and evolutionary. Plants are grouped according to relationships based on characteristics from these sources. The flower plays a significant role in plant taxonomy because it is a very stable organ across different environments.

2: TAXONOMY IS A WORK IN PROGRESS

Taxon. A taxonomic group of organisms (e.g., family, genus, or species).

What is the basis for assigning plants to certain categories? There are seven general taxonomic groups in botanical or scientific classification of plants (Figure 1). *Kingdom* is the most inclusive group; *species* is the least inclusive. Each group is called a **taxon**

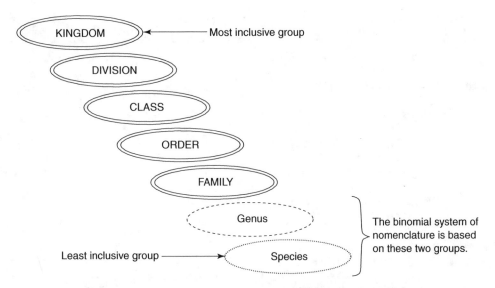

FIGURE 1 The seven basic taxonomic groups of organisms. Between kingdom and division, there are *subkingdom* and *superdivision*. Similarly, *subclass* may follow class. Conventional plant breeding is limited to sexual gene transfer that is possible mainly within species. Recombinant DNA technology enables gene transfer to occur across the whole spectrum of categories.

(plural is *taxa*). Carolus Linnaeus developed a two-part name, called the *binomial nomenclature,* for plants. This consists of the *genus* and the *species* names. Taxonomy is a work in progress. As new information becomes available, scientists revise the existing classification, reassigning certain plants to new groups. Similarly, scientists assign new names to old names (e.g., the grass family used to be called Gramineae but is now called Poaceae). An example of scientific or binomial nomenclature is presented in Table 1.

There are five major groups (kingdoms) of all organisms: *Plantae, Animalia, Protoctista, Fungi,* and *Monera* (Table 2). Plants belong to the kingdom Plantae (plant kingdom). Should crop science students be concerned about the other four kingdoms apart from kingdom Plantae? Yes. Crop production is also concerned about the other four kingdoms because organisms in these groups pose significant problems for crops by causing diseases and being pests. In this role, these organisms decrease crop productivity. Organisms that are beneficial to plants occur in these groups as well.

The kingdom Plantae consists of two major groups—**bryophytes** *(non-vascular plants)* and **trachaeophytes** *(vascular plants). Non-vascular plants are also called lower*

Table 1 Examples of Scientific Classification of Plants

Plantae	**Kingdom**	Plantae
Magnoliophyta	**Division**	Magnoliophyta
Liliopsida	**Class**	Magnoliopsida
Cyperales	**Order**	Rosales
Poaceae	**Family**	Fabaceae
Zea	**Genus**	*Glycine*
mays	**Species**	*max*
"PJ457"	**Cultivar**	"Kent"

Table 2 The Five Kingdoms of Organisms as Described by Whitaker

1. **Monera** (have prokaryotic cells)
    Bacteria
2. **Protoctista** (have eukaryotic cells)
    Algae
    Slime molds
    Flagellate fungi
    Protozoa
    Sponges
3. **Fungi** (absorb food in solution)
    True fungi
4. **Plantae** (produce own food by the process of photosynthesis)
    Bryophytes
    Vascular plants
5. **Animalia** (ingest their food)
    Multicellular animals

Divisions in the Kingdom Plantae

	Division	*Common Name*
Bryophytes	Hepaticophyta	Liverworts
(non-vascular;	Anthocerotophyta	Hornworts
no seed)	Bryophyta	Mosses
Vascular plants	Trachaeophyta	
(a) Seedless	Psilotophyta	Whisk ferns
(spore-bearing)	Lycophyta	Club mosses
	Sphenophyta	Horsetails
	Pterophyta	Ferns
(b) Seeded	Pinophyta	Gymnosperms
(cone-bearing		(non-flowering)
naked seed)	Subdivision: Cycadicae	Cycads
	Subdivision: Pinicae	
	Class: Ginkgoatae	*Ginko*
	Class: Pinatae	Conifers
	Subdivision: Gneticae	*Gnetum*
(c) Seeded	**Magnoliophyta**	**Angiosperms (flowering)**
(seeds borne	Class: Liliopsida	Monocots
in fruits)	Class: Magnoliopsida	Dicots

plants. Similarly, vascular plants are also called *higher plants* and may bear seeds or be seedless. They are large-bodied and comprise three major vegetative organs—stem, leaf, and root. Higher plants have *conducting tissues* (or *vascular tissue*). More than 80% of all species in the plant kingdom are flowering plants. There is enormous variation in plants. Some are naturally occurring and maintained and are called *botanical varieties,* while others are human-made (created through plant breeding) and are called *cultivars,* a contraction of two terms—*culti*vated *var*iety. This term is often used synonymously with *variety.*

2.1 FLOWERING PLANTS BELONG TO THE DIVISION MAGNOLIOPHYTA

Division Magnoliophyta consists of plants that bear true seeds that are contained in fruits. This is the most important division in terms of crop production, because practically all the economically important plants used for food, feed, and fiber belong to this group. The division is further separated into two classes: Liliopsida (have one cotyledon—monocot) and Magnoliopsida (have two cotyledons—dicot). A common classification of crop plants is on the basis of the number of cotyledons (i.e., either monocots or dicots). The distinguishing external and internal features of these two groups of subclasses of plants are described later in this chapter. Selected field crop families in the division Magnoliophyta are presented in Table 3.

Table 3 Selected Field Crop Families in the Division Magnoliophyta (Flowering Plants)

Monocots

Poaceae (Gramineae) *(grass family)*
In terms of numbers, the grass family is the largest of flowering plants. It is also the most widely distributed.
Examples of species: wheat, barley, oats, rice, corn, fescues, bluegrass

Aracaceae *(palm family)*
The palm family is tropical and subtropical in adaptation.
Examples of species: oil palm *(Elaeis guineensis),* coconut palm *(Cocos nucifera)*

Amaryllidaceae *(amaryllis family)*
Plants with tunicate bulbs characterize this family.
Examples of species: onion, garlic, chives

Dicots

Brassicaceae (Cruciferae) *(mustard family)*
The mustard family is noted for its pungent herbs.
Examples of species: cabbage, radish, cauliflower, turnip, broccoli

Fabaceae (Leguminosae) *(legume family)*
The legume family is characterized by flowers that may be regular or irregular.
The species in this family are an important source of protein for humans and livestock.
Examples of species: dry bean, mung bean, cowpea, pea, peanut, soybean, clover

Solanaceae *(nightshade family)*
This family is noted for the poisonous alkaloids many of them produce (e.g., belladonna, nicotine, atropine, solanine).
Examples of species: tobacco, potato, tomato, pepper, eggplant

Euphobiaceae *(spurge family)*
Members of the spurge family produce milky latex and include a number of poisonous species.
Examples of species: cassava *(Manihot esculenta),* castor bean

Asteraceae (Compositae) *(sunflower family)*
The sunflower family has the second-largest number of flowering plant species.
Example of species: sunflower, lettuce

Apiaceae (Umberliferae) *(carrot family)*
Plants in this family usually produce flowers that are arranged in umbels.
Examples of species: carrot, parsley, celery

Cucurbitaceae *(pumpkin family)*
The pumpkin or gourd family is characterized by prostrate or climbing herbaceous vines with tendrils and large, fleshy fruits containing numerous seeds.
Examples of species: pumpkin, melon, watermelon, cucumber

2.2 CLASSIFYING AND NAMING PLANTS IS A SCIENCE GOVERNED BY INTERNATIONAL RULES

Who decides what name to give a particular plant so it is universally recognizable? The science of plant taxonomy is coordinated by the *International Board of Plant Nomenclature,* which makes the rules. The Latin or Greek language is used in naming plants. Sometimes, the names given reflect specific plant attributes or use of the plant. For example, some specific epithets indicate color, such as, *alba* (white), *variegata* (variegated), *rubrum* (red), and *aureum* (golden); others are *vulgaris* (common), *esculentus* (edible), *sativus* (cultivated), *tuberosum* (tuber bearing), and *officinalis* (medicinal). The ending of a name is often characteristic of the taxon. Class names often end in *opsida* (e.g., Magnoliopsida), orders in *ales* (e.g., Rosales), and families in *aceae* (e.g., Rosaceae). Certain specific ways of writing the binomial name are strictly adhered to in scientific communication. These rules are as follows:

1. It must be underlined or written in italics (because the words are non-English).
2. The genus name must start with an uppercase letter, and the species name (specific epithet) always starts with a lowercase letter. The term *species* is both singular and plural and may be shortened to sp. or spp.
3. Frequently, the scientist who first named the plant adds his or her initial to the binary name. The letter *L* indicates that Linnaeus first named the plant. If revised later, the person responsible is identified after the *L,* for example, *Glycine max* L. Merr (for Merrill).
4. The generic name may be abbreviated and can also stand alone. However, the specific epithet cannot stand alone. Valid examples are *Zea mays,* and *Zea, Z. mays,* but not *mays.*
5. The cultivar or variety name may be included in the binomial name—for example, *Lycopersicon esculentum* Mill cv. "Big Red," or L. *esculentum* "Big Red." The cultivar name (cv), however, is not written in italics.

2.3 OPERATIONAL CLASSIFICATION SYSTEMS

What if one does not have an interest or a need to communicate in scientific terms, using names that are often difficult to pronounce, let alone memorize? Crop plants may be classified for specific purposes—for example, according to seasonal growth, kinds of stem, growth form, and economic part or agronomic use.

Seasonal Growth Cycle

Annual plant. A plant that completes its lifecycle in one growing season.

Biennial plant. A plant that completes its lifecycle in two growing seasons.

Perennial plant. A plant that grows year after year without replanting and usually produces seed each year.

Plants may be classified according to the duration of their lifecycle (i.e., from seed, to seedling, to flowering, to fruiting, to death, and back to seed). On this basis, crop plants may be classified as **annual**, **biennial**, **perennial**, or **monocarp** (Figure 2).

Annual   Annual plants (annuals) complete their lifecycle in one growing season. Examples of such plants include corn, wheat, and sorghum. Annuals may be further categorized into *winter annuals* or *summer annuals.* Winter annuals (e.g., wheat) utilize parts of two seasons. They are planted in fall and undergo a critical physiological inductive change called *vernalization* that is required for flowering and fruiting in spring. In cultivation, certain non-annuals (e.g., cotton) are produced as though they were annuals.

Biennial   A biennial is an herb that completes its lifecycle in two growing seasons. In the first season, it produces only basal leaves; then it grows a stem, produces

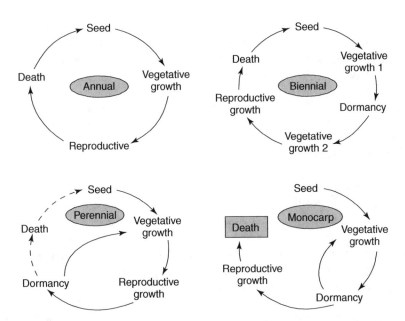

FIGURE 2 Classification of flowering plants according to the duration of their growth cycle from seed to seed. Variations occur within each category, even for the same species, due in part to the activities of plant breeders.

flowers and fruits, and dies in the second season. The plant usually requires a special environmental condition or treatment, such as exposure to a cold temperature (vernalization), to be induced to enter the reproductive phase. Examples are sugar beet and onion. Even though annuals and biennials rarely become woody in temperate regions, these plants may sometimes produce secondary growth in their stems and roots.

Perennial Perennials may be herbaceous or woody. They persist all year round through the adverse weather of the non-growing seasons (winter, drought) and then flower and fruit after a variable number of years of vegetative growth beyond the second year. Herbaceous perennials survive the unfavorable season as dormant underground structures (e.g., roots, rhizomes, bulbs, and tubers) that are modified primary vegetative parts of the plant. Examples of herbaceous perennials are grasses with rhizomes (e.g., indiangrass) or stolons (e.g., buffalograss).

Woody perennials may be vines (e.g., grape), shrubs, or trees. These plants do not die back in adverse seasons but usually suspend active growth. Although some perennials may flower in the first year of planting, woody perennials flower only when they become adult plants. Woody perennials may be categorized into two types:

1. *Evergreen.* These are perennials that have green leaves all year round. Some leaves may be lost, but not all at one time. Examples are citrus and pines.
2. *Deciduous.* These plants shed their leaves during one of the seasons of the year (dry, cold). New leaves are developed from dormant buds upon the return of favorable growing conditions. Examples are oak and elm. Intermediate conditions occur in these groups of plants, whereby only partial loss of leaves occurs (*semideciduous*).

Monocarp Monocarps are characterized by repeated, long vegetative cycles that may go on for many years without entering the reproductive phase. Once flowering occurs, the plant dies. Common examples are bromeliads. The top part dies, so that new plants arise from the root system of the old plant.

Stem Type

There are three general classes of plants based on stem type. However, intermediates do occur between these classes.

Herbs These are plants with soft, non-woody stems. They have primary vegetative parts and are not perennials. Examples are corn, many potted plants, many annual bedding plants, and many vegetables.

Shrubs A shrub has no main trunk. It is woody and has secondary tissues. Branches arise from the ground level on shrubs. Shrubs are perennials and are usually smaller than trees. Examples are dogwood, kalmia, and azalea.

Trees Trees are large plants that are characterized by one main trunk. They branch on the upper part of the plant, are woody, and have secondary tissues. Examples are pine and orange.

Common Stem Growth Form

Certain plants can stand upright without artificial support; others cannot. Based on this characteristic, plants may be classified into groups. The common groups are as follows:

1. *Erect.* Erect plants can stand upright without physical support, growing at about a 90-degree angle to the ground. This feature is needed for mechanization of certain crops. Plant breeders develop erect (bush) forms of non-erect (pole) cultivars for this purpose. There are both pole and bush cultivars of crops such as bean (*Phaseolus vulgaris* L.) in cultivation.
2. *Decumbent.* Plants with decumbent stem growth form, such as peanuts (*Arachis hypogea),* are extremely inclined with raised tips.
3. *Creeping (repent).* Plants in this category, such as strawberry (*Fragaria* spp. white clover (*Trifolium repens)),* have stems that grow horizontally on the ground.
4. *Climbing.* Climbers are plants with modified vegetative parts (stems or leaves) that enable them to wrap around a nearby physical support, so they do not have to creep on the ground. An example is yam (*Dioscorea* spp.). Climbers are vines that, without additional support, will creep on the ground. There are three general modes of climbing. Twiners are climbing plants that simply wrap their stringy stems around their support, as occurs in sweet potato. Another group of climbers develops cylindrical structures, called tendrils, that are used to coil around the support on physical contact (e.g., garden pea). The third mode of climbing is by adventitious roots formed on aerial parts of the plant (e.g., English ivy).
5. *Despitose (bunch or tufted).* Grass species, such as buffalograss, have a creeping form, whereas others, such as tall fescue, have a bunch form and hence do not spread by horizontal growing stems.

Agronomic Use

Crop plants may be classified according to agronomic use. Examples are as follows:

1. *Cereals.* These are grasses such as wheat, barley, and oats that are grown for their edible seed.
2. *Pulses (grain legumes).* These are legumes grown for their edible seed. (e.g., peas, beans).
3. *Grains.* Crop plants grown for their edible dry seed or caryopsis (e.g., corn, soybean, cereals).
4. *Small grains.* Grain crops with small seed (e.g., wheat, oats, barley).
5. *Forage.* Plants grown for their vegetable matter that is harvested and used fresh or preserved as animal feed (e.g., alfalfa, red clover).
6. *Roots.* Crops grown for their edible (swollen) roots (e.g., sweet potato, cassava).
7. *Tubers.* Crops grown for their edible modified (swollen) stem (e.g., Irish potato, yam).
8. *Oil crops.* Plant grown for their oil content (e.g., soybean, peanut, sunflower).
9. *Fiber crops.* Crop plant grown for use in fiber production (e.g., jute, flax, cotton).
10. *Sugar crops.* Crops grown for use in making sugar (e.g., sugar cane, sugar beet).
11. *Green manure crops.* Crop plants grown and plowed under the soil while still young and green, for the purpose of improving soil fertility (e.g., many leguminous species).
12. *Cover crops.* Crops grown between regular cropping cycles, for the purpose of protecting the soil from erosion and other adverse weather factors (e.g., many annuals).
13. *Hay.* Grasses or legume plants that are grown, harvested, and cured for feeding animals (e.g., alfalfa, buffalograss).
14. *Silage crops.* Crops preserved in succulent condition by the process of fermentation.
15. *Green chop (soilage crop).* Forage that is harvested daily and brought fresh to livestock.
16. *Drug crops.* Crops grown for their medicinal value.
17. *Trap crops.* Crops planted to protect the main cash crop from a pest.
18. *Companion crops.* Crops along with another crops for mutually beneficial impact, and harvested separately.
19. *Rubber crops.* Crops grown for their latex.

3: VISUAL IDENTIFICATION OF PLANTS REQUIRES FAMILIARITY WITH PLANT MORPHOLOGY

Student agronomy clubs may participate in crop judging contests. To be successful, participants need to study morphological attributes that distinguish among plant species. Crop inspectors and crop extension agents also need to be able to identify plant species. Certain morphological features of plant parts, such as the leaf, flower, and stem, may be used to identify crop plants. The descriptive features are categorized into those for dicots and those for monocots. One of the most visible distinguishing features of these two subclasses of flowering plants is the leaf.

The leaf is the primary photosynthetic organ of plants. A typical leaf has three components: thickened *leaf base (pulvinus),* a slender *petiole* (or *leaf stalk*), and a flat *lamina*

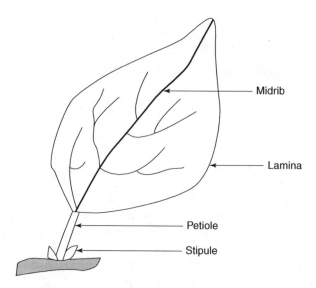

FIGURE 3 A simple leaf. The prominent part of the leaf is the lamina. It varies in size, shape, thickness, and other characteristics among species. Some leaves may not have a petiole and are attached directly to the branch.

(or *leaf blade*) (Figure 3). A leaf is sessile if it lacks a petiole. The leaf blade consists of veins, the middle one, or midrib, normally being larger than the rest. The pattern of veins *(venation)* in dicots is branched and rebranched to form a weblike or netted venation (called *reticulate venation*). Monocot leaves normally have *parallel venation,* in which the veins are not webbed but run parallel to the dominant midrib. In dicots, a pair of scale-like structures called *stipules* occurs at the leafbase. Further, an axillary bud occurs in the leaf axil. Monocots are generally called *narrow leaf* plants because of the lamina shape, while dicots are generally called *broadleaf* plants for a similar reason.

3.1   IDENTIFYING BROADLEAF (FOLIAGE) PLANTS

Broadleaf plants may be described by foliage leaf form, shape, margin, arrangement, attachment, tip, and base.

1. *Leaf form.* The *form* of the leaf refers to the shape of a single lamina. Leaf forms range from needle shape to circular (Figure 4).
2. *Leaf shape.* Leaf *shape* refers to the complexity of the leaf. The leaf may have an undivided lamina and is said to be a *simple leaf.* On the other hand, the leaf blade may be divided into several smaller leaflets arranged on either side of the midrib, or *rachis,* or secondary veins *(rachilla).* Such a leaf is described as a *compound leaf.* There are several arrangements of leaflets on a compound leaf (Figure 5). There are two basic types of compound leaves: *palmate* or *digitate* (leaflets arising from one point on the tip of the petiole) and *pinnate* (leaflets arranged like a feather). Second-degree pinnate arrangement is called *bipinnate,* while third-degree pinnate is called *tripinnate.*
3. *Leaf margin.* Lamina margin types range from *unindented* and smooth to *toothed* (slight indentation) to *lobed* (deeply incised) (Figure 6). Intermediate margin types occur.

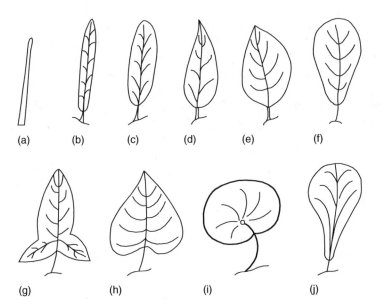

FIGURE 4 Selected leaf forms. The shape of the lamina varies from narrow and needlelike to round: (a) filiform, (b) linear, (c) oblong, (d) lanceolate, (e) ovate, (f) abovate (g) sagittate, (h) cordate, (i) peltate (j) spatulate.

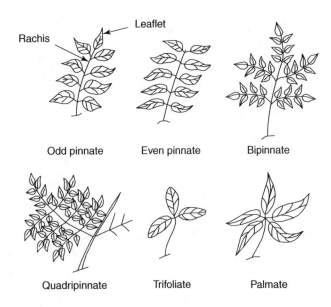

FIGURE 5 Compound leaf shapes. Instead of one solid lamina, some leaves consist of several to many small leaflets. Variation in the palmate and other shapes occur.

4. *Leaf arrangement.* Leaf arrangement may be one of three basic types: *alternate, opposite,* or *whorl* (Figure 7).
5. *Leaf attachment.* Bud leaves attach to stems several ways. It may be petioled or sessile (i.e., with or without petiole). The leaf may also clasp round the stem (Figure 8).
6. *Tips and bases.* Plant leaves differ in the leaf tip and base shape (Figure 9).

FIGURE 6 Variation in leaf margins. The leaf margin may be intact and smooth or be rough and incised to varying extents.

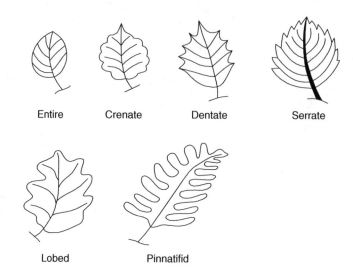

Entire   Crenate   Dentate   Serrate

Lobed   Pinnatifid

FIGURE 7 Common types of leaf arrangement.

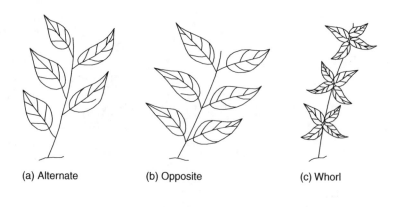

(a) Alternate   (b) Opposite   (c) Whorl

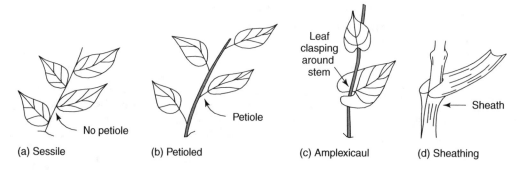

(a) Sessile   (b) Petioled   (c) Amplexicaul   (d) Sheathing

FIGURE 8 Common types of leaf attachment.

3.2 IDENTIFYING GRASS PLANTS

Just like broadleaf plants, grasses are identified on the basis of the characteristics of plant parts.

Leaf

Grass leaves have one basic form—linear. However, they differ in other features, including venation, blade (or lamina), sheath, collar, ligule, and auricles (Figure 10).

1. *Venation.* This is the arrangement of the young leaf in the bud shoot. The leaf may be folded (e.g., Kentucky bluegrass) or rolled (e.g., tall fescue).
2. *Blade (or lamina).* This is the often broad and expanded main body of the leaf. This is the primary site of *photosynthesis,* the process by which plants manufacture food.

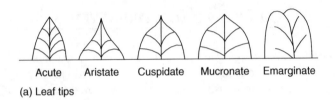

Acute   Aristate   Cuspidate   Mucronate   Emarginate

(a) Leaf tips

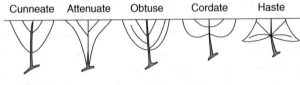

Cunneate   Attenuate   Obtuse   Cordate   Haste

(b) Leaf bases

FIGURE 9 Selected common leaf tips and bases.

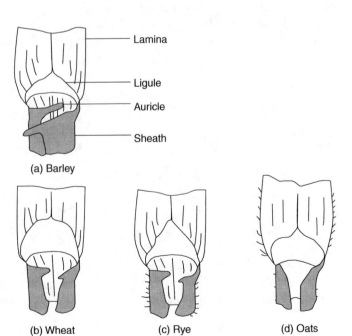

(a) Barley

(b) Wheat   (c) Rye   (d) Oats

FIGURE 10 Grasses have certain unique features at the junction between the lamina and the stem: sheath, collar, and ligule. The sheaths in these small grains are split. The sheaths of rye and oats and the leaf margins of oats have pubescence. They may overlap or be closed in other species. The ligules vary in shape and size. Wheat has a large and rounded ligule. The auricles in barley are long and clasping, while rye has very short auricles. Oats have no auricles.

3. *Sheath.* The lower portion of the grass blade that usually encloses the stem is called the *sheath.* Grass blades attach to the stem by a sheathing. The sheath may be split and just touching, split and overlapping, or closed and entirely fused.
4. *Collar.* The leaf blade and sheath join in a region called the *collar.* The collar may be narrow or broad. It may also be divided into two sections by the midvein.
5. *Ligule.* This is a translucent membrane or a ring of hairs that occurs at the leaf junction on the inside of the leaf blade and the sheath. The ligule may be membranous or ciliate (hairy).
6. *Auricles. Auricles* are clawlike appendages that project from either side of the collar to the inside of the leaf blade and extend partially around the stem in a clasping fashion.

4: FLOWERS ARE VERY RELIABLE MEANS
OF PLANT IDENTIFICATION

Flowers are very stable plant organs under varying environmental conditions. They are thus very important in taxonomic studies. Flowers may occur individually *(solitary)* and are called *simple flowers.* They may also occur in groups and are then called *inflorescence.*

4.1 SIMPLE FLOWER

Gynoecium. The female part of a flower or pistil formed by one or more carpels and composed of the stigma, style, and ovary.

Androecium. The male part of a flower composed of the anther and filament.

The typical simple flower has four main parts: a *petal* (the showy and colorful part), *sepal* (the protective cover for the flower in bud stage), *pistil* (the female reproductive organ), and *stamen* (the male reproductive organ) (Figure 11). A pistil consists of a basal *ovary* (the part that usually forms the fruit), a median *style* (passage connecting the ovary to the stigma), and the terminal *stigma* (the pollen receptive area). The ovule-bearing unit that is part of the pistil is called the *carpel.* Some flowers have more than one carpel. The carpels together form the **gynoecium.** The ovules of the carpels develop into seed. The petals collectively form the *corolla,* while the collectivity of sepals is called the *calyx.* The stamens consist of a stalk, or *filament,* and pollen-bearing structure called *anther.* The anther consists of pollen sacs. The stamens together form the **androecium.**

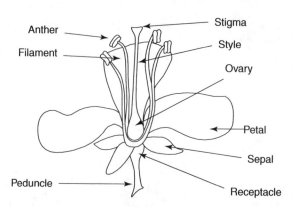

FIGURE 11 Parts of a typical flower. A complete flower has four parts: sepal, petal, stamen, and pistil.

A flower that has the full complement of appendages (sepals, petals, stamens, carpels) is said to be complete. A flower in which one or more of these appendages are missing is called an incomplete flower. Similarly, a flower in which both the stamen and carpels are present is called a perfect flower, whereas a flower in which either the stamens or the carpels are missing is called an imperfect flower.

4.2 INFLORESCENCE

There are two groups of inflorescence: *indeterminate* and *determinate.* In indeterminate inflorescence, the apical bud continues to grow for an indefinite period. The different types of indeterminate inflorescence are *raceme* (elongated axis with pedicelled flowers), *spike* (like a raceme but with sessile flowers), *corymb* (pedicels gradate in length), and *panicle* (a compound inflorescence consisting of clusters of other inflorescence types) (Figure 12). In determinate inflorescence, the terminal bud becomes a flower. This type of inflorescence is called a *cyme.* There are different types of cymes. A third group of inflorescence produces a flat-top but without a definite central axis. The types in this group are *umbel* and *head.* The flowers in a head are sessile.

4.3 A TYPICAL LEGUME FLOWER

Certain flowers have unique characteristics that readily and exclusively identify the particular family of plants. The subfamily of the legume family, Papillionoideae, is the most important of legume subfamilies in terms of agronomic importance. Examples of papillionacious crops are peanut, soybean, and dry bean. Members of this subfamily are capable of nodulation. Also, they are characterized by flowers that have a five-petal corolla—a standard, two wings, and one keel petal (Figure 13). The flower has five petals: one standard, two wing, and two fused together to form a *keel.* The female structure has one carpel that may contain many ovules. The mature fruit of members of the family Fabaceae is called a legume (has one carpel and splits on both sides).

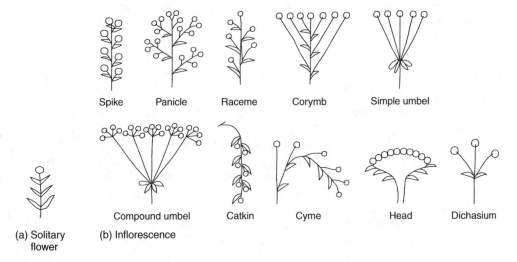

Spike   Panicle   Raceme   Corymb   Simple umbel

Compound umbel   Catkin   Cyme   Head   Dichasium

(a) Solitary flower   (b) Inflorescence

FIGURE 12 Types of inflorescence. A simple flower is also solitary, occurring alone on a pedicel. An inflorescence consists of numerous florets arranged in a variety of ways. There are three basic types of inflorescence: head, spike, and umbel.

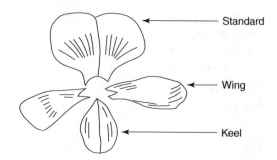

FIGURE 13 The petals of a papillionacious legume flower are unique, having a standard, two wings, and one folded keel petal.

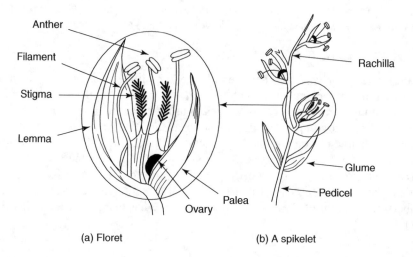

(a) Floret

(b) A spikelet

FIGURE 14 The grass family has three basic kinds of inflorescence: panicle, raceme, and spike. The flower consists of subunits called spikelets that bear florets.

4.4 TYPICAL GRASS FLOWER

The grass family (Poaceae) is characterized by a flower with a spike inflorescence (Figure 14). The basic unit of a grass inflorescence is a spikelet, which is comprised of flowers (florets) that are surrounded by sterile bracts. The grass floret consists of a *lemma* and *palea* (both structures are equivalent to petals) that enclose the reproductive parts of the plant. The glumes constitute the sepals. Grass flowers are *incomplete*. In plants such as corn, the sexes are located on different parts of the plant. Thus, flowers of corn are *imperfect*. Corn is also called a **monoecious plant** (both types of flowers occur on the same plant but at different locations). A **dioecious plant** has imperfect flowers but the sexes occur on separate plants.

4.5 TYPICAL COMPOSITE FLOWER

The sunflower plant (family Asteraceae) has two kinds of florets that are arranged on a receptacle (Figure 15).

Monoecious plant. A plant with separate male and female flowers on the same plant.

Dioecious plant. Plant species in which individual plants may have either staminate (male) or pistillate (female) flowers, but not both.

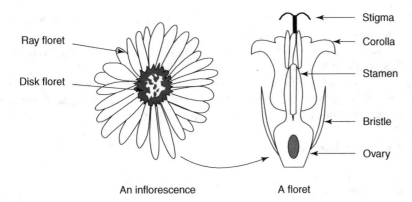

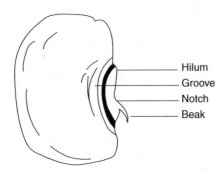

FIGURE 15 The inflorescence of the family Asteraceae (sunflower family) is a head with numerous florets.

FIGURE 16 Features of a dicot seed. The hilum may have distinct color in a ring form, as occurs in black eye pea. A notch is an indentation in the region of the hilum. The beak is a pointed structure protruding from the notch, while a groove is a troughlike depression near the hilum.

5: SEED IDENTIFICATION

Dicot seed and monocot seed have certain fundamental differences.

5.1 *LEGUME SEED*

Legume seed can be identified on the basis of morphology by the **testa** (seed coat) color, texture, shape, and size:

Testa. The seed coat formed from the integument(s) of the ovule.

1. *Color.* This characteristic is reliable in fresh seed. As seed ages, its color deteriorates.
2. *Texture. Seed texture* refers to the seed coat appearance. It may be smooth, rough, dull, or shiny.
3. *Shape.* This is the most stable and reliable identification characteristic. It is defined by three elements (Figure 16):
    a. *Notch.* An indentation in the region of the *hilum* (a scar representing the point of attachment of the seed to the ovary wall). It may be shallow or deep.

b. *Beak.* This feature occurs in the notch of the hilum as a pointed protrusion. It may also occur on the surface.

c. *Groove.* The groove is a troughlike indentation that leads away from the hilum down the side of the seed.

4. *Size.* Size is highly influenced by the environment. Seeds shrivel under adverse weather. Seed size is determined by weight (e.g., 100 seed weight, or the number of seeds per gram), rather than by visual examination.

5.2   GRASS GRAIN

Caryopsis. A small, one-seeded, dry fruit with a thin pericarp surrounding and adhering to the seed occuring in grasses (commonly called grain or kernel)

The fruit of grass species is called the *grain.* Even though the term *seed* is used on occasion (e.g., seed corn), it is an imprecise reference. Grass grain (kernel or **caryopsis**) is identified on the basis of color, endosperm (food storage tissue of grain) type, shape, and size.

1. *Color.* The color of the grain is found in the pericarp (outer covering), aleurone layer (protein-rich area at the outer edge of the endosperm), and the endosperm. For example, the corn may have red or colorless pericarp, blue or colorless aleurone layer, while the endosperm may be yellow or white.

2. *Type of endosperm.* The endosperm characteristics differ in chemistry and physical structure (Figure 17). In corn, the endosperm may be described as sugary, starchy, or flinty. In wheat, the endosperm may be of soft or hard starch (vitreous or glassy).

3. *Texture.* The kernel may be dull, shiny, or glossy in texture.

4. *Shape.* In rice, for example, classification for the market is also based on shape and length of grain. There are slender, long, medium, and short grain rice types. The kernel may be pointed at both ends, as in barley, while that is not the case in wheat.

5. *Brush.* Tiny bristles or brush may cap one end of the kernel. Barley has no brush, but wheat does. However, the Durum wheat has no brush.

5.3   FORAGE GRASS GRAIN

Identification of forage grass grain is based on the characteristics of the spikelet (e.g., glumes, lemma, and palea). The lemma varies in size, shape, texture, color, nerves (or veins), and other factors. These structures are usually attached to the grain.

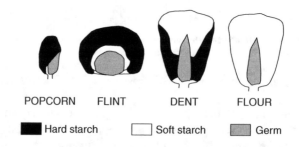

FIGURE 17 Types of endosperm in corn. Popcorn has very little soft starch, while flint corn is mostly hard starch. On the other hand, dent corn is about 50% soft starch, while flour corn is all soft starch. (Source: USDA)

6: PLANT INTERNAL STRUCTURE

6.1 FUNDAMENTAL UNIT OF ORGANIZATION

The **cell** is the fundamental unit of organization of organisms (Figure 18). Some organisms consist entirely of one cell *(unicellular)*. Other organisms consist of many cells working together *(multicellular)*. In crop production, the producer cultivates multicellular organisms only, even though unicellular ones (e.g., bacteria) are of importance to production. Except bacterial cells, which lack compartmentalization into organelles with specific functions (called *prokaryotes*), all other cells consist of a membrane-bound nucleus and other membrane-enclosed organelles. These organisms are called *eukaryotes*. Animal and plant cells differ in significant ways (Table 4).

Cell. The basic structure and physiological unit of plants and animals.

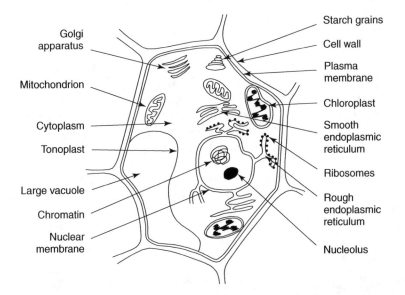

FIGURE 18 The parts of a plant cell.

Table 4   A Comparison of Animal and Plant Cells

Cell Part	Animal Cell	Plant Cell
Cell wall	−	+
Plasma membrane	+	+
Nucleus	+	+
Peroxisome	+	+
Mitochondrion	+	+
Chloroplast	−	−
Central vacuole	−	−
Ribosomes	+	+
Golgi apparatus	+	+
Cytoskeleton	+	+
Rough endoplasmic reticulum	+	+
Lysosome	+	Not in most
Centriole	+	Not in most
Flagellum	+	Not in most

Cell Structure

The eukaryotic cell consists of many organelles and structures with distinct as well as interrelated functions.

Cell Wall   How is the plant cell wall different from the animal cell wall? The outer membrane of the cell is called the *plasma membrane* (or *plasmalemma*). In plants, an additional structure called the *cell wall* forms around the plasma membrane. The cell wall consists of cellulose, hemicellulose, protein, and other pectic substances. Cellulose, the most abundant of the cell wall constituents, is not digestible by animals. As the cell matures and ages, the cell wall becomes rigid and inelastic through the process of *lignification,* or lignin deposition. All cells have a standard, or *primary, cell wall.* In addition, certain cells develop another wall *(secondary cell wall)* inside the primary one that consists of cellulose and lignin. Adjacent cells are held together by a pectin-rich material called the *middle lamella.* This layer breaks down during fruit rot to release the characteristic slimy fluid.

Nucleus   The *nucleus* is a densely staining body that is usually spheroidal and is the primary location of hereditary material, deoxyribose nucleic acid (DNA). It is composed of DNA, ribose nucleic acid (RNA), protein, and water. The DNA occurs in structures called *chromosomes.* Each species has a specific number of chromosomes per cell (Table 5). The number of chromosomes in the sex cell (gametic cell—e.g., pollen grain) is half (haploid, *n* number) that of the somatic or body cell (diploid, *2n* number).

Vacuoles   Vacuoles are cavities in the cell that contain a liquid called vacuolar sap, or *cell sap.* They also store water-soluble pigments called *anthocyanins* that are responsible for the red and blue colors of many flowers and fruits and the fall colors of some leaves. Vacuoles also absorb water to create a turgor pressure that is neces-

Table 5   Number of Chromosomes per Cell Possessed by a Variety of Plant Species

Species	Scientific Name	Chromosome Number (n)
Broad bean	*Vicia faba*	6
Potato	*Solanum tuberosum*	24
Corn	*Zea mays*	10
Bean	*Phaseolus vulgaris*	11
Cucumber	*Cucumis sativus*	7
Sorghum	*Sorghum bicolor*	10
Sugarcane	*Saccharum officinarum*	40
Wheat	*Triticum aestivum*	7
Oat	*Avena sativa*	7
Field pea	*Pisum arvense*	7
Flax	*Linum usitatissimum*	15
Sweet potato	*Ipomea batatas*	15
Peanut	*Arachis hypogeae*	10
Cotton	*Gossypium hirsitum*	26
Sugar beet	*Beta vulgaris*	9
Sunflower	*Helianthus annus*	17

sary for physical support in plants. The turgor pressure of guard cells controls the opening and closing of stomata (pores in the epidermis of leaves).

Plastids Do genes occur exclusively in the nucleus? *Plastids* are protein-containing structures capable of synthesizing some of their own protein (they are semiautonomous). The genes they contain are, however, not subject to Mendelian laws of inheritance. Plastids are dynamic and occur in different forms. One form that contains **chlorophyll**, the green pigment of green leaves, is called a *chloroplast*. Chloroplasts are sites of photosynthesis. Chloroplasts occur only in plants and are involved in the variegation of leaves (the development of patchy white or purple coloration found in green leaves). Some plastids are colorless and are called *leucoplasts;* others are called *chromoplasts* and produce numerous pigments found in fruits and flowers. Pigments of bright yellow, orange, or red are called *carotenoids.* The various forms of plastids are interconvertible. As such, when plants are grown in darkness, chloroplasts change to another form of cells called *etioplasts,* cells that cause spindly growth (etiolation). The abnormality is corrected upon exposure to normal light.

Chlorophyll. A complex organic molecule in plants that traps light energy for conversion into chemical energy through photosynthesis.

Mitochondria **Mitochondria** are double-membraned structures that are sites of the energy-production processes of the cell, called respiration. The food synthesized by photosynthesis is converted into chemical energy by respiration. Like chloroplasts, mitochondria have their own DNA, and hence they are semiautonomous.

Mitochondria. Organelles found in the cytoplasm of eukaryotic cells that is associated with cellular respiration.

Other Organelles The cell contains other **organelles** with distinct functions. The *ribosomes* are tiny structures consisting of RNA and protein and are the sites of protein synthesis. They occur on the *endoplasmic reticulum* (a network of sacs and tubes). The *Golgi apparatus* consists of flattened sacs that have secretory functions. There are also substances in the cell called *ergastic substances* that are metabolites (e.g., tannins and resins), some of which are toxic (phytotoxins) to animals and insect pests and thus protect plants from herbivores and insect attack.

Organelle. A membrane-bound region in the cell with specialized function.

7: PLANT CELLS AGGREGATE TO FORM DIFFERENT TYPES OF TISSUES

Aggregates of cells produce a **tissue**. There are two types of tissue—*simple tissue* (consisting of one cell type) and *complex tissue* (consisting of a mixture of cell types). There are three basic types of simple tissue—*parenchyma, collenchyma,* and *sclerenchyma.* They differ in their cell wall characteristics.

Tissue. A group of cells of similar structure that performs a special function.

7.1 SIMPLE TISSUE

Parenchyma

Parenchyma cells have a thin cell wall. The tissue they form is called parenchyma tissue. It is found in actively growing parts of the plant called meristems. These cells are undifferentiated (they do not have any particular assigned functions). The fleshy and succulent parts of fruits and other swollen underground structures (e.g., tubers and roots) are comprised of large amounts of this simple tissue. Some parenchyma cells have secretory roles, while others (e.g., chlorenchyma) have synthetic roles in photosynthesis.

Collenchyma

The primary cell wall of collenchyma cells is thicker than those of parenchyma cells. Collenchymatous tissue occurs in plant parts such as the leaf, where it has a mechanical role in the plant support system by strengthening the parts. It is found in the petiole, leaf margins, and veins of leaves. This mechanical role is confined to regions of the plant where active growth occurs. Fruit rinds that are soft and edible contain collenchyma tissue.

Sclerenchyma

This type of cell has the thickest cell wall of the three primary cells. This is caused by the presence of both primary and secondary cell walls. Sclerenchymatous tissue has primarily a strengthening or mechanical role in the plant. It is elastic and resilient and occurs in places where movement is needed—for example, in the leaf petiole. Structurally, there are two basic sclerenchyma cell types—*short cells (sclereids)* and *long cells (fibers)*. Field crops that are grown for fiber, such as cotton, kenaf, and flax, have large amounts of this tissue.

7.2   COMPLEX TISSUE

Complex tissues are comprised of combinations of the three basic simple tissues. They are found in the epidermis, secretory structures, and conducting tissue of the plant.

Epidermis

Epidermis. The outer layer of cells on all parts of the primary body of the plant, except meristems.

The outermost layer of the plant is called the **epidermis**. By virtue of its location, this structure is involved in a variety of roles, including structural (protective), physiological, regulation of water and gaseous movement between the external and internal part of the plant, and anatomical variability. In some plants, an additional protective layer of polymerized fatty acids called *cutin* produces a waterproof layer called a *cuticle*. Pores called *stomata* occur in the epidermis for gaseous exchange. In some species, pubescence (hairlike structures) may occur on the epidermis. This plays a role in pest control by interfering with oviposition, or egg deposition.

Secretory Tissue

There are numerous locations on the plant where secondary tissues perform secretory functions (Table 6). Some of these tissues are on the surface of the plant, while others occur on the inside.

Conducting Tissue

Xylem. Specialized cells in plants that transport water and minerals from the soil through the plant and constitute the woody tissue of woody plants.

Phloem. Specialized cells in plants through which carbohydrates and other nutritive substances are translocated through the plant.

Vascular plants conduct inorganic materials up to the leaves and photosynthates down through a network of conducting tissues. The tissue for upward transportation of minerals and water is called **xylem**, and that for conducting assimilates is called the **phloem**.

Xylem constitutes the wood of woody plants and consists of two types of conducting cells—*tracheids* and *vessel elements*. Collectively, they are called *tracheary elements*. Water with nutrients moves up the xylem conducting tissue by water potential. The movement is caused by passive transport, since the xylem cells lack protoplasm and hence function essentially as dead cells. The two types of xylem cells have lateral perforations called *pits* that function in the cell-to-cell flow of fluids. The phloem conducting elements are called sieve elements. The sieve elements consist of two cell types—*sieve cells* (primarily parenchyma cells) and *sieve tube members*. Unlike xylem

Table 6 Secretory Tissues of Plants

Those Found Outside the Plant

Nectaries: Occur on various parts of the plant. In flowers, they are called floral nectaries and they secrete nectar that attracts insects for pollination.

Hydathodes: Secrete pure water. Droplets of water may form along leaf margins of certain plants due to secretory activities.

Salt glands: Found in plants that grow in desert or brackish areas

Osmophores: Secrete fragrance in flowers. Repulsive odor of aroids is attributed to the amines and ammonia secreted by osmophores.

Digestive glands: Found in insect-eating (insectivorous) plants (e.g., pitcher plant)

Adhesive cells: Secrete materials that aid attachment between host and parasite

Those Found Inside the Plant

Resin ducts: Found commonly in woody species. They secrete sticky resin.

Mucilage cells: Slimy secretions found at the growing tip of roots and believed to aid the passage of roots through the soil.

Oil chambers: Secrete aromatic oils

Gum ducts: Cell wall modification results in the production of gums in certain trees.

Laticifers: Latex-secreting glands

Myrosin cells: Secrete an enzyme called myrosinase, which when mixed with its substrate, thioglucosides, produces a toxic oil called isothiocyanate. This occurs when cells are ruptured by insects or animals during chewing.

cells, which are nonliving (lack protoplasm) and hence play a passive role in the movement of materials, phloem cells are living and thus are actively involved in movement of food. These two cells also have associated cells called *companion cells* in angiosperms (flowering plants) and *albuminous cells* in non-angiosperms. These cells aid in phloem loading of newly synthesized sugars into cells for transport to other parts of the plant. Phloem cells are not durable and must be replaced constantly.

Meristems

Do plants grow in the same fashion as animals? **Meristems** are areas of active growth in plants. The cells at these locations divide rapidly. They are also undifferentiated. When meristems occur at the tip (or apex) of the plant, they are called *apical meristems*. Those that occur at the leaf axil are called *axillary meristems*. Unlike animals, in which growth is a diffused process (i.e., growth occurs throughout the entire individual), plants have localized growth (growth is limited to specific areas—the meristems). Meristems occur in other parts of the plant (basal, lateral, intercalary). Localized growth permits juvenile and mature adult cells to coexist in a plant, provided favorable conditions exist. In some species, the plant can continue to grow indefinitely without any limit to final size, while certain organs and tissues are fully mature and functional. This is called an *indeterminate* growth pattern. In certain plant species, the apical meristem dies at some stage. Such plants are described as *determinate* in growth pattern. Even though it appears many plants have predictable sizes that are characteristic of the species, this feature is believed to be a largely environmental and statistical phenomenon. Under optimal and controlled conditions, many annual plants have been known to grow perennially. What are the advantages and disadvantages of determinacy and indeterminacy in crop production?

Meristem.
Undifferentiated tissue whose cells can divide and differentiate to form specialized tissues.

FIGURE 19 The shoot system of a dicot plant.

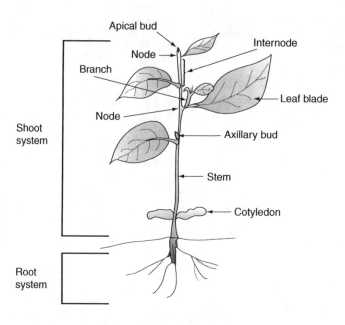

8: THE SHOOT SYSTEM

The shoot system comprises the part of the plant that grows above ground. Shoot growth occurs in two phases—*vegetative* and *reproductive.* When in the vegetative phase, the shoot comprises the stem or cylindrical axis, to which appendages or lateral organs are attached (Figure 19). These appendages are leaves and axillary or lateral buds or branches. When a plant enters the reproductive phase, additional appendages arise, depending on whether it is an angiosperm or a gymnosperm. These include cones, sporangia, flowers, and fruits. In terms of external morphology, the shoot has certain features. The leaves attach to the stem at jointlike regions called *nodes.* The space between nodes are *internodes.* A shoot has an apical meristem inside the tip of each terminal bud and axillary bud. This tissue is responsible for forming bud scales, leaves, and, in the reproductive phase, flowers or cone parts. The axillary (lateral) buds give rise to lateral branches of the shoot system. The number of leaves attached to each node determines the leaf arrangement of the shoot system. A single leaf attached to each node produces an *alternate* arrangement that usually forms a spiral pattern up the shoot. When two leaves occur at each node, directly across from each other, the arrangement produced is called *opposite,* while three or more leaves at each node produces a *whorled* arrangement. When a leaf drops off the plant, it leaves a *leaf scar.* In some cases (e.g., grasses), the leaf base is expanded into a *leaf sheath.*

9: THE LEAF

Leaf morphology used in plant identification was discussed earlier in this chapter. There are five types of leaves: *foliage leaves, budscales, floral bracts, sepals,* and *cotyledons.* Foliage leaves are the most prominent.

The epidermis on the upper side of the leaf is called the *adaxial side;* the opposite side, the lower side, is called the *abaxial side.* The distribution of stomata is not always equal on both sides. In most plants, very few stomata occur on the upper side. However, in wheat and onions, there are equal numbers of stomata on both sides of the leaf. Both sides of the leaf may be covered with *trichomes* (pubescence). In species such as hemp *(Cannabis),* the trichomes contain certain compounds (e.g., cannabinoid hydrocarbons in *Cannabis*).

Older leaves on trees eventually drop. Some leaves drop during certain seasons of the year (summer, fall). Leaf fall is called *abscission.* In crop production, some producers use artificial methods to induce premature leaf abscission (e.g., in cotton production) to facilitate crop harvesting and to obtain a high product quality. Leaf abscission occurs in a specialized region, called the *abscission zone,* where the petiole detaches from the node, leaving leaf scar.

9.1 FUNCTIONS

The functions of leaves include the following:

1. Food synthesis. Leaves manufacture food by the process of photosynthesis. Foliage leaves conduct this function. Are leaves the only plant organs capable of photosynthesis?
2. Protection. This role is performed by non-foliage leaves (bud scale, floral bracts, and sepals) through protection of vegetative and floral buds.
3. Storage. Cotyledons, or seed leaves, store food that is used by seeds during germination.

Can you name additional functions of leaves?

9.2 INTERNAL STRUCTURE

The internal structure of the leaf is shown in Figure 20. The parts and functions of leaf internal structure are summarized in Table 7.

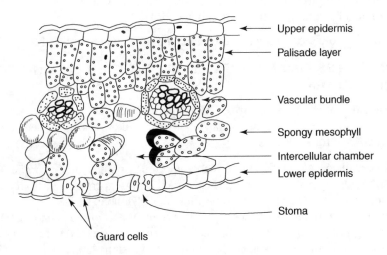

FIGURE 20   Internal structure of a dicot leaf.

Table 7	Internal Structure of the Leaf and Functions of Parts

Cuticle: A layer of waxlike material called cutin. It protects the leaf and prevents evaporative loss through the epidermis. It is water repellent.

Epidermis: A layer of cells that form the outer protective layer of the leaf. There is an upper epidermis and a lower epidermis.

Mesophyll: Layers of cells beneath the epidermis. Consists of two types of cells:

    Palisade parenchyma: Blocky or rectangular cells that are arranged on the shorter side against the epidermis. They contain chloroplast for photosynthesis.

    Spongy parenchyma: Consists of irregularly shaped cells that are loosely arranged, allowing large intercellular spaces to occur between them. They have chloroplasts. The spaces allow for gases to move through the leaf.

Vascular bundle: Comprised of the conducting tissues, xylem and phloem. Xylem tissue conducts water and minerals from the roots, while phloem conducts photosynthates and other materials from the leaf to other parts of the plant.

Bundle sheath: A ring of cells around the vascular bundles of leaves of certain species. May be involved in storage of photosynthates.

Stomata: Pores in the epidermal layer defined by two special cells called guard cells. The closing and opening of the guard cells regulate the rate of movement of carbon dioxide and water between the leaf and the atmosphere.

9.3 MODIFIED LEAVES: WHEN LEAVES DON'T LOOK LIKE LEAVES

Leaves may be modified to perform functions other than photosynthesis or to carry on photosynthesis under unusual environmental conditions. Some leaf modifications are as follows:

1. *Glands.* For secretion.
2. *Spines or thorns.* For protection against herbivores.
3. *Storage tissue.* For food storage, as in bulbs (e.g., onions).
4. *Thickened leaf surface.* To reduce moisture loss under xeric (dry) conditions.
5. *Thin cuticle and gas chamber.* For survival under submerged conditions.
6. *Tendrils.* Stringlike structures for additional support. The terminal leaflet of the trifoliate of pea may be modified into a tendril.

Can you think of other economically useful plant parts that are modified leaves?

9.4 SUMMARY OF LEAF-RELATED CROP MANAGEMENT PRACTICES

The management practices summarized here represent decisions a producer must make in order to have success with crop establishment. The factors discussed here are similar to those presented for stems.

1. *Photosynthetic surface.* The leaves are the primary photosynthetic organs of the plant. Reduced photosynthetic surface directly impacts crop productivity. Many of the practices presented next impact the photosynthetic surface.
2. *Forage management and harvesting.* The principal part of the plant removed during grazing or harvesting is the leaf. Overgrazing excessively removes the herbage, reducing regrowth and promoting soil erosion. Ample amount of leaf

area must be left after grazing or harvesting to allow the plant to photosynthesize enough to meet the carbohydrate needs of the plants for regrowth. Younger leaves are more nutritious and digestible, making higher-quality hay.

3. *Drought management.* Most of the moisture lost through transpiration occurs through the leaves. Cultivars used in dryland production should have drought tolerance traits.

4. *Light interception.* Photosynthesis is the harnessing of light energy and its conversion into chemical energy. Leaves absorb light. The effectiveness of light interception depends on the leaf angle and arrangement. Some cultivars have upright and narrow leaves that reduce leaf shading in the canopy for more effective light interception.

5. *Plant density.* Proper spacing of plants is essential for establishing an ideal leaf area index (total leaf area per unit area) for effective use of the land for high crop productivity.

6. *Planting date.* A crop is seeded at a certain time to take advantage of environmental conditions or to avoid hazards. The management of time of planting in crop production can allow plants to take advantage of a longer growing season. That is, plants can photosynthesize for a longer period.

10: THE STEM

The stem is the central axis of the shoot of a plant. It produces various appendages—leaves, axillary buds, floral buds—from the shoot apical meristem. The dermal tissue consists of epidermal cells, stomata, and trichomes. The guard cells of the stomata have chloroplast; hence, the stem, at least in early growth, is green and is capable of photosynthesis. The stem in grasses is called a *culm* and may be hollow (e.g., in rice, wheat) or solid (e.g., in corn). The hollow or central cavity arises when the central pith matures and stops growth earlier than in the peripheral epidermis and cortex. As a result, the central tissue is torn apart as the internodes extend, creating a hollow center.

10.1 FUNCTIONS

The functions of the stem include the following:

1. Provision of mechanical support to hold branches, leaves, and reproductive structures (flowers). It is important that the leaves are well displayed to maximize light interception for photosynthesis.
2. Conduct water and minerals up to leaves and assimilates from leaves to other parts of the plant. This function occurs through the vascular system.
3. Usable as material for crop propagation (e.g., in yam and Irish potato).
4. Modified stems for food storage that is of economic value in crops (e.g., Irish potato and yam).

Can you think of additional functions of the stem?

10.2 INTERNAL STRUCTURE

The outer layer of the stem is the epidermis and the inner layer is the *cortex*. Dicots and monocots differ in the internal structure of the stem regarding the arrangement of the vascular structures (xylem and phloem). The vascular tissues form a central cylinder called the *stele*. The stele consists of units called *vascular bundles*. The vascular bundles are arranged in a ring in dicots while they are scattered in monocots (Figure 21).

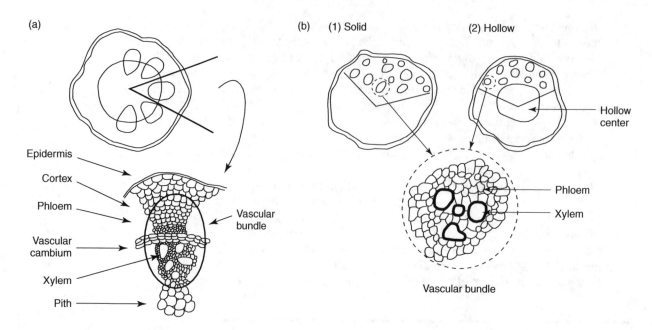

FIGURE 21 Internal structure of (a) dicot stem and (b) monocot stem. The key distinguishing feature is the arrangement of the vascular bundles in a ring in dicots, while they are scattered in monocots. Further, the stem may be solid, as in a corn plant, or hollow, as in rice.

Table 8 Internal Structure of the Stem and Function of the Parts

Epidermis: Outer protective layer of the stem. It is usually one cell thick and often bears trichomes.

Vascular bundles: Comprised of the conducting tissues, xylem and phloem. Xylem tissue conducts water and minerals from the roots, while phloem conducts photosynthates and other materials from the leaf to other parts of the plant. Vascular bundles are arranged in a single ring in most dicots, while they are scattered throughout the ground tissue of monocots.

Ground tissue: Mostly parenchyma tissue that occurs in two regions in dicots:
1. **Cortex:** Ground tissue that occurs between the epidermis and the ring of vascular tissue.
2. **Pith:** Ground tissue in the center of the stem. It is specialized for storage. Not readily discernable in monocots.

In the center of the stem lies a region of purely parenchyma cells called the *pith*. The stem internal structures and their functions are presented in Table 8.

10.3 STEM MODIFICATION: WHEN STEMS DON'T LOOK LIKE STEMS

Rhizome. An unusually thickened and horizontally growing underground stem.

Just like the leaf, stem modifications occur, some of which are the economic parts of the plant for which the crops are produced. Most stem modifications occur underground. Some important world food crops are modified stems. These include tubers such as Irish potato and yam *(Dioscorea)*, both of which are swollen ends of stems. A grass plant may have a vertical stem and may have modified stems of one of two kinds: **rhizomes** or

(a)

(b)

(c)

FIGURE 22 Stem modifications. Modified stems feature prominently in the list of crops that feed the world. (a) Potatoes are modified stems, (b) onions are stems modified as bulbs, and (c) ginger is a stem modified as a rhizome, or an underground storage organ.

stolons. A rhizome is a lateral stem that grows underground (e.g., in ginger and indiangrass), while a stolon is a modified stem that grows horizontally on the surface of the ground (Figure 22). Can you name other examples of economic plant parts that are modified stems?

Stolons are also called *runners*. They develop **adventitious roots** at sites along the stem where their shoot tips turn upward. Stolons and rhizomes are a natural means of

Stolon. An unusually slender and prostrate above-ground stem.

Adventitious roots. Plant structures arising from unusual places (e.g., adventitious root or bud).

propagation. Corms, such as tubers, are fleshy underground stems. They are erect and bear scale leaves (e.g., *Crocus* and *Gladiolus*).

10.4 SUMMARY OF STEM-RELATED CROP MANAGEMENT PRACTICES

The management practices summarized here are discussed in detail in appropriate sections of the book. These represent decisions a producer must make in order to have success with crop establishment.

1. *Plant density.* Plant population and spacing are decisions made by the grower to obtain the optimal number of plants for optimal yield under a specific cultural system. Plant spacing depends on several factors, including the planting equipment, the crop species and cultivar, and the moisture available (dryland or irrigated farming). The closer the spacing, the less the branching of some plants or tillering of grasses. Also, closer spacing promotes elongation of the stem (etiolation) and lodging. Consequently, dwarf environmentally responsive cultivars are selected for high-density planting. High-density planting promotes the development of a closed canopy, which reduces weeds in the field. However, extreme density may be counterproductive.

2. *Grazing management and forage harvesting.* Perennial forage species, both grasses and non-grasses, must be carefully removed (grazing or cutting) such that the remainder can sustain regrowth and protect the plant from damage. A rule of thumb is "take half leave half." The time of harvesting determines the quality of the product. Grasses are best cut at or before flowering. Alfalfa is cut in the early bloom for high yield and long-term survival of the plants. The carbohydrate content of the stem and roots is critical in determining the best times for harvesting forage.

3. *Weed control.* Species with horizontal stems, underground stems (rhizomes), or above-ground stems (stolons) (e.g., johnsongrass) are difficult to control by tillage. Herbicides should be applied at the proper stage of stem growth to minimize or avoid injury to the crop. As previously indicated, high density of the crop provides a more effective ground cover for shading out weeds.

4. *Fertilization.* Tall cultivars are generally susceptible to lodging, which is exacerbated by high nitrogen fertilization. Dwarf cultivars are more responsive to high fertilization. Phosphorus promotes rooting, whereas potassium promotes the development of strong stems.

5. *Cultivar morphology.* Grass crop cultivars differ in tillering habits, some being low tillering while others are high tillering. In crops such as soybean, there are thin-line varieties, determinate-stemmed and indeterminate-stemmed, branching and less branching types. In cotton, there are the picker varieties and stripper varieties. In pea, there are bush and pole types, whereas peanut has bunch and runner varieties.

11: THE ROOT

Roots are underground vegetative organs of plants. There are two types of roots—*seminal* (derived from seed) and *adventitious* (derived from organs of the shoot system rather than the root system). A germinated seed provides a young root called a *radicle*. It grows to become the primary root from which secondary or lateral roots emerge. The tip of the root is

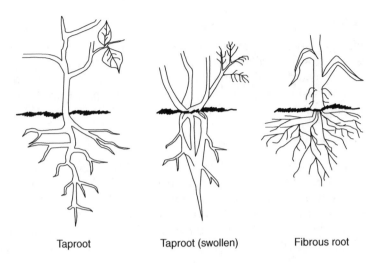

Taproot   Taproot (swollen)   Fibrous root

FIGURE 23 Root systems. Dicots have a taproot system in which the central axis may or may not be swollen. Moncots have a fibrous root system that lacks a defined central axis.

protected by a *root cap. Root hairs* are tiny roots that develop from larger ones and serve as structures for absorbing water and minerals from the soil. There are two basic root systems (distribution of roots in the soil)—*taproot* and *fibrous roots* (Figure 23).

In the taproot root system, there is a primary root consisting of a large central axis and several lateral roots. The taproot is usually deeply penetrating and is found in dicots and gymnosperms. Sometimes, it is swollen and is harvested as the economic part (e.g., carrot and sugar beet).

Fibrous roots occur in the grass family (e.g., rice, corn, wheat) and other monocots (e.g., onion, banana). This root system lacks a dominant central axis and is shallowly penetrating. The seminal not senesces after completion of seedling growth. Fibrous roots have more soil-binding effect and are used in erosion control in soil conservation practices.

Adventitious roots may occur on rhizomes (underground) or on aerial shoots (above ground). Adventitious roots develop in some species when the nodes and internodes of the stem come into contact with the soil or are buried in it (e.g., in currant, gooseberry). When plants are propagated by cuttings (pieces of shoot—stem, leaf, root—used for propagation), sometimes an application of rooting powder to the cut surface prior to planting is needed to promote rapid rooting. Aerial roots are produced by many vines and epiphytes (plants that grow on other plants), such as orchids and bromeliads. Other forms of aerial roots are *prop roots,* which grow down from the stem to the soil (e.g., in corn).

11.1 FUNCTIONS

The functions of the root include the following:

1. Roots anchor plants in the soil, holding stems and leaves upright and preventing toppling by wind.
2. Roots absorb the nutrients and water used by plants in photosynthesis and other physiological functions.
3. Modified roots have storage roles, as occurs in sweet potato where they are the economic part of the plant. Aerial roots occur in certain species, where they provide additional support for the plant through attachment to physical support. Prop roots of corn are aerial roots.

11.2   INTERNAL STRUCTURE

The pericycle is a meristematic region that produces, among other structures, lateral or branch roots that grow outwardly through the cortex and the epidermis. The pericycle together with the vascular cylinder form the *stele* (Figure 24). The solution of water and nutrients from the soil enters the inner tissue through the permeable endodermal cell walls and the protoplast.

11.3   ROOT MODIFICATION

Why is sweet potato a root, while Irish potato is a stem, even though they both occur underground? Do all roots grow underground? As previously mentioned, roots do not always come from the seed but can develop from other parts of the plant. However, true roots can be modified to become swollen, as in sweet potato or cassava, where they store water and foods (Figure 25). Some roots provide additional support to the plant stem by becoming modified for attachment, as in aerial roots and prop roots (for such species as corn).

11.4   ROOT NODULE

Through symbiotic association between a plant host and bacteria, localized root modifications, called *root nodules,* appear on roots as roundish structures. This symbiotic association occurs between legumes (e.g., soybean, peanut, bean) and a soil bacterium, *Rhizobium.* Nodulation starts when the appropriate strain of bacterium enters a root hair and changes into bacteroids (irregularly shaped bacteria). These bacteroids enter the cortical cell of the root, invading the cytoplasm of the root cells. These invaded cells divide, proliferating into tumorlike structures (nodules). A nodule is hence cortical cells that are filled with bacteroids. The bacteria derive nourishment from the plant and in turn incorporate molecular nitrogen from the air into the plant by the process of biological nitrogen fixation.

11.5   SUMMARY OF ROOT-RELATED CROP MANAGEMENT PRACTICES

The management practices summarized here are discussed in detail in appropriate sections of the book. These represent decisions a producer must make in order to have success with crop establishment.

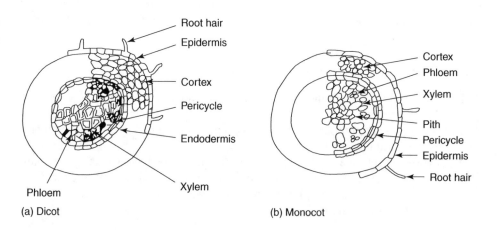

FIGURE 24 Internal structure of roots: (a) dicot root, (b) monocot root.

(a) Dicot

(b) Monocot

FIGURE 25 Modified root, represented by sugar beet (*Beta vulgaris*).

1. *Depth of irrigation.* The goal of irrigation is to provide water in the root zone of the plant. Plants vary in root depth and spread. Depth of irrigation for grasses is different from depth of irrigation suitable for deep-rooted plants.
2. *Cultivation.* Cultivation of growing crops may be undertaken to control weeds. Shallowly rooted plants are more susceptible to damage from cultivators.
3. *Tillage.* In preparing the land for planting, deep-rooted plants require deep soil for proper growth. Tillage, in this case, should be deep. Using heavy implements in tillage can cause subsoil compaction, which affects deep-rooted species more than shallow-rooted species in terms of soil volume available for exploiting. However, shallow rooting predisposes plants to root lodging.
4. *Fertilization and fertilizer placement.* Deep-rooted plants can benefit from deep placement of fertilizer as well as leached nutrients. Phosphorus tends to promote good rooting. Starter application of fertilizer usually contains a high amount of phosphorus for this reason.
5. *Grazing management and harvesting.* Deep-rooted species are more resistant to damage from uprooting by grazing animals. The carbohydrate content of roots is an important factor in grazing management.

12: THE FLOWER

12.1 REPRODUCTION

The female reproductive part of the flower is the *gynoecium*. It is made up of one or more *carpels* (or pistils), consisting of an enlarged ovary, an elongate style, and a receptive stigma. The male reproductive part of the flower is the *androecium* and consists of a

FIGURE 26 Reproductive parts of a dicot flower.

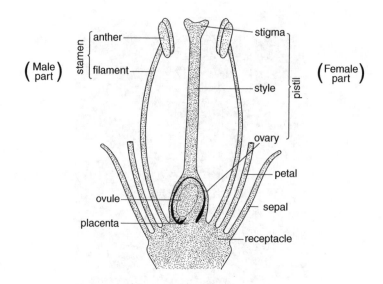

filament and a distal *anther.* The anther contains four pollen sacs, or microsporangia. When mature, the anthers dehisce to shed the pollen grains that contain the haploid number of chromosomes for the species (Figure 26).

12.2 POLLINATION

Pollen grains are transferred to the stigma of a flower by the process of *pollination,* using a variety of agents. Flowers may be *self-pollinated* (receive pollen only from the same plant or genotype) or *cross-pollinated* (receive pollen from a different plant or a different genotype). Agents of pollination include insects (e.g., bees, wasps, flies), birds (e.g., hummingbirds), bats, and wind. Bees tend to pollinate flowers that are showy and that are blue or yellow. Bees are the most important insect pollinators. Growers of certain crops sometimes rent colonies of bees from bee keepers for use during the growing season for effective pollination for a good fruit set. Wind-pollinated species produce large amounts of smooth, small pollen grains. Flowers that are self-pollinated often have some amount of cross-pollination, and vice versa. Hence, it is best to describe plants as *predominantly* either self- or cross-pollinated.

12.3 FERTILIZATION

Fertilization is the union of gametes (pollen and egg in plants). It starts with the germination of pollen on a receptive stigma and subsequent growth of the pollen tube through the style to the ovule of the ovary. The pollen tube enters the embryo sac and discharges two sperm nuclei, one of which fuses with the egg to form a zygote (2*n*). The other fuses with two polar nuclei to form the primary endosperm nucleus (a triploid, 3*n*). These two fertilization events constitute what is called *double fertilization.* The primary endosperm nucleus builds a nutritive endosperm around the developing embryo. Fertilization does not always follow pollination. The process of embryo formation is called *embryogenesis.*

12.4 SUMMARY OF FLOWER-RELATED CROP MANAGEMENT PRACTICES

The management practices summarized here are discussed in detail in appropriate sections of the book. These represent decisions a producer must make in order to have success with crop production.

1. *Effectiveness and type of pollination.* In flowering species where the economic part is the fruit, seed, or grain, crop yield depends on effective pollination. Some growers may rent hives of bees for use during the growing season for effective pollination. Spraying of pesticides at flowering should not be done to avoid killing insect pollinators. Some flowers are predominantly self-pollinated (receive pollen from the same flower or plant), while others are predominantly cross-pollinated (can use pollen from any compatible source). Hybrids of cross-pollinated species are developed such that seed cannot be saved for planting the next season's crop. Self-pollinated cultivars breed true. Hence, seed can be saved for planting the next season's crop.

2. *Fruit set.* The yield of the crops depends on the number of flowers that develop fully to desired harvest maturity. Fruit set is affected by environmental factors, such as drought, frost, and pests. Growth regulators may be sprayed to control fruit set so that only a desirable number of flowers are permitted to develop, resulting in larger fruits.

3. *Plant identification.* Flowers are less environmentally labile. They maintain their properties across a wide range of environments, making them desirable as a means of identifying crop species.

13: THE FRUIT

Embryogenesis leads to the production of a fruit. The mature ovary with the associated parts form the *fruit*. In some species, the fruit develops without fertilization, a phenomenon called *parthenocarpy*. Parthenocarpic fruits are seedless—for example, "Cavendish" banana, "Washington navel" orange, and many fig cultivars. The natural function of the fruit is to protect the seed, but the fruit is what is most desired by animals and humans.

A typical fruit has three regions: the *exocarp* (which is the outer covering, or skin), the *endocarp* (which forms a boundary around the seed and may be hard and stony or papery), and the *mesocarp* (the often fleshy tissue that occurs between the exocarp and the endocarp).

A common way of classifying fruits is according to the succulence and texture on maturity and ripening. On this basis, there are two kinds of fruits—fleshy fruits and dry fruits. However, anatomically, fruits are distinguished by the arrangement of the carpels from which they develop. A carpel is sometimes called the pistil (consisting of a stigma, a style, and an ovary), the female reproductive structure, as previously described. A fruit may have one or more carpels. Even though the fruit is basically the mature ovary, some fruits include other parts of the flower in their structure and are called accessory fruits. Combining carpel number, succulence characteristics, and anatomical features, fruits may be classified into three kinds—*simple, multiple,* or *aggregate* (Figure 27).

13.1 SIMPLE FRUITS

Simple fruits develop from a single carpel or sometimes from the fusing together of several carpels. This group of fruits is very diverse. When mature and ripe, the fruit may be soft and fleshy, may be dry and woody, or may have a papery texture.

Fleshy Fruits

There are three types of fleshy fruits—drupe, berry, and pome.

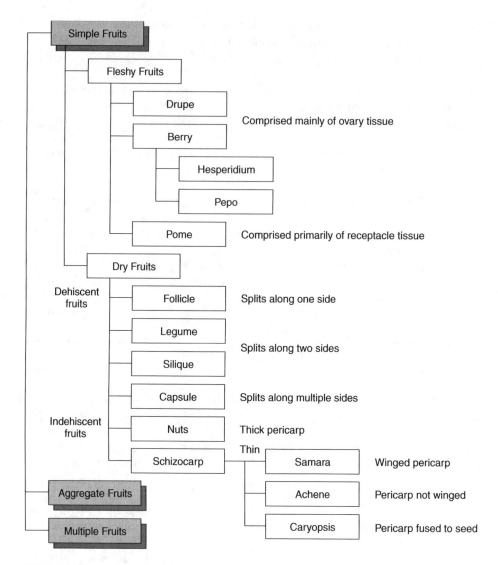

FIGURE 27 A classification of fruits.

Drupe Drupes are simple fleshy fruits with a hard, stony endocarp (or pit) that encloses a single seed. The mesocarp may not always be exactly fleshy in the true sense of the word. The coconut (*Cocos nucifera* L.) has a fibrous layer of a combination of mesocarp and exocarp called a *husk*. This is a source of fiber for a variety of crafts. The edible part of the fruit is the seed, which occurs as a thick, white layer and can be scooped with a spoon if the fruit is young. The seed is hollow and contains a liquid that is casually referred to as coconut "milk." The seed is covered by a hard endocarp. Sometimes, this kind of fruit is described as fleshy-dry. Examples include peaches, plums, cherries, apricots, almonds, and olives (Figure 28).

Berry A berry originates from a compound ovary. Usually, it contains more than one seed. The pericarp of berries is fleshy. There are distinguishable variations among berries. A true berry has a thin exocarp. At maturity, the pericarp is usually soft. Common examples include the tomato, grape, banana, eggplant, and pepper

(Figure 29). Exceptions to this description are date and avocado, which are fleshy fruits with one seed, as opposed to the typical multiple seeds. Just because a fruit has the word *berry* in its common name does not make it one. For example, blackberry, strawberry, and raspberry are not berries at all. In species such as orange, lemon, and lime, the pulp juice sacs are enclosed in a leathery rind (Figure 30). The fruit in this case is called a *hisperidium*. Another kind of fleshy fruit called a *pepo* is exemplified by melon, squash, and cucumber (the gourd family) (Figure 31). The pericarp forms a much harder rind than in the citrus family.

Pome Pomes originate from the receptacle located around the ovary called the *hypanthium*. In apples, the same adjacent tissue is involved in the development of

FIGURE 28 A drupe, represented by a peach *(Persica spp.)*.

FIGURE 29 A berry, represented by tomato *(Lycopsersicon esculentum)*.

FIGURE 30 A hesperidium, represented by Citrus *(Citrus spp.)*. (Source: USDA)

FIGURE 31 A pepo, represented by muskmelon. (Source: USDA)

the fruit (Figure 32). The edible part of the fruit occurs outside the seed. Quince and pear are examples of pomes.

13.2 AGGREGATE FRUITS

Aggregate fruits are formed from a single flower with many pistils. Each of these pistils develops into a fruit (sometimes called *drupelet*). However, these tiny fruits form a cluster on a single receptacle upon maturity. Examples of aggregate fruits are strawberry, blackberry, and raspberry (Figure 33).

13.3 MULTIPLE FRUITS

Multiple fruits are distinguished from aggregate fruits by the fact that they are produced by many individual flowers occurring in one inflorescence. Like aggregate fruits, the individual flowers produce separate tiny fruits, or fruitlets, which develop together into a larger fruit. Common examples are fig and pineapple.

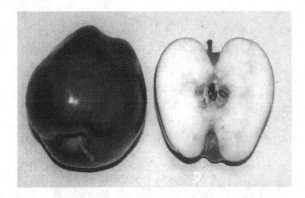

FIGURE 32   A pome, represented by an apple *(Pyrus malus).*

FIGURE 33   Aggregate fruit, represented by strawberry. (Source: USDA)

Dry Fruits

As the name implies, dry fruits are not juicy. Some have one seed; others have many. The exocarp, mesocarp, and endocarp may be fused into one layer, called the **pericarp,** which surrounds the seeds as a thin layer. When mature and dry, the fruit may split open and discharge the seed (*dehiscent fruits*) or retain it (*indehiscent fruits*). Based on this characteristic, there are two kinds of dry fruits.

Dehiscent Fruits   There are a number of dehiscent fruits, which may be distinguished according to how they split. When the fruit splits along one side only, it is called a follicle. Follicles include peony (*Paeonia* spp.), milkweed (*Asclepias* spp.), and larkspur (*Delphinium* spp.). Certain dehiscent fruits split along both sides of the fruit, as typified by legumes, such as pea, lentil, garbanzo bean, and lima bean. Follicles and legumes are collectively called *pods* (Figure 34). Siliques are fruits that split along both seams but whose seed is borne on a structure between the two halves of the split fruit. Sometimes the fruit is long and is called a *silicle*. Plants that bear this kind of fruit include those in the mustard family (Brassicaceae), such as cabbage, radish *(Raphanus sativus),* watercress *(Nasturtium officinale),* and broccoli. Plants such as poppy, lily, snapdragon, and iris are classified as capsules. They split in a variety of ways and consist of two or more carpels.

Indehiscent Fruits   Fruits in this category do not dehisce because the seed is united in some way to the pericarp. One kind is the *achene* (one-seeded dry fruit with firm pericarp), as found in buttercup and nettle. The other kind is called a *caryopsis* and is the seed (or fruit) of grasses (such as corn, wheat, and sorghum). The pericarp is

FIGURE 34 A lugume or pod, represented by garden bean *(Phas eolus vulgaris).*

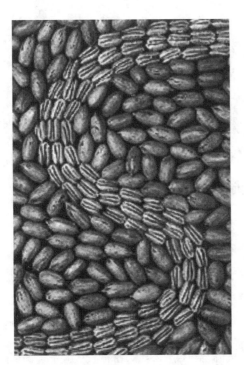

FIGURE 35 A nut, represented by pecan *(Carya illinoensis)*. (Source: USDA)

not separable from the seed. The third indehiscent dry fruit is the nut, which is similar to the achene, except that nuts usually are much larger and have a thicker, harder pericarp which must be cracked to reach the edible seed. True nuts include chestnut (*Castanea* spp.) and hazelnut (*Corylus* spp.). Just like berries, there are many fruits that have *nut* in their common names but are not true nuts. For example, walnut and pecan *(Carya illinoensis)* are actually drupes (Figure 35).

The seed is a mature, or ripened, ovule. It develops in the ovary portion of the carpel as the ovary is differentiating into a fruit. Seeds are the end products of sexual reproduction in seed plants, the means by which they are propagated. All seeds are covered by a seed coat (testa) comprised of fused inner and outer integuments of the ovule. The seed coat surrounds the endosperm and the embryo. The space occupied by the embryo in the seed is variable among species. In grasses, the embryo is more differentiated.

14: THE SEED AND CARYOPSIS

The seed is the propagational unit of flowering species. The economic part of grass crops is not seed but rather the entire fruit, called a *grain* or *caryopsis*.

14.1 DICOT SEED

Dicot seeds are so called because they have two *cotyledons,* or seed leaves, the structures that contain the stored food of the seed. The outer covering is called the *testa* (Figure 36). Legumes have this seed type. The parts of seed and their functions are summarized in Table 9.

Dicot. A subclass of flowering plants with two cotyledons.

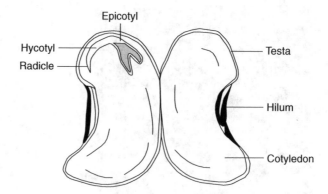

FIGURE 36 Structure of a dicot seed. Dicot seed can be split into two halves, exposing a fragile embryo.

Table 9 Parts and Functions of a Legume Seed

Raphe: A ridge on seeds formed by the stalk of the ovule (in seeds in which the funiculus is sharply bent at the base of the ovule).

Hilum: Present as a scar, it represents the point of attachment of the seed to the pod and through which nourishment was transferred to the seed during development. In species such as soybean, the hilum occurs in different colors that are used as a tool for seed identification purposes.

Micropyle: Opening representing the point of entry into the ovule for the purpose of fertilization.

Embryo area: A region (on the opposite side of the raphe when it occurs) where the embryonic axis is located.

Testa: The seed coat of a legume seed. It has protective functions.

Hypocotyl: The part of the stem tissue between the epicotyl and the radicle. The elongation of this structure causes the arching characteristic of epigeal seedling emergence.

Radicle: The part of the embryonic axis that becomes the primary root. It is the first part of the embryo to start growth during germination.

Epicotyl: The upper portion of the embryonic axis or seedling, above the cotyledons and below the first true leaves.

Cotyledons: A pair of seed leaves that contain food reserves for use by the embryonic axis and seedlings in early stages of growth.

14.2 MONOCOT CARYOPSIS

Monocot. A subclass of flowering plants with a single cotyledon.

Monocots have one cotyledon, also called the *scutellum* (Figure 37). The storage tissue is called the *endosperm*. The cereal grain or kernel, is called a *caryopsis*. The fruit cover, or *pericarp,* is not loose like the testa of a legume seed. It is fused to the aleurone. The parts of the cereal caryopsis and their functions are summarized in Table 10.

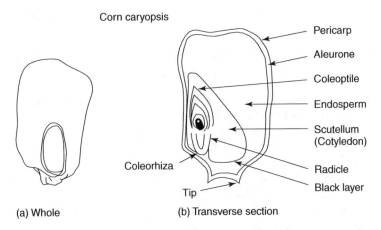

Corn caryopsis

Pericarp

Aleurone

Coleoptile

Endosperm

Scutellum
(Cotyledon)

Coleorhiza

Radicle

Tip

Black layer

(a) Whole

(b) Transverse section

FIGURE 37 Structure of a monocot caryopsis. Corn caryopsis and other monocot kernels cannot be split naturally into two-parts.

Table 10	Parts and Functions of a Cereal Caryopsis

Pericarp: The outer covering of the kernel. May contain red color in corn. Consists primarily of ovary tissue and hence its characteristics are subject to maternal inheritance.

Aluerone layer: Lines the inside of the pericarp and consists of several layers of the outer part of the endosperm occurring to the inside. Its characteristics are subject to biparental inheritance. Produces enzymes that break down the endosperm to release nutrients during seed germination.

Endosperm: Represents the bulk of the mature cereal kernel and is a source of nourishment during the germination and early seedling stages. May be starchy (soft) or flinty (hard) and variable in color (e.g., reddish, yellow, white). In wheat, rye, and triticale, the endosperm contains *gluten* (a proteinaceous substance that is responsible for the stickiness and elasticity of dough). Soft starch may shrink upon drying to cause a dent to form on top of the kernel in corn (hence *dent corn*).

Scutellum: This is the equivalent of the cotyledon. It contains enzymes that are released during the germination process to digest the endosperm to release energy for the young seedling.

Coleoptile: Occurs at the top of the embryonic axis as a protective sheath for the tender and emerging leaf.

Epicotyl: Or plumule. This is the portion of the embryonic axis above the cotyledon.

Apical meristem: The growing point of the embryo.

Scutellar node: The point of attachment to the cotyledon or scutellum to the embryonic axis.

Radicle: The part of the embryonic axis that becomes the primary root. It is the first part of the embryo to start growth during germination.

Coleorhiza: A protective sheath surrounding the radicle and through which the young developing root emerges.

Tip: Or pedicel. This is the point of attachment of the kernel to the flower stock.

Other parts found in certain cereal grains:

Brush: A patch of pubescence or hairs. Occurs at the upper tip of rice caryopsis, for example.

Black layer: A black layer formed near the tip of corn as an indicator of physiological maturity.

14.3 SUMMARY OF SEED-RELATED CROP MANAGEMENT PRACTICES

The management practices summarized here represent decisions a producer must make in order to have success with crop establishment.

1. *Tillage and seedbed preparation.* Tillage precedes seeding as an operation designed to disturb the soil to provide a suitable environment for seed germination. A key consideration in this operation is seed size—the smaller the seed, the finer and firmer the seedbed needed to provide an effective seed-soil contact for imbibition of moisture for germination.

2. *Seeding method and equipment.* The method of seeding depends on seed size. Larger seeds are easier to plant at predetermined equidistant spacing using row planters (e.g., in cotton, corn, peanuts), whereas smaller seeds (e.g., wheat, rice, barley) are best closely spaced using grain drills or broadcast using broadcast seeders.

3. *Seeding depth.* The depth of planting is relative to seed size. Smaller seeds are shallowly planted, while larger seeds are planted deeper in the soil. Seeds differ in the mode of emergence. Those that are epigeal (cotyledons emerge above the soil) are best planted at a shallower depth than those with hypogeal emergence (cotyledons remain in the ground). Soil texture and soil moisture are important in determining seeding depth. Seeding is deeper in sandy soil, especially, under dry conditions. Seeding deeper allows the seed a better chance of obtaining moisture for initiate germination.

4. *Seed treatment.* When seeding into a soil with pest problems (e.g., nematodes, wireworm, and other fungal problems), the producer should consider seed dressing with appropriate pesticides. Some seed treatments are designed to protect the seed against herbicide injury. Seeding into soil that previously received a herbicide treatment, or to allow the seed to resist certain herbicides in the current season, growers should know about any susceptibility of the seed to the herbicide. For example, Lassso herbicide is injurious to sorghum seedling. However, treating the seed with Screen prior to seeding protects it from such injuries. These chemicals are called safeners or protectants. Inoculation of legume seed with *Rhizobium* bacteria is a common practice in the production of crops such as soybean. This seed treatment enhances biological nitrogen fixation for enhancement of crop performance. Sometimes, seeds need special treatment to break dormancy before germination can occur. Dormancy can be broken by physical or chemical methods.

5. *Date of seeding.* Seeds require appropriate temperature and moisture conditions for germination. Extreme cold or drought may kill the seed. Sometimes, a producer may delay seeding to allow volunteer plants and certain weeds to emerge and be controlled by tilling before seeding.

6. *Seeding rate.* Each crop has an ideal seeding rate to obtain the optimal plant density for optimal yield under a specific cultural practice. The planter used for seeding must be properly adjusted to seed at the desired rate.

SUMMARY

1. Diversity is a fact of nature.
2. The enormous natural biological variability needs to be classified to facilitate its use. There is consensus in classifying and naming plants.

3. Plant taxonomy is the science of classifying and naming plants based on information from various sources, including cytology, anatomy, and ultrastructural properties.
4. Taxonomy is a work in progress. Changes are made as new information becomes available.
5. Taxonomy follows certain universal rules so that a particular crop plant name means the same thing to all users worldwide. The system of classification is the binomial nomenclature, which assigns two names to a plant type: a genus name and a species name.
6. Plants may be operationally classified according to seasonal growth cycle as annual, biennial, or perennial. Plants may also be classified according to stem type, stem growth form, agronomic use, and adaptation, among others.
7. Important crop plant families include Poacea (grass family—e.g., corn, wheat, and sorghum), Fabaceae (legume family—e.g., soybean, peanut), and Solanaceae (e.g., tomato, potato).
8. Crop plants are identified by using morphological factors, including leaf shape, form, margin, arrangement, and attachment in broadleaf plants. In grasses, the leaf characteristics of importance include venation, sheath, ligule, collar, and auricles.
9. Flowers are important in the taxonomy of flowering plants because they are stable in expression over environments.
10. Seeds are important in identifying seed-forming plants. They vary in shape, color, size, and other features.
11. The cell is the fundamental unit of organization of organisms. Some organisms are unicellular; others are multicellular.
12. Plant cells have a cell wall around the plasma membrane. This wall may be lignified in certain situations.
13. The nucleus is the most prominent cell organelle. It contains the primary hereditary material (DNA). Other major organelles are the mitochondria (site of respiration), chloroplast (site of photosynthesis), and plastids.
14. There are two groups of tissues—simple tissues and complex tissues. There are three types of simple tissue—parenchyma (have thin walls), collenchyma (have medium wall thickness), and sclerenchyma (have thick walls). Thin-walled cells occur in fleshy and succulent parts, while thick-walled cells occur in strengthening tissue.
15. Complex tissues have a mixture of basic cell types. The major ones are the epidermis (occurs on the outside of plant parts and provides protection), secretory tissue (secretes various substances), and conducting tissue (or vascular system), consisting of the xylem (conducts raw materials up the plant for photosynthesis) and phloem (conducts photosynthates to plant parts).
16. There are different types of leaves; foliage leaves are the most prominent. They are the primary organs in which photosynthesis occurs. Monocot leaves have a parallel venation, while dicot leaves have a reticulate venation.
17. The stem is the central axis of the shoot of a plant. It provides mechanical support for plant parts and conducts nutrients and photosynthates. It may also be modified for food storage and used for propagation in certain species.
18. Roots are underground plant structures. They provide anchorage to the plant and absorb water and nutrients. There are two basic types of root systems—taproot (in dicots) and fibrous roots (in monocots).
19. Seeds are propagational units for flowering plants. Dicot seeds have two cotyledons and are characteristic of legumes. Monocot seeds (caryopsis) characteristic of grasses have one cotyledon.
20. The flower is the reproductive structure of flowering plants.

REFERENCES AND SUGGESTED READING

Acquaah, G. 2002. *Horticulture, principles and practices.* Upper Saddle River, NJ: Prentice Hall.

Benson, L. 1979. *Plant classification.* Washington, DC: Heath and Co.

Esau, K. 1977. *Anatomy of seed plants.* 2d ed. New York: Wiley.

Hayward, H. E. 1967. *The structure of economic plants.* New York: Lubrect & Crammer.

Kaufman, P. B., T. F. Carlson, P. Dayanandan, M. L. Evans, J. B. Fisher, C. Parks, and J. R. Wells. *Plants, their biology and importance.* New York: Harper & Row.

Mauseth, J. D. 1988. *Plant anatomy.* San Francisco, CA: Benjamin/Cummings.

Moore, R., and W. D. Clark. 1994. *Botany: Form and function.* Dubuque, IA: Wm. C. Brown.

SELECTED INTERNET SITES FOR FURTHER REVIEW

http://www.csdl.tamu.edu/FLORA/gallery.htm

Photo gallery of vascular plants, with good description.

http://www.csdl.tamu.edu/FLORA/Wilson/tfp/ham/history.htm

A great site on plant taxonomy.

http://www.cgiar.org/centers.htm

List, location, and functions of all international agricultural research centers.

OUTCOMES ASSESSMENT

PART A

Answer the following questions true or false.

1. T F Linnaeus developed the binomial nomenclature for plants.
2. T F In binomial nomenclature, the genus name must always start with an uppercase letter.
3. T F The stamen is the male reproductive part of the flower.
4. T F Flowers occurring in a cluster form an inflorescence.
5. T F Corn has a spike inflorescence.
6. T F In taxonomy, a name ending in *aceae* is likely to be genus name.
7. T F Some perennials are cultivated as annuals.
8. T F Angiosperms are non-flowering plants.
9. T F All plant cells have a secondary cell wall.
10. T F Chloroplasts have DNA.
11. T F Photosynthesis occurs in the mitochondria.
12. T F Meristems consist of parenchyma cells.
13. T F Xylem vessels conduct raw materials for photosynthesis.
14. T F Seminal roots are derived from seeds.

PART B

Answer the following questions.

1. The science of classifying and naming plants is _____.

2. The bionomial name of a plant consists of a two-part name: _____ and _____.

3. Classify plants according to seasonal growth cycle.

4. Give the four main parts of a typical flower.

   _____

   _____

   _____

   _____

5. The collectivity of petals is called the _____.

6. Give four important plant families, in terms of world food production.

   _____

   _____

   _____

   _____

7. Give an example of a type of indeterminate inflorescence.

   _____

   _____

8. Give two examples of annual crops.

   _____

   _____

9. List, giving two examples each, four operational classes of crops.

   _____

   _____

10. Leaf shape may be simple or _____.

11. Give the three basic types of plant cells.

   _____

   _____

   _____

12. Give three functions of roots.

_____

_____

_____

13. Give three functions of leaves.

_____

_____

_____

14. Give three functions of stems.

_____

_____

_____

15. The two basic root systems are _____ and _____.

PART C

Write a brief essay on each of the following topics.

1. Distinguish between a botanical variety and a cultivar.
2. Classify plants on the basis of temperature adaptation.
3. Describe a typical grass flower.
4. Discuss the features used in identifying grasses.
5. Compare and contrast the dicot seed and monocot.
6. Compare and contrast the dicot stem and monocot stem.
7. Discuss the structure and function of plastids.
8. Discuss the structure and function of conducting tissues.

PART D

Discuss or explain the following topics in detail.

1. Develop your own operational system of classification of plants and justify its utility. (Do not use any example from the text.)
2. Why is it important for an agronomist to understand plant structure and function?
3. How will knowledge of plant structure and function help someone become a better crop producer?
4. How important are modified plant parts in U.S. agriculture?

Photosynthesis

Photosynthesis uses light energy to produce organic molecules.

An Overview of Photosynthesis

Photosynthesis produces food, molecular building blocks, and O_2, which support almost all life on Earth

Photosynthesis uses light energy to convert CO_2 and H_2O into sugars

The processes of photosynthesis and respiration are interdependent

Converting Light Energy to Chemical Energy: The Light Reactions

Chlorophyll is the principal light-absorbing molecule of photosynthesis

Light energy enters photosynthesis at locations called *photosystems*

The light reactions produce O_2, ATP, and NADPH

In the light reactions, ATP is synthesized using energy from chemiosmosis

Converting CO_2 to Sugars: The Calvin Cycle

The Calvin cycle uses ATP and NADPH from the light reactions to make sugar phosphates from CO_2

The Calvin cycle is relatively inefficient at converting CO_2 into sugars

The enzyme rubisco also functions as an oxygenase, resulting in photorespiration

The C_4 pathway limits the loss of carbon from photorespiration

CAM plants store CO_2 in a C_4 acid at night for use in the Calvin cycle during the day

From Chapter 8 of *Introduction to Botany*, First Edition, Murray W. Nabors. Copyright © 2004 by Pearson Education, Inc. Published by Pearson Benjamin Cummings. All rights reserved.

Sugarcane is a perennial, tropical plant that grows up to 5 meters (16.4 feet) in height. It has been cultivated in Asia and in the Americas as a source of sugar for thousands of years. In 510 B.C., the Persian King Darius I saw it growing on the banks of the Indus River. Later, Alexander the Great (356–332 B.C.) brought plants back to Greece from India. The Persians and Greeks were both surprised to find a plant that produced sweetener without the need for bees to make honey. The Chinese had also been extracting sugar from sugarcane for millennia before Marco Polo found large sugar mills in China when he visited in the 1200s.

The European explorations of the Americas in the 1500s and 1600s introduced many Europeans to sugar produced from sugarcane. Christopher Columbus himself brought the plant back from the Caribbean and established a sugarcane plantation there. Sugar became a wildly popular and expensive replacement for honey and provided a sure sign of affluence.

Unfortunately, slavery in the Americas got an economic impetus from the need for workers on sugar plantations in Central America, the Caribbean, and the southern British colonies that would become the United States. An insatiable sweet tooth made Europe the prime market for sugar. During the 1600s and 1700s, sugar was a key element in the so-called *triangular trade* that carried cane sugar and rum (made from sugarcane) from the Americas to Europe; tools, weapons, and other trade goods from Europe to Africa; and ultimately more than 11 million enslaved Africans to the Americas. It is tragic

Sugar beets are primary sources of processed sugar.

to note that the sweetness of sugar played a role in changing the course of history and the lives of so many enslaved Africans.

Eventually, a source of cheaper sugar undermined the market for cane sugar. In 1744, a German chemist named Andreas Marggraf discovered sugar in the juice of certain types of beets (*Beta vulgaris*). By mostly haphazard selection, growers eventually produced sugar beets with markedly increased concentrations of sugar. Sugar-beet production in continental Europe increased slowly over the next half century. By 1802, the first large factory for the extraction of beet sugar was built in Germany. By this time, the production of sugar from sugar beets in several European countries began to reduce the market for more expensive cane sugar brought by boat from the Americas and played a role in ending slavery in the Americas.

The importance of sugar in human history reminds us of the vital role played by plants in supplying our food. As you know, humans and other animals ultimately depend on photosynthesis for all of their food. Sugar in particular is produced as a direct result of photosynthesis and serves as a source of both energy and organic molecules for all living organisms. Understanding photosynthesis and protecting plants and other organisms that carry it out are therefore of vital interest.

Sugarcane being harvested on St. Kitts in the Caribbean.

An Overview of Photosynthesis

Photosynthesis makes the basic organic molecules a plant needs to survive, prosper, and reproduce. In general, photosynthetic organisms make the lives of nonphotosynthetic organisms possible.

Photosynthesis produces food, molecular building blocks, and O₂, which support almost all life on Earth

Like it or not, your molecular ingredients are remarkably similar to those of broccoli and earthworms. All organisms use carbon-based molecules as building blocks for assembling and maintaining themselves. In almost all cases, photosynthesis is the ultimate source of those molecules. Plants, algae, and photosynthetic bacteria, of course, rely on photosynthesis directly and are known as *autotrophs* because they make their own food (Figure 1). Since they get their energy through photosynthesis, they are known more specifically as **photoautotrophs.** Most nonphotosynthetic life-forms, such as animals and fungi, are heterotrophs, depending totally on other organisms for organic molecules to build their bodies, energy to function, and oxygen. You can consume all the carbon dioxide gas (CO_2) you want—that is what makes carbonated drinks bubbly—but as an animal you cannot use CO_2 to produce organic molecules. Through photosynthesis, however, plants can convert CO_2 and H_2O into sugars that form the basis of thousands of other organic molecules that make up all living organisms.

Since most heterotrophs rely either directly or indirectly on photosynthetic organisms for nutrition, photosynthetic organisms underlie almost every food chain. In terrestrial food chains, land animals either eat plants or eat animals that have eaten plants. For example, cows eat grass, and humans eat cows. Meanwhile, fungi absorb energy-rich compounds from the remains of organisms whose organic carbon molecules were originally produced by plants and other photosynthetic organisms. In aquatic food chains, animals eat algae or eat animals that have eaten algae. For example, sea urchins eat algae, and sea otters eat sea urchins. The only organisms that do not rely on photosynthesis are bacteria known as **chemoautotrophs,** which get their carbon from CO_2 and their energy from inorganic chemicals (see *The Intriguing World of Plants* box on the next page).

Every carbon atom in your body has existed at some previous point in a photosynthetic organism and has been processed by that organism from CO_2 and the energy of sunlight. The carbon-containing molecules produced by photosynthesis are responsible for more than 94% of the dry weight of living organisms. They are combined with minerals from the soil to produce the many different kinds of molecules found in living organisms. When you die, your body will eventually become CO_2, water, and a few minerals. Those substances will again be used in photosynthesis.

Photosynthesis also sustains life by releasing oxygen (O_2). In 1771, Joseph Priestley, an English clergyman and scientist, used closed-container experiments to show that plants "restore" air, thereby allowing a candle to burn and a mouse to survive. Later he discovered oxygen. A citation associated with a medal he received for this discovery said, "For these discoveries we are assured that no vegetable grows in vain . . . but cleanses and purifies our atmospheres." Later, in 1779, Dutch physician Jan Ingenhousz repeated and extended Priestley's observations, showing that oxygen was restored by plants only in the presence of sunlight and only by green plant parts.

Figure 1 Photosynthetic organisms. Photosynthetic species—which include almost all plants, algae, and some bacteria—harvest solar energy to produce organic molecules.

Nonphotosynthetic Plants

Some plants are actually nonphotosynthetic, depending entirely on decaying organic matter for their nutrition. Indian pipe (*Monotropa uniflora*) is a saprophytic flowering plant. Only the nonphotosynthetic flowering stalks appear above-ground. The remainder of the plant is underground, where it does not parasitize other plants but obtains nutrients from decaying plant material. A Cherokee legend says that after a week of watching quarreling chiefs of several tribes smoke the peace pipe, the Great Spirit changed the chiefs into the flowers called Indian Pipes to remind everyone that smoking the peace pipe was supposed to end quarreling. According to the legend, the flowers grow wherever people have quarreled. In the western United States, the snow plant (*Sarcodes sanguinea*) is a saprophytic member of the family that includes huckleberries and blueberries.

Indian pipe (*Monotropa uniflora*).

Snow plant (*Sarcodes sanguinea*).

O_2 in the atmosphere is split by ultraviolet (UV) light into molecular oxygen, which combines with O_2 to produce ozone (O_3). The ozone layer in the atmosphere absorbs harmful UV light from the Sun and thereby helps to make life on land possible.

Photosynthesis uses light energy to convert CO_2 and H_2O into sugars

Photosynthesis in plants and algae takes place in microscopic organelles called *chloroplasts*. Typically around 3–5 μm in diameter, chloroplasts can be circular or elongated and are most common in leaf tissue, where a typical cell may contain between 5 and 50 chloroplasts.

The process of using light energy to convert CO_2 and H_2O into sugars consists of two series of reactions: the light reactions and the Calvin cycle (Figure 2). The **light**

Chloroplasts

H_2O (usually from roots)

CO_2 (from air)

Stroma (fluid surrounding thylakoids)

Light

Chloroplast

Light reactions

NADP⁺

NADPH

ADP

+ P i

ATP

Calvin cycle

Stack of thylakoids (granum)

O_2 (to air)

Sugars (used—sometimes with minerals—to make other molecules)

Figure 2 An overview of photosynthesis. The light reactions use chlorophyll to capture light energy that is transferred to ATP and NADPH, in electrons supplied by water. The Calvin cycle uses ATP, NADPH, and CO_2 to make simple three-carbon sugar phosphates, which become building blocks for more complex molecules.

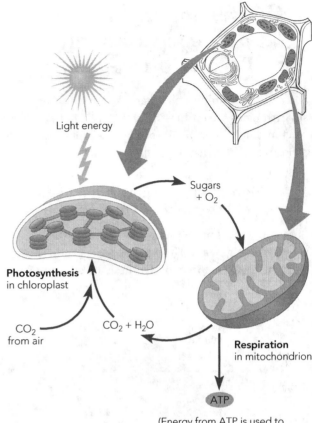

reactions, which occur within the thylakoid membranes, are the *photo* part of photosynthesis because they capture light energy. They use light energy and H_2O to generate chemical energy in the form of ATP and NADPH, and they release O_2 as a by-product. The **Calvin cycle,** the *synthesis* part of photosynthesis, assembles (synthesizes) simple three-carbon sugars, using ATP and NADPH from the light reactions and CO_2 from the air. The Calvin cycle takes place in the stroma, the fluid-filled region surrounding the thylakoids.

The simple three-carbon sugars produced by the Calvin cycle become building blocks for complex molecules such as glucose ($C_6H_{12}O_6$). Photosynthesis can be summarized in terms of the amount of CO_2 and H_2O needed to produce one molecule of glucose:

$$6CO_2 + 12H_2O + \text{light energy} \rightarrow C_6H_{12}O_6 + 6O_2 + 6H_2O$$

The use of bold in this equation indicates that oxygen atoms from H_2O combine to form molecules of O_2. We can simplify the formula by noting only the net consumption of H_2O:

$$6CO_2 + 6H_2O + \text{light energy} \rightarrow C_6H_{12}O_6 + 6O_2$$

This formula shows that CO_2, water, and light energy are used to make sugar and oxygen. We can further simplify it by dividing the previous formula by 6. Now we have the basic formula for making sugars and other carbohydrates (molecules with the basic structure CH_2O) one carbon at a time:

$$CO_2 + H_2O + \text{light energy} \rightarrow CH_2O + O_2$$

In summary, photosynthesis captures light energy from the Sun and uses it to assemble CO_2 into sugars. We will look at specific reactions of the process later in the chapter.

The processes of photosynthesis and respiration are interdependent

Before we look at the light reactions and the Calvin cycle, it is worth keeping in mind that photosynthesis by itself does not sustain life. Photosynthesis produces food, but all organisms—whether or not they are photosynthetic—must then extract energy from that food in a process known as *respiration*. In **respiration,** which takes place in mitochondria, organisms break down organic molecules in the presence of oxygen and convert the stored energy into the form of ATP. Cells then use the energy in ATP to do work. In other words, respiration harvests energy from the food produced by photosynthesis. Each process relies on products of the other, as respiration uses sugars and O_2 in producing CO_2, H_2O, and ATP,

Figure 3 The interdependence of photosynthesis and respiration. The products of photosynthesis—sugars and O_2— are used in respiration to produce the ATP that powers most cellular work. The by-products of respiration—CO_2 and H_2O—are used in photosynthesis.

while photosynthesis uses CO_2 and H_2O in producing sugars and O_2 (Figure 3).

Respiration is an exergonic process, resulting in a net output of free energy in the form of ATP, while photosynthesis is an endergonic process, resulting in a net input of free energy.

Section Review

1. **How do nonphotosynthetic organisms obtain the carbon molecules necessary for life?**
2. **How do heterotrophs and autotrophs differ?**
3. **What is the source of the oxygen produced during photosynthesis?**
4. **Briefly summarize how photosynthesis relates to respiration.**

Converting Light Energy to Chemical Energy: The Light Reactions

Since sunlight supplies the energy to drive photosynthesis, organisms are ultimately solar-powered. In the light reactions, light energy absorbed by chlorophyll is used to make two energy-rich compounds: ATP and NADPH.

Chlorophyll is the principal light-absorbing molecule of photosynthesis

Photosynthesis is made possible by light-absorbing molecules called **pigments.** The types of pigments that absorb light energy for use in photosynthesis are either attached to or part of the thylakoid membranes of chloroplasts. The pigment that is directly involved in the light reactions is the green pigment **chlorophyll** (Figure 4).

Each type of photosynthetic pigment absorbs light energy at certain wavelengths. Visible light and all other forms of electromagnetic energy move through space as packets of energy called **photons,** which vary in their energy content, depending on their wavelengths. A photon with a shorter wavelength has more energy than a photon with a longer wavelength (Figure 5a). For instance, photons that are visible as blue light contain more energy than photons visible as red light. Chlorophyll absorbs photons from the red and blue portions of the visible spectrum but either transmits or reflects photons from the green portion (Figure 5b). In other words, the green color is what is visible after chlorophyll has absorbed the

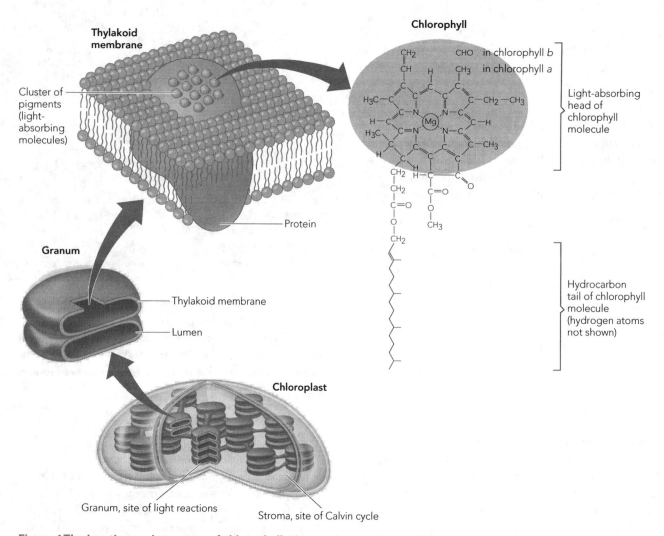

Figure 4 The location and structure of chlorophyll. Photosynthesis in plants and algae occurs within organelles called *chloroplasts,* which in plants are found in cells in leaves and some stems. Within the chloroplast, membrane-bound structures called *thylakoids* are stacked together to form grana. The thylakoid membranes absorb light through clusters of pigments, with the green pigment chlorophyll *a* being directly involved in the light reactions.

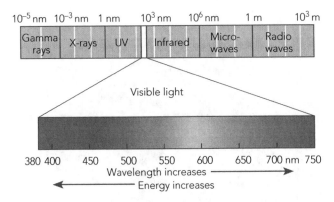

(a) Electromagnetic spectrum

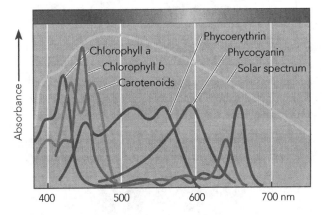

(b) Absorption of pigments

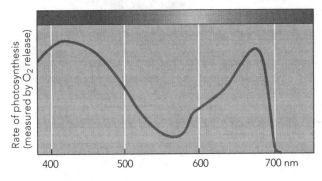

(c) Action spectrum

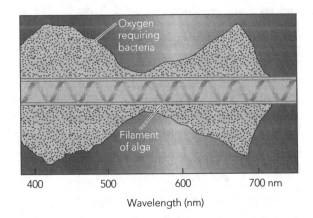

(d) Engelmann's experiment

light used in the light reactions of photosynthesis. As a result of the thylakoid membranes reflecting green light, the photosynthetic parts of plants—leaves and some stems—typically appear green.

There are two main types of chlorophyll in plants and green algae, known as chlorophyll *a* and chlorophyll *b*. In plants, **chlorophyll *a*** is the only pigment directly involved in the light reactions. It primarily absorbs light from the blue-violet and red ranges of the spectrum and appears dark green because it mainly reflects green light. In photosynthesis, a chlorophyll *a* electron that has absorbed a photon from the blue portion of the spectrum loses the extra energy as heat and ends up with the same energy as an electron that has been energized by a photon from the red portion of the spectrum. In other words, blue light is not used directly in photosynthesis in plants. **Chlorophyll *b*** does not take part directly in the light reactions but instead transmits absorbed energy to those chlorophyll *a* molecules that are directly involved. Chlorophyll *b* is therefore known as an **accessory pigment.** Some other accessory pigments, known as *carotenoids,* primarily absorb blue-green light and reflect yellow or yellow-orange light. In plants, these accessory pigments are typically not visible until chlorophyll breaks down as when leaves of deciduous plants change color. It is the carotenoids that cause autumn coloration after short days and cold temperatures have slowed photosynthesis and chlorophyll has broken down.

Measuring O_2 production as a function of wavelength reveals the **action spectrum** for photosynthesis—that is, a profile of how effectively different wavelengths of light promote photosynthesis. The action spectrum for photosynthesis has peaks in the blue and red regions of the spectrum, corresponding closely to chlorophyll's **absorption spectrum**—the range of a pigment's ability to absorb wavelengths of light. This correlation indicates that chlorophyll is the primary pigment involved in photosynthesis (Figure 5b and c). The action spectrum of photosynthesis can also be demonstrated by placing oxygen-requiring bac-

Figure 5 Chlorophyll absorbs light. (a) The electromagnetic spectrum contains a relatively narrow band of visible light. **(b)** Chlorophyll absorbs in both the blue and red regions of the absorption spectrum but transmits green. **(c)** The action spectrum of photosynthesis corresponds to the absorption spectrum of chlorophyll and accessory pigments. **(d)** In 1883, Thomas Engelmann placed single-celled oxygen-requiring bacteria along a filament of photosynthetic algae. The bacteria congregated around the regions of the algal cells receiving blue and red light from a prism. In this way, he demonstrated which wavelengths of light were causing oxygen production by promoting photosynthesis.

As you can see, the distribution of the bacteria correlates with the action spectrum of photosynthesis.

teria next to a strand of photosynthetic algae and then exposing the algae to different wavelengths of light. The bacteria cluster where O_2 is being released as a by-product of photosynthesis—the areas receiving blue and red light (Figure 5d).

One could reasonably ask why photosynthesis does not use all available light, in which case plants would appear black. One possible answer might be that in Earth's early days, more than 2.5 billion years ago, some other life-form absorbed green light first, making it unavailable for photosynthesis. Perhaps this life-form floated on the ocean's surface, where it was first to get the light. For example, the prokaryote *Halobacterium* absorbs green light. Some photosynthetic prokaryotes called *cyanobacteria* absorb light primarily in the green but also in the blue regions of the spectrum.

Light energy enters photosynthesis at locations called photosystems

Within the thylakoid membranes, chlorophyll *a*, chlorophyll *b*, and other pigments such as carotenoids form clusters of pigments, with each cluster consisting of about 200 to 300 pigment molecules, along with associated protein molecules. Experiments indicate that light reactions in each cluster are triggered by one chlorophyll *a* molecule, which absorbs the energy of a photon and ejects an electron that is then absorbed by a molecule known as a *primary electron acceptor*. Together, this chlorophyll *a* molecule and the primary electron acceptor are called a **reaction center.** The reaction center and accessory pigments in each cluster work together as a light-harvesting unit known as a **photosystem** (Figure 6). Each photosystem absorbs light energy on the outside—the stroma side—of the thylakoid membrane.

There are two types of photosystems, known as photosystem I and photosystem II. The numbers designate the order in which they were discovered. Photosystem I has little chlorophyll *b*, whereas photosystem II has more chlorophyll *b*, in almost equal amounts with chlorophyll *a*. These photosystems occur repeatedly throughout the thylakoid membranes. The accessory pigments are critical components. The chlorophyll *a* molecule that triggers the light reactions is not going to get hit directly by photons very often because it represents less than 1% of the pigments in a photosystem. Accessory pigments, however, funnel the energy from the photon to the chlorophyll *a* in the reaction center. These accessory pigments, along with chlorophyll *a* molecules that transfer energy to the chlorophyll *a* molecule in the reaction center, are sometimes called *antenna pigment molecules* because they

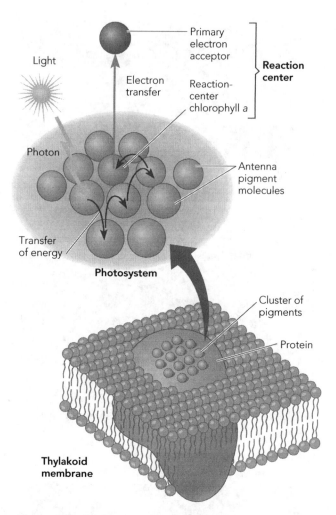

Figure 6 Each photosystem is a light-harvesting complex. A photosystem consists of a reaction center and antenna pigment molecules that transfer light energy to the chlorophyll *a* molecule in the reaction center. The reaction center also includes a primary electron acceptor. Light energy causes an electron to be ejected from the chlorophyll *a* in the reaction center and transferred to the primary electron acceptor. This process is carried out repeatedly in each photosystem.

function like an antenna in receiving and transmitting energy, somewhat like a satellite dish. Energy can be transferred in the form of energized electrons, or the energy itself can move from molecule to molecule.

The chlorophyll *a* molecule in the reaction center absorbs energy at slightly longer wavelengths (lower energy) than chlorophyll in general. The reaction center chlorophyll *a* molecule in photosystem II is called *P680,* with the *P* standing for pigment and the number indicating that it absorbs light best at a wavelength of 680 nm. In photosystem I, the chlorophyll *a* molecule in the reaction center is called *P700* because it absorbs light best at 700 nm. As a result of the energy transfer from the antenna pigment molecules, much more light energy can reach the

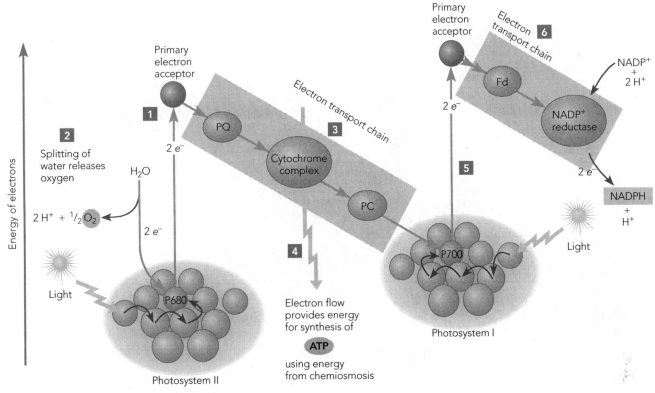

Figure 7 Movement of electrons in the light reactions. This zigzag diagram, known as the *Z scheme*, provides an overview of the flow of energy in the light reactions. As each electron flows through the electron carriers—plastoquinone (PQ), a cytochrome protein complex, plastocyanin (PC), ferredoxin (Fd), and NADP⁺ reductase—each carrier attracts the electron more strongly than the previous carrier. The numbered steps are described in the text.

chlorophyll *a* molecule in the reaction center than it would have absorbed on its own. Each time the reaction center chlorophyll *a* molecule is activated, an energized electron is transferred to the primary electron acceptor.

The light reactions produce O₂, ATP, and NADPH

The two light-absorbing photosystems are linked together in a zigzag pattern sometimes called a *Z-scheme* (Figure 7). The Z-scheme consists of a series of protein-based electron carriers that form a pathway for the movement of electrons. Keep in mind that this pathway is repeated thousands of times within a typical thylakoid membrane. The movement of electrons in each Z-scheme constitutes the light reactions.

We will now follow the flow of energy to see how the light reactions produce O₂, ATP, and NADPH. The steps correlate with Figure 7. Although each electron passes through the light reactions one at a time, notice that the figure shows two electrons, the number needed at the end of the light reactions in order to transform one molecule of NADP⁺ into one molecule of NADPH.

1 When light energy reaches the chlorophyll *a* in the reaction center, it energizes an electron in the chlorophyll *a* molecule. This electron is transferred to the primary electron acceptor.

2 Each ejected electron is quickly replaced by an electron from H_2O, after an enzyme splits an H_2O molecule into 2 electrons, 2 hydrogen ions (H^+), and one oxygen atom. (A hydrogen ion is a solitary proton.) The chlorophyll *a* is positively charged because it lost an electron, so it attracts the negatively charged electron from water. In addition to replacing the electron in the chlorophyll *a* molecule, the splitting of water produces oxygen gas, releasing one molecule of O_2 for every two molecules of H_2O that are split.

3 Each electron ejected from the chlorophyll *a* molecule passes from the primary electron acceptor and gradually loses energy by transfer through a series of electron carriers known as an **electron transport chain.** The movement from carrier to carrier occurs in a series of oxidation-reduction (redox) reactions.

4 The energy that is released by the flow of electrons is indirectly used to power the synthesis of ATP, a process we will look at shortly.

Figure 8 Chemiosmosis and ATP synthesis in the light reactions. This diagram shows the flow of hydrogen ions (H⁺) through ATP synthase, a process called *chemiosmosis*. Some of the hydrogen ions come from the splitting of water, while others are pumped through the membrane by the energy released through the flow of electrons in the electron transport chain. ATP synthase uses the energy of chemiosmosis to add an inorganic phosphate (P_i) to ADP to form ATP.

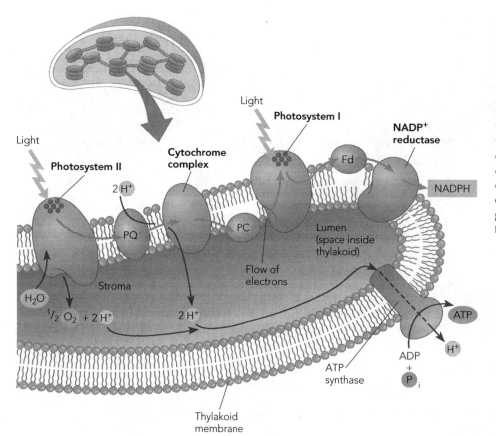

5 Each electron that passes through the electron transport chain neutralizes the positively charged chlorophyll *a* molecule in the reaction center of photosystem I. This chlorophyll *a* molecule is positively charged because the absorption of a photon has already ejected a reenergized electron that is transferred to a primary electron acceptor.

6 Each electron ejected from photosystem I passes through another electron transport chain. The last electron carrier in this chain is an enzyme that transforms $NADP^+$ to NADPH. As noted previously, 2 electrons must pass through the light reactions before one NADPH can be synthesized.

So, the light reactions use the energized electrons ejected from photosystem II in producing energy-rich ATP and use the reenergized electrons ejected from photosystem I in producing NADPH. The light reactions capture 32% of the sunlight absorbed by chlorophyll, making them more efficient than any energy-capturing device made by humans. For example, solar panels typically capture, as electricity or heat, around 5% of the solar energy they absorb. As you will see, the ATP and NADPH produced by the light reactions will be used in the Calvin cycle to make CO_2 into simple sugar phosphates.

In the light reactions, ATP is synthesized using energy from chemiosmosis

As electrons move through the electron transport chain between photosystem II and photosystem I, they lose energy. This energy is used to pump protons from the stroma into the thylakoid compartment, causing a concentration difference in H⁺ ions across the thylakoid membrane (Figure 8). The charge difference is also a pH difference, creating a kind of battery that stores energy for doing work. In a process known as **chemiosmosis** (from the Greek *chemi-*, referring to "chemical," and *osmos*, meaning "a push"), H⁺ ions move back across the membrane, resulting in a release of energy. Many of these H⁺ ions flow through an enzyme called **ATP synthase,** which uses the energy to add an inorganic phosphate (P_i) to ADP, thereby forming ATP. This phosphorylation is known as **photophosphorylation** because the energy to carry it out comes originally from light.

Electrons typically move from photosystem II to photosystem I, in what is called *noncyclic electron flow*. During the light reactions as they occur naturally in plants, the synthesis of ATP relies on this noncyclic electron flow and is therefore known as *noncyclic photophosphorylation*. In some bacteria and in laboratory experiments with plants, it is possible to achieve what is called *cyclic photophosphorylation,* which only involves photosystem I. Electrons flow in a cycle from the reaction center of photosystem I to the electron transport chain and back to the same reaction center, indirectly producing ATP but no NADPH. However, plant physiologists continue to debate whether cyclic photophosphorylation occurs in plants in nature.

Section Review

1. Describe the role of chlorophyll in photosynthesis.
2. How does light energy enter the light reactions?
3. Identify the products of the light reactions and explain how they are formed.

Converting CO_2 to Sugars: The Calvin Cycle

As you have seen, the light reactions use light energy and H_2O to yield chemical energy in the form of ATP and NADPH. These products fuel the second part of photosynthesis—the Calvin cycle, which makes simple sugar phosphates. The Calvin cycle is named after Melvin Calvin, who—together with his graduate student Andrew Benson and later James Bassham—in 1953 determined the pathway by which plants convert CO_2 into sugars. In 1961, Calvin won the Nobel Prize for this discovery, which resulted from experiments involving exposure of photosynthetic algae to radioactive CO_2 for shorter and shorter lengths of time (Figure 9). After 5 seconds of exposure to the radioactive CO_2, the principal radioactive compound in the algae was a three-carbon molecule known as 3-phosphoglycerate (PGA). The rest of the Calvin cycle was worked out by similar experiments. Since the first product has three carbons, the Calvin cycle is sometimes known as the C_3 pathway.

The Calvin cycle uses ATP and NADPH from the light reactions to make sugar phosphates from CO_2

The reactions of the Calvin cycle are sometimes called the *dark reactions* or the *light-independent reactions* because they can take place in the dark, as long as the products of the light reactions—ATP and NADPH—are supplied. However, these terms can be misleading because they

Figure 9 Calvin's experiment. Melvin Calvin, working with Andrew Benson and other colleagues, conducted an experiment in which they traced the process of photosynthesis in green algae, using radioactive CO_2, in this "lollipop" apparatus. After varying lengths of time, the lollipop contents were emptied into boiling alcohol, thereby killing the algae so that the progress of the radioactivity through various compounds could be followed. In this way, Calvin and his colleagues were able to identify how CO_2 fixation occurs in photosynthesis.

imply that the Calvin cycle can continue indefinitely in the dark, which is not the case. Cellular stockpiles of ATP and NADPH last only a few seconds or minutes at most. Cells do not store large quantities of either ATP or NADPH, so the Calvin cycle must rely on these molecules being resupplied by the light reactions.

As you have seen, in plants and algae the Calvin cycle occurs outside the thylakoids, in the stroma of chloroplasts. In the case of plants, CO_2 enters through the pores called *stomata* in the leaf epidermis and then diffuses into mesophyll cells, where photosynthesis takes place. The Calvin cycle uses the energy-rich products of the light reactions—ATP and NADPH—to incorporate three CO_2 molecules (one at a time) into a three-carbon sugar phosphate. You might imagine that synthesis of sugars occurs by linking together molecules of CO_2 while adding needed electrons and hydrogens. However, this is not the case. In fact, the Calvin cycle adds one CO_2 to a five-carbon compound. After the cycle repeats three times, enough carbon has been added to account for one molecule of a three-carbon sugar phosphate called *glyceraldehyde-3-phosphate* (*G3P*), also known as *3-phosphoglyceraldehyde* (*PGAL*). Outside of the Calvin cycle, molecules of G3P are used to produce molecules of several types of six-carbon sugars, including fructose and glucose, which can be combined to form sucrose, composed of 12 carbons. Sucrose is the principal sugar used in translocation of carbohydrates from the leaves to other parts of the plant.

The Calvin cycle incorporates CO_2 and uses ATP and NADPH from the light reactions to create building blocks of life. The carbon atoms fixed into sugar by the Calvin cycle will ultimately become the carbons of all of the organic molecules found in plants, animals, and almost all other life-forms. Figure 10 provides an overview of one turn of the Calvin cycle:

1 One ATP powers addition of a phosphate to a five-carbon sugar phosphate to make a sugar phosphate molecule with two phosphates. The addition of this second phosphate energizes the five-carbon molecule. Specifically, one ATP is used to make ribulose-1,5-bisphosphate (RuBP) from ribulose-5-phosphate (Ru5P).

2 Carbon dioxide is added to the five-carbon sugar phosphate. Specifically, the enzyme **rubisco** adds CO_2 to RuBP. The name *rubisco* is the abbreviation for <u>ru</u>bulose 1,5-<u>bis</u>phosphate <u>c</u>arboxylase/<u>o</u>xygenase. Rubisco is called a *carboxylase* because it can add carbon from CO_2 to another molecule. In this case, the resulting short-lived six-carbon compound immediately breaks down into two molecules of a three-carbon organic acid, 3-phosphoglycerate (PGA). This is called **carbon fixation** because the carbon from CO_2 is incorporated ("fixed" or bound) into a nongaseous, more complex molecule.

3 Two molecules of ATP add phosphates to the three-carbon organic acids. The addition of phosphates energizes the three-carbon organic acids. Specifically, two molecules of ATP are used to convert two molecules of PGA into two molecules of 1,3-bisphosphoglycerate (BPG).

4 Two molecules of NADPH add electrons to the three-carbon organic acid phosphates, reducing each BPG into one molecule of glyceraldehyde-3-phosphate (G3P). The result is two G3P molecules, representing a total of six carbons.

5 After three turns of the Calvin cycle, enough carbon has been fixed to allow one molecule of G3P to leave the cycle and become available for making other sugars, while still leaving enough carbons to regenerate Ru5P to complete the cycle.

6 Most G3P continues through the rest of the Calvin cycle. Other reactions of the cycle make four-carbon, six-carbon, and seven-carbon sugar phosphates. Eventually, the cycle regenerates the five-carbon Ru5P molecule, which initiates another turn of the cycle.

Here is the overall equation reflecting the products of three turns of the Calvin cycle:

$$3CO_2 + 6NADPH + 9ATP + 6H^+ \rightarrow 1G3P + 6NADP^+ + 9ADP + 8P_i + 3H_2O$$

This equation reflects the three CO_2 molecules required for the sugar, the nine ATP molecules, and the six NADPH molecules used for three turns of the Calvin cycle. The products $NADP^+$, ADP, and P_i return to the light reactions as reactants.

Glucose, an important sugar of living cells, is produced indirectly from two molecules of G3P formed in the Calvin cycle. The metabolic fates of G3P include:

- Conversion in respiration to CO_2 and H_2O, with energy stored in ATP.
- Conversion to intermediate compounds in respiration that are synthesized into amino acids and other compounds.
- Conversion to fructose 6-phosphate (F6P) and fructose bisphosphate.
- Conversion of F6P into glucose 6-phosphate (G6P) and glucose 1-phosphate (G1P).
- Use of G1P to form cellulose in cell walls and starch for energy storage.
- Use of G1P and F6P to make sucrose for transport throughout the plant.

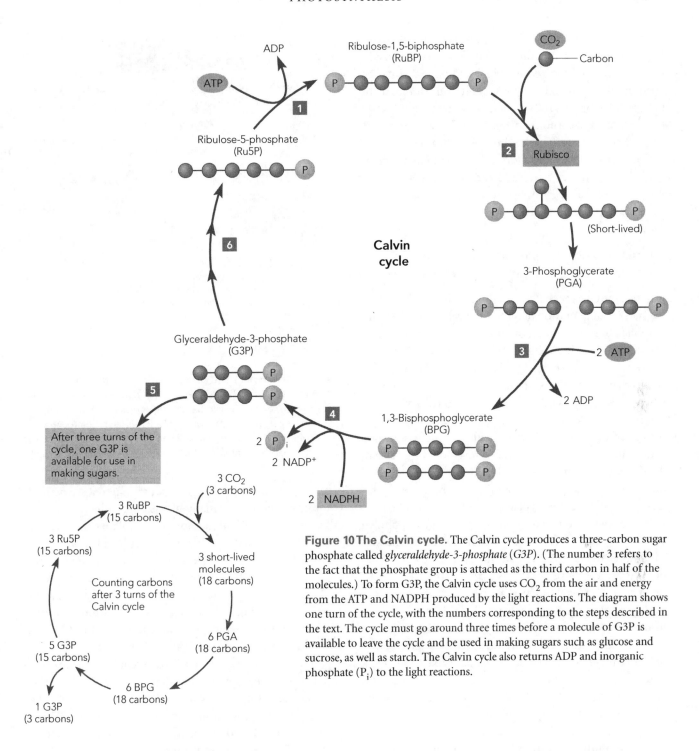

Figure 10 The Calvin cycle. The Calvin cycle produces a three-carbon sugar phosphate called *glyceraldehyde-3-phosphate* (*G3P*). (The number 3 refers to the fact that the phosphate group is attached as the third carbon in half of the molecules.) To form G3P, the Calvin cycle uses CO_2 from the air and energy from the ATP and NADPH produced by the light reactions. The diagram shows one turn of the cycle, with the numbers corresponding to the steps described in the text. The cycle must go around three times before a molecule of G3P is available to leave the cycle and be used in making sugars such as glucose and sucrose, as well as starch. The Calvin cycle also returns ADP and inorganic phosphate (P_i) to the light reactions.

The Calvin cycle is relatively inefficient at converting CO_2 into sugars

The efficiency of the Calvin cycle is the amount of chemical energy it actually uses to convert CO_2 compared to the amount of light energy received by the light reactions. The Calvin cycle's efficiency can be measured by comparing how much energy the cycle uses to fix CO_2 and how much light energy is needed to generate the NADPH that enters the cycle. The theoretical maximum for photosynthetic efficiency has been calculated to be around 35%. In the real world, however, most plants and algae achieve only between 1% and 4%. This reduced efficiency results in part from the fact that the Calvin cycle may waste up to half of the carbon it fixes. This occurs in a process known as *photorespiration*, which we will look at shortly.

Since production totals for photosynthesis involve large numbers that are difficult to imagine, let us consider a summary that involves one plant and one person. One corn plant fixes 0.23 kg (about a half pound) of carbon per season. A 45-kg (100-lb.) person contains about 6.8 kg (15 lbs.) of fixed carbon. Corn kernels that are eaten contain 10% or less of that carbon. A typical large ear of cooked corn has 100 kilocalories (kcal), so to maintain an adult human would require 25 ears of corn per day—or 9,125 ears of corn per year—equivalent to approximately a third of an acre of production.

The enzyme rubisco also functions as an oxygenase, resulting in photorespiration

Rubisco, the enzyme that fixes carbon in the Calvin cycle, is the most abundant protein on Earth. Every carbon of your body has been processed by rubisco because the carbon comes directly or indirectly from plants. In the summer, rubisco can cause up to a 15% decrease in daytime atmospheric concentrations of CO_2. Within plant canopies, where most photosynthesis takes place, the decrease is as much as 25%. Plants grow more rapidly if the CO_2 concentration of their atmosphere is artificially increased, as is sometimes done in greenhouses. The gradual increase in the CO_2 concentration of Earth's atmosphere as a result of the burning of fossil fuels by humans may be slowed by increased photosynthesis by plants.

The oxygen produced by the light reactions of photosynthesis actually inhibits net carbon fixation by rubisco. This is because rubisco, in addition to its role as a carboxylase (an enzyme that adds carbon from CO_2 to another molecule), can function as an oxygenase, an enzyme that adds oxygen to another molecule (Figure 11). Rubisco does not bind CO_2 strongly, and at higher temperatures and lower CO_2 concentrations rubisco is just as likely to bind oxygen. In this case, no carbon is fixed. One PGA and one molecule of 2-phosphoglycolate (a two-carbon compound) result from ribulose 1,5-bisphosphate. The phosphoglycolate is eventually broken down into CO_2. The production of CO_2 as a result of rubisco activity is known as **photorespiration** because it occurs in the light, produces CO_2, and uses O_2. Unlike respiration, photorespiration does not produce ATP. Photorespiration begins with rubisco activity and involves chloroplasts, peroxisomes, and mitochondria. At low CO_2 concentrations and high O_2 concentrations, the oxygenase function of rubisco predominates.

Overall, on bright, sunny days, when the temperature is around 25°C, O_2 may reduce the rate of CO_2 fixation

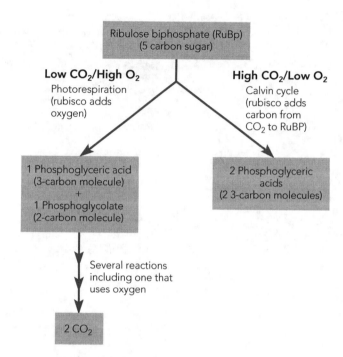

Figure 11 Rubisco and photorespiration. Rubisco, the fixation enzyme of the Calvin cycle, can function as a carboxylase (fixing carbon) or as an oxygenase (fixing oxygen), depending on oxygen concentration. As a carboxylase, rubisco facilitates production of sugars. As an oxygenase, it converts two carbons of ribulose bisphosphate back into CO_2, the process known as *photorespiration*.

by rubisco by 33%. As temperatures increase, the photorespiration rate of many plants equals the rate of photosynthesis. At higher temperatures, plants also begin to close their stomata, preventing water loss. Consequently, less CO_2 enters the leaf, less O_2 is released, and photorespiration results. Photorespiration reduces the growth rate of many plants, particularly on bright, hot days. Overall, photorespiration reduces net carbon fixation because it releases into the atmosphere a large amount of CO_2 that would otherwise be fixed in sugars. The situation is analogous to collecting sugar in a box, except that the box has a hole in it so that some of the sugar escapes.

By converting some fixed carbon back into CO_2, photorespiration wastes a significant fraction of the ATP and NADPH produced by the light reactions. Indirectly, in terms of productivity, it wastes minerals, water, light, and any other resources needed by plants to live and reproduce. In an environment in which one or more necessary resources are scarce, a plant that wastes up to 50% of fixable CO_2 may have difficulty surviving on its own and will be easily outcompeted for necessary resources by a more efficient plant.

Rubisco has been around at least 2 billion years and became the carbon fixation enzyme at a time when the at-

EVOLUTION

Evolution and O_2 Concentration

If you think about it, the O_2 produced in photosynthesis should be used up by respiration in both photosynthetic and nonphotosynthetic organisms. So, why does our current atmosphere have 21% O_2 when the Earth started out with none? In general, the idea that O_2 concentrations have gradually increased from zero to the current 21% is far too simple. The course and causes of changes in atmospheric O_2 concentration are areas of very active research.

After the Earth cooled enough so that gravity could retain an atmosphere, that atmosphere had a high concentration of CO_2—maybe up to 80%—and no O_2. When photosynthesis evolved in bacteria around 3.5 billion years ago, plenty of CO_2 was available. For the first 2 billion years or so, the O_2 produced by photosynthesis was taken up by iron deposits on the ocean floor. Then O_2 began to gradually appear in the atmosphere. Photosynthetic organisms evolved into a number of different forms, and so did nonphotosynthetic bacteria, thanks to the biomass and O_2 production of their photosynthetic kin.

Around 2.5 to 1.9 billion years ago, there was a surge in the amount of atmospheric O_2. Some investigators think the cause was an increased runoff and erosion from the continents, resulting in a buildup of ocean sediments that buried and killed many of the nonphotosynthetic bacteria living on the ocean floor. Thus, photosynthetic organisms, which absorbed light near the surface, predominated, causing the rapid increases in O_2 concentrations. Increased levels in O_2 may have made possible the evolution of eukaryotic cells around 2.2 billion years ago.

A second surge in O_2 concentrations occurred just before the Cambrian period, around 600 million years ago, and quite possibly for the same geologic reason. This increase in O_2 concentration may have fueled the huge adaptive radiation in invertebrate animals around that time. By the late Cambrian period, O_2 concentration had reached at least 2%, enough to allow the survival of land-based eukaryotes. Starting around 430 million years ago, the evolution and rapid spread of land plants caused the O_2 concentration to increase to a high of around 35% in the Carboniferous period, around 370 million years ago. This may account for the giant, two-foot dragonflies and other huge insects that existed then. The inefficient oxygenation system of insects puts an upper limit on insect size for any given O_2 concentration.

By the end of the Permian period, around 250 million years ago, the percentage of O_2 had crashed to 15%. The decline may have been caused in part by a large die-off of organisms, followed by their decay. Following these mass extinctions, photosynthetic organisms again predominated, and O_2 levels again increased.

---

mosphere had little or no free oxygen. The fact that the enzyme has an oxygenase function is a historical accident that only became significant when oxygen concentrations gradually increased as a result of the actions of photosynthetic organisms. Evidently, no single mutation can change the enzyme to eliminate photorespiration while retaining carbon fixation, because in the long history of competition and natural selection, such a mutation would surely have occurred. The resulting plant would have had a tremendous selective advantage and would have rapidly taken over most environments (see the *Evolution* box on this page).

In the future, it might be possible for genetic engineering to design a rubisco that has little or no oxygenase function and therefore up to twice the photosynthetic efficiency in plants. A computer that could simulate the effect of particular mutations on enzyme structure and function might demonstrate what specific amino acid changes would produce rubisco with no oxygenase function and a strong carboxylase function.

The C_4 pathway limits the loss of carbon from photorespiration

Remember that photosynthesis first evolved among bacteria and later algae in the water, where moderate light levels and temperature prevailed. On land, plants may have to contend with lack of water, higher light levels, and more extreme temperatures. These environmental conditions lead to closure of stomata, which helps plants by preventing water loss but also hinders photosynthesis by keeping CO_2 from entering the leaves. When the stomata close, the CO_2 concentration in leaves falls as a result of Calvin cycle activity, while the O_2

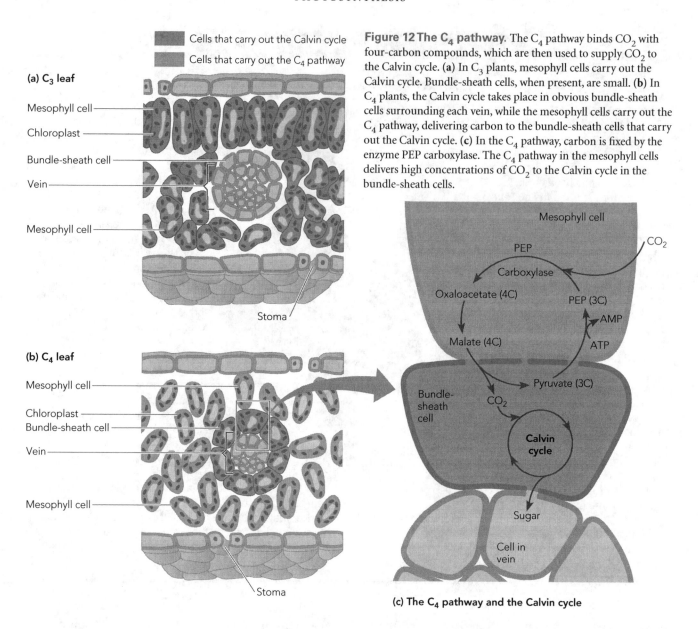

(a) C$_3$ leaf

Cells that carry out the Calvin cycle

Cells that carry out the C$_4$ pathway

Mesophyll cell

Chloroplast

Bundle-sheath cell

Vein

Mesophyll cell

Stoma

(b) C$_4$ leaf

Mesophyll cell

Chloroplast

Bundle-sheath cell

Vein

Mesophyll cell

Stoma

Figure 12 The C$_4$ pathway. The C$_4$ pathway binds CO$_2$ with four-carbon compounds, which are then used to supply CO$_2$ to the Calvin cycle. (**a**) In C$_3$ plants, mesophyll cells carry out the Calvin cycle. Bundle-sheath cells, when present, are small. (**b**) In C$_4$ plants, the Calvin cycle takes place in obvious bundle-sheath cells surrounding each vein, while the mesophyll cells carry out the C$_4$ pathway, delivering carbon to the bundle-sheath cells that carry out the Calvin cycle. (**c**) In the C$_4$ pathway, carbon is fixed by the enzyme PEP carboxylase. The C$_4$ pathway in the mesophyll cells delivers high concentrations of CO$_2$ to the Calvin cycle in the bundle-sheath cells.

Mesophyll cell

PEP

Carboxylase

Oxaloacetate (4C)

PEP (3C)

AMP

Malate (4C)

ATP

Pyruvate (3C)

Bundle-sheath cell

CO$_2$

Calvin cycle

Sugar

Cell in vein

CO$_2$

(c) The C$_4$ pathway and the Calvin cycle

concentration increases as a result of the light reactions. Under these conditions, rubisco is likely to add O$_2$ to other molecules instead of adding CO$_2$, leading to increased photorespiration and reduced photosynthesis.

Plants that waste energy in photorespiration also waste resources such as water and mineral nutrients. Natural selection will favor any change that aids photosynthesis in hot, sunny conditions. Among flowering plants, a number of tropical monocots and some dicots have an add-on to the Calvin cycle called the *C$_4$ pathway*. The **C$_4$ pathway** binds CO$_2$ into four-carbon compounds, which are then used to supply an increased concentration of CO$_2$ to the Calvin cycle. Scientists discovered the C$_4$ pathway in the 1960s, when they noticed that in sugarcane the first product of carbon fixation is a four-carbon molecule, hence the term *C$_4$* (Figure 12).

The C$_4$ pathway either prevents or limits photorespiration because its carbon-fixing enzyme, known as PEP carboxylase, only binds CO$_2$ and not O$_2$. Unlike rubisco, PEP carboxylase keeps binding CO$_2$ to carbon compounds even when the CO$_2$ concentration is low within the leaf.

Plants that have the C$_4$ pathway are known as **C$_4$ plants** and are more common in the Tropics, in arid regions, and in hot, dry, sunny environments. Plants that only carry out the Calvin cycle for carbon fixation are known as **C$_3$ plants.** Most C$_4$ plants have a different leaf anatomy than C$_3$ plants, a difference that is crucial to the operation of the C$_4$ pathway. In C$_3$ plant leaves, the Calvin cycle occurs in all photosynthetic cells, but in leaves of C$_4$ plants it typically occurs only in bundle-sheath cells, which appear in a prominent single or double layer surrounding each leaf vein (Figure 12a and b).

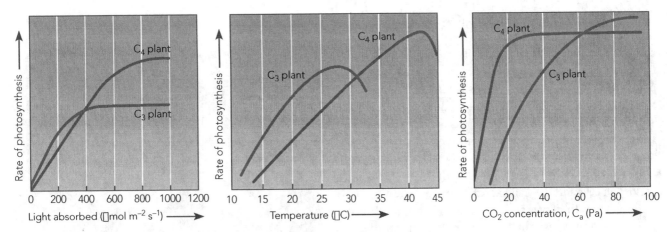

Figure 13 C$_4$ plants are more efficient than C$_3$ plants. When light intensity or temperature is high, or when CO$_2$ concentration is low, C$_4$ plants are much more efficient at photosynthesis, and therefore at utilization of water and minerals, than are C$_3$ plants. These conditions are often found in deserts and temperate grasslands.

This ringlike arrangement is often called *Kranz anatomy*, from the German word *kranz*, meaning "wreath or halo." All of the mesophyll cells in a C$_4$ leaf have only the C$_4$ pathway. These mesophyll cells feed CO$_2$ trapped in organic compounds to the bundle-sheath cells, where it is released and refixed by the Calvin cycle. Thus, the bundle-sheath cells have high concentrations of CO$_2$, allowing rubisco to fix CO$_2$ rather than O$_2$.

Apparently a C$_4$ pathway evolved several times in plants. It occurs in more than 19 families of flowering plants. Many cereals and other grasses are C$_4$ plants, but the pathway exists in some dicots as well. As you can see in Figure 12c, the enzyme PEP carboxylase fixes CO$_2$ in mesophyll cells of C$_4$ plants. The more efficient carbon fixation by PEP carboxylase is especially notable at low CO$_2$ concentrations, when rubisco would tend to bind O$_2$ to other molecules. PEP carboxylase attaches bicarbonate to PEP to make oxaloacetate. This four-carbon acid is typically converted to malate, a process that uses NADPH from the light reactions. Malate—or, in some plants, aspartate—moves into the bundle-sheath cells through plasmodesmata. The bundle-sheath cells break it down to pyruvate, a common metabolite in cells, regenerating both CO$_2$ and NADPH. Pyruvate—or, in some plants, alanine—is then moved back to the mesophyll cells, where PEP is regenerated by enzyme action.

The C$_4$ pathway would seem to be a relatively energy-inefficient process because ATP is needed to convert pyruvate to PEP, in addition to the three molecules of ATP used in the Calvin cycle. Despite this inefficiency, the C$_4$ pathway combined with the Calvin cycle will outperform the Calvin cycle alone on hot, sunny days, when photosynthesis is rapid and leaf CO$_2$ concentrations may drop (Figure 13). When temperatures are cooler and as the CO$_2$ concentra-

tion increases, the Calvin cycle alone—the C$_3$ pathway—is more energy-efficient because it requires less ATP.

The relative efficiency of C$_4$ plants can be demonstrated by a competition experiment. Wheat (*Triticum aestivum*), a C$_3$ plant, is put into competition in a closed container with corn (*Zea mays*), a C$_4$ plant. PEP carboxylase, the C$_4$ enzyme, is much more efficient at fixing carbon than is rubisco. Therefore the C$_4$ plant takes up most of the CO$_2$ in the air, the CO$_2$ produced by photorespiration in the C$_3$ plant, and the CO$_2$ produced by respiration in the C$_3$ plant. Before long, the C$_4$ plant is flourishing and the C$_3$ plant dies. If the plants occupy separate closed containers, each does well. Another common example of a C$_4$ plant outcompeting C$_3$ plants is found when the C$_4$ plant crabgrass (*Digitaria sanguinalis*) overgrows more desirable C$_3$ lawn grasses, such as Kentucky bluegrass (*Poa pratensis*), during hot, dry summer days.

Earth's atmosphere has a current CO$_2$ concentration of 365 parts per million (ppm), or 0.0365%. C$_4$ plants achieve maximum photosynthesis rates at around 50 ppm (0.005%) CO$_2$. Even on hot days with high light intensities, photosynthesis is occurring at maximum rates in the leaves of these plants. C$_3$ plants usually increase their photosynthesis rates as CO$_2$ concentrations increase up to 500 ppm (0.05%) and in some cases at even higher concentrations. These increases relate to the fact that increased CO$_2$ concentration in the leaves lowers the rate of photorespiration.

CAM plants store CO$_2$ in a C$_4$ acid at night for use in the Calvin cycle during the day

Some plants have a variation of the C$_4$ pathway called **crassulacean acid metabolism** (CAM), in which they take up CO_2 at night using the C_4 pathway and then carry out the Calvin cycle during the day (Figure 14). The name comes from the Crassulaceae family of succulent desert plants, in which the process was first discovered. Like C_4 plants, **CAM plants** live in regions where high temperatures necessitate closing the stomata during the day to avoid excessive water loss. CAM plants and C_4 plants differ in where and when they carry out the C_4 pathway and the Calvin cycle. In C_4 plants, both processes occur at the same time but in different locations: the C_4 pathway in mesophyll cells and the Calvin cycle in bundle-sheath cells (Figure 14a). In contrast, CAM plants carry out both processes in the mesophyll cells, but at different times: the C_4 pathway at night and the Calvin cycle during the day. At night, when it is cool, mesophyll cells use the C_4 pathway to bind CO_2 temporarily in malate within the vacuoles (Figure 14b). During the day, malate is transferred to the chloroplasts and converted to pyruvate and CO_2, which enters the Calvin cycle. During the day, CAM plants rapidly use the CO_2 stored during the night, so their overall photosynthetic production is less than that of other plants.

Like the C_4 pathway, CAM has also arisen several times in the evolution of plants. A typical environment favoring CAM is one with high temperatures during the day, high light intensity, and low water availability. Currently CAM exists in 18 or more plant families, mostly dicots. Some nonsucculent examples are pineapple and several seedless vascular plants, including some ferns.

Section Review

1. What are the main reactions of the Calvin cycle?
2. Describe the difference between the C_3 and C_4 pathways.
3. Compare and contrast C_4 plants and CAM plants.

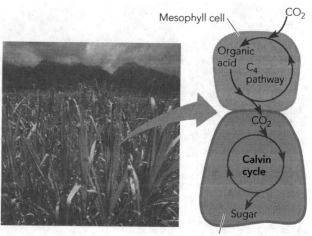

Sugarcane (C_4 plant)

(a) C_4 plants, such as sugarcane, run the C_4 pathway and the Calvin cycle simultaneously during the day. The C_4 pathway is carried out in mesophyll cells, while the Calvin cycle is carried out in bundle-sheath cells.

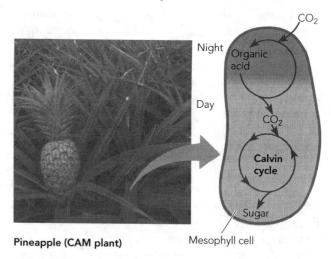

Pineapple (CAM plant)

(b) CAM plants, such as pineapple, run the C_4 pathway at night, allowing organic acids to accumulate in the vacuole. During the day, these organic acids are used to supply CO_2 to the Calvin cycle. The CAM pathway allows plants to keep stomata closed during hot, dry days while using CO_2 accumulated the previous night for photosynthesis.

Figure 14 Comparing C_4 and CAM plants.

SUMMARY

An Overview of Photosynthesis

Photosynthesis produces food, molecular building blocks, and O_2, which support almost all life on Earth

Plants, algae, and photosynthetic bacteria are photoautotrophs, getting all their energy from photosynthesis. Most nonphoto-synthetic organisms are heterotrophs, depending totally on other organisms for organic molecules. Photosynthesis provides the building blocks of life and sustains life by supplying O_2.

Photosynthesis uses light energy to convert CO_2 and H_2O into sugars

The light reactions take electrons from water and use sunlight absorbed by chlorophyll to energize them. Solar energy is used first to produce ATP and then to deposit energy-rich electrons in NADPH. Chlorophyll and other light-absorbing molecules are located in the thylakoids of chloroplasts. The Calvin cycle uses ATP and NADPH from the light reactions, as well as CO_2, to produce three-carbon sugars.

The processes of photosynthesis and respiration are interdependent

In photosynthesis, electrons from H_2O are energized by the Sun and linked with CO_2 to form sugars. In respiration, the carbons in sugars are used to make CO_2 while the energy in sugar is transferred to ATP and the de-energized electrons are added to O_2 to produce H_2O.

Converting Light Energy to Chemical Energy: The Light Reactions

Chlorophyll is the principal light-absorbing molecule of photosynthesis

Chlorophyll and other light-absorbing pigments are located inside the thylakoid membranes of chloroplasts. Chlorophyll uses blue and red light while transmitting green light.

Light energy enters photosynthesis at locations called *photosystems*

Solar energy energizes electrons in chlorophyll within light-harvesting units called photosystem I and photosystem II. These photosystems occur repeatedly throughout the thylakoid membranes. The light reactions capture about a third of the sunlight absorbed by chlorophyll.

The light reactions produce O_2, ATP, and NADPH

In the light reactions, electron flow first leads from water to a chlorophyll *a* molecule in photosystem II, where the electron is energized and transferred to an accepter. The electron gradually loses energy, which is transferred to ATP. The de-energized electron is transferred to a chlorophyll in photosystem I, where the electron is energized and transferred to NADPH.

In the light reactions, ATP is synthesized using energy from chemiosmosis

Between photosystem II and photosystem I, an electron transport chain uses light energy to pump H^+ ions across the thylakoid membrane. Some H^+ ions release energy as they move back across the membrane and through the enzyme ATP synthase, a process called *chemiosmosis*. ATP synthase uses the energy from chemiosmosis to produce ATP by phosphorylation.

Converting CO_2 to Sugars: The Calvin Cycle

The Calvin cycle uses ATP and NADPH from the light reactions to make sugar phosphates from CO_2

The Calvin cycle, which occurs in the stroma of chloroplasts, uses CO_2 from the air and ATP and NADPH from the light reactions to produce sugars. After three turns of the cycle, enough

CO_2 has been added to produce one molecule of G3P, which is used to make other sugars.

The Calvin cycle is relatively inefficient at converting CO_2 into sugars

The theoretical maximum for photosynthetic efficiency in synthesizing sugars is about 35%, but actual efficiency is between 1% and 4%, in part because the Calvin cycle may waste up to half of the carbon it fixes.

The enzyme rubisco also functions as an oxygenase, resulting in photorespiration

Rubisco, the carbon-fixing enzyme in the Calvin cycle, is the most abundant protein on Earth. At higher temperatures and lower CO_2 concentrations, rubisco binds O_2. When oxygen is bound, no carbon is fixed and two carbons are eventually released as CO_2, a process known as *photorespiration*. On bright, hot days, rubisco can be involved in carbon loss as frequently as in carbon fixation.

The C_4 pathway limits the loss of carbon from photorespiration

The C_4 pathway adds CO_2 to a three-carbon compound to produce a four-carbon oxaloacetate. C_4 plant anatomy features the C_4 pathway in mesophyll cells and the C_3 pathway in bundle-sheath cells surrounding vascular bundles in leaves. Malate from C_4 cells moves into bundle-sheath cells, where it is broken down into pyruvate and CO_2. Thus, high concentrations of CO_2 are supplied to the Calvin cycle, reducing photorespiration. C_4 plants are particularly efficient on hot, sunny days when leaf CO_2 concentrations are low and O_2 concentrations are high.

CAM plants store CO_2 in a C_4 acid at night for use in the Calvin cycle during the day

Some succulent, desert plants have a variation of the C_4 pathway called *crassulacean acid metabolism* (*CAM*). By taking up CO_2 at night through the C_4 pathway and using it in the Calvin cycle during the day, they can keep stomata closed during hot days.

Review Questions

1. What is the importance of photosynthesis for life on the planet?
2. Explain how photosynthesis and respiration are interdependent.
3. Describe the function of chlorophyll in photosynthesis.
4. Describe how a photosystem captures light energy.
5. What are the products of the light reactions and the Calvin cycle?
6. How do the light reactions and the Calvin cycle depend on each other?

7. Trace the pathway of an electron through the light reactions. Where does each electron begin, and where does it end?
8. Explain how ATP is synthesized during the light reactions.
9. How does the Calvin cycle provide building blocks for making more complex molecules?
10. Explain how the process of making sugar phosphates is a cycle.
11. Explain how rubisco is involved in photorespiration.
12. What is the difference between an oxygenase and a carboxylase?
13. How does the anatomy of a C_3 leaf differ from that of a C_4 leaf?
14. What types of environments favor C_4 plants? Why?
15. Compare and contrast C_4 plants and CAM plants.

Questions for Thought and Discussion

1. What kinds of life-forms do you think would exist after 6 billion years on Earth if photosynthesis had never developed? What life-forms would you expect if photosynthetic organisms were the only ones to evolve?
2. Suppose the Earth becomes warmer and has ever-higher concentrations of CO_2 over the next 500 million years. What types of plants might evolve?
3. If an asteroid strikes Earth and kicks up a thick cloud of dust that lowers the rate of photosynthesis by 90%, what immediate and long-term effects would you expect to find in animal and plant populations?
4. Suppose you own a greenhouse that produces salad greens and vegetables. Would it be worth your while to artificially increase the CO_2 concentration in your greenhouse's atmosphere? Explain.
5. Some scientific studies have shown that spraying methanol (CH_2OH) on plants increases carbon fixation by photosynthesis. What is happening?

6. From considerations of input and output of CO_2, O_2, H_2O, ATP, NADPH, and glucose, draw a flow diagram to illustrate the interdependence of respiration, the light reactions of photosynthesis, and the carbon-fixation (Calvin cycle) reactions of photosynthesis. It is suggested that you start by drawing three rectangular boxes side by side and label these, from left, "light reactions," "Calvin cycle," and "respiration." You can then indicate processes that occur within each box and the chemicals that flow from one box to another and interconnect the processes.

Evolution Connection

Biologists believe that the first living organisms on Earth, some 3.8 to 4 billion years ago, were chemoheterotrophs that utilized organic molecules formed in the Earth's atmosphere and oceans by nonbiological chemical processes, and that photosynthesis evolved later, once the supply of these organic compounds became depleted. From your knowledge of the processes involved, do you think that non-cyclic photophosphorylation evolved first and cyclic photophosphorylation evolved later, or was it more likely the other way around? Defend your answer.

To Learn More

Visit The Botany Place Website at www.thebotanyplace.com for quizzes, exercises, and Web links to new and interesting information related to this chapter.

Hessayon, G. D. *The House Plant Expert: The World's Best-Selling Book on House Plants.* London: Sterling Publications, 1992. Correct lighting is a key to having happy house plants.
Hobhouse, Henry. *Seeds of Change: Five Plants That Transformed Mankind.* New York: HarperCollins Publishers, 1999. Sugarcane is one of these five influential plants.

Respiration

Skunk cabbage (*Lysichiton americanum*).

An Overview of Nutrition

All living organisms need sources of energy and carbon

Plants use photosynthesis to store light energy in sugars and use respiration to transfer the energy from sugars to ATP

The breakdown of sugar to release energy can occur with or without oxygen

Respiration

Glycolysis splits six-carbon sugars into two molecules of pyruvate

The Krebs cycle generates CO_2, NADH, $FADH_2$, and ATP

The electron transport chain and oxidative phosphorylation transfer energy from the energy-rich electrons of NADH and $FADH_2$ to ATP

The energy yield from respiration is high

In some plants, the electron transport chain can generate excess heat

Plants, unlike animals, can make fatty acids into glucose

Fermentation

In the absence of oxygen, pyruvate produced by glycolysis is converted to ethanol or lactate

Some important industries rely on fermentation

Fermentation has a low energy yield compared to that of respiration

From Chapter 9 of *Introduction to Botany*, First Edition, Murray W. Nabors. Copyright © 2004 by Pearson Education, Inc. Published by Pearson Benjamin Cummings. All rights reserved.

Energy is vital for carrying out the biochemical and physiological functions necessary for life, both to construct organisms and to maintain them. In fact, living organisms are islands of order in a universe that is overall becoming more disordered. Living organisms use ATP and electron carriers such as NADH, NADP, and FADH$_2$ to facilitate chemical reactions. Non-photosynthetic organisms rely on photosynthetic organisms for organic molecules that can be broken down to obtain energy.

In photosynthesis, plants make ATP in the light reactions and use all of it in the Calvin cycle. Therefore, even though plants and other photosynthetic organisms can make their own food, they still must break down that food to produce the ATP and electron carriers necessary to build and maintain themselves. Unlike photosynthesis, which requires light and therefore occurs during the day, the breakdown of sugar and related molecules to obtain metabolic energy can occur around the clock.

An Indonesian corpse flower (*Amorphophallus titanum*) in Kew Gardens.

are too cold, they produce more body heat by breaking down more sugar and then breaking down the resulting ATP. In some cases, they use an alternate pathway to break down sugar, while releasing all of the energy as heat.

In contrast to mammals and birds, the temperatures of plants—as well as those of reptiles, amphibians, and fish—are usually close to that of the outside environment. Such organisms are much less active in using metabolic energy directly to control temperatures. Plants, for example, cease photosynthesis and respiration when temperatures are too cold. They may lose their leaves and may also enter a dormant state in which metabolism is slower or suspended until suitable temperatures return.

While plants do not maintain a constant body temperature, a few plants can maintain temperatures considerably warmer than the surrounding air by generating heat instead of producing ATP. In some plant species, the heat is used to melt snow and ice, enabling the plant to take

Environment can considerably influence how much metabolic energy an organism must use to survive. As a result of their biochemistry, living organisms can tolerate only a limited range of temperatures. Many environments have seasonal temperature extremes below or above those optimal for life. A number of different structures, physiological mechanisms, and behaviors have evolved that enable organisms to survive extreme temperatures.

As you will learn in this chapter, the process of breaking down sugar to transfer the energy to ATP is not totally efficient. Some energy is always lost as heat. Some animals, such as mammals and birds, maintain a constant body temperature by trapping this heat, using fur, feathers, and body fat as insulating materials. When conditions

advantage of sunny but cold days in early spring. In other plants, such as the corpse flower, the heat evaporates fragrant molecules from the flowers, attracting particular pollinating organisms.

The corpse flower and other "hot plants" are unusual examples of how plants use energy produced through respiration. In this chapter, we will examine how plants use respiration to obtain ATP and heat from sugars produced in photosynthesis and from other organic compounds. During respiration, these organic molecules are broken down in the presence of oxygen into CO_2 and H_2O, releasing energy that is either transferred to ATP or given off as heat. We will also look at an alternative metabolic pathway, known as *fermentation,* which occurs sometimes in plants and other organisms when oxygen is absent.

An Overview of Nutrition

The processes by which an organism takes in and uses food substances are known as **nutrition.** Once food is produced, it must be broken down by a series of biochemical reactions in order to release the energy it contains. In plants, animals, and fungi, respiration is the process that breaks down sugars, in the presence of O_2, into CO_2 and H_2O while using the energy released to make ATP and heat.

All living organisms need sources of energy and carbon

Organisms need carbon and energy in order to create organic compounds, which form the structural and energetic basis of life as we know it. Based on their source of carbon, organisms can be classified as either autotrophs or heterotrophs (Table 1). Plants are examples of autotrophs, organisms that obtain carbon from CO_2 and use it to make their own organic compounds. Animals are examples of heterotrophs, organisms that must obtain carbon by consuming organic compounds from other organisms.

Both autotrophs and heterotrophs can be further classified based on their energy source. Plants and most other autotrophs are photosynthetic organisms and are known as *photoautotrophs* because they get energy from light. Nonphotosynthetic autotrophs, consisting of a few types of prokaryotes, are known as *chemoautotrophs* because they get energy from inorganic chemical compounds rather than light. Most heterotrophs, including humans, get both their energy and their carbon from organic compounds, which means that you qualify as a **chemoheterotroph.** Some heterotrophs, consisting of a few types of prokaryotes, are **photoheterotrophs,** getting their energy from light but their carbon from organic compounds.

In addition to carbon, most organisms—whether they are autotrophs or heterotrophs—need mineral nutrients and specific organic molecules such as vitamins. However, only plants and other autotrophs can make their own organic molecules.

Plants use photosynthesis to store light energy in sugars and use respiration to transfer the energy from sugars to ATP

Like all organisms, plants and other photosynthetic organisms carry out respiration. Figure 1 provides an overview of the relationship between photosynthesis and respiration. The overall relationship between the two processes can be described as follows:

◆ Plants and other photosynthetic organisms collect solar energy to make ATP and NADPH. These reactions constitute the light reactions of photosynthesis.

◆ They use the energy of ATP and the energy-rich electrons of NADPH to convert CO_2 to sugars. These reactions constitute the Calvin cycle reactions of photosynthesis.

◆ The sugars produced as a result of photosynthesis are combined with minerals from the soil to make a host of different organic molecules, which are used as a source of energy and as a source of structural components such as carbon skeletons.

◆ If oxygen is available, the process of respiration converts some of the sugars produced by photosynthesis to CO_2 and H_2O, while the energy is released as heat or transferred to ATP.

The net result of the processes of photosynthesis and respiration is the transfer of light energy to chemical energy in ATP and various organic molecules.

As in photosynthesis, the synthesis of ATP during respiration involves phosphorylation—the addition of a phosphate group to a molecule. In the case of ATP synthesis, the phosphorylation is the addition of an inorganic phosphate (P_i) to an ADP molecule to make ATP.

Table 1 Sources of Energy and Carbon for Organisms

Type of nutrition	Energy source	Carbon source	Types of organisms
Autotroph			
Photoautotroph	Light	CO_2	Photosynthetic prokaryotes, plants, algae
Chemoautotroph	Inorganic compounds	CO_2	Some prokaryotes
Heterotroph			
Photoheterotroph	Light	Organic compounds	Some prokaryotes
Chemoheterotroph	Organic compounds	Organic compounds	Many prokaryotes and protists, fungi, animals, some parasitic plants

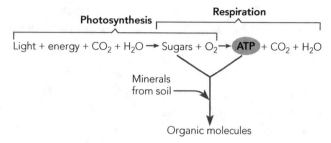

(a) Summary of the relationship of respiration to photosynthesis. Photosynthesis begins with carbon dioxide and water, and respiration ends with the same compounds.

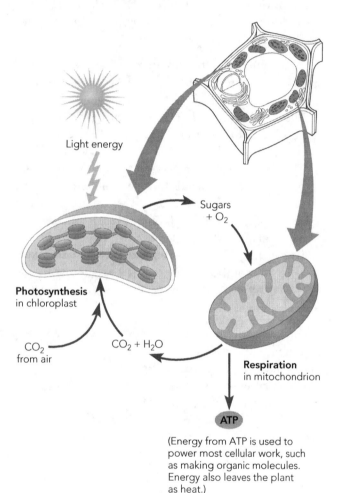

(b) Locations of respiration and photosynthesis in plant cells. In plants, photosynthesis occurs in chloroplasts, while respiration occurs in mitochondria.

Figure 1 Respiration and photosynthesis: An overview.

ATP synthesis can be carried out in several ways. The synthesis of ATP during photosynthesis is called *photophosphorylation* because it is powered by light energy. That is, light energy stimulates the electron flow through an electron transport chain that causes hydrogen ions (H^+) to move across the membrane—the movement known as *chemios-*

mosis. The enzyme ATP synthase then uses chemiosmotic energy to make ATP. In respiration, ATP is synthesized by two other types of phosphorylation: substrate-level phosphorylation and oxidative phosphorylation.

In **substrate-level phosphorylation,** an enzyme transfers a phosphate group from one phosphate-containing organic molecule to ADP, producing ATP (Figure 2a). This type of phosphorylation is so named because it involves an enzyme acting on two substrates: an ADP molecule and another phosphate-containing molecule. Chemiosmosis and ATP synthase are not involved, and the phosphorylation can occur with or without oxygen.

Oxidative phosphorylation is quite similar to photophosphorylation because it involves an electron transport chain, chemiosmosis, ATP synthase, and oxygen (Figure 2b). However, in oxidative phosphorylation it is energy from NADH—rather than light energy—that stimulates the electron flow for chemiosmotic synthesis of ATP. The process is called *oxidative phosphorylation* because it begins with oxidation, the loss of electrons. Specifically, NADH loses electrons to the electron transport chain, starting the flow of energy that ultimately powers the synthesis of ATP.

The breakdown of sugar to release energy can occur with or without oxygen

In plants, as well as in all other eukaryotes and some prokaryotes, the breaking down of sugars to obtain energy in the form of ATP follows one of two general pathways. One pathway is **aerobic,** which means it uses oxygen. The other is **anaerobic,** which means it does not use oxygen. Both pathways begin with a series of anaerobic enzymatic reactions known collectively as **glycolysis,** which takes place in the cytosol, the fluid part of the cell's cytoplasm. Glycolysis splits a six-carbon sugar into two molecules of pyruvate and also produces ATP and NADH.

Respiration is the aerobic pathway, in which cells ultimately require oxygen when breaking down organic molecules and converting the energy into the form of ATP. This process within cells is often called *cellular respiration,* to distinguish it from the use of the word *respiration* to refer to supplying oxygen to cells, as in the case of breathing in animals. In scientific usage, however, the term *respiration* means cellular respiration.

Respiration begins with glycolysis in the cytosol of the cell. The pyruvate produced by glycolysis then enters the mitochondrion, where it is broken down to form a compound called *acetyl coenzyme A,* or *acetyl CoA* (Figure 3). Next, acetyl CoA is broken down to supply two-carbon fragments that enter the phase of respiration known as the **Krebs cycle.** The Krebs cycle generates ATP by substrate-

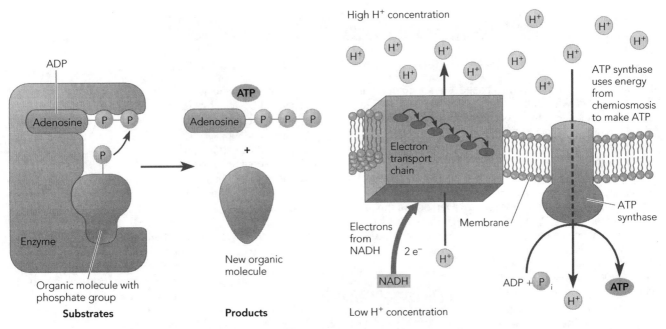

(a) Substrate-level phosphorylation. In synthesis of ATP through substrate-level phosphorylation, an enzyme transfers a phosphate from one substrate molecule to ADP, thereby forming ATP. Since this method relies only on enzyme action, it can occur with or without oxygen.

(b) Oxidative phosphorylation. In oxidative phosphorylation, ATP synthase produces ATP by using energy from chemiosmosis–the flow of hydrogen ions (H^+) from a region of high concentration to low concentration.

Figure 2 ATP synthesis by substrate-level phosphorylation and oxidative phosphorylation.

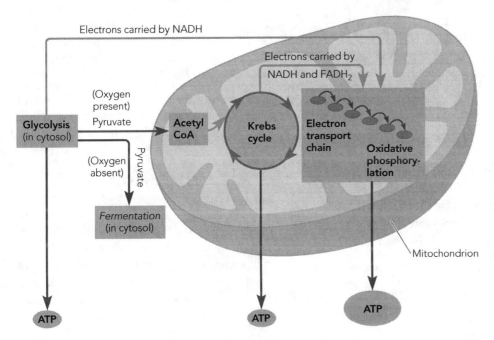

Figure 3 An overview of ATP production in respiration and related processes. Glycolysis takes place in the cytosol of the cell and produces a small amount of ATP. If oxygen is present, respiration occurs. First, the pyruvate from glycolysis proceeds to the mitochondria. Within the mitochondria, the following phases of respiration take place: the conversion of pyruvate to acetyl CoA, the Krebs cycle, the electron transport chain, and oxidative phosphorylation. The Krebs cycle produces a small amount of ATP. The greatest yield of ATP comes from oxidative phosphorylation, which is powered by chemiosmosis. If oxygen is absent, the pyruvate from glycolysis goes through the process of fermentation, and the only ATP produced is the small amount that came from glycolysis.

level phosphorylation. It also supplies the electron carriers NADH and $FADH_2$ to the last phase of respiration, consisting of an electron transport chain and synthesis of large amounts of ATP by oxidative phosphorylation. By definition, the term *respiration* refers to an energy-yielding process that uses oxygen. Actually, only the electron trans-

port chain directly requires oxygen. However, the Krebs cycle cannot occur unless oxygen is available for the electron transport chain.

If oxygen is not present, organic molecules are broken down through the anaerobic pathway, which is known as **fermentation** and takes place completely within the

CONSERVATION BIOLOGY

Global Warming and the Greenhouse Effect

Living organisms are carbon based, consisting of organic molecules, with carbon frameworks that were originally made by plants in photosynthesis. As you know, respiration breaks glucose and other sugars down to CO_2 and transfers the energy to ATP. Indeed, when any organically based material is burned, either metabolically or in a fire, the carbon is converted into CO_2.

Burning of large amounts of fossil fuels releases large amounts of CO_2 into the atmosphere. Even before the advent of civilization, CO_2 was released into the atmosphere as a result of volcanoes and forest fires. However, civilization has increased the release of CO_2 by burning fossil fuels. During the past century, scientists have monitored increasing atmospheric concentrations of CO_2 and noted increasing average temperatures.

Scientists theorize that temperatures might be increasing because of what is known as the greenhouse effect. This theory suggests that the gases that accumulate in the atmosphere, like CO_2, prevent heat from radiating into space. Instead, this heat is reflected back onto the earth's surface, raising temperatures, similar to the way a greenhouse traps heat. Scientists worry about the prospect of continued global warming as a result. They note

that, in this scenario, polar ice caps would melt, increasing the level of oceans, eventually inundating coastal cities.

In fact, the consequences of the greenhouse effect and of global warming are complex. Aside from human contributions to global warming, some scientists believe that warm temperatures may alternate naturally with cool temperatures in a cycle of hundreds or thousands of years. Consider the following scenario, which has been proposed by some researchers:

◆ As CO_2 concentrations and temperatures increase, so does photosynthesis. Rubisco performs very well at high CO_2 concentrations, and warmer temperatures encourage plant growth in temperate and even in subpolar regions.

◆ As a result of increased global photosynthesis, CO_2 concentrations in the atmosphere drop, causing temperatures to fall and global photosynthesis to decline. Polar ice caps once again begin to increase in size, and climates worldwide become colder.

◆ The colder temperatures cause plants to die off again. The plants are degraded by bacteria, releasing considerable CO_2 back into the atmosphere through respiration. This, of course, causes a renewed greenhouse effect and the whole cycle begins again.

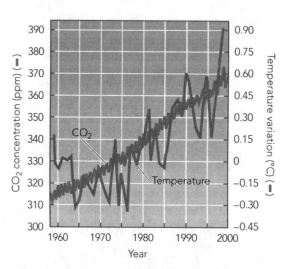

This graph shows the steady increase of atmospheric CO_2 (blue line) and a general warming trend (red line) since 1958.

---

cytosol. In fermentation, pyruvate is converted into either ethanol or lactate, depending on the organism. The process of fermentation is carried out by enzymes without an electron transport chain, and the only ATP produced is the small amount that came from glycolysis (see the *Conservation Biology* box on this page).

Section Review

1. **Describe how organisms differ in their modes of nutrition.**
2. **Describe the relationship between photosynthesis and respiration.**
3. **How does substrate-level phosphorylation differ from oxidative phosphorylation?**
4. **How do respiration and fermentation differ?**

Respiration

Respiration is usually described as including glycolysis, the Krebs cycle, and the electron transport chain with associated oxidative phosphorylation. We will describe glycolysis in connection with respiration because in plants and most other types of organisms respiration occurs more often than fermentation. Keep in mind, though, that glycolysis is necessary for both respiration and fermentation.

Glycolysis splits six-carbon sugars into two molecules of pyruvate

The term *glycolysis* (from the Greek *glyco*, "sweet" or "sugar," and *lysis*, "splitting") reflects the fact that the process involves splitting six-carbon sugars into two molecules of pyruvate, a three-carbon molecule (Figure 4).

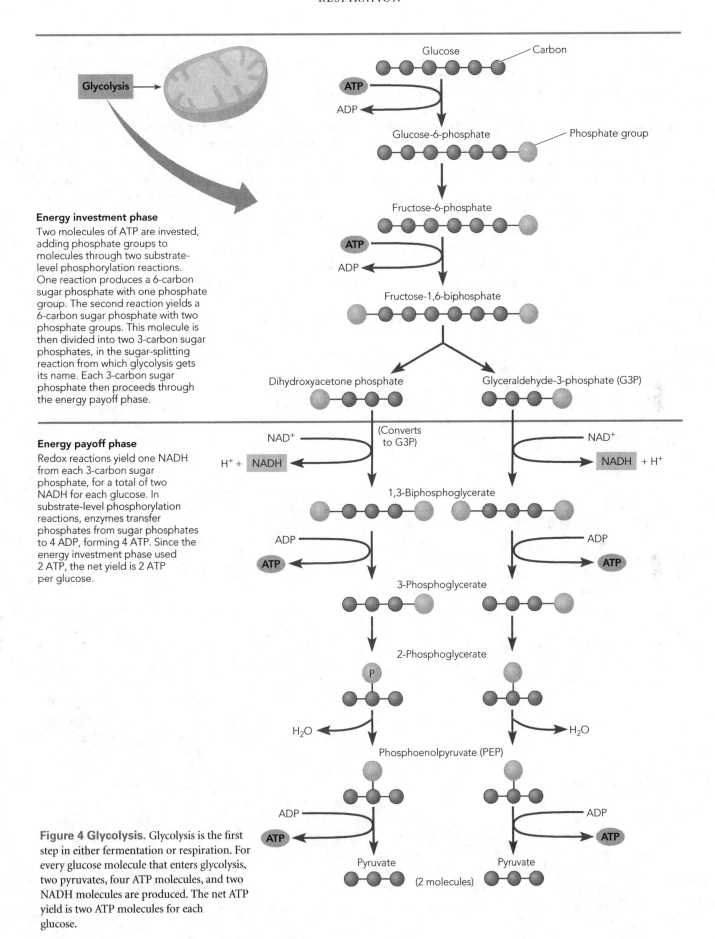

Glycolysis

Glucose — Carbon

ATP
ADP

Glucose-6-phosphate — Phosphate group

Fructose-6-phosphate

ATP
ADP

Fructose-1,6-biphosphate

Dihydroxyacetone phosphate

Glyceraldehyde-3-phosphate (G3P)

(Converts to G3P)

NAD⁺
H⁺ + NADH

NAD⁺
NADH + H⁺

1,3-Biphosphoglycerate

ADP
ATP

ADP
ATP

3-Phosphoglycerate

2-Phosphoglycerate

P

H₂O

H₂O

Phosphoenolpyruvate (PEP)

ADP
ATP

ADP
ATP

Pyruvate   Pyruvate
(2 molecules)

Energy investment phase

Two molecules of ATP are invested, adding phosphate groups to molecules through two substrate-level phosphorylation reactions. One reaction produces a 6-carbon sugar phosphate with one phosphate group. The second reaction yields a 6-carbon sugar phosphate with two phosphate groups. This molecule is then divided into two 3-carbon sugar phosphates, in the sugar-splitting reaction from which glycolysis gets its name. Each 3-carbon sugar phosphate then proceeds through the energy payoff phase.

Energy payoff phase

Redox reactions yield one NADH from each 3-carbon sugar phosphate, for a total of two NADH for each glucose. In substrate-level phosphorylation reactions, enzymes transfer phosphates from sugar phosphates to 4 ADP, forming 4 ATP. Since the energy investment phase used 2 ATP, the net yield is 2 ATP per glucose.

Figure 4 Glycolysis. Glycolysis is the first step in either fermentation or respiration. For every glucose molecule that enters glycolysis, two pyruvates, four ATP molecules, and two NADH molecules are produced. The net ATP yield is two ATP molecules for each glucose.

Glycolysis occurs in a series of ten reactions, each catalyzed by a specific enzyme.

The reactions of glycolysis resemble an assembly line, with the enzymes serving as metabolic control points. If the activity of one enzyme slows or stops as a result of being inhibited, so does the entire assembly line. A good example is phosphofructokinase, the enzyme that catalyzes the conversion of fructose-6-phosphate into fructose-1,6-bisphosphate. A molecule of ATP breaks down to supply the energy and the phosphate gained in this reaction. Inhibitors of phosphofructokinase include molecules such as ATP that indicate the cell has a good energy supply. Activators of phosphofructokinase include molecules such as ADP that indicate the cell may not have enough ATP.

For each molecule of glucose that enters glycolysis, two molecules of ATP are used in carrying out reactions and four molecules of ATP are produced, for a net gain of two ATP molecules. Meanwhile, two molecules of NADH are formed. The fact that glycolysis produces ATP and NADH tells us that two pyruvates contain fewer calories than one glucose, which can be confirmed with a calorimeter. Glycolysis generates an apparently meager amount of ATP and NADH for such a lengthy series of reactions. The reactions do, however, also produce intermediate compounds that are important sources of organic molecules for various cell processes. Glycolysis supplies sugars to make sucrose, the principal form of sugar transported from leaves to other parts of the plant. In addition, polysaccharides that help form cell walls originate from glycolysis. Glycolysis also supplies carbon frameworks for the synthesis of nucleic acids, some amino acids, and lignin, as well as glycerol used in the synthesis of lipids.

Scientists believe that the earliest organisms, which were prokaryotes that first evolved around 3.5 billion years ago, may have produced ATP solely through glycolysis. Respiration probably did not evolve until after significant oxygen accumulated in the atmosphere around 2.7 billion years ago (see the *Plants & People* box.

The Krebs cycle generates CO_2, NADH, $FADH_2$, and ATP

If oxygen is present, each pyruvate produced by glycolysis enters the mitochondrion and is transformed into a compound called *acetyl coenzyme A*, known more commonly as *acetyl CoA* (Figure 5). To form acetyl CoA, first a carbon is removed as CO_2 from pyruvate. The remaining two-carbon fragment is converted to become acetate, a process that generates one NADH. The acetate is then linked to a large cofactor called *coenzyme A*, forming acetyl CoA. Then acetyl CoA is broken down, with the coenzyme A (CoA) being recycled for use with another pyruvate, while the two-carbon fragment enters the Krebs cycle. Accordingly, this conversion process forms the link between glycolysis and the Krebs cycle.

The Krebs cycle takes place in the mitochondrial matrix, the part of the mitochondrion that is interior to both mitochondrial membranes. The conversion of pyruvate to acetyl CoA and the Krebs cycle itself generate all of the CO_2 produced by respiration. Meanwhile, each turn of the Krebs cycle involves considerable energy transfer, producing one ATP, one $FADH_2$, and three NADH molecules. The cycle begins when a four-carbon molecule, oxaloacetate, combines with a two-carbon fragment from acetyl CoA to make citrate. Since citrate is the first compound formed, the Krebs cycle is sometimes called the *citric acid cycle*. The resulting six-carbon citrate compound is converted to isocitrate. In each of the next two conversions, a carbon leaves the cycle in the form of CO_2 and one NADH is generated. The remaining reactions involve a series of four-carbon compounds and yield 1 ATP, 1 $FADH_2$, and 1 NADH. The cycle is completed with the regeneration of oxaloacetate, which can accept another two-carbon fragment from an acetyl CoA to begin the cycle again. The NADH and $FADH_2$ molecules produced by the Krebs cycle supply energy-rich electrons to the next phase of respiration: the electron transport chain and oxidative phosphorylation.

The electron transport chain and oxidative phosphorylation transfer energy from the energy-rich electrons of NADH and $FADH_2$ to ATP

The synthesis of ATP in the inner mitochondrial membrane depends on the electron transport chain. The oxidative phosphorylation of ADP to ATP is powered by the energy supplied by chemiosmosis—the flow of hydrogen ions (H^+) across the membrane. These ions have been pumped out by the electron transport chain. Some of them move back across the membrane in association with the enzyme ATP synthase, which uses this chemiosmotic movement of hydrogen ions as a source of energy to synthesize ATP. The process is quite similar to ATP synthesis in the light reactions of photosynthesis, which also involve an electron transport chain, chemiosmosis, and ATP synthase. As noted previously, though, in respiration the flow of electrons is caused by the oxidation of NADH (the removal of electrons from NADH) rather than by light energy. That is why the ATP synthesis during this phase of respiration is called *oxidative phosphorylation*.

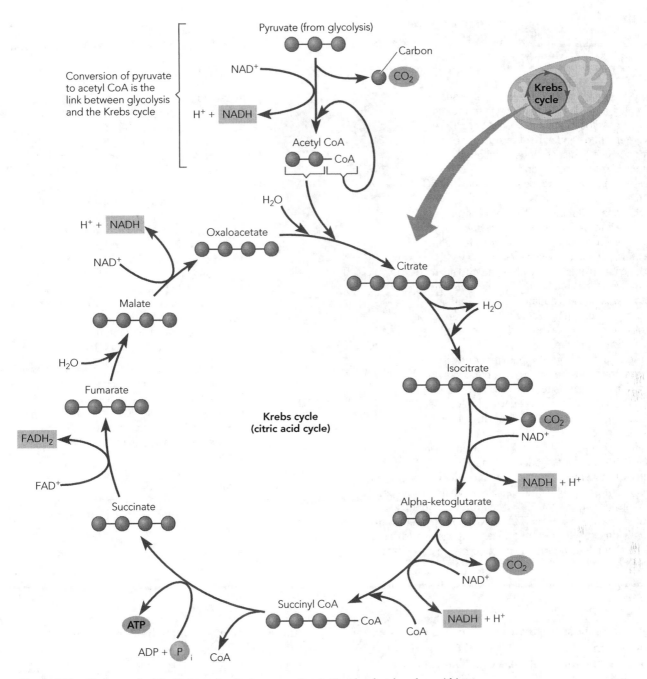

Figure 5 The Krebs cycle. The Krebs cycle, also known as the *citric acid cycle*, takes place within the mitochondrial matrix, the interior region of each mitochondrion. The conversion of pyruvate to acetyl CoA provides the link between glycolysis and the Krebs cycle. As acetyl CoA is broken down, a two-carbon fragment enters the Krebs cycle, combining with a four-carbon compound to produce citrate. Although the Krebs cycle generates only a small amount of ATP, it plays a key role in supplying the electron carriers NADH and $FADH_2$ to the electron transport chain, which makes possible the high yield of ATP from oxidative phosphorylation. Each turn of the Krebs cycle produces one ATP, one $FADH_2$, and three NADH molecules. Since glycolysis breaks each glucose into two pyruvates, the yield of the Krebs cycle per molecule of glucose is two ATP, two $FADH_2$, and six NADH molecules.

As in the light reactions, electrons pass from one electron carrier to another. Most of these electron carriers are protein complexes, with each electron carrier attracting the electron more strongly than the previous carrier. In this way, oxidation/reduction (redox) reactions move electrons along the electron transport chain while energy is released and transferred. The energy released by the electron transport chain pumps hydrogen ions into the

PLANTS & PEOPLE

Sucrose and Fructose: Sweeteners of Choice

When it comes to sweeteners, sucrose and fructose are used far more often in foods than glucose. After all, we sweeten coffee and almost everything else with sucrose (a disaccharide composed of fructose linked to glucose), and the most common sweetener in prepared foods is high-fructose corn syrup.

Sucrose, or table sugar, is so common partly because it tastes quite sweet as sugars go. The main reason, though, is that sucrose is the transport form of sugar in plants. Glucose is made in the chloroplasts and synthesized into sucrose for transport in the phloem. Sucrose is isolated from plants such as sugarcane and sugar beets, where it is found in high concentrations. Selection by plant breeders has resulted in varieties of the plants with high levels of sugar.

High-fructose corn syrup is frequently found in prepared foods because it is produced at low cost from corn kernels, which are rich in starch. The starch is converted by enzymes to glucose, which is then made into fructose. To our taste, fructose is considerably sweeter than glucose. On a weight basis, HFCS is 75% sweeter than sucrose. A 12-ounce soda sweetened with HFCS would require 10 teaspoons of sucrose for equivalent sweetness. HFCS consists of 14% fructose, 43% dextrose (glucose), 31% disaccharides, and 12% other products. The choice between sucrose and HFCS as a sweetening agent is frequently driven by sweetness considerations as well as by the market price and availability of corn, sugarcane, and sugar beets.

High-fructose corn syrup is the major sweetener in most processed foods.

In general, humans and other animals should consume only moderate levels of these sweeteners. All natural sweeteners add significant numbers of calories to a diet that contains them. Dangers of diets high in sweeteners such as sucrose or HFCS include diabetes, heart problems, and cholesterol buildup. In a United States Department of Agriculture (USDA) study, rats fed diets high in fructose and low in copper begin dying in five weeks instead of living a normal two years. Human studies on related diets were stopped when some subjects developed heart abnormalities. In general, diets high in sweeteners require relatively high levels of minerals such as magnesium, chromium, and copper to prevent known health risks.

Artificial, non-caloric sweeteners have come into use during the last century. They include

- aspartame, marketed as Nutrasweet, which is a dipeptide of two amino acids. Aspartame is 200 times sweeter than sugar.
- saccharin, which was discovered accidentally in 1879 in research designed to find food preservatives. Saccharin is 300 times sweeter than sugar.
- sorbitol, which is used mainly in pharmaceuticals, is 50% as sweet as sugar.
- sucralose, marketed as Splenda, is a modified form of glucose. Sucralose is 600 times as sweet as sugar.
- Acesulfame potassium is 130 times as sweet as sugar.

All artificial sweeteners are associated with health risks for some people who consume them.

---

intermembrane space between the inner and outer mitochondrial membranes (see Figure 6). The charge separation between the hydrogen ions outside the inner membrane and the electrons in the electron transport chain forms a potential energy gradient—a kind of battery that is measured as a pH difference between the solutions on each side of the membrane. The movement of the hydrogen ions back across the membrane and through ATP synthase then powers ATP synthesis. For every three hydrogen ions that move through ATP synthase, one ATP is synthesized.

The last electron carrier in an electron transport chain is known as the *terminal electron acceptor*. In the case of respiration, the terminal electron acceptor is an oxygen atom from the air, which is why organisms that carry out respiration require oxygen. The electrons and hydrogen ions unite on the inside of the inner membrane with O_2 from the air to become H_2O.

In theory, the energy in each NADH gives rise to three molecules of ATP, while the energy of each $FADH_2$ gives rise to two molecules of ATP because the electrons in $FADH_2$ carry less energy than those in NADH. Actually, the number of ATP molecules for each NADH could be higher or lower, depending on whether the NADH comes from glycolysis or from the Krebs cycle and also on how much ATP is already present in the cell.

ATP synthase has been called "a molecular machine" and is composed of three parts: a cylindrical rotor, a rod or "stalk," and a knob, with each part consisting of protein subunits. The cylindrical rotor spans the membrane and surrounds a channel through which the hydrogen ions flow. In the center of the channel is a rod connecting the rotor to the knob. The knob, which protrudes into the mitochondrial matrix, contains sites where inorganic phosphate (P_i) is joined to ADP to make ATP. The most interesting feature of ATP synthase is that both the cylindrical rotor and the rod spin, activating sites in the knob where ATP is synthesized.

The energy yield from respiration is high

Figure 7 summarizes the estimated energy yield from glycolysis, the Krebs cycle, and oxidative phosphorylation for one molecule of glucose: 36 molecules of ATP. This is an ideal value based on the assumption that chemiosmotic pumping of hydrogen ions from one NADH and associated hydrogen ions will yield three molecules of ATP, and that each $FADH_2$ will yield 2 molecules of ATP. As noted

earlier, the actual value can be higher or lower and would be expected to vary from one type of cell to the other.

The total yield of ATP from one glucose is sometimes calculated as 38 molecules. However, that does not account for the fact that two ATP molecules must be used in shuttling electrons across the mitochondrial membrane—specifically the electrons from the NADH produced in glycolysis. This shuttling is necessary because the inner mitochondrial membrane is impermeable to NADH. Subtracting these two ATP molecules gives the net ATP yield of 36.

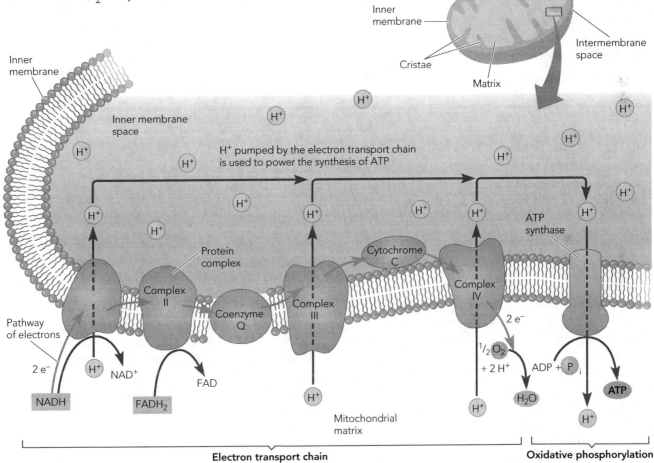

Figure 6 The electron transport chain and oxidative phosphorylation. While the Krebs cycle occurs in the mitochondrial matrix, the electron transport chain and oxidative phosphorylation occur within the inner mitochondrial membrane. Actually, many copies of the chain occur in the inner membrane, made possible by the increased surface area provided by fingerlike projections called *cristae*. NADH and $FADH_2$ enter each chain, which consists mainly of electron-carrying protein complexes. Complex I removes high-energy electrons and associated protons from NADH. Complex II removes high-energy electrons and associated protons from $FADH_2$. Complex III transfers the electrons to Complex IV, where they are combined with oxygen to make water. At complexes I, III, and IV, the energy released from the electrons pumps hydrogen ions into the intermembrane space. Chemiosmosis—the flow of hydrogen ions back across the membrane and through ATP synthase—provides the energy to synthesize ATP by oxidative phosphorylation.

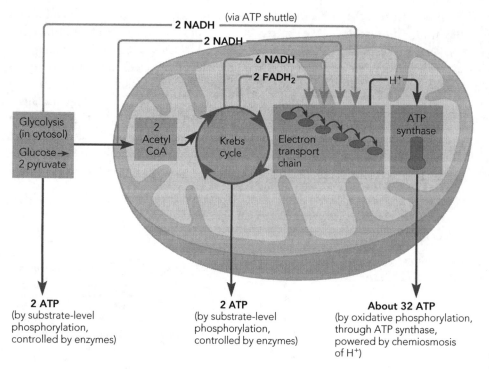

2 NADH (via ATP shuttle)

2 NADH

6 NADH

2 FADH$_2$

H$^+$

Glycolysis (in cytosol)

Glucose → 2 pyruvate

2 Acetyl CoA

Krebs cycle

Electron transport chain

ATP synthase

2 ATP
(by substrate-level phosphorylation, controlled by enzymes)

2 ATP
(by substrate-level phosphorylation, controlled by enzymes)

About 32 ATP
(by oxidative phosphorylation, through ATP synthase, powered by chemiosmosis of H$^+$)

Figure 7 Summary of estimated maximum ATP production in respiration. The numbers reflect the estimated maximum ATP yield per molecule of glucose. The estimates are based on the energy in each NADH being converted to 3 ATP and the energy in each FADH$_2$ being converted to 2 ATP. Since each glucose is converted into two pyruvates, two turns of the Krebs cycle are involved. Glycolysis produces 2 ATP, the Krebs cycle produces another 2 ATP, and the yield from the electron transport chain and oxidative phosphorylation is 32 ATP. At first it may appear that the latter figure should be 34 ATP. After all, the diagram shows 10 NADH and 2 FADH$_2$ entering the electron transport chain. However, we need to subtract the 2 ATP used in shuttling electrons from the NADH molecules produced in glycolysis. Therefore,

The synthesis of 36 molecules of ATP requires 262.8 kilocalories (kcal), representing 38% of the energy contained in glucose. The rest of the 686 kcal of energy in each glucose is released as heat. Actually, an energy yield of 38% is reasonably efficient. The useful yield in a gasoline engine is typically less than 25%, with 75% of the energy converted to heat or incompletely oxidized exhaust products, such as carbon monoxide (CO).

The synthesis and use of ATP in living cells is an undertaking of considerable magnitude. The average person who is neither a couch potato nor a lumberjack uses around 2,000 kcal per day, equivalent to about 0.45 kg (1 pound) of glucose per day. Calculations reveal that an average human cell produces and uses around 10 million ATP molecules per second. The overall metabolic rates of plants are 10 to 100 times less than those of most animals, but the number of ATP molecules produced and used in each typical living plant cell every second is still often in the millions. In short, the process of ATP synthesis and breakdown occurs on a phenomenal scale in living cells.

In some plants, the electron transport chain can generate excess heat

In some plants, an enzyme called *alternative oxidase* moves electrons from NADH to O$_2$ without leading to oxidative phosphorylation. When this alternative oxidase moves electrons, no ATP results, and the energy is all released as heat. This type of mechanism is used by plants to produce "hot" flowers that can melt snow, allowing the plants to take advantage of sunny but cold days. This is the same mechanism that enables bears to produce enough heat to survive during hibernation.

A few plants, particularly those in the Family Araceae, can metabolically maintain their flowers at a temperature considerably above that of their environment, for short periods of time, and even keep their temperatures at constant values. Why do they devote energy to this endeavor?

Many tropical plants in the Family Araceae—such as philodendrons, caladiums, elephant ears, dieffenbachias, and anthuriums—are grown as houseplants or in gardens in warm regions. These plants frequently have foul-smelling flowers that attract insects such as flies and beetles. A notable example is the corpse flower, which you saw at the beginning of the chapter. This extremely large Indonesian flower grows up to 3.7 m (12 feet) tall and is supported by a fleshy root weighing more than 46 kg (90 pounds). The corpse flower's common name comes from its aroma. The heating of the flower parts causes a large amount of aromatic molecules to evaporate into the air, thereby more effectively attracting pollinators. Presumably, plants with stronger odors attracted more flies and eventually produced more seeds, initiating the next generation. In this way, selection for flowers that were warmer and had a stronger odor occurred over successive generations (see *The Intriguing World of Plants* box on the next page).

THE INTRIGUING WORLD OF PLANTS

Skunk Cabbage

Among the examples of "hot plants" in North America are several species of skunk cabbage, such as *Symplocarpus foetidus,* found in the eastern United States, and *Lysichiton americanum,* found in the west. These members of the Araceae family bloom in January or February, and the heat produced by the flower bud can raise its temperature as high as 16°C (60°F). The bud frequently melts surrounding snow and readily survives many nights with temperatures considerably below freezing. The heat released also activates fragrant molecules from the flowers, giving the plant its distinctive name. Skunk cabbage maintains its high floral temperatures by converting starch, stored in a large fleshy root, into glucose or CO_2. The advantage of a skunk cabbage's high metabolism continues to be the subject of debate. Not many pollinating insects are out and about in January and February. On the other hand, pollinating insects are often

Skunk cabbage (*Lysichiton americanum*) melting surrounding snow.

found in the swamps of eastern and western Canada and the United States, where skunk cabbage grows. Any "early bird" flies would profit from using skunk cabbage as a food source and as a source of life-sustaining warmth, while the plants would profit by having pollinating organisms early in the season. Beginning growth so early in the season also gives the plant weeks of direct sunlight and, therefore, of photosynthesis without being shaded by other plants.

Some have suggested that skunk cabbage simply retains an adaptation that was useful in the Tropics (where the plant's strong odor would increase its chances of being pollinated) but has no use in temperate regions. This seems unlikely because the various species of skunk cabbage devote considerable energy to producing heat. A variety that saved the energy probably would have rapidly multiplied to become the dominant form in the population.

Plants, unlike animals, can make fatty acids into glucose

Animals can obtain energy from several sources. Starches and other carbohydrates break down or change into glucose that is metabolized by respiration. Fats break down to acetyl CoA that enters the Krebs cycle. Proteins break down to amino acids that enter the Krebs cycle at various places. Most organisms, including humans, can metabolize fats to glycerol and acetyl CoA units that can enter glycolysis and the Krebs cycle to produce energy (Figure 8). Hibernating animals, for example, have a sophisticated hormonal control system to regulate this process. Thus, organisms can store energy as fat, when extra food is available, and use fat to obtain ATP when food is in short supply. However, most animals—including all mammals—cannot convert fatty acids into glucose.

In contrast, plants and some bacteria can break down fatty acids into acetyl CoA, which is then used to make glucose. In this way, plants are more versatile than animals because they can use fatty acids as either a source of energy or as a source of glucose, which is water-soluble and readily convertible into forms that can be moved

throughout the plant. The ability of plants to use fatty acids for energy or for structural molecules may explain why so many plants have oil as a storage compound used to nourish germinating seeds.

Plants can convert fatty acids into sugars by virtue of the glyoxylate cycle, which occurs partly in microbodies called *glyoxysomes* and partly in mitochondria. Basically, the glyoxylate cycle is nothing more than the Krebs cycle with two additional enzymes that bypass the two steps of the Krebs cycle that release some carbon as CO_2. Since these carbons are not lost, they are available to synthesize glucose.

Section Review

1. **Describe the relationship between glycolysis and the Krebs cycle.**
2. **Explain the roles of the electron transport chain and ATP synthase in the production of ATP.**
3. **Summarize the products of glycolysis, the Krebs cycle, the electron transport chain, and oxidative phosphorylation.**

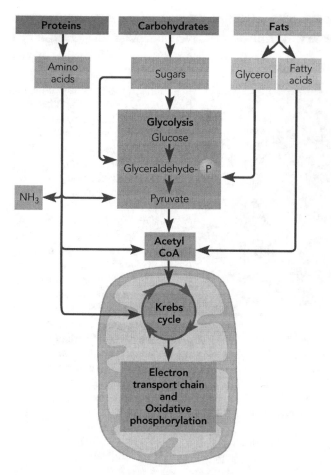

Figure 8 Substrates other than glucose can be used in respiration. Proteins, carbohydrates, and fats all feed into respiration at various locations.

Fermentation

Before photosynthesis evolved, respiration was not possible because of lack of oxygen. In today's world, anaerobic environments still occur where oxygen is excluded or when oxygen is used more rapidly than it can be replaced. Under such conditions, fermentation can occur. Some microorganisms, known as *obligate anaerobes,* require anaerobic conditions to survive. Others, known as facultative anaerobes, have the ability (faculty) to carry out respiration if oxygen is present or to carry out fermentation if oxygen is absent.

In the absence of oxygen, pyruvate produced by glycolysis is converted to ethanol or lactate

Fermentation converts pyruvate to other organic molecules, such as ethanol or lactate, while transferring electrons to NAD^+ (Figure 9). Because the NAD^+ concentration in living cells is very low, it must be rapidly regenerated so that glycolysis can continue and the cell can thereby obtain ATP. In the absence of O_2, the electron transport chain produces no NAD^+, so the regeneration of NADH to NAD^+ becomes the purpose of fermentation. In the early days of life on Earth, before photosynthesis had evolved, the atmosphere contained very little if any free oxygen, so glycolysis combined with fermentation was the only source of ATP. Living cells used primitive forms of glycolysis and fermentation to break down sugars and other molecules produced spontaneously in shallow, ancient oceans. Today, fermentation is restricted to certain environments where specialized bacteria live and to certain times in the life of all cells, but it plays a role in physiology, commercial uses, and disease. For example, yeasts are fungi that are used in the production of beer and wine by fermentation. (The term *fermentation* comes from the Latin word for yeast, *fermentum.*) Anaerobic bacteria of the genus *Clostridium* cause diseases such as gangrene and tetanus.

Most plant cells produce ethanol if deprived of oxygen; however, some species produce lactate, malate, glycerol, or both ethanol and lactate. Plants encounter oxygen deprivation when their roots are flooded because oxygen diffuses three million times more slowly in pure water than in air. In bogs and swamps, where many organisms compete for a limited supply of oxygen, seeds sometimes undergo oxygen deprivation during the early phases of germination. A lack of oxygen promotes grass seed germination, probably by stimulating synthesis of the plant hormone ethylene.

Animal cells typically cannot carry out alcoholic fermentation. If they could, then humans could get drunk simply by holding their breath. Instead, when oxygen is scarce, a process called *lactic acid fermentation* converts pyruvate to lactate. Typically, lactic acid fermentation occurs when the animal uses ATP to move muscles, which may become sore as a result of the buildup of lactate. If the circulatory system cannot keep up by supplying enough oxygen for oxidative phosphorylation, respiration is inhibited by lack of oxygen, but the organism still continues to produce pyruvate and ATP by glycolysis. In fact, both respiration and fermentation can occur in an organism at the same time. Unlike alcohol fermentation, lactic acid fermentation is reversible. When oxygen is again available, lactate converts to pyruvate, and respiration proceeds.

Some important industries rely on fermentation

The ability of yeast, a facultative anaerobe, to metabolize pyruvate into ethanol gave rise to the brewing and baking industries (Figure 10). In winemaking, sugary fruit juice, mixed with yeast cells, ferments until the alcohol concentration reaches 12%. At this point, the yeast cells die as a result of the alcohol they have produced. Any alcoholic beverage with a higher concentration of ethanol is fortified, meaning that alcohol that is concentrated by distillation was added to make the final product. If oxygen enters the process before completion, bacteria from the air rapidly convert ethanol to acetic acid. A solution of 9% acetic acid is vinegar. To make beer, wheat or some other starch-containing grain is germinated long enough to break down some of its starch to maltose, which can serve as food for yeast. When yeast is added, alcohol fermentation begins.

The fermentation process that produces ethanol also yields CO_2, which in turn causes the solution to bubble and appear active. In winemaking the CO_2 usually dissipates, whereas in the brewing of beer the CO_2 remains.

In the baking industry, yeast is mixed with a starchy, sugary dough that provides an anaerobic environment. The CO_2 produced by glycolysis and fermentation of sugar causes the dough to rise, and the alcohol that is produced evaporates during the baking process. People who say they love to be in the kitchen when bread bakes may be responding to the alcohol-enhanced aroma of the bread.

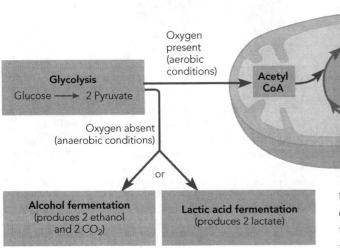

(a)

Fermentation has a low energy yield compared to that of respiration

Keep in mind that in fermentation, the conversion of pyruvate to ethanol or to lactate does not produce any additional ATP. The only ATP comes from glycolysis, which produces two ATP molecules per glucose. Each ATP has 7.3 kcal of energy, while glucose has 686 kcal. The energy yield of glycolysis plus fermentation is therefore 14.6/686, or just over 2%.

In contrast, respiration can generate a maximum of about 38 ATPs per glucose, for an energy yield of approximately 40%. One of the reasons you do not find anaerobic organisms dancing or playing basketball is that they do not have the energy and could not get it without consuming massive amounts of glucose or other foods.

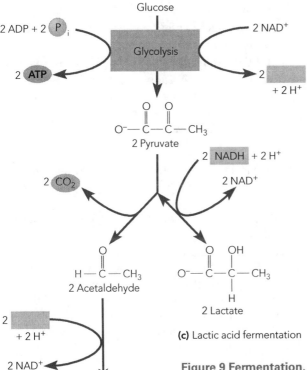

(c) Lactic acid fermentation

(b) Alcohol fermentation

Figure 9 Fermentation. (a) In the absence of oxygen, the Krebs cycle and the electron transport chain cannot function. Instead, pyruvate is converted to ethanol or to lactate in the cytosol. The production of both ethanol and lactate in fermentation serves to regenerate NAD^+, enabling the limited ATP production of glycolysis to continue. (b) Alcohol fermentation occurs in yeasts, most plant cells, and some bacteria. (c) Lactic acid fermentation occurs in a variety of cells in many types of organisms, including animal muscle cells. Lactic acid fermentation by some fungi and bacteria is used to make cheese and yogurt.

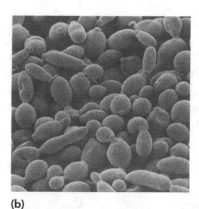

(b)

Figure 10 Some commercial uses of fermentation. During the making of beer and wine, yeast converts sugar to pyruvate and then to ethanol. In wine, the CO_2 produced is allowed to escape, whereas in beer it is retained in the final product. **(a)** Modern wineries and breweries such as this microbrewery often use stainless steel containers. **(b)** This scanning electron microscope image of yeast (Saccharomyces cerevisiae) shows yeast in the process of "budding" or reproducing.

(a)

Section Review

1. What is fermentation, and how does it differ from respiration?
2. How does fermentation play a role in making beer, wine, and bread?
3. Why do anaerobic organisms have less available energy than aerobic organisms?

SUMMARY

An Overview of Nutrition

All living organisms need sources of energy and carbon
Most autotrophs are photoautotrophs, obtaining energy from light and carbon from CO_2. A few are chemoautotrophs, obtaining energy from inorganic compounds. Most heterotrophs are chemoheterotrophs, obtaining both energy and carbon from organic compounds, but a few are photoheterotrophs, obtaining energy from light instead.

Plants use photosynthesis to store light energy in sugars and use respiration to transfer the energy from sugars to ATP
In respiration, organisms break down sugars and other organic compounds to make ATP. During respiration, ATP synthesis occurs by substrate-level phosphorylation and oxidative phosphorylation.

The breakdown of sugar to release energy can occur with or without oxygen
Through either respiration or fermentation, all living cells break down glucose to CO_2 and H_2O, yielding ATP. Both fermentation and respiration use glycolysis to break glucose into pyruvate. Under aerobic conditions, respiration occurs, which involves the breakdown of pyruvate to acetyl CoA, the Krebs cycle, the electron transport chain, and oxidative phosphorylation.

Respiration

Glycolysis splits six-carbon sugars into two molecules of pyruvate
Glycolysis consists of ten reactions that convert a six-carbon sugar into two molecules of pyruvate. From one glucose, gly-

colysis produces two molecules of ATP and two molecules of NADH. Intermediate compounds serve as reactants to form various compounds.

The Krebs cycle generates CO_2, NADH, $FADH_2$, and ATP

As pyruvate leaves glycolysis, it is converted to two molecules of acetyl CoA and two molecules of CO_2. In the Krebs cycle, the acetyl groups are converted to CO_2. In two turns of the cycle, energy from one glucose is transferred to two molecules of ATP, while energy-rich electrons and accompanying hydrogens are incorporated into six molecules of NADH and two molecules of $FADH_2$.

The electron transport chain and oxidative phosphorylation transfer energy from the energy-rich electrons of NADH and $FADH_2$ to ATP

Energy released from the electron transport chain moves hydrogen ions across a membrane. This chemiosmotic coupling creates a charge difference and pH difference across the membrane, which functions as a battery to power oxidative phosphorylation by ATP synthase. The electrons from the electron transport chain, along with associated hydrogen ions, are combined with oxygen to produce water.

The energy yield from respiration is high

The net maximum energy yield from one glucose is 36 molecules of ATP, representing about 40% of the energy in glucose. The remaining energy is released as heat.

In some plants, the electron transport chain can generate excess heat

Using an alternative oxidase, electrons can bypass the electron transport chain, resulting in almost all of the stored energy being released as heat.

Plants, unlike animals, can make fatty acids into glucose

Plants and animals can convert fatty acids into acetyl CoA, which is metabolized to CO_2 in the Krebs cycle. Plants can also break down fatty acids into acetyl CoA, which is used to make glucose, without production of CO_2.

Fermentation

In the absence of oxygen, pyruvate produced by glycolysis is converted to ethanol or lactate

Fermentation converts pyruvate to other organic molecules, such as ethanol or lactate, while transferring electrons from NAD^+ to NADH.

Some important industries rely on fermentation

The baking, brewing, and winemaking industries are based on the ability of yeast to ferment sugars into ethanol and CO_2.

Fermentation has a low energy yield compared to that of respiration

The ATP yield of fermentation per molecule of glucose consists only of the two ATP molecules produced by glycolysis, or about 2% of the energy in glucose.

Review Questions

1. What is the difference between autotrophs and heterotrophs?
2. What is the net result of the processes of photosynthesis and respiration?
3. Distinguish between the three types of ATP synthesis.
4. What is the function of ATP and of NADH in cells?
5. What are the end products of glycolysis?
6. What enters the Krebs cycle and what are the end products?
7. Compare and contrast glycolysis and the Krebs cycle.
8. Explain how oxidative phosphorylation is both separate from and dependent upon the electron transport chain.
9. Describe in general how glycolysis, the Krebs cycle, the electron transport chain, and oxidative phosphorylation are related.
10. Describe ATP synthase and what it does.
11. How does fermentation differ from respiration in terms of process and the amount of ATP yielded?
12. What can plants do with fat that animals cannot do? Explain why.

Questions for Thought and Discussion

1. If you hold your breath, what happens to the glucose molecules in your cells that are being used for energy?
2. Which do you think evolved first, photosynthesis or respiration? Explain.
3. Why do most eukaryotes die if oxygen is cut off? Why are they unable to survive using fermentation?
4. Plants produce ATP in photosynthesis, so why do they need to carry out respiration?
5. When ATP is broken down some energy is released as heat. Does this mean that the temperature of a plant will always be somewhat higher than the outside temperature? Explain.
6. Make a series of diagrams to illustrate the process of aerobic respiration in a plant. Your diagrams should be, in order: (a) an entire plant; (b) an individual plant cell; (c) a close-up of a portion of the cytoplasm of a plant cell, showing an individual mitochondrion; and (d) a close-up of a portion of a mitochondrion. In each diagram, draw and label the individual processes and reactions to a degree of detail appropriate to the diagram.

Evolution Connection

Biologists believe that the reactions of glycolysis and fermentation evolved early on in the history of life on Earth and that the Krebs cycle was added later. Explain why this hypothesis is reasonable. Is there any evidence to support it?

To Learn More

Visit The Botany Place Website at www.thebotanyplace.com for quizzes, exercises, and Web links to new and interesting information related to this chapter.

Gardenway Staff and P. Hobson. *Making Cheese, Butter, and Yogurt.* North Adams, MA: Storey Books, 1997. This book is packed with information about cheese and has a variety of recipes.

Mathews, C. K., Van Holde, K. E., and K. G. Ahern. *Biochemistry.* San Francisco: Benjamin Cummings, 2000. This excellent text contains detailed information on respiration.

Robbins, Louise. *Louis Pasteur: And the Hidden World of Microbes.* New York: Oxford Portraits in Science, 2001. This book examines Pasteur's experiments of microbes in fermentation and various diseases, as well as the changes in medicine and public perception of disease that resulted from his work.

Transport in Plants

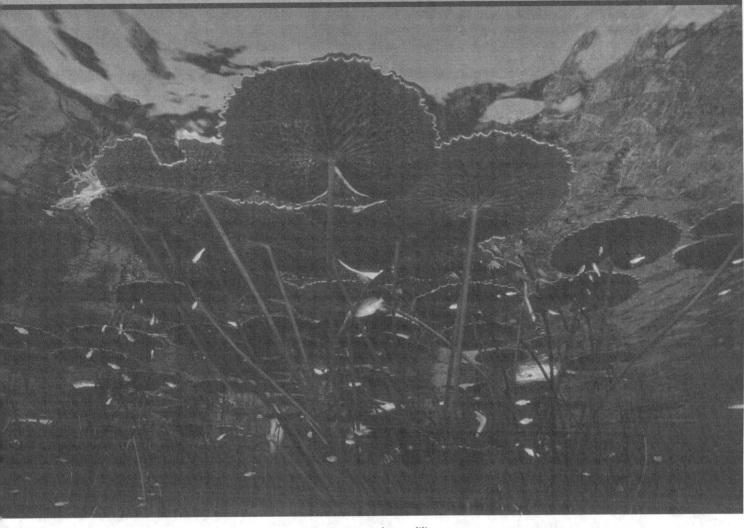

Long-stemmed water lilies.

Molecular Movement Across Membranes

Diffusion is the spontaneous movement of molecules down a concentration gradient

Facilitated diffusion and active transport use proteins to assist in movement across membranes

Exocytosis and endocytosis transport large molecules

Osmosis is the movement of water across a selectively permeable membrane

In plant cell growth, the osmotic potential inside the cell interacts with pressure generated by the cell wall

Movement and Uptake of Water and Solutes in Plants

Water evaporation from leaves pulls water through the xylem from the roots

Stomata control gas exchange and water loss for the plant

Sugars and other organic molecules move from leaves to roots in the phloem

Soil, Minerals, and Plant Nutrition

Soil is made of ground-up particles of rocks surrounded by negative charges that bind water and minerals

Plants require 17 essential elements, most of which are obtained from soil

Soil particles bind water and mineral ions

Bacteria in the soil make nitrogen available to plants

From Chapter 10 of *Introduction to Botany*, First Edition, Murray W. Nabors. Copyright © 2004 by Pearson Education, Inc. Published by Pearson Benjamin Cummings. All rights reserved.

What are plants made of? Today we tend to answer that question by mentioning molecules such as DNA and enzymes, sugars and amino acids, and hormones that a plant makes out of simpler inorganic components. In any case, our answer involves the system of chemistry we have studied. Human understanding of chemistry used to be much simpler, back when everything was thought to consist of only four elements. The Greek philosopher Empedocles (around 450 B.C.) and later Aristotle (384–322 B.C.) believed that everything in the universe consisted of various combinations of earth, air, fire, and water. Some Greek philosophers added a fifth element, called *quintessence,* which characterized the celestial as opposed to the terrestrial realm.

In truth, some reasonably good science was done under the earth, air, fire, and water system of what we will call the "old" chemistry. Around 1600, the Belgian chemist Jan Baptista van Helmont conducted an experiment to determine the relative contributions of earth and water to plant growth. He planted a 2.3 kilogram (5 pound) willow tree in a tub containing 90.9 kg (200 pounds) of oven-baked, dry soil. For five years, he watered and cared

for the tree. At the end of that time, the tree weighed 76.9 kg (167 pounds), but the soil had lost only 57 mg (2 ounces). Observing that the tree had absorbed large quantities of water but only a small amount of soil, van Helmont concluded that it was made almost completely of water. Indeed, even modern chemistry would concede that water is the most common molecule found in a plant, accounting for perhaps 60% of its weight.

In 1699, an Englishman named John Woodward carried out an experiment in London using spearmint plants, arriving at a conclusion distinctly different from van Helmont's. He placed plants in four water sources: rainwater, Thames River water, Hyde Park sewer water, and Hyde Park sewer water plus garden soil. After 77 days he collected the following data on the weight gain of the four groups of plants:

Water source	Weight gain [in grains, 1 grain = 64.8 milligrams (mg) = 0.002 ounce (oz)]
Rain	17.5
Thames River	26.0
Hyde Park sewer	139.0
Hyde Park sewer and garden soil	284.0

Woodward observed that plant growth increased in proportion to the amount of soil or silt in each water source. He concluded that plants are made primarily from earth. We now know that minerals from the soil are essential for plant growth, but actually they contribute only a small percentage of a plant's weight.

Farmers have known for centuries that plant growth improved when animal manure was added to the soil. In the 1700s, they began to take note of the fact that various naturally occurring mineral deposits worked as well in the fields as manure. For example, marl—which we know as lime or calcium carbonate ($CaCO_3$)—was known to be useful if worked into the soil.

Farmers recognized also that saltpeter (potassium nitrate, KNO_3) from decaying plant and animal remains could help plants grow. Around 1731, an English agriculturalist named Jethro Tull asserted that saltpeter was a fifth element in plants. Tull was probably the first investigator to propose that the old four-element chemistry could not adequately describe the composition of plants. He also believed that plant roots had tiny mouths that they used to eat the earth, and that plowing the earth into bite-sized pieces would make it easier for plants to consume.

Around this same time, scientists began to identify the chemical elements recognized by chemists today. For example, in 1771, Joseph Priestley determined that plants produced something that enabled candles to burn and animals to survive. He had discovered oxygen. Scientists continued to define individual elements of the new chemistry, and in 1866, Demitri Mendeleev published the first periodic table, listing some 46 elements. The old chemistry was officially dead.

We now know that plants require at least 17 elements to compose their biochemical structures. Carbon comes from the air as CO_2, plants can obtain the oxygen and hydrogen they need by splitting water molecules, and other elements come from the soil. Since water and mineral absorption occurs in the roots and photosynthesis takes place in the leaves, plants need a system of transport to move molecules to where they are needed. In this chapter, we will look at how inorganic and organic molecules are transported between cells and throughout the plant as a whole.

Molecular Movement Across Membranes

Plant cells have several ways to import and export molecules that are important for cellular growth and development. These molecules include both water and various **solutes,** molecules that dissolve in water. Some solutes used by plants are mineral ions, such as potassium and phosphorus, found in the soil. Others are organic molecules such as sugars that are synthesized by plants in particular cells and needed by cells throughout the plant.

Molecules can move through the interior of cells or within cell walls. Movement through the interior of cells is known as **symplastic transport** (from the Greek *sym,* "with") because molecules move within the cytoplasm. The continuum of cytoplasm between cells, joined by the channels called *plasmodesmata,* is known as the *symplast* of a plant. The plasma membrane is selectively permeable, governing entry of molecules into the cytoplasm of each cell, often restricting movement of some molecules while enhancing movement of others.

The continuum of cell walls throughout the plant is known as the *apoplast* (from the Greek *apo,* "away from").

The movement of molecules within the cell walls is called **apoplastic transport,** in which molecules pass around ("away from") the cytoplasm of cells. Apoplastic transport can be rapid because the molecules are not being filtered through the plasma membrane and cytoplasm of cells, but the cells have no control over the types of molecules being transported.

The movement of a molecule through a plant typically involves both apoplastic transport and symplastic transport. We will now look at the types of symplastic transport across plasma membranes: diffusion, facilitated diffusion, active transport, the movement of large molecules by exocytosis and endocytosis, and osmosis.

Diffusion is the spontaneous movement of molecules down a concentration gradient

If you place a drop of red food coloring in one end of a filled bathtub and a drop of blue food coloring in the other end, the molecules in each drop will spontaneously spread out until the concentration of each food coloring is uniform throughout the tub. The tendency of molecules to spread out spontaneously within the available space is called **diffusion** (Figure 1a). In diffusion, solutes

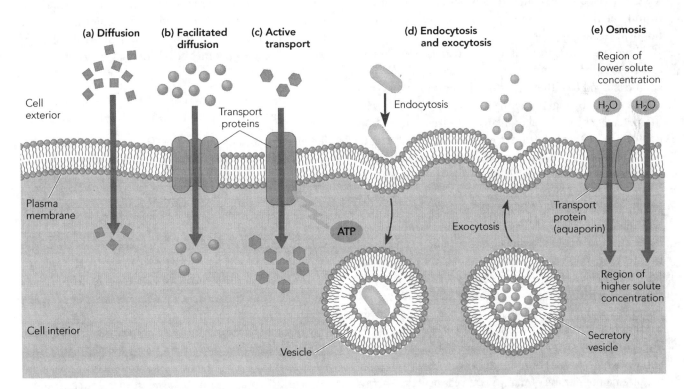

Figure 1 Transport of molecules across membranes. (a) In diffusion, a solute moves spontaneously to a region of lower solute concentration. **(b)** In facilitated diffusion, transport proteins help solutes diffuse more rapidly through the membrane. **(c)** Unlike diffusion and facilitated diffusion, active transport requires energy, as transport proteins move solutes "uphill" to a region of higher solute concentration. **(d)** Vesicles move large molecules into a cell (endocytosis) or out of a cell (exocytosis). **(e)** Water movement across a membrane, called *osmosis,* occurs with or without transport proteins. Water moves to a region of higher solute concentration (lower water concentration).

gradually move through a **concentration gradient,** a transition between regions of higher and lower concentrations. In diffusion, the movement is *down* a concentration gradient, from a region of higher concentration to a region of lower concentration. Such movement leads to an **equilibrium**—a random, equal distribution. Diffusion is passive transport because it does not require energy. It can occur in open solutions or between two solutions separated by a membrane, particularly for lipid-soluble substances that move readily through membranes.

Facilitated diffusion and active transport use proteins to assist in movement across membranes

For many water-soluble molecules, transport proteins assist diffusion through the plasma membrane, a process called **facilitated diffusion** (Figure 1b). The transport proteins are typically embedded in the plasma membrane. When a transport protein binds with a solute, the protein changes shape in a manner that delivers the solute to the other side of the membrane. Facilitated diffusion is similar to regular diffusion because the solute moves from a region of higher solute concentration to a region of lower solute concentration. Also, as with all types of diffusion, the transport is passive, which means that it does not involve any input of energy.

Some transport proteins appear to act alone. Others associate to form channels in the plasma membrane and can be shaped to either block or open a so-called *gated channel,* thereby regulating the transport of solutes. The diameter of the channel regulates the size of molecules that can move through from one side of the membrane to the other. Specific binding sites also control whether specific solutes can enter the channel. The channels can be opened or closed by specific solutes to be transported or by other molecules that control diffusion.

Sometimes transport across a membrane moves *up* a concentration gradient, from a region of lower concentration to a region of higher concentration. Since this transport requires energy to move up the gradient, it is not passive, like diffusion, but is instead called **active transport** (Figure 1c). The energy for most active transport is supplied by ATP or by the release of energy in electron transport chains. Active transport can involve a single protein or two proteins. For example, a transport protein in the plasma membrane of many plant cells uses the energy from ATP to pump hydrogen (H^+) ions to the outside of the cell. A second protein, called a *cotransporter protein,* then allows the H^+ ions to flow back across the membrane if accompanied by a sucrose molecule. Chemiosmosis is a form of active transport that uses energy from an electron transport chain to pump H^+ ions across the plasma membrane. The battery-like charge differential across the membrane is then used as a source of energy to synthesize ATP as the H^+ ions flow back across the membrane through the enzyme ATP synthase.

Exocytosis and endocytosis transport large molecules

Large molecules and multimolecular components often leave plant cells by **exocytosis,** a process in which small membrane-bound vesicles containing specific molecules fuse with the plasma membrane to release their contents from the cell (Figure 1d). Mucigel secretion from the root cap, placement of cell wall components, and the release of digestive enzymes of carnivorous plants are all examples of exocytosis in plants. Plant cells can also take up large molecules—a process known as **endocytosis,** in which the plasma membrane surrounds a large molecule and pinches off, enclosing the molecule within a vesicle inside the cell. In other words, endocytosis is the reverse of exocytosis. Since plant cells have cell walls, endocytosis is not as important a process as in animal cells. Many single-celled algae are photosynthetic and can absorb organic molecules as well. Individual molecules are taken up by facilitated diffusion, while larger fragments of many molecules can sometimes be taken up by endocytosis.

Osmosis is the movement of water across a selectively permeable membrane

The term **osmosis** (from the Greek *osmos,* meaning "a push") refers to the movement of water or any other solvent across a selectively permeable membrane. In the case of cells, of course, the solvent is always water. Water flows spontaneously from a region of lower solute concentration (higher water concentration) to a region of higher solute concentration (lower water concentration) (Figure 1e). Although water can pass directly through the membrane, transport proteins called *aquaporins* usually facilitate osmosis by forming channels that specifically admit water.

The idea that water moves spontaneously to a region of *higher* solute concentration may not be intuitive. After all, diffusion of a solute involves spontaneous movement "downhill" to a region of *lower* solute concentration. However, keep in mind that water is the solvent, not a solute. Its movement is actually "downhill" to a region of lower concentration as well. It is just that water moves to a region of lower *water* concentration. In a region of higher solute concentration, some water molecules are bound to the solute molecules, so there are fewer water molecules that are free to move, resulting in a lower water concentration. In an area of lower solute concentration, there are fewer solute molecules, so there are more unbound water molecules that are free to move. Therefore, water moves to an area of lower water concentration (higher solute concentration). Osmosis is similar to the diffusion of solutes in the sense that each substance moves spontaneously toward a region where it is less concentrated. Like other substances that move across a membrane, water tends to flow to equalize its concentration.

In plant cell growth, the osmotic potential inside the cell interacts with pressure generated by the cell wall

Living plant cells contain about 70–80% water. Since water takes up space, a cell taking up additional water must increase in size. Recall that plant cells have rigid cell walls that resist expansion. Therefore, cell enlargement requires both increased water and a weakening of the cell wall. Growth of a plant cell resembles enlargement of a water balloon that is surrounded by a cardboard box. To make the balloon larger, you can increase the internal pressure by putting more water in the balloon, but you must also weaken the walls of the box or increase its size.

The cell contents take up water as a result of a force called **osmotic potential,** the measurement of water's tendency to move across a membrane as a result of solute concentrations. Osmotic potential is also called *solute potential.* Since water moves to a region of higher solute concentration, the direction of its movement depends on the solute concentrations inside and outside of the cell. Frequently, osmotic potential is demonstrated by placing a membrane-bound bag of sugar solution into a container of pure water. The sugar molecules are large solutes that cannot cross the selectively permeable membrane, whereas the smaller water molecules can pass through. The sugar solution inside the bag has a higher solute concentration than the solution outside, and it is therefore described as being **hypertonic** (from the Greek *hyper,* "above") with respect to the solution outside. The solution with the lower solute concentration is said to be **hypotonic** (from the Greek *hypo,* "below"). Under these conditions, water flows into the bag, expanding the bag. The osmotic flow is from a region of lower solute concentration (higher water concentration) to a region of higher solute concentration (lower water concentration). If the two solutions were to have equal solute concentrations, they would be called **isotonic** solutions (from the

Greek *isos,* "equal"), characterized by equilibrium, with no net flow of water in either direction.

The bag of sugar solution can be compared to a protoplast—the contents of a plant cell minus the cell wall. The solute concentration of a plant cell—which includes minerals and organic molecules such as sugars and amino acids—is typically higher than that of the cell's surroundings. Like the bag of sugar solution, the typical cell is surrounded by a hypotonic solution, resulting in a net flow of water into the cell (Figure 2a). The protoplast spontaneously takes up water from the surroundings until the pressure of the surrounding cell wall, known as **pressure potential,** prevents further expansion of the protoplast. Under these conditions, the plasma membrane is pressed against the cell wall, making the cell turgid, or stiff, which is the normal, desirable state for a plant cell. If the solute concentrations inside and outside of the cell are isotonic, or equal, the protoplast is flaccid, or limp (Figure 2b). If many of a plant's cells become flaccid, stems and leaves may droop. If the solute concentration outside the cell exceeds the solute concentration inside the cell, there is a net flow of water out of the cell, causing the plasma membrane to shrink away from the cell wall, a condition known as **plasmolysis** (Figure 2c). When plasmolysis occurs, plants wilt and cell-to-cell cytoplasmic connections are broken, so transport through the phloem is restricted. In extreme cases of plasmolysis, the plant dies.

The ideal state of a plant cell differs from that of an animal cell. Since animal cells do not have cell walls, they expand or shrink as water moves in or out of the cell, potentially bursting or shriveling. In the normal animal cell, the solute concentrations inside and outside the cell are isotonic. In contrast, the desirable state for a plant cell is turgidity, in which the cell has a higher solute concentration than its surroundings.

The term **water potential** is used to refer to a measurement that predicts which way water will tend to flow between a plant cell and its surroundings or between different parts of a plant, such as roots and leaves. Water potential is defined as the combination of the osmotic potential (the effect of solute concentrations) and the pressure potential (the effect of cell wall pressure). These potentials are measured by the same units, represented by the Greek letter *psi* (ψ). Water potential is identified as ψ_w, pressure potential as ψ_P, and osmotic potential (solute potential) usually as ψ_O. The equation for water potential is $\psi_w = \psi_P + \psi_O$. Osmotic potential is always zero or a negative number, while pressure potential is always a positive number. Water potential can be positive, zero, or negative, depending on whether the cell is shrinking, at equilibrium, or expanding. If the osmotic potential

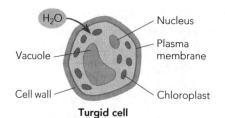

Outside of cell:
• Lower solute concentration
• Higher water potential

Inside of cell:
• Higher solute concentration
• Lower water potential

Turgid cell

(a) Plant cell surrounded by hypotonic solution. If the solution outside the cell is hypotonic, there is a net flow of water into the cell. This is the normal condition for a plant cell – being turgid. The expanded protoplast presses the plasma membrane against the cell wall.

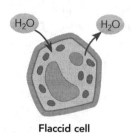

Outside and inside of cell:
• Equal solute concentrations
• Equal water potentials

Flaccid cell

(b) Plant cell in isotonic conditions. If the solutions inside and outside have equal solute concentrations, there is equilibrium. The plant cell is flaccid, and the loss of turgor may cause stems and leaves to droop.

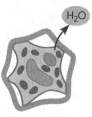

Outside of cell:
• Higher solute concentration
• Lower water potential

Inside of cell:
• Lower solute concentration
• Higher water potential

Cell in state of partial plasmolysis

(c) Plant cell surrounded by hypertonic solution. If the outside solution is hypertonic, there is a net flow of water out of the cell. This loss of water can result in plasmolysis.

Figure 2 Osmosis and regulation of water balance. In osmosis, water moves from an area of higher water potential (lower solute concentration) to an area of lower water potential (higher solute concentration). In a hypotonic environment, the cell wall prevents a plant cell from taking in too much water and bursting. However, the cell wall cannot prevent a cell from losing water in a hypertonic environment, which can result in plasmolysis.

and pressure potential balance each other, the water potential is zero and the cell neither expands nor shrinks. If the osmotic potential is more negative—that is, stronger—than the pressure potential, then the water potential is negative and the cell expands by taking up water.

For most living plant cells, the water potential is either zero or negative, indicating that if the cell wall were not there, the protoplast would take up water. Since we are dealing with negative numbers, "higher" and "lower" water potentials mean "less negative" and "more negative," which can be confusing. Mathematically, a lower water potential is indeed a lower (more negative) number. Physically, however, a cell or plant organ with a lower (more negative) water potential has *more* capacity to take up water. With water potential, therefore, you might say that "less is more." Just remember that a more negative water potential means greater capacity to absorb water. Water

moves from a region of higher water potential to a region of lower water potential—that is, from where the water potential is zero or negative to where it is more negative. In terms of the overall flow of water in a plant, water potential becomes increasingly negative—that is, increasingly strong—as water moves from the roots to the leaves. Leaf cells have more capacity to take up water than do root cells.

The pressure of water potential can be expressed mathematically in a variety of ways, such as atmospheres, pounds per square inch, millimeters (mm) of mercury, and kilopascals (KPa). For example, if you are at sea level, the pressure of all the atmospheric gases can be expressed as 1 atmosphere, 14.7 pounds per square inch, 760 mm of mercury, or 101.3 KPa, or 0.101 megapascal (MPa). By comparison, growing shoots and roots generate water potentials in the range of 33 to 165 pounds per square inch.

THE INTRIGUING WORLD OF PLANTS

The Power of Plants

The force of water potential by which the cell expands and takes up water is frequently in the range of 30 to 100 pounds per square inch. Germinating seeds use the pressure generated by water potential to push their way up through the soil, leaves, and other materials that have covered them. Meanwhile, as roots expand, they generate substantial pressures that help in penetrating the soil. Think about the effort needed to dig a hole with a shovel in dry, hard ground, and yet plant roots can penetrate this dense material.

Sidewalk damage caused by roots.

One obvious effect of the power of plants is on city sidewalks, which are frequently pushed out of place, raised, and even broken by the growth of plant roots. Less obviously, many home sewer systems have been damaged by roots growing toward a source of water.

In nature, tree seedlings sometimes germinate in crevices on the top of large boulders and end up splitting enormous boulders entirely in two. Also, houseplants sometimes split open their pots as a result of root growth. Even individual small seedlings sometimes lift rocks many times their size during germination.

You can see why growing roots can raise sections of sidewalk and topple retaining walls (see *The Intriguing World of Plants* box on this page).

The water potential generated by a plant cell or organ can be measured in different ways. The cell or organ can be put in competition for available water with an external solution containing a solute that does not enter the plant cell. The minimum concentration of the solution that stops expansion of the cell or plant organ is equal to the water potential. Alternatively, plant tissue can be allowed to absorb water in a closed chamber from a small water supply, with the water temperature closely monitored. As water evaporates, the temperature of the remaining water cools, indicating the rate of evaporation. The rate of evaporation is monitored electronically to measure water movement into the plant cell or organ.

Section Review

1. **Explain the difference between symplastic transport and apoplastic transport.**
2. **How does facilitated diffusion differ from diffusion?**
3. **Compare and contrast osmosis and diffusion of solutes.**
4. **How do variations in solute concentrations affect a plant cell?**
5. **What is water potential?**

Movement and Uptake of Water and Solutes in Plants

Having explored transport at the cellular level, we will now look at the overall movement of water and solutes in a plant. Plants derive water and minerals from the soil and use the xylem to transport them from the roots to the rest of the plant. Leaves need both water and minerals to carry out photosynthesis and to synthesize the many types of molecules used by plants. In the leaves, photosynthesis and other biochemical processes make sugar and other organic molecules, which are then transported throughout the plant by the phloem (Figure 3).

Water evaporation from leaves pulls water through the xylem from the roots

The vascular system transports water, minerals, and organic molecules throughout the plant. Xylem is composed of tracheids and, in the case of flowering plants, vessel elements. These dead cells handle transport of water and minerals from the roots to stems and leaves, where water evaporates through the stomata—the process called *transpiration*.

A large tree in a forest can transpire between 700 and 3,500 liters (185 and 925 gallons) a day during the summer. By comparison, typical crop plants transpire much

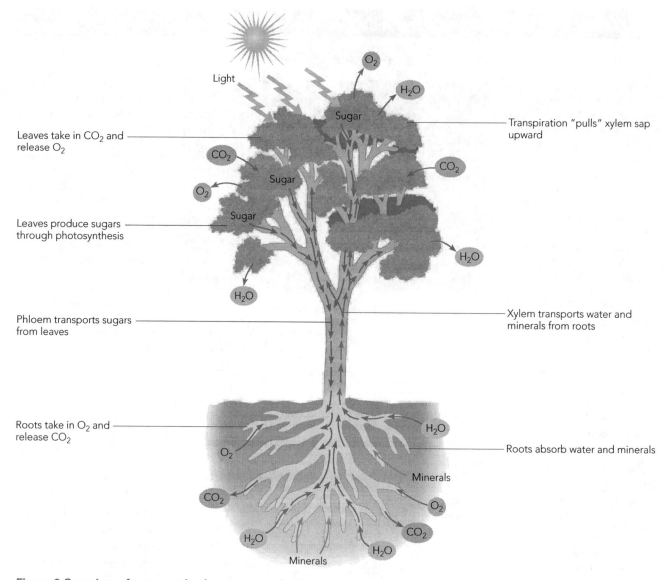

Figure 3 Overview of water and solute transport in plants.

less. Corn, for instance, transpires approximately 2 liters (0.53 gallon) a day per plant. However, that amount is still significant, equating to a daily transpiration of 60,000 liters (15,850 gallons) per acre, an area roughly the size of a football field. During a growing season, an acre of corn will use 6 million liters (about 1.6 million gallons). If applied all at once, this amount of water would cover the acre about 2 feet deep. Plant breeders are therefore interested in developing crop plants that require less water (see the *Biotechnology* box on the next page). The plant needs water for cell growth and photosynthesis and to provide minerals for the biosynthesis of proteins, nucleotides, and other molecules. However, small amounts of water would supply these needs.

Transpiration, which appears to waste water, actually serves two necessary functions. First, it cools the leaves, which are considerably heated by the sunlight absorbed

in photosynthesis. Second, it serves as the pump to pull water and water-soluble minerals up from the roots. The fact that a plant pumps water from the top was puzzling to plant physiologists, considering how mechanical pumps, such as a well pump, work. A pump located at the top of a water well can only pump water 10.36 m (34 feet) or less because water columns pulled higher than 10.36 m (34 feet) will break as a result of their weight. For this reason, most wells have pumps at the bottom, where this limitation does not apply. How, then, is water pumped from the top of a plant?

Plants, and in particular tall trees, are able to "pump" from the top of the water column because of the design of xylem tissue and the characteristics of water. Water is a **polar molecule**—a molecule with positively charged and negatively charged ends. Therefore, the positively charged end of

BIOTECHNOLOGY

Water-Efficient Crops

Can scientists develop plants that use less water and are more efficient at transpiration? Indirectly, *any* increased efficiency of the plant translates into water saved. If the plant has a shorter time to maturity, or decreased photorespiration, or an architecture that produces more grain on each plant, the net effect saves water. For example, the following traits help wheat tolerate drought:

◆ Large seed size provides more food for germination in dry, hard soil.
◆ Long coleoptiles (the sheath covering the first leaves that push up through the soil) allow for deep sowing where the soil is cooler and has more moisture.
◆ Thinner, wider leaves shade the soil and radiate heat more rapidly.
◆ Prostrate (horizontal) growth habit shades the soil.
◆ High photosynthetic capacity of flowering spike ensures rapid grain development.
◆ Rapid adjustment to osmotic stress means that the cells produce extra solute molecules to prevent water loss.
◆ Accumulation of abscisic acid controls the closing of stomata and thus regulates water loss.
◆ Hairy, waxy leaves diffuse sunlight and prevent water loss through epidermal cells.
◆ Heat tolerance offers protection from high temperatures that often accompany drought.

Wheat with these traits can be obtained by traditional breeding and by genetic engineering if specific genes have been identified.

Irrigated fields in Oregon.

The use of genetic engineering to improve drought tolerance is attracting increasing interest and following many experimental routes. Here are three examples that provide an introduction.

Scientists are interested in producing genetically engineered plants that convert table sugar, sucrose, into sugar polymers called *short-chain fructans,* produced naturally by some plants, such as the onion. These molecules taste sweeter than sucrose but provide no calories to humans. Currently short-chain fructan synthesis involves an expensive, industrial process. An agronomic side benefit of this research has been the discovery that plants, genetically transformed to produce short-chain fructans, also have increased drought tolerance. They may increase drought tolerance because of interactions with membranes or because the molecules serve as an osmotic protectant that is not translocated out of the cells.

The successful introduction of the C_4 photosynthetic pathway into rice should markedly increase production under the high temperature, high light intensities in which rice grows.

Scientists at the University of California produced *Arabidopsis* that are hypersensitive to abscisic acid and close their stomata more rapidly in response to increasing stress. When plants were not watered for 12 days, the engineered plants looked healthy, whereas normal plants had wilted and shriveled.

While these plants are not yet found in farmer's fields, such fascinating results imply that further research is warranted.

---

one water molecule attracts the negatively charged end of another. This characteristic helps explain three behaviors of water molecules: adhesion, cohesion, and tension.

◆ **Adhesion** is the attraction between different kinds of molecules. In plants, there is adhesion between water molecules and the cell wall molecules. Water moves to the top of plants in a continuous stream sometimes thought of as a column of water. Actually, the column passes through millions of narrow xylem cells, where cellulose walls adhere to water molecules, binding and supporting tiny segments of the column. Therefore, the column is in no danger of breaking as a result of its own weight. Paper towels, made from wood pulp, provide a good demonstration of adhesion of cellulose to water molecules.

◆ Water columns in xylem also exhibit **cohesion**—the attraction between molecules of the same kind. Since they are highly polar, water molecules bind to each other, which helps support the water column.

◆ Water columns in xylem experience **tension,** the negative pressure on water or solutions. In the xylem, tension is caused by transpiration through stomata. Water evaporating from the stomata into the air "pulls" the water column up, in much the same way as a person sucking on a straw "pulls" the fluid up through the straw. In plants, tension is transmitted down the stem or trunk. In fact, the diameter of tree trunks actually shrinks during transpiration, as in the way a straw starts to collapse when you suck hard.

Most physiologists use the **tension-cohesion theory** to explain transport in the xylem (Figure 4). Actually, while both tension and cohesion are important, adhesion is crucial. A water well that is 15.2 m (50 feet) deep cannot be successfully pumped from the top, but through transpiration a 15.2 m (50-foot) tree can "pull" water from the bottom of the tree to the top. Two important differences explain the failure of the well and the success of the tree. In both cases, the column of water has cohesion between water molecules and tension created by the pump. One difference is that the pipe carrying water up from the well does not shrink in response to tension, so the tension created by the pump is not transmitted down the column, in contrast with the tree. The other difference is that the well pipe provides little or no adhesive component.

Studies using radioactive isotopes dissolved in water have indicated clearly that xylem transports water. Sometimes the tension of the water column in a stem causes the water column to break and air bubbles to form. In some cases, plants can repair the damage by redissolving the air bubble, usually at night. This occurs because the pressure of surrounding tissues drives water back into the cell with the air bubble, reducing the size of the bubble and finally eliminating it. Since there are many single cells in the xylem, air bubbles are usually confined to just a few tracheids, and the water stream simply flows around them. In the case of vessels, the breaking of a water column interrupts transport in the entire vessel, not just one vessel element. Taller trees have more danger of broken water columns. Higher rates of transpiration increase tension on the columns and increase the danger of breakage. The tallest trees, coast redwoods, live in moist habitats with considerable fog and low or moderate levels of transpiration.

As a result of transpiration, water potential becomes more and more negative as water moves from the soil to the leaves. For example, the water potential of soil might be –0.3 MPa whereas the water potential of root hairs is –0.6 MPa. Thus, water will flow from the soil into the root. Midway up a tree trunk the water potential would be –0.7 MPa, whereas in the leaf it would drop to –3.0

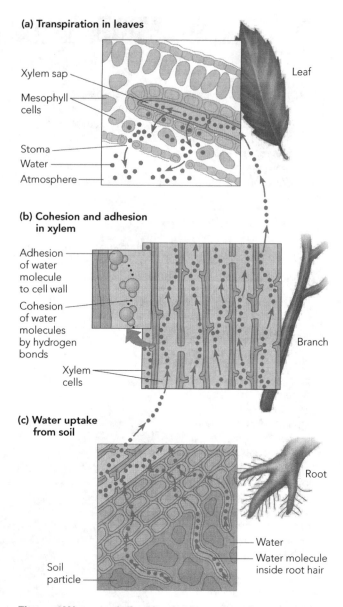

(a) Transpiration in leaves

Xylem sap
Mesophyll cells
Stoma
Water
Atmosphere
Leaf

(b) Cohesion and adhesion in xylem

Adhesion of water molecule to cell wall
Cohesion of water molecules by hydrogen bonds
Xylem cells
Branch

(c) Water uptake from soil

Root
Water
Water molecule inside root hair
Soil particle

Figure 4 Water and dissolved solutes flow from roots to shoots. (a) The evaporation of water through stomata creates a gradient of water potential that is most negative at the top of the tree. **(b)** Cohesion of water molecules to each other and adhesion of water molecules to the cellulose walls of tracheids keep the column of sap intact. **(c)** Roots take up water from soil.

MPa. The water potential of air outside the leaf could be between –5.0 and –100.0 MPa. Thus, increasingly negative water potential keeps water flowing from the soil, into and up the stem (trunk), and out the leaves into the air.

Water absorption in roots occurs through elongated epidermal cells known as *root hairs,* which develop just above the root apical meristem. The water potential of root hairs reflects whether the plant needs water or not. The root hairs also compete directly with soil particles for water and can either win or lose the competition, depending on how dry the soil is. Between the root hairs and the

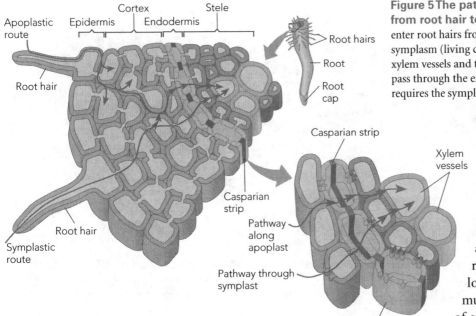

Figure 5 The pathway of minerals and water from root hair to xylem. Water and mineral ions enter root hairs from the soil and flow through the symplasm (living cells) or apoplasm (cell walls) to xylem vessels and tracheids. As water and mineral ions pass through the endodermis, the Casparian strip requires the symplastic route.

and disrupts the supply of both nutrients and hormones necessary to maintain the plant and control its functioning. As a result of the high rate of transpiration necessary for leaf cooling and for pumping water from the roots, dangerous amounts of water loss can occur quickly. The plant must be able to respond to a variety of environmental stimuli to control water balance, which occurs when the water potential of a cell or a tissue is zero.

The waxy layer, called the cuticle, on the outside of most epidermal cells of leaves allows very little water loss. Ninety percent of water loss by a plant occurs through the stomata, the pores surrounded by guard cells. Stomata occur in the epidermis of all aboveground parts of the plant, with most occurring on the undersides of leaves, where the temperature is lower and where they are less likely to become clogged by dust deposited by the air. Up to 10,000 stomata can occur per square centimeter of leaf surface.

When sufficient water is available, the photosynthetic guard cells of stomata take up water and become curved, like overinflated balloons, to open a pore that allows gas exchange with the air spaces that make up 15–40% of the inside of a leaf (Figure 6). Stomata open in response to decreasing internal concentrations of CO_2 and to light from the blue portion of the visible spectrum. They close in response to increasing internal concentrations of CO_2, high temperatures, wind, low humidity, and the hormone **abscisic acid** (**ABA**). On a typical summer day, stomata are closed at daybreak. As sunlight stimulates photosynthesis, the CO_2 concentration in the leaf drops and the stomata open in response to the CO_2 level and to blue light, remaining open until nightfall unless conditions that promote water loss occur.

Abscisic acid controls the opening and closing of the pores of stomata by guard cells. When high levels of ABA occur in guard cells, they lose water, and the pore closes. Abscisic acid, produced in roots in response to dry soil, is transported to leaves and provides advance warning of drought. When low levels of ABA occur in guard cells, they take up water, and the pore opens.

endodermis, water can flow between cells—apoplastic transport—or through the cytoplasm of cells—symplastic transport (Figure 5). However, when water reaches the endodermis, the Casparian strip ensures that water and dissolved minerals must be filtered through the endodermal cells, thereby giving the membrane the opportunity to control the uptake of ions.

The negative water potential of root cells causes enough water uptake to generate root pressure. If a stem is removed, roots continue to push water up the stem. The water pushed into the stem by root pressure may end up leaving the leaves as droplets through specialized epidermal regions, in a process called **guttation.** Early investigators thought root pressure was responsible for the movement of water to the tops of tall trees, operating much like a pump at the bottom of a well. However, root pressure can only move water a few feet and is at its lowest during the day, when maximal transpiration occurs. The water potential of plant organs can be measured by applying pressure within an airtight container. For instance, a stem can be placed in such a container, with a cut end of the stem sticking through a hole at the top. Pressure is applied until water appears at the protruding end of the cut stem or in the stomata of leaves. At this point, the applied pressure equals the water potential of the stem.

Stomata control gas exchange and water loss for the plant

Plants must maintain enough water in tissues to prevent loss of turgor and consequent wilting, which occurs when the plasma membrane is not pushing against its cell wall. A loss of turgor interrupts cell-to-cell communication

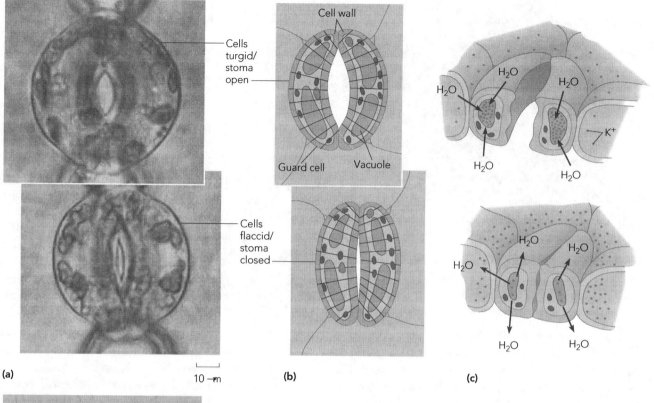

(a)

10 —m

(b)

(c)

High water
potential

Guard
cell

Low water
potential

(d)

Figure 6 The opening and closing of stomata. (**a**) Open and closed stomata of a spider plant (*Chlorophytum colosum*) leaf. (**b**) The orientation of cellulose microfibrils causes guard cells to elongate rather than thicken as they take up water. This leads to buckling that opens the stomatal pore to the inner leaf. (**c**) Potassium (K^+) ions move into guard cells to cause water uptake and opening of the stomatal pore. (**d**) Inside the leaf, water vapors are abundant, humidity is high, and water potential is negative. Outside the leaf, water vapor is less abundant, humidity is lower, and water potential is very negative.

By controlling the diameter of the stomata, the plant can regulate the rate of water loss caused by transpiration. On hot, dry, windy days, stomata will be closed. Of course, closing the stomata saves water but also reduces the uptake of CO_2 required for photosynthesis. Under these conditions the plant will lose carbon through photorespiration. Plants are constructed so that stomata close, resulting in lower photosynthesis, before photorespiration markedly increases.

Sugars and other organic molecules move from leaves to roots in the phloem

In plants, transport of sugar and other organic molecules takes place in the phloem. In the phloem of flowering plants, organic molecules are transported through sieve-tube members and their companion cells. Phloem moves sap from a sugar source to a sugar sink. A **sugar source** is a part of a plant—usually leaves and also green stems—that produces sugar. A **sugar sink** is a part of a plant that mainly consumes or stores sugar, such as roots, stems, and fruits. Sugar transport is driven by water uptake by osmosis and therefore requires the selectively permeable plasma membrane of a living cell.

As with water and minerals, sugar and other organic molecules can be moved by either symplastic transport or apoplastic transport. In the case of sugar, the sugar synthesized in leaf mesophyll cells must be transported to the cells of the phloem (Figure 7a). Symplastic transport is most common in plants from warm environments,

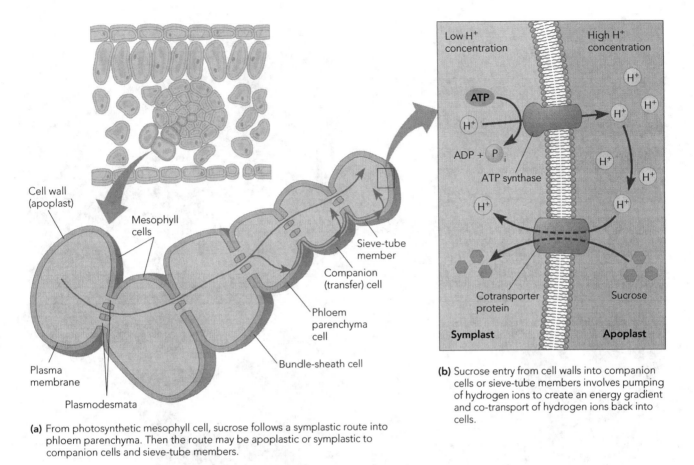

(a) From photosynthetic mesophyll cell, sucrose follows a symplastic route into phloem parenchyma. Then the route may be apoplastic or symplastic to companion cells and sieve-tube members.

Figure 7 Loading sucrose into the phloem.

(b) Sucrose entry from cell walls into companion cells or sieve-tube members involves pumping of hydrogen ions to create an energy gradient and co-transport of hydrogen ions back into cells.

with molecules remaining inside cells to pass through plasmodesmata (the channels between cells) from mesophyll cells into phloem cells. Apoplastic transport is most common in plants from temperate or cold environments, with molecules following a pathway outside the plasma membrane as they move from mesophyll cells to the phloem. Frequently, these plants store sugar in the cell walls of cells near the phloem. Companion cells take up the sugar and pass it to sieve-tube members through plasmodesmata. Some companion cells have cellular protrusions and ingrowths that increase the surface area between them and sieve-tube members. Such modified companion cells are known as *transfer cells.*

Energy is required when molecules transported in the apoplastic pathway enter sieve-tube members, as ATP is used to pump H^+ ions out of the cells (Figure 7b). Then the H^+ ions and sugar molecules enter the cell together, with the help of a cotransporter protein. The mechanism of phloem transport differs from the transpiration-driven movement of water and minerals in the xylem. In the phloem, the sugar that enters sieve-tube members generates osmotic potential and water uptake. The turgor pressure developed by water uptake moves water and sugar down the phloem until the sugar is downloaded into root cells and other cells requiring energy. Open pores at each end of a sieve-tube member allow direct connections between cells so the sugary solution can move easily through the phloem. Building high pressure at the leaf end (sugar source) and reducing it at the root end (sugar sink) keeps the phloem sap moving. When sugar reaches sugar sinks, such as roots, water then leaves the sieve-tube members, along with solutes like sugar. The mechanism for phloem transport, first proposed by Ernst Munch in 1927, is known as the **pressure-flow hypothesis** (Figure 8). Although living cells are required, the actual transport process, driven by osmosis, is passive.

Phloem-feeding aphids have provided useful information about phloem transport. Phloem sap contains between 10–20% sugar and small percentages of other organic molecules such as amino acids. A typical aphid feeds by sticking its pointed, straw-like stylet through leaf or stem tissue and into the sugary phloem. The turgor pressure of sieve-tube members then pushes phloem sap through the aphid's gut to emerge as drops of "honeydew"

Figure 8 Pressure flow in sieve-tube members. In this example, the sugar source is a leaf cell and the sugar sink is a root cell.

1 Entry of sugar reduces water potential in the sieve-tube members, causing the tube to take up water.

2 Water pressure forces sap to flow through sieve-tube members.

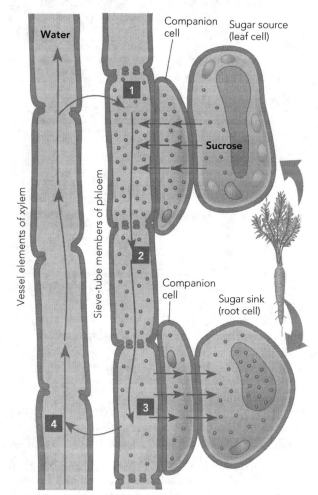

3 As sugar is unloaded at the sink, the pressure in the sieve tubes drops, creating a pressure gradient. Most of the water then diffuses back to the xylem.

4 Xylem recycles water from the sugar sink (root) to the sugar source (leaf).

on the tip of the aphid's abdomen. If the aphid is anesthetized to prevent stylet withdrawal, and the rest of its body is removed, the stylet exudes pure phloem sap for several hours, serving as a tap that botanists can use to measure the flow (Figure 9). Phloem sap moves at speeds of up to 1.0 m per hour. Neither diffusion nor cytoplasmic streaming can account for such high speeds. The pressure developed in phloem cells of leaves by osmotic uptake of water accounts for the observed transport rates.

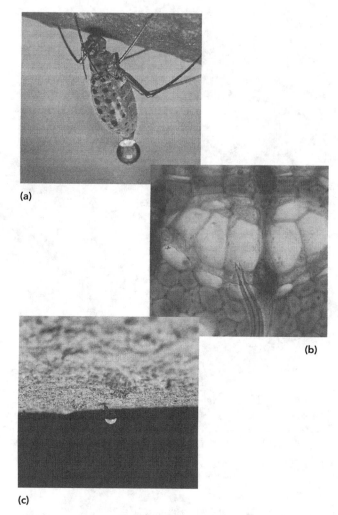

Figure 9 Using aphids to study flow of phloem sap. (**a**) The sieve tube pressure pushes phloem sap into the aphid. (**b**) The aphid sticks its stylet directly into a phloem sieve-tube member. (**c**) If the insect is removed, phloem sap can be collected from the stylet to measure flow.

Section Review

1. Define transpiration and explain how water gets to the top of tall trees.
2. How do stomata control gas exchange and water loss?
3. How does sugar get from the leaves to the roots?

Soil, Minerals, and Plant Nutrition

You already know that plants obtain the minerals they need from the soil. The uptake of mineral ions occurs through root hairs at the same time as water uptake, and transport of the solution occurs through the xylem. In this section, you will learn about the structure of soil and how it binds solute molecules and water.

Soil is made of ground-up particles of rocks surrounded by negative charges that bind water and minerals

Rocks, weathered by wind and rain and fractured by water expanding into ice, break down to produce stones and gravel and eventually become soil. Bacteria, algae, fungi, lichens (associations of algae and fungi), mosses, and plant roots all secrete acids that contribute to the breakdown of rocks into soil. Classified by size, soil particles include **sand,** which contains particles 0.02 to 2 mm (0.0008–0.08 inch) in diameter; **silt,** which contains particles 0.002 to 0.02 mm (0.00008–0.0008 inch) in diameter; and **clay,** which contains particles smaller than 0.002 mm (0.00008 inch) in diameter.

Soil occurs in layers called **horizons** (Figure 10). In a simplified view, the uppermost horizon, or A horizon, consists of **topsoil,** which contains the smallest soil particles and is most suited to support plant growth. Topsoil ranges in depth from a few millimeters to several feet and generally contains soil particles of the three basic sizes (sand, silt, and clay); decaying organic material called *humus;* and various organisms such as bacteria, fungi, nematodes, and earthworms. Ideal garden topsoil is loam, which contains roughly equal amounts of sand, silt, and clay. Loam is most suited for planting because the soil particles are small enough to permit the growth of roots between them and because the soil has enough surface area to bind sufficient water and minerals to support growth. Plant roots can penetrate sand easily, but the particles are large and the total surface area of sandy soil is insufficient to support most plant growth. The second horizon, the B horizon, contains larger and less-weathered particles of sand and rocks, as well as less organic matter. The deepest horizon, the C horizon, is quite rocky but supplies raw materials for soil produced in the upper horizons. Groundwater, in the form of underground deposits known as **aquifers,** occurs in various locations in or below the C horizon. Wells tap into groundwater, replenished by rain, which percolates through the soil horizons. Below the C horizon is rock, the Earth's crust or bedrock, which can extend 40 kilometers (15.4 miles).

Plants require 17 essential elements, most of which are obtained from soil

By the mid-1800s, scientists realized that plants depended on soil to supply water and minerals. This conclusion was supported by experiments in supplying plants with solu-

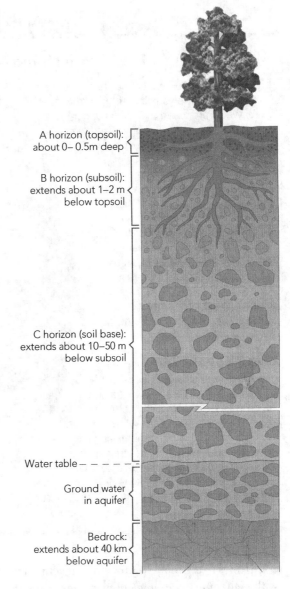

A horizon (topsoil):
about 0–0.5m deep

B horizon (subsoil):
extends about 1–2 m
below topsoil

C horizon (soil base):
extends about 10–50 m
below subsoil

Water table

Ground water
in aquifer

Bedrock:
extends about 40 km
below aquifer

Figure 10 Soil horizons. This simplified soil profile shows the A, B, and C horizons. In general, soil becomes rockier the deeper you go.

tions of water and minerals in a lab and also by the invention of **hydroponics** (from the Greek *hydor,* "water," and *ponos,* "labor or toil"), or soil-less gardening. In hydroponics, the mineral nutrients normally supplied by the soil are mixed into a liquid solution, which is used to water the plant roots. The first hydroponics recipe—containing KNO_3, $Ca(NO_3)_2$, KH_2PO_4, $MgSO_4$, and $FeSO_4$—supported the growth of many kinds of plants in liquid culture or in sand. It seemed that plant mineral nutrition was totally understood (see the *Plants & People* box on the next page). By the 1900s, however, plants were no longer growing consistently with this mineral recipe. Had the laws of plant nutrition changed? As it turns out, chemical

Justus von Liebig—A Father of Modern Agriculture

In the early 1800s, most agricultural scientists believed in some variation of the humus theory, which proposed that all major components of plants consisted of soil and water taken in through the roots. After all, people had known for thousands of years that soil fertilized with organic matter such as manure grew much better crops than unfertilized soil. The contribution of air to plant growth was not widely recognized.

In 1840, however, German chemist Justus von Liebig put the humus theory to rest. He presented strong evidence that most or all of the carbon in plants comes from atmospheric CO_2, while the necessary minerals and water come from the soil. He developed a Law of the Minimum, which states that plant growth is limited by the necessary mineral present in the smallest amount. He called this limiting factor the "minimum." Liebeg's Law of the Minimum has been supported by experiments and has governed soil testing and fertilizer application for nearly 150 years. Liebig invented the first artificial fertilizer, a combination of chemical elements known to promote plant growth. Unfortunately, several ingredients formed a concrete-like

Justus von Liebig.

substance, and his venture into the marketplace failed. Two British scientists, J. B. Lawes and J. H. Gilbert, developed the first commercially successful artificial fertilizers in 1843. In 1862, German scientist W. Knop published a list of five chemicals that allowed for hydroponics, or gardening without soil. The nutritional contribution of soil to plants had been defined in chemical terms.

Through his views and the students he trained, Justus von Liebig played an indirect but important role in improving the productivity of American agriculture. When Abraham Lincoln created the Department of Agriculture in 1860, he appointed one of Justus Liebig's students as the department's first scientist. The passage of the Homestead Act in 1862 furthered the expansion of American agriculture by giving 1.29 square km (0.25 square mile) of free land for farming to any head of a family or anyone at least 21 years old. The Land Grant College Act, passed that same year, led to the establishment of agricultural colleges in each state. Meanwhile, Liebig and his students influenced the establishment of agricultural experimental stations throughout Europe and the United States.

companies had simply begun to manufacture chemicals with higher purity, leaving out many impurities that were actually essential for plant growth.

Plants contain 60 or more chemical elements, but only 17 of them are currently believed to be essential. These are classified as either macronutrients or micronutrients (Table 1). **Macronutrients** are used in large amounts for producing the body of the plant and for carrying out essential physiological processes. The air supplies oxygen and carbon, while the other macronutrients come from the soil. **Micronutrients** are usually necessary cofactors for enzymes and are therefore recycled by the plant. Plants exhibit characteristic deficiency symptoms when inadequately supplied with one or more essential nutrients. Some minerals may be required by plants at such low concentrations that adequate amounts are supplied by dust, and deficiencies would be very difficult to demonstrate. Plants with inadequate mineral nutrition pass on these inadequacies to animals that consume

them. Humans and other animals require several minerals (selenium, chromium, and fluoride) that are usually found in plants but typically not required by them.

When soils in a region lack sufficient quantities of a micronutrient, plants and animals may develop deficiency symptoms. The United Nations estimates that micronutrient malnutrition afflicts more than 40% of the world's people. For example, soil in parts of China commonly lacks sufficient selenium. Common human signs of the deficiency are heart and bone defects. A soil study revealed that in regions with low levels of soil selenium, three times as many people died from cancer as in the regions with high levels of soil selenium. Studies in which people received selenium supplements showed dramatic decreases in the incidence of many types of cancer.

Agriculture removes nutrients from the soil and reduces soil fertility. Nutrient depletion is particularly a problem where farming has occurred for thousands of years. Soil testing can determine soil fertility with respect

Table 1 Essential Nutrients for Most Vascular Plants

Element	Chemical symbol	Form available to plants	Importance to plants
Macronutrients			
Carbon	C	CO_2	Major element in organic compounds
Oxygen	O	CO_2	Major element in organic compounds
Hydrogen	H	H_2O	Major element in organic compounds
Nitrogen	N	NO_3^-, NH_4^+	Elements in nucleotides, nucleic acids, amino acids, proteins, coenzymes, and hormones
Sulfur	S	SO_4^{2-}	Elements in proteins, coenzymes, and amino acids
Phosphorus	P	$H_2PO_4^-$, HPO_4^{2-}	Elements in ATP and ADP, several coenzymes, nucleic acids, and phospholipids
Potassium	K	K^+	Cofactor in osmosis and ionic balance, action of stomata, and protein synthesis
Calcium	Ca	Ca^{2+}	Essential for stability of cell walls, in maintaining membrane structure and permeability, acting as enzyme cofactor, and regulating some stimulus responses
Magnesium	Mg	Mg^{2+}	Enzyme activator and a component of chlorophyll
Micronutrients			
Chlorine	Cl	Cl^-	Essential in water-splitting step of photosynthesis that produces oxygen and functions in osmosis and ionic balance
Iron	Fe	Fe^{3+}, Fe^{2+}	Activator of some enzymes, forms parts of cytochromes and nitrogenase, and is required for chlorophyll synthesis
Boron	B	$H_2BO_3^-$	Required for chlorophyll synthesis; might be involved in nucleic acid synthesis, carbohydrate transport, and membrane integrity
Manganese	Mn	Mn^{2+}	Activator of some enzymes, active in the formation of amino acids, required in water-splitting step of photosynthesis, and involved in the integrity of chloroplast membrane
Zinc	Zn	Zn^{2+}	Activator of some enzymes, involved in formation of chlorophyll
Copper	Cu	Cu^{2+}, Cu^+	Activator of some enzymes involved in oxidation/reduction reactions, component of lignin-biosynthetic enzymes
Molybdenum	Mo	MoO_4^{2-}	Involved in nitrogen fixation and nitrate reduction
Nickel	Ni	Ni^{2+}	Cofactor for an enzyme that functions in nitrogen metabolism

to specific nutrients. Application of the appropriate fertilizer to soil can remedy specific problems.

Soil particles bind water and mineral ions

Approximately 93% of the Earth's crust consists of **silicates** (SiO_4^{-4}). Therefore, soil particles display negative charges on their outside layers. Being polar molecules, water molecules have a positively charged side and a negatively charged side, so rings of water form around each soil particle. In the water, some mineral ions dissolve as cations (positively charged ions) and others as anions (negatively charged ions). The first ring of water surrounding a soil particle has cations, the next has anions, and so on. Some cations dissolve in the water, while others bind directly to soil particles.

Water, dissolved mineral ions, and dissolved O_2—together known as the **soil solution**—occupy around 50% of soil volume and provide the source of these nutrients for plants (Figure 11a). Soil binds water molecules with a force called the **matrix potential,** which is a negative number. Think of all the soil as consisting of a matrix of particles of various sizes, which are separated by

281

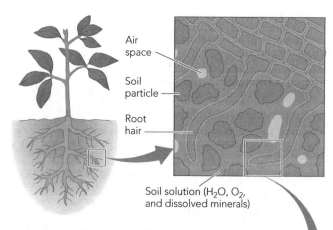

Air space

Soil particle

Root hair

Soil solution (H_2O, O_2, and dissolved minerals)

(a) Soil particles and soil solution. Root hairs cannot absorb minerals directly from soil particles. Instead, they absorb soil solution that includes water, dissolved oxygen, and dissolved minerals, which are present as either positively charged ions (cations) or negatively charged ions (anions).

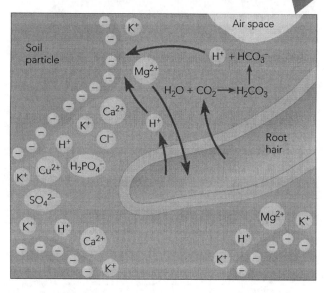

Air space

Soil particle

K^+

Mg^{2+}

$H^+ + HCO_3^-$

$H_2O + CO_2 \rightarrow H_2CO_3$

H^+

Ca^{2+}

K^+

Cl^-

H^+

Root hair

Cu^{2+} $H_2PO_4^-$

K^+

SO_4^{2-}

K^+ H^+

Ca^{2+}

K^+

Mg^{2+} K^+

H^+

K^+

K^+

(b) Cation exchange. Since cations are positively charged, they bind closely to the negatively charged soil particles, but they can be displaced by H^+ ions, the process known as cation exchange. When dislodged, they are available for absorption. The diagram shows a magnesium ion (Mg^{2+}) displaced by two H^+ ions. Root hairs supply the H^+ ions directly by secreting them and indirectly by producing CO_2, causing a chemical reaction that yields H^+. Negatively charged ions usually do not bind as closely to soil particles, and are therefore more readily absorbed but also more easily drained from the soil.

Figure 11 Absorption of minerals by root hairs.

water and air. For a root hair to absorb water, its water potential must be more negative than the matrix potential of the soil.

Ions bind to soil particles in a preferential order, depending on the relative strength of their positive or negative charges. For example, cations bind to soil parti-

cles according to three rules: Cations with more positive charges bind first, smaller ions bind before larger ions, and ions at high concentrations bind before ions at low concentrations. For example, according to the first two rules, Ca^{2+} binds before Na^+. High concentrations of Na^+ bind before low concentrations of Ca^{2+}, according to the third rule.

These rules become important for plants when toxic ions occur in the soil solution. For example, in regions with salty soil, the concentration of sodium ions (Na^+) is high and Na^+ displaces ions that the plant needs from soil particles. The sodium ions remain in the soil, while the useful ions end up in the groundwater, where they are largely unavailable to plants. For that reason, salty soil is nutrient-poor soil. Large regions of the southwestern United States, which was an ocean millions of years ago, suffer from this problem.

The order in which ions bind to soil particles also plays an important role in acidic soils, which occur in regions of high rainfall. In rain, CO_2 dissolves in water to produce H^+ ions according to the following reaction: $CO_2 + H_2O \rightarrow H_2CO_3$ (carbonic acid) $\rightarrow H^+ + HCO_3^-$ (bicarbonate). Hydrogen binds tightly to soil particles, displacing other cations, including those important to plants. Also, acidic soil brings previously insoluble and highly toxic aluminum ions into the soil solution. Acidic soil is therefore nutrient-poor and often contains toxic aluminum.

The displacement of the mineral cations by H^+ ions plays a role in normal mineral uptake by roots (Figure 11b). Both water molecules and mineral ions bind directly to soil particles. Since anions are not found in the first binding layer, directly next to the soil particles, they are more easily drained away from the soil and "lost" to plants in the groundwater, a process known as *leaching*. As roots penetrate the soil, they release CO_2 produced in respiration, which combines with water to become bicarbonate and H^+ ions. Roots can also secrete H^+ ions directly. The CO_2 dissolves to produce H^+ ions, which replace the mineral cations bound to the soil, a process known as **cation exchange**. In this way, the minerals are released from the soil and made available in the soil solution for uptake by roots.

Bacteria in the soil make nitrogen available to plants

Some plants form associations with bacteria. Plants need nitrogen, but they cannot absorb nitrogen gas (N_2) from the air. They must absorb it from nitrogen compounds in the soil, primarily as nitrate (NO_3^-) but also as ammonium (NH_4^+). Some soil bacteria carry out **nitrogen fixation**—the conversion of nitrogen gas into nitrate or ammonium (Figure 12). In some soils, nitrifying bacteria convert ammonium to nitrite (NO_2^-) and then into nitrate. In addition to nitrogen-fixing bacteria, there are ammonifying bacteria that release ammonium by breaking down organic matter called *humus* and denitrifying bacteria that convert nitrate back to N_2.

Nitrogen-fixing bacteria first convert nitrogen gas into ammonia (NH_3), through the action of the enzyme nitrogenase. Ammonia then picks up an H^+ ion from the soil solution to become ammonium NH_4^+. Some nitrogen-fixing bacteria are free-living, but most form mutualistic associations with certain plants, particularly legumes such as alfalfa, peas, beans, and clovers. Some non-legumes such as alder trees and a genus of water ferns (*Azolla*) form similar associations. Plants that have associations with nitrogen-fixing bacteria take less nitrogen from the soil than other plants and actually add nitrogen back to the soil. Therefore, farmers often rotate legumes with other crops to enrich the soil. In a single growing season, a legume crop can add 300 kg (660 pounds) of fertilizer per 1 hectare (2.47 acres). The bacteria associated with one legume plant yield between

1 and 3 grams (0.035–0.11 ounce) of fixed nitrogen. The crop is then plowed back into the soil to release additional nitrogen by normal decay. *Azolla* ferns floating in rice paddies supply nitrogen to the rice after they die as a result of shading by the rice and absence of water in the paddy.

Nitrogen fixation by bacteria is a complex process. In legumes, bacteria of the genus *Rhizobium* enter roots through a modified root hair called an *infection thread*. In response to the infection thread, the plant produces a flavonoid that activates a series of chemical signals, resulting in the plant forming **root nodules** where the bacteria will live (Figure 13). Once inside the nodules, the bacteria change into an enlarged form called *bacteroids*, which live in vesicles inside root cells.

Nitrogen can also be fixed commercially, but the process is energy-intensive and expensive. Nevertheless, farmers frequently use commercially produced nitrogen fertilizer because it eliminates the need for crop rotation with legumes and is easily applied along with other fertilizers. In developing countries, where artificial fertilizer is often prohibitively expensive, farmers sometimes grow legumes side-by-side with a non-nitrogen-fixing crop. Once the latter is harvested, the legume crop is plowed

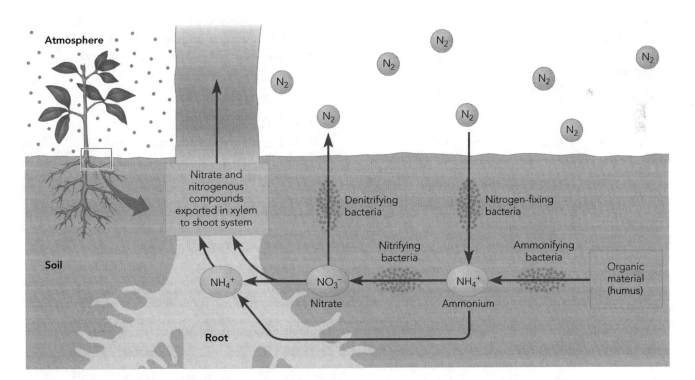

Figure 12 Soil bacteria regulate the soil nitrogen available to plants. Plants can absorb either nitrate or ammonium from the soil. Most soil nitrogen is nitrate because of the presence of nitrifying bacteria that convert ammonium, from decaying organic matter and from nitrogen-fixing bacteria, to nitrate.

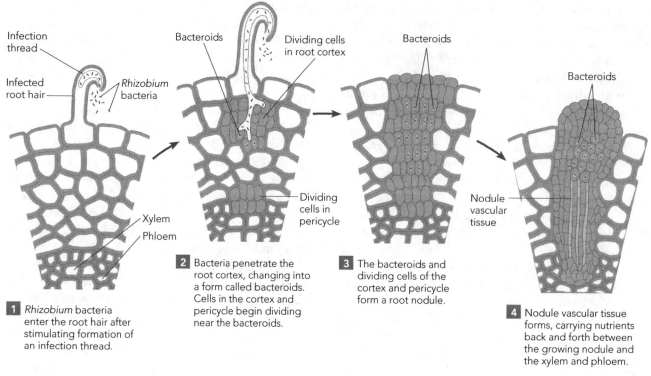

Figure 13 Formation of root nodules.

1 *Rhizobium* bacteria enter the root hair after stimulating formation of an infection thread.

2 Bacteria penetrate the root cortex, changing into a form called bacteroids. Cells in the cortex and pericycle begin dividing near the bacteroids.

3 The bacteroids and dividing cells of the cortex and pericycle form a root nodule.

4 Nodule vascular tissue forms, carrying nutrients back and forth between the growing nodule and the xylem and phloem.

under to provide more nitrogen through the decay process. In the case of legumes like peas and beans, a crop can be harvested before the rest of the plant is returned to the soil.

Since commercially produced nitrogen fertilizer is expensive, scientists have long dreamed of transferring the ability to form nitrogen-fixing bacterial associations to all crop plants. Although one primary enzyme, nitrogenase, carries out the fixation, the bacterial colonization process involves several genes and complex signaling between the host plant and bacteria. Each legume species associates with a specific bacterium species, and the signaling molecules vary with each association. Trans-

ferring the nitrogen-fixing process to a new plant would involve introducing a number of genes and an overall greater knowledge of how the association works.

Section Review

1. Describe the three soil horizons.
2. Describe the interaction between soil, water, and mineral ions.
3. What is the difference between macronutrients and micronutrients?
4. How do bacteria supply nitrogen to plants?

SUMMARY

Molecular Movement Across Membranes

Diffusion is the spontaneous movement of molecules down a concentration gradient
Solute molecules move spontaneously from a region of higher solute concentration to a region of lower solute concentration.

Facilitated diffusion and active transport use proteins to assist in movement across membranes
In facilitated diffusion, proteins bind solutes and transport them across membranes from a region of higher solute concentration to a region of lower solute concentration. In active transport, solutes move up a concentration gradient with the help of energy supplied by the cell.

Exocytosis and endocytosis transport large molecules

Molecules leave the cell by exocytosis and enter by endocytosis. In exocytosis, molecules are packaged in membrane-bound vesicles, which fuse with the plasma membrane. In endocytosis, the plasma membrane forms pockets around molecules, which become vesicles.

Osmosis is the movement of water across a selectively permeable membrane

In osmosis, water moves from a region of lower solute concentration (higher water concentration) to a region of higher solute concentration (lower water concentration). Osmosis can occur with or without transport proteins, called *aquaporins*.

In plant cell growth, the osmotic potential inside the cell interacts with pressure generated by the cell wall

Cells grow when their water potential is negative. Water potential is the sum of the osmotic potential and pressure potential. Osmotic potential is generated by the cell's solute concentration. Pressure potential is generated by cell wall resistance to protoplast expansion.

Movement and Uptake of Water and Solutes in Plants

Water evaporation from leaves pulls water through the xylem from the roots

Transpiration through stomata creates tension in water columns of xylem. Cohesion of water molecules to each other and adhesion to cell walls help support the water in tracheids and vessel elements. Transpiration is regulated by the opening and closing of stomata in response to light, CO_2, and abscisic acid.

Stomata control gas exchange and water loss for the plant

A full 90% of a plant's water loss occurs through stomata, which open in response to lowered CO_2 concentrations or to blue light and close due to increases in abscisic acid.

Sugars and other organic molecules move from leaves to roots in the phloem

According to the pressure-flow hypothesis, osmotic pressure caused by production of sugars in photosynthesis pushes a sugar solution from its source in leaves to sinks in stems, roots, and fruits.

Soil, Minerals, and Plant Nutrition

Soil is made of ground-up particles of rocks surrounded by negative charges that bind water and minerals

Soil occurs in layers called *horizons* and consists of a mixture of sand, silt, and clay mixed with organic matter.

Plants require 17 essential elements, most of which are obtained from soil

Plants require nine macronutrients and at least eight micronutrients. Mineral deficiencies in soils are passed onto the food chain to nonphotosynthetic organisms.

Soil particles bind water and mineral ions

The soil solution consists of water and dissolved minerals bound to negatively charged soil particles by a matrix potential. Cations bind to soil particles, depending on the relative charges and their concentrations.

Bacteria in the soil make nitrogen available to plants

Plants absorb nitrogen as nitrate or ammonium ion from the soil. All nitrogen in the soil is secured by nitrogen-fixing bacteria, which convert ammonium (NH_4^+) to nitrate (NO_3).

Review Questions

1. How do symplastic transport and apoplastic transport differ?
2. Explain the difference between diffusion, facilitated diffusion, and active transport.
3. Name some cellular processes in plants that use exocytosis.
4. If a selectively permeable membrane separates a solution and fresh water, in which direction will water flow? Why?
5. Why is a plant cell like a water balloon inside a cardboard box?
6. How does water potential affect the flow of water in a plant?
7. Describe plasmolysis and how it occurs.
8. How does transpiration relate to transport?
9. How do the properties of water facilitate transport in plants?
10. Why are pumps placed at the bottom of water wells?
11. Explain how stomata function and why they are important.
12. How does rainfall produce acidic soils?
13. Give three examples of macronutrients and three examples of micronutrients, explaining the importance of each.
14. Describe the conversion of nitrogen gas to nitrate by bacteria.
15. Why does farming result in nutrient-poor soils?

Questions for Thought and Discussion

1. During droughts, trees lining irrigation ditches have sometimes been cut to save water. Is this a sound idea? Explain.
2. As the relative humidity approaches 100%, transpiration decreases. Does this result in plants being nutrient-poor? Explain.

3. Describe some creative ways to maintain soil fertility on agricultural land.

4. The presence of cell walls in plants is thought by some scientists to indicate that plants evolved in fresh water rather than from oceanic algae. Why are cell walls useful to plant cells surrounded by fresh water?

5. Why do cells that are carrying out photosynthesis take up water?

6. Diagram the pathway taken by a single water molecule that, by chance, is carried from the soil to a leaf of a tall tree and then returns from the leaf to the roots of the same plant. Include in your diagram the key cells and tissues through which this movement occurs.

Evolution Connection

As you have read in this chapter, agronomists hope to one day transfer the ability to fix atmospheric nitrogen from certain microorganisms to crop plants. Why do you think this ability has apparently never evolved naturally in plants.

To Learn More

Visit The Botany Place Website at www.thebotanyplace.com for quizzes, exercises, and Web links to new and interesting information related to this chapter.

Brady, Nyle and Ray Weil. *The Nature and Properties of Soils.* Upper Saddle River, NJ: Prentice Hall, 2001. The physical, chemical, and biological properties of soil are explored.

Gleick, Peter H. *The World's Water 2002–2003: The Biennial Report on Freshwater Resources.* Washington, D.C.: Island Press, 2002. An interesting general view of all aspects of water availability, conflicts, and sanitation.

Postel, Sandra. *Pillar of Sand: Can the Irrigation Miracle Last?* New York: W. W. Norton, 1999. She discusses the role of irrigation in human history; the present status of insufficient resources; and how the future of irrigated agriculture might be improved.

Taiz, Lincoln, and E. Zieger. *Plant Physiology.* Sunderland, MA: Sinauer Associates, 2002. This excellent text explores all areas of plant physiology including mineral nutrition and water relations of cells and whole plants.

Plant and Soil Water

From Chapter 9 of *Principles of Crop Production: Theory, Techniques, and Technology*, Second Edition, George Acquaah.
Copyright © 2005 by Pearson Education, Inc. Published by Pearson Prentice Hall. All rights reserved.

Plant and Soil Water

PURPOSE

The purpose of this chapter is to discuss the properties of soil water, its movement in the soil and the plant, and its management for crop production under rainfed and irrigated conditions.

EXPECTED OUTCOMES

After studying this chapter, the student should be able to:

1. Discuss the hydrologic cycle.
2. Classify soil water according to availability to plants.
3. Discuss how water moves in the soil.
4. List the primary goals of soil water management.
5. Discuss water use efficiency and factors that affect it.
6. Discuss water management in rainfed production in humid conditions.
7. Discuss water management in rainfed production in dry conditions.
8. Discuss water management in production under irrigated conditions.
9. Discuss the methods of irrigation and the role of water quality.

KEY TERMS

Aquifer	Cohesion	Furrow irrigation
Available water	Embolism	Gravitational water
Capillary rise	Evapotranspiration	Hydraulic conductivity
Capillary water	Fallow	Hydrologic cycle
Cavitation	Field capacity	Hydrophytes

Hygroscopic water
Infiltration
Irrigation
Matric potential
Mesophytes
Microirrigation

Percolation
Permanent wilting point
Salinization
Saturated flow
Sprinkler irrigation

Subirrigation
Surface irrigation
Unsaturated flow
Water-use efficiency
Xerophytes

TO THE STUDENT

Water for crop production is stored in the soil. The capacity of soil to store water depends on several factors, including its depth, texture, structure, and organic matter content. The amount of water stored in the soil at some point in time depends on how much was received (through rain or irrigation) and how much was lost (transpiration, evaporation, percolation). Certain regions of crop production have climatic conditions that support production solely on water received as rain. In other areas, no crop production can occur without irrigation. Because of the uncertainty of the weather, drought periodically devastates crop production when it is conducted under solely rainfed conditions. Whenever possible, provisions should be made for supplemental irrigation, in case of droughty days. Since water for crop production is stored in the soil, the producer should adopt cultural practices to manage the soil so that it does not lose moisture.

Regarding the crop being produced, the grower needs to know certain factors, including the root system and stage of crop development (affect the time when the plant needs water the most). Apart from soil and plant factors, effective management should take into account the effects of local weather. Weather modifies crop needs for water. In this chapter, you will learn how water is managed under various crop production systems and the various methods used to provide supplemental moisture in crop production. Pay attention to the soil-plant-water relationship and how the atmosphere impacts it.

Water can exist in three states in nature: *solid, liquid,* and *gaseous.* The liquid state is the most useful to plants. Soil water is the solvent in which all the soil nutrients needed for plant growth and development are dissolved. A soil may have high concentrations of nutrients but will be unproductive if there is no soil water to dissolve them for root absorption. Water needed for photosynthesis is absorbed from the soil (or growing medium) by plant roots. Other physiological processes such as transpiration and translocation depend on water.

1: HYDROLOGIC CYCLE

Water in the soil, plants, and the atmosphere exists in a continuum. Just like soil nutrients, soil water is a dynamic system influenced by factors that deplete it or replenish it. There is a relationship between water in the atmosphere and soil water that is described by the **hydrologic cycle** (Figure 1). This cycle is a complex phenomenon of movement of water that includes factors that add water to the system and factors that remove water from it. Plants act as conduits for the flow of water from the soil through plant organs (e.g., roots, stem, leaves) into the atmosphere. This pathway of water movement is called the *soil-plant-atmosphere continuum.* The movement of water through plants into the atmosphere constitutes transpiration, while the direct loss of water into the atmosphere from the soil is evaporation.

Hydrologic cycle. The circuit of water movement from the atmosphere to the earth and back to the atmosphere through various processes, such as precipitation, runoff, percolation, storage, evaporation, and transpiration.

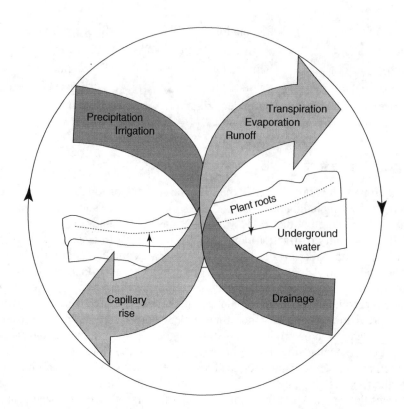

FIGURE 1 The hydrologic cycle operates on the principle that water evaporates from the earth's surface, including water bodies, and returns in the form of precipitation. Life on earth depends on the hydrologic cycle. The cycle described in this figure is in particular reference to plants. Precipitation and irrigation are the main avenues for replenishing soil water from above ground. Underground, water can reach plant roots from the underground water pool through capillary rise. Similarly, water is lost through transpiration, evaporation, surface runoff, and drainage from the root zone into the underground water pool.

Soil water is stored at different depths (levels) of the soil. Plant roots draw water from different depths of the soil and store it in their organs. For crop production, the water stored in the root zone is of importance. The level or amount of this water depends on a balance between factors that increase it and those that deplete it, as already stated.

1.1 THREE FORCES ARE INVOLVED IN SOIL WATER MOVEMENT AND RETENTION

Hydraulic conductivity. An expression of the soil's ability to transmit flowing water through a solid, such as soil, in response to a given potential gradient.

Matric potential. The amount of work an infinitesimal quantity of water in the soil can do as it moves from the soil to a pool of free water of the same composition and at the same location.

How does water move in the soil? The rate of water flow depends on the *potential gradient* (the driving force) and the **hydraulic conductivity** (the ease of flow through pore spaces in a particular medium). Water can perform work when it moves. *Soil water potential* is the work performed when a quantity of water moves from its present state to a pool of pure, free water at the same location and at normal atmospheric pressure. This potential has several components. The effect of the surface area of soil particles and micropores, called **matric potential**, and the effect of dissolved substances (*osmotic potential*) are key components.

Other key components are the *pressure potential* (effects of atmospheric gas) and the effect of the water's elevation as compared with a specified position (*gravitational potential)*, the latter not related to soil properties. Water flows from an area of high water potential (usually wetter soil) to low water potential (usually drier soil). Soil water potential is mostly matric potential (work done when a quantity of water in the soil moves from the soil to a pool of free water of the same composition and at the same location). Matric potential nearly equals water potential in non-salty soils.

Three forces are involved in soil water movement and retention. Water enters the soil by infiltration through the pore spaces. The infiltration capacity of a soil depends on its physical characteristics (e.g., texture, structure, and the presence of impediments such as impervious layers, like pans). When downward movement of water encounters an obstruction, or the rate of infiltration is overwhelmed by the rate at which water is supplied, water pools or ponds on the soil surface. Where there is a slope, surface runoff occurs as a consequence.

Water flow may be classified into two categories: **saturated flow** and **unsaturated flow**. Soil is said to be saturated when all the pores (both macropores and micropores) are filled with water. Under this state, water movement depends on *hydraulic force* (usually gravitational pull) and hydraulic conductivity. Sandy and loamy soils have higher hydraulic conductivity than clay soils. Why is this so?

The process by which water (rain or irrigation) enters the soil body is called water **infiltration**. Infiltration wets the soil profile. More water then moves through the wetted soil by the process called **percolation** (the process responsible for leaching of dissolved salts).

Water infiltration is influenced by various soil factors:

1. Soil texture (the percentage of sand, silt, and clay in the soil). Infiltration is rapid in coarse sands and slow in clay soils.
2. Soil structure (particle arrangement). Infiltration is high in a soil with granular structure and poor in structureless soil such as clay.
3. Soil organic matter. Organic matter improves infiltration. Mulching also protects soil structure by protecting against destruction of soil aggregation. Infiltration is facilitated by good soil aggregation.
4. Presence of impervious layers, such as pans (clay pan, plow pan) and other obstructions such as bedrock, which impedes infiltration. The problem is more significant if the depth of the impervious layer is shallow. Can you explain why?
5. Compaction. Soil compaction reduces pore spaces and slows water infiltration.
6. Soil temperature. Cold soils absorb water slowly.
7. Soil moisture status. Wet soils have low infiltration rates.

Unsaturated flow of soil water occurs when its potential is low (less than -20 to -33 kPa). Under such conditions, water moves in any direction but from regions of high potential (relatively wet) to those of low potential (relatively dry). The rate of this flow is fastest when the water potential gradient between the wet and the dry areas is high. This flow is also faster when soil moisture is near field capacity.

Under unsaturated soil conditions, the matric potential gradient is more important than hydraulic conductivity and hydraulic force. Hydraulic conductivity is higher in sand than clay when matrix potential is high. However, under drier soil conditions, water movement through clay has the advantage of higher capillarity.

Capillary rise (water movement in micropores) is responsible for the loss of water from the soil by evaporation (Figure 2). While gravity moves water downward, the retention of water by soil depends on two surface forces, namely **cohesion** (the force of attraction between water molecules) and *adhesion* (the force of attraction between soil particles and water molecules). The ability of the soil to retain water is called its *water-holding capacity*.

Saturated flow. The movement of water through the soil by gravity flow, as in irrigation or during a rainstorm (i.e., saturated soil).

Unsaturated flow. The movement of water in soil that is not filled to capacity with water (i.e., soil is not water-saturated).

Infiltration. Entry of water downward through the soil surface.

Percolation. The downward movement of water through the soil, especially the downward flow of water in saturated or nearly saturated soil.

Capillary rise. Rise of water in small or capillary pores against gravity.

Cohesion. Force holding a liquid or solid together because of attraction between like molecules.

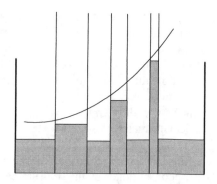

FIGURE 2 The upward capillary rise of water through tubes depends on the diameter of the bore. The rise is higher in tubes with finer bores than those with wider bores. Similarly, the capillary rise in the soil is higher in finer-textured soils (more micropores) than coarse-textured soils (more macropores).

1.2 WATER UPTAKE BY PLANTS OCCURS LARGELY WITHOUT ENERGY EXPENDITURE

How does soil water enter plant roots? More than 90% of water entering plants is absorbed by *passive absorption* (no energy involved). As plants transpire, a force is generated that pulls a continuous column of water through plant cells. The trend is for water to move from the region of highest water potential to one of lowest water potential in the soil. Water is moved through xylem conducting vessels. This movement is possible because of the strong cohesive bond among water molecules. This movement of water is called the *cohesion-tension theory* of water movement. The cohesiveness of water molecules allows water to withstand tension and retain the continuous column. Water in the xylem vessels is held against gravity by capillarity. Capillary flow can be obstructed when air bubbles interrupt the continuity of the water in the water column (**cavitation**). The condition in which capillary flow is cavitated is called **embolism**. An embolized tracheary element is incapacitated and unable to conduct water.

Water enters the plant from the soil through the root hairs. Once inside, water moves through the root cortex into the tracheary elements. Transpiration is negligible at night. As such, root pressure is known to play a role in water movement during this period. Ions build up in the xylem to a high concentration to initiate osmosis and cause water to enter the vascular tissue through neighboring cells. This *active absorption* requires energy expenditure.

Water occurs in the soil in the pore spaces and is adsorbed to soil particles. Not all soil water is accessible to plants for use. The portion of stored soil water that can be readily absorbed by plants is called plant-**available water**. This water is held within a potential of between −33 and −1,500 kPa. At water potential greater than −1,500 kPa, water absorption is slower than moisture loss through transpiration. This results in wilting of plants. The water content of soil at a water potential of −1,500 kPa is called the *wilting point* (or **permanent wilting point**). Plants such as corn show signs of wilting even at −100 to −200 kPa, as occurs on a hot, dry day. Plants usually recover during the cool of the night. This is because the wilting is only temporary.

Soil water at a soil water potential of −33 kPa is called **field capacity**. This is the maximum amount of water a soil can hold after wetting and free drainage. The difference between the soil water content at field capacity and the soil water content at permanent wilting point is the plant-available water. The water available depends on soil texture (Figure 3). Explain the trends in the figure based on your knowledge of the physical properties of soil.

The difference between the total water potential between two locations in the soil is called *water-potential gradient*. Water in micropores (**capillary water**) moves in all directions when a water-potential gradient exists.

Cavitation. An interruption in the continuity of flow in a pore by air bubbles.

Embolism. The cavitation of a capillary flow.

Available water. The portion of water in a soil that can be readily absorbed by plant roots.

Permanent wilting point. The largest amount of water in the soil at which plants will wilt and not recover when placed in a dark, humid atmosphere.

Field capacity. The amount of water remaining in a soil after being saturated and then freely drained.

Capillary water. The water held in capillary or small pores of a soil that is available to plants.

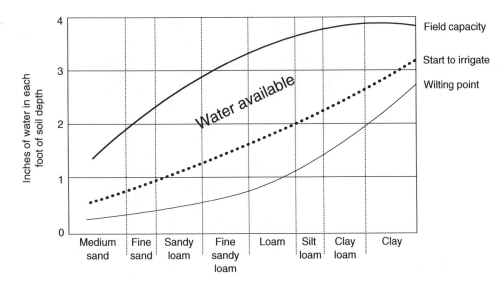

FIGURE 3 The water available for plant use depends on the soil texture. Field capacity and wilting coefficient are also influenced by soil texture. Field capacity increases as soil texture increases, leveling off as soil becomes finer in texture. Loamy soil drains well, has good water-holding capacity, and is recommended for cropping.

1.3   NOT ALL FORMS OF SOIL WATER ARE AVAILABLE TO PLANTS

How useful is a heavy downpour of rain to crop in the field? Based on the degree of wetness (which depends on the tightness with which the moisture film is held around the soil particles), soil water may be classified into three forms: gravitational, capillary, and hygroscopic (Figure 4).

1. **Gravitational water**. Gravitational water occupies the macropores as well as the micropores after a heavy rain or excessive irrigation. It drains under gravity and is therefore not available to plants for growth and development.
2. *Capillary water*. Capillary water is held in the micropores, after the macropores have been drained by gravitation pull. This is the only important source of water for plants.
3. **Hygroscopic water**. Hygroscopic water is held too tightly around soil particles and therefore not available to plants. It can be removed by air-drying of the soil.

Plants differ in their capacity to grow and produce under varying moisture regimes. In this regard, there are three general categories of plants:

1. **Hydrophytes** are plants that can live and can be productive under waterlogged conditions (e.g., paddy rice).
2. **Mesophytes** are plants that prefer normal rainfall conditions. Most field crops are mesophytes (e.g., corn, wheat, cotton).
3. **Xerophytes** are plants adapted to conditions of moisture deficit (drought). Drought tolerance is an important breeding objective for areas that are prone to erratic rainfall (e.g., *Agave* spp., such as sisal).

1.4   SOME PLANTS USE WATER MORE EFFICIENTLY THAN OTHERS

What makes certain species use water more efficiently that others? The water needs of plants change as they grow and develop. Most of the water that is used by most of the

Gravitational water. Water that moves into, through, or out of the soil under gravitational force.

Hygroscopic water. The component of soil water that is held by adsorption to surface of soil particles and is not available to plants.

Hydrophytes. Plants that grow in an exceptionally moist habitat, usually partly or entirely submerged in water.

Mesophytes. Plants requiring moderate or intermediate amounts of water for optimum growth.

Xerophytes. Plants that tolerate and grow in or on extremely dry soils.

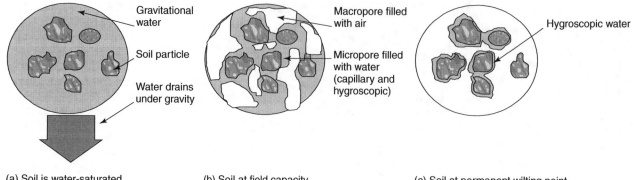

(a) Soil is water-saturated   (b) Soil at field capacity   (c) Soil at permanent wilting point

FIGURE 4 Forms of water. Water in a saturated soil drains freely under gravitational force (gravitational water). This water is not available for plant use. When water is drained out of the macropores, drainage ceases, the remainder of the water being held against gravity in micropores. After plants use up this water, or after it is lost to evaporation, there is some water held too tightly to soil particles to be accessible to plant roots. This is the hygroscopic water.

cultivated crop plant species is drawn from the top 5 feet (1.5 meters) of the soil profile. Some crops, such as alfalfa, have a deep root system and thus are capable of extracting more water from lower depths of the soil than other species. Similarly, drought-tolerant species (such as sorghum with its extensive root system) are able to extract more water from the soil than other grasses.

Plants differ in the water needed for development and productivity. Corn, for example, requires between 30 and 100 cm (11.8 and 39.4 inches) of water per month in cultivation for proper development and productivity. As previously indicated, it is important that moisture be available during the critical periods of the crop plant's lifecycle. Crops may be able to grow and produce well using the cropping season's rainfall or stored soil moisture. However, under certain cultural conditions, irrigation may be necessary to supplement soil moisture for maximum productivity. Irrigation may be needed because of seasonal variation in soil moisture.

Water use efficiency. The dry matter or harvested portion of a crop produced per unit of water consumed.

The role of water in photosynthesis has been previously discussed. Crop plants differ in their **water-use efficiency**. Moisture stress causes stomata to close and, consequently, carbon dioxide assimilation is reduced. Certain species are more efficient at fixing carbon dioxide under low water conditions by keeping stomatal aperture open for a longer time. This, of course, means opportunity for water loss is extended. *Transpiration ratio* is a measure of the effectiveness of a crop plant in photosynthesis under moisture stress through moderating moisture loss while allowing sufficient carbon dioxide to be assimilated. This is calculated as follows:

Transpiration ratio = amount of water transpired/amount of carbon dioxide fixed

Water-use efficiency is a measure of the total amount of water required to produce a unit of dry matter. This total amount of water includes usable water (for plant growth) and water lost (through drainage, transpiration, evaporation, and surface runoff). In order for water to be used efficiently, the producer should experience the most advantage from the least amount of water.

There are several ways of measuring water-use efficiency. The transpiration ratio is a measure of water-use efficiency that is obtained by determining the effectiveness in moderating water loss while allowing sufficient carbon dioxide uptake for photosynthesis.

The amount of dry matter produced depends on the amount of carbon dioxide fixed. It is clear that transpiration ratio and water use efficiency are closely linked. In fact the transpiration ratio may be defined as the amount of water transpired per unit of dry matter produced. The reciprocal of transpiration ratio is the water-use efficiency (i.e., WUE = 1/transpiration ratio). Water use efficiency ranges from 1/200 to 1/1,000, the common range being 1/300 to 1/700. As the climate becomes hot and dry, values decline sharply. Insufficient water causes stomata to close and photosynthesis to cease. Crops with high water-use efficiencies are able to produce high yields under drought conditions by keeping their stomata open for longer periods of time for carbon dioxide fixation. Drought-tolerant species such as sorghum (or C_4 plants) have higher WUE than others such as wheat (or C_3 plants).

In crop production, certain biotic and abiotic factors will influence the ability of plants to utilize the water available. Weeds compete with crop plants for water. They disrupt the patterns of water use and cause shortages at critical times in the crop cycle, leading to reduced yield. Weed control is important under rainfed production.

Pathogens cause diseases that reduce physiological activities and deprive plants of energy for growth and development. Those that affect leaves reduce photosynthetic surface; those that are soil borne may destroy roots and reduce their ability to absorb water and nutrients, resulting in reduced photosynthesis, growth, and development.

Plants that receive balanced nutrition develop properly and exploit water and other resources effectively. However, excessive nitrogen causes luxuriant and early growth and greater leaf area that may place a greater demand on water. Plants growing under low fertility and moisture stress have reduced plant growth. However, water is better distributed between vegetative and reproductive functions for maximizing yield under the given environmental conditions even though the yield is low.

The loss of moisture from leaves (transpiration) and from any exposed surface (evaporation) together constitutes the combined effect called **evapotranspiration**. Evapotranspiration is influenced by solar radiation, increasing on a clear, sunny day. It is also affected by the leaf area index (LAI). As such, evapotranspiration is high when plants are younger and the ground in the field is more exposed (because of low LAI). Evaporation occurs when the atmospheric vapor pressure is less than that at the immediate leaf or soil surface. Drier and windy atmospheric conditions accelerate evapotrans-piration. Evapotranspiration is also higher when the soil is near field capacity than when it is drier.

Crop producers may reduce evapotranspiration through mulching, weed control, or **irrigation**. Certain irrigation methods, such as drip, are more effective in this regard. In corn under irrigation, narrower spacing and higher plant population density (28,000 plants per acre or 69,188 plants per hectare) produce higher WUE than spacing at 14,000 plants per acres (34,594 plants per hectare).

Evapotranspiration. The sum of water transpired by vegetation and evaporated from soil in a given area within a given period of time.

Irrigation. The intentional application of water to the soil.

1.5 SOIL WATER CONTENT CAN BE MEASURED IN A VARIETY OF WAYS

Soil water content is measured by several methods, the most classic and standard being the *gravimetric method*. The soil sample is weighed (wet) and then dried at 105° to 110°C (221° to 230°F) to constant weight. The following calculations are then made:

Mass water ratio = mass of water/mass of oven-dry soil

Mass water percentage = mass water ratio × 100

Soil water is frequently expressed in terms of volume:

Volume water ratio = volume water/volume of soil

= (weight of water/density of water)/(weight of oven-dry soil/soil bulk density)

Volume water % = volume water ratio × 100

For the purpose of irrigation, it is important to know the reservoir of water in a soil volume or the amount of water required to wet the soil by irrigation or rain. Plant roots explore a volume of soil for water.

A variety of instruments are available for quick estimates of soil water status. One such instrument is the *tensiometer* that measures the matric potential of soil moisture. Some growers of crops such as sugarcane and potatoes use tensiometers to schedule irrigation. One instrument is placed such that it monitors moisture at the depth of maximum root density and activity, and another near the bottom of the active root zone. When the tensiometer readings at the top and lower soil levels are, for example, −50 kPa and −40 kPa, respectively, an automatic irrigation system is triggered into action.

Tensiometers are, however, unable to measure soil matric potential at levels low enough to warn against the danger of wilting. Other instruments for measuring soil water are the *neutron probe* and the *gamma ray absorption unit.*

2: GOALS OF SOIL WATER MANAGEMENT

The goal of water management in crop production is to optimize water use. Water should be supplied when plants need it so it is not wasted. The general goals of managing soil water in crop production are

1. To optimize the use of soil water while it is available
2. To minimize nonproductive soil water losses. Irrigation is prone to evaporative and percolative losses.
3. To optimize the use of supplemental moisture when it is applied. Supplemental moisture is supplied at additional costs to crop production. It is therefore uneconomical to irrigate crops at the wrong time and in the wrong amounts.

2.1 WHAT IS DRYLAND AGRICULTURE?

Dryland agriculture comprises systems of production that rely exclusively on rainfall as the source of moisture for crops and pasture production. Consequently, moisture is often the limiting factor in production during at least part of the cropping season. Dryland areas receive less than 20 inches of annual rainfall. Crop rotations are commonly practiced on dryland farms. The principal environmental problems that dryland farmers face include susceptibility to soil erosion (by both wind and water), increased soil salinity and acidification, soil structure deterioration, and soil and nutrient depletion.

Drylands are called by different names all over the world—e.g., plains, grasslands, savannas, steppes, and pampas. They are among the most productive ecosystems in the world, accounting for about 75% of the world's food supply. The major crops grown include potato, cassava, wheat, corn, and rice. Dryland farming occurs in arid and semiarid regions of the world, which make up about 40% of the world's total land area, and is home to over 700 million people. Most (about two-thirds) of this land area is in developing countries. The natural resource base of these areas is fragile. The soils generally are low in fertility and organic matter, as well as low in water-holding capacity. In the United States, dryland farming is common in the eastern and central states.

As energy costs rise and water resources for irrigation decline, dryland production will be increasingly important in producing food to meet the needs of the growing populations of the world.

2.2 CROP PRODUCTION UNDER RAINFED CONDITIONS DEPENDS ON THE HYDROLOGIC CYCLE

There are two basic soil water management practices, depending on whether the production will be rainfed or irrigated. In managing soil water for production under rainfed conditions, the features of the hydrologic cycle of importance are

1. *Rainfall.* The aspects of rainfall of importance are total rainfall per year, time of year of rainfall, and reliability of the rain.
2. *Crop.* The water requirement of the crop is important.
3. *Atmosphere.* Water is lost to the atmosphere through evaporation and transpiration.

The role of the weather in rainfed (non-irrigated) crop production is critical. Precipitation is depended upon for all the water used in production. The schedule of watering is dictated by nature. Since the weather is unpredictable, how can rainfed crop producers ensure reasonable success in their operations? The crop producer operating under rainfed conditions should adopt a cropping system that exploits soil water while it is available. Production decision making under such circumstances is based largely on years of experience. It is important to know when the rainfall season starts and, more important, the reliability of the rainfall, timing, frequency, and intensity. Crop cultivars selected for production should mature within the growing season. Early-maturing cultivars are suited to regions of a short wet season. Crop production decisions regarding planting density and fertilization should be made with caution to avoid premature exhaustion of stored soil moisture before the cropping season is over. Cultivars with drought resistance are important in rainfed crop production systems because they provide insurance against unexpected drought occurrences.

Is crop production in the world predominantly rainfed or irrigated? Most crops are produced under rainfed conditions. Rain may be supplemented with irrigation to varying degrees. Rainfed production strategies may be categorized into two, according to rainfall characteristics—practices for *wet conditions* and those for *dry conditions*. Humid regions of the world experience large quantities of rainfall. Unfortunately, the rain does not fall in amounts that are ideal for cropping. Occasional drought is possible even under humid and wet conditions. The more common problem, however, is excessive rainfall that causes a variety of problems, including water erosion, surface flooding, waterlogging, and leaching. Low-lying lands may require drainage to be productive as agricultural lands. Further, these lands usually have cold soils.

Excessive rainfall delays crop production activities such as tillage, planting, and harvesting of produce. Grain dryers may be needed to keep harvested grains in good condition. Humid conditions provide opportunities for diseases and pests to thrive. Producing hay in wet regions is problematic. Instead, ensilaging may replace haying. Weeds are also problematic in wet agriculture. Cloud cover in wet regions is greater than in dry regions. This reduces production potential. However, the abundant moisture compensates for the deficiency.

2.3 IN RAINFED CROP PRODUCTION, DISTRIBUTION OR VARIABILITY IN RAINFALL PATTERNS IS MORE IMPORTANT THAN THE TOTAL AMOUNT OF RAINFALL

The rainfed producer should select crops and cultivars very judiciously. The crops and cultivars should have developmental cycles that avoid or tolerate periods in the growing period when water shortage occurs. Further, they should be able to optimize the use of available water for high productivity.

Plants whose economic yield is vegetative (non-grain or seed) are more successful under conditions of unpredictable water supply. Such species include grasses and other forage species. Roots and tubers are adapted to rainfed agriculture because they are able to halt the growth cycle temporarily but resume with rainfall to add more dry matter. Cassava *(Manihot esculenta)* is exceptionally suited to drought-prone regions.

Plants with determinate stem types are very susceptible to fluctuations in rainfall during the growing season. Crop yield is significantly reduced when drought occurs near flowering time (anthesis). Under such unpredictable conditions, short-duration cultivars, even though less productive, are best to use to avoid water stress.

To use water efficiently under rainfed conditions, the grower should select cultivars with high water-use efficiency. All the water that is available under the production system should be fully utilized for crop production. The crop should be planted such that stress is avoided; otherwise, the crop should be able to tolerate transient water shortages. Further, the soil water should be used such that it supports vegetative and reproductive growths.

2.4 DRYLAND PRACTICES

Fallow. Cropland left idle and free of weeds for a period of time to restore productivity through accumulation of water, nutrients, or both.

Irrigation is usually not the practical solution to drought in dryland production. Rather, farmers adopt practices such as **fallow**, mulching, alternative plant arrangement in the field, use of catch crops, and xerophytic crops to conserve or efficiently use moisture in production. Sometimes, it is also prudent to plan for crop failure by purchasing crop insurance policies.

Crop producers use fallow under rainfed conditions to accumulate moisture for crop production. The land is idled for a period of time weed-free. The success of this practice depends on the climate, soil, and management skill of the producer. The soil should have good water-holding capacity. Part of fallow management includes improving soil infiltration or penetration, minimizing losses by evaporation and drainage. Sandy soils have high penetration but low water-storage capacity. The efficiency of a fallow (the proportion of the total rainfall that contributes to crop production during the subsequent cropping) depends on the soil type, rainfall amount and distribution, and evapotranspiration. The efficiency of a fallow can be enhanced by implementing water conservation practices that increase the irregularities on the soil surface (e.g., ridges, plant residues on soil). These structures trap surface water by pooling and allowing more time for infiltration to occur, while reducing surface runoff.

Sometimes, soil structure must be improved through incorporation of organic matter, addition of soil amendments, and tillage. Tillage may be used to break up pans and control weeds. However, frequent tillage to control weeds during a fallow is expensive. Application of a mulch or maintenance of surface residue will control weeds, increase infiltration, protect the soil surface from destruction, and help the soil to retain water for a longer time. In spite of management practices adopted, a fallow is subject to losses by evaporation, transpiration by weeds, and drainage below the root zone.

There are two basic kinds of fallow systems in crop production—conventional and conservation. These systems are associated with certain tillage practices.

Conventional Fallow System

The chief characteristic of the conventional system is the lack of plant residues on the surface of the soil. The bare soil is vulnerable to both wind and soil erosion. Extensive tillage is used in conventional tillage systems to control weeds and conserve moisture. Tillage raises soil temperature and increases aeration, thereby accelerating the decomposition of soil organic matter and the recently incorporated crop residues. In addition to a decline in soil organic matter, the nutrients resulting from the mineralization of soil organic matter are susceptible to leaching or volatilization, as the case may be. The reduced soil organic matter also adversely impacts soil structure, reducing the infiltration of precipitation and thereby increasing surface round off.

Conservation Fallow Systems

Conservation fallow systems aim at minimizing soil erosion during the fallow period by leaving plant residue on the soil surface. An estimated minimum residue cover of about 1,300 lb/acre is required to protect the soil sufficiently from soil erosion. Residue cover is reduced by natural processes (e.g., microbial activity, oxidation) as well as by producer activities, such as tillage. Various conservation fallow systems are in use:

1. *Chemical summer fallow.* Chemical fallow provides an alternative to tillage for controlling weeds. Herbicides are used to control weeds. Vegetative growth during the fall or summer months is controlled by applying one or two consecutive applications of suitable herbicides. The herbicides kill weeds and leave plant residue on the soil surface for protection against soil erosion. The potential risk of using herbicides is the risk of contaminating groundwater and other water resources. Such potential risks can be minimized by the timely application of herbicides with short residual and limited mobility in the soil. The chemicals should be applied at the right rates and under the proper environmental conditions. One practice involves an early spring application of 24-D to control winter annual weeds and a late spring application of glyphosate or paraquat mixed with an appropriate phenoxy herbicide for a broad spectrum control of all broad weeds and volunteer grains until July. This approach eliminates three or four tillage operations.
2. *Eco-fallow.* This is similar to chemical fallow that is solely dependent on herbicides. In eco-fallow, a tillage operation (e.g., subsurface sweep) is performed to spread the plant residue. The tillage application follows a previous application of a herbicide, such as atrazine. This application into plant residue may miss weeds that were covered by the debris. The tillage controls volunteer crop plants and weeds that were hidden under the windrow or some other debris during the first chemical application.
3. *Stubble mulch fallow.* Stubble is the basal parts of plants that are left after the straw has been harvested. Stubble mulch fallow is designed to leave the field covered with straw residue during the non-cropping period. Wide-sweep blades undercut the stubble and weeds without pulverizing the soil surface. The mulch cover prevents soil erosion and conserves soil moisture. The amount of residue left on the soil surface depends on the implement used for the tillage operation. A wide blade cultivator or offset disc leaves only about 35 to 65% residue cover after each pass.

Cover Crops

Cover crops are critical to the success of any dryland annual cropping system that strives for sustainability. Cover crops are grown primarily to prevent soil erosion, to suppress weeds, and to conserve moisture. To be effective, cover crops should provide a high percentage of ground cover as quickly as possible. Leguminous cover crops enrich the soil with nitrogen. There are different types of cover crops. When cover crops are incorporated as green manures, they recycle other essential nutrients (nitrogen, phosphorus, potassium) and improve soil organic matter for improved soil physical conditions.

1. *Winter cover crop.* This crop is sown in late summer or fall to provide soil cover during the winter. In northern climates, hardy species, such as hairy vetch and rye, are desirable cover crops. In the southern region, adapted varieties of clovers, vetches, or field peas may be used. Other cereals are also grown as cover crops.
2. *Living mulch.* A living mulch is a cover crop that is inter-planted with an annual or a perennial cash crop. These living mulches suppress weeds, reduce soil erosion, enhance soil fertility, and enhance water infiltration. Examples of living mulches are overseeding hairy vetch into corn at the last cultivation or sweet clover drilled into small grains. In perennial crop fields (e.g., vineyards, orchards), grasses or legumes may be planted in the alleyways between crop rows.
3. *Catch crop.* A catch crop is one that is planted to reduce nutrient leaching following a main crop. These nutrients would have been lost to future crops. The term is also applied to a short-term cover crop that occupies a niche in a crop rotation. An example is planting cereal rye following corn harvest to scavenge the residual nitrogen from fertilizing corn. Some catch crops are winter-killed (e.g., buckwheat, oats, spring wheat, crimson clover), while others overwinter (hairy vetch, fall rye).

Skip-Row Planting

Skip-row planting is the practice of eliminating certain rows in the field to allow the producer to move through the field with implements without damaging crops or to reduce the effective crop area to reduce irrigation needs. This tactic can buy time while the farmer waits for rain and reduces the risk of crop failure.

Crop-Rotation

When crop rotation is practiced in dryland agriculture, the primary goal is to optimize the use of soil moisture for optimal crop yields. Rotations may or may not include a fallow (e.g., wheat-corn-millet-fallow or wheat-corn-millet-no fallow) as used by growers in Colorado. Producers using crop rotations have recorded 10 to 30% increase in income. Crop rotations are discussed in detail later in this book.

3: IRRIGATED CROP PRODUCTION

Whenever feasible and affordable, irrigated production can dramatically boost crop yield. Irrigation is one factor responsible for the great productivity of crops in places such as the Pacific states of the United States, especially California. About 50 million acres of the over 300 million acres of cropland in the United States are under irrigated production.

Irrigated crop production depends on a reliable source of clean water. Irrigation may be used to supplement rainfall during crop production at times when drought spells occur. However, in arid and semiarid conditions, irrigation may be used as the sole source of water for crop production.

Water for irrigation may be derived from a variety of sources:

1. *Surface water.* Surface water for crop irrigation includes rivers, lakes, streams, and ponds. To increase the volume of water available, the river or stream may be dammed.
2. *Groundwater.* Water may be pumped through wells from an **aquifer** (water stored underground) for irrigation. The aquifer can be overdrawn. Thus, management of irrigation water from this source includes methods for replenishment as well as safe withdrawal. There has to be a way of monitoring the withdrawal of the aquifer by various producers operating in the same general regions and drawing from a common pool. Not all aquifers can be recharged, leading some to question if irrigated production is sustainable.
3. *Surface runoff.* Rainwater may be collected and stored in, for example, ponds for use in irrigation.

Aquifer. A geologic formation, usually a permeable layer such as sands, gravel, and vesicular rock, that transmits water underground under ordinary water pressures.

3.1 IRRIGATION WATER SHOULD BE FREE FROM POLLUTANTS

What are the sources of irrigation water? How do they differ in terms of water quality for irrigation? The quality of irrigation water depends on its source. Rainfall contains salts and dissolved pollutants. In certain regions, the pH may be very low (acid rain) and have corrosive effects on plants. Direct surface runoff is relatively salt-free. However, running water (streams, rivers), by virtue of the fact that it contains water that has percolated through soil and underlying rock minerals, contains high concentrations of dissolved salts. Groundwater is created from accumulation of deeply percolated water and hence has the highest concentration of dissolved salts. The most common ions of dissolved salts found in irrigation water are Na^+, Cl^-, Ca^{2+}, Mg^{2+}, K^+, HCO_3^-, CO_3^{2-}, NO_3^-, SO_4^{2-}, and BO_3^{3-}. The kinds of ions and their concentrations vary from one place to another and depend on the geology, leaching, and hydrologic cycles, among others. Na^+ and Cl^- ions are more common in arid regions. When they combine with weak anions such as HCO_3^- or CO_3^{2-}, they produce alkaline soil (pH greater than 8.5). Low rainfall produces less leaching. As such, the salts are trapped in the top layers (B horizon).

The suitability of water for irrigation is determined by its salt content (total dissolved solids) and the sodium adsorption ratio:

$$SAR = [Na^+]/\sqrt{[Ca^{2+}][Mg^{2+}]}$$

The accumulation of salts in the soil is called **salinization.** All water used for irrigation has some soluble salts. As irrigation becomes more efficient, less water is applied to the crops, reducing the amount available to leach salts out of the soil profile. Consequently, salt accumulates as the added water evaporates and is transpired. Irrigation-induced salinization is a problem with irrigation, especially in arid climates (Figure 5).

Salinization. The accumulation of soluble salts in the soil.

Irrigation itself is a significant contributor to accumulation of salts in the soil through the use of water with high salt content. The salt accumulates over a period and may reach toxic proportions in the crop root zone. At this stage, leaching is needed to wash excess salts away to avoid reduction in the crop productivity.

Crops differ in tolerance to salinity. Grasses generally are more salt-tolerant than legumes. Highly sensitive crops include common bean, chickpea, strawberry, white clover, and red clover. Corn, alfalfa, rice, and oats are moderately sensitive to salts, while wheat, tomato, cotton, soybean, and sorghum are moderately salt-tolerant. Crops such as barley, cotton, sugar beet, and bermudagrass are tolerant of salts.

FIGURE 5 Irrigation-induced salinization, showing a field covered with salts that have been drawn in the evaporative stream and deposited on the soil surface. (Source: USDA)

The two most important factors to consider in irrigation water quality analysis are the total dissolved solids (TDS) and the sodium adsorption ratio (SAR). The TDS is basically a measure of the concentration of soluble salts in the water sample (i.e., salinity), while the TDS is measured in terms of electrical conductivity (dS/m). The U.S. salinity laboratory has developed a suitability classification system for irrigation water that combines salinity and sodicity. A classification of C2-S2 indicates water with high sodicity and medium salinity. Generally, irrigation water with electrical conductivity of 2 dS/m or a SAR of more than 6 could be harmful for irrigation. The SAR value can be lowered by adding calcium using a source that has high solubility (e.g., $CaCl_2$).

3.2 IRRIGATION WATER MAY BE APPLIED IN ONE OF SEVERAL WAYS

How is irrigation water applied in crop production? What determines the method selected for application? Which methods are most water-efficient? Techniques of irrigation may be categorized in several ways, one of which is the degree of control they offer the producer over application rate and distribution. Technologies of irrigation also differ in cost of installation and maintenance. Generally, the higher the producer's control over the amount and placement of the water applied, the higher the cost of the system. Another useful way of categorizing irrigation application systems is according to the energy or force needed to distribute water—by *gravity* or *pressurized*. Surface irrigation systems are gravity application systems, while sprinkler systems are pressurized application systems that depend on pumps to move water.

The choice of an irrigation system depends upon several factors, including

1. *Cost.* Irrigation is a capital-intensive undertaking. It requires a high initial capital investment for installation and then maintenance.
2. *Profitability of the enterprise.* Irrigation is justifiable if the returns on investment are high.
3. *Topography.* Terrain affects the method of distribution of water. Sometimes, land leveling is needed for successful use of certain techniques.
4. *Soil physical properties.* Soil infiltration is a key factor in the choice of a method of irrigation. Coarse-textured soils (sandy) have high infiltration. In surface techniques (e.g., flood), high soil infiltration is undesirable.

5. *Salinity.* Crops differ in tolerance of salinity. The source of water differs in salinity.
6. *Severity of frost.* In cold regions, water in irrigation pipes buried in the ground may freeze during certain times.
7. *Crop.* Certain crops may not tolerate the pool of water needed for certain methods of irrigation. Also, certain methods are expensive to operate and thus suited to crops with high economic value.
8. *Rainfall.* Some producers need irrigation to supplement rainfall in certain regions. In other regions, production may totally depend on irrigation.

3.3   METHODS OF IRRIGATION

The methods of irrigation may be classified operationally as follows:

1. Surface irrigation
   a. Gravity flow
      • Flood
      • Furrow
      • Border/basin
   b. Sprinkler systems
      • Center pivot
      • Mechanical move
      • Hand move
      • Solid set and permanent
   c. Low-flow irrigation (drip/trickle)
2. Subirrigation

Surface Irrigation

Surface irrigation is a technique of irrigation in which water is spread over the soil surface. Sometimes, the entire land area is covered such that the plants stand in water, as in the case of *flood irrigation.* In one variation of flooding, called *border strip,* small levees are built around strips of leveled land and then flooded (Figure 6). In other practices, the water flows between close rows (called *corrugations*), as in **furrow irrigation** (Figure 7). Furrow irrigation is the oldest method of crop irrigation in agriculture. About 40% of all crop land is furrow irrigated. It is applicable to row crops such as corn and cotton. Since water moves by gravity in surface irrigation, the land requires grading to create a gentle slope. A steep slope promotes soil erosion. Further, smooth furrows allow faster flow of water and reduced percolation. The ideal slope should be less than 0.25% (no more than 2%). Some producers plant Kentucky bluegrass in the furrows to reduce erosion on steep slopes. This method is not suitable for soils of high infiltration (e.g., sandy soil). Water would have to be run rapidly, but such high rates would cause erosion. In some production areas, such as California, the furrows are deliberately smoothed by dragging a steel cylinder filled with concrete with a cone cap (called a *torpedo*) down the furrow. Up to 30% faster water flow has been achieved in some cases as a result of this treatment.

Another method of flooding, called *basin irrigation,* is used on impermeable soil for growing crops that tolerate flooding (Figure 8). In paddy rice cultivation, clay soils are deliberately tilled in such a way (by puddling) that it further decreases the soil impermeability. Water is thus held in the basin so that plants grow in water for a long period. Infiltration under this condition is uniform.

Surface irrigation. The intentional application of water to plants from aboveground.

Furrow irrigation. A method of surface irrigation in which water is delivered to the field through shallow ditches between ridges on which plants are growing.

FIGURE 6 Flood irrigation is suited to soils that are not readily permeable. The land surface should be level to permit unimpeded and even water flow without surface erosion. (Source: USDA)

FIGURE 7 In furrow irrigation, water flows through furrows or corrugations by gravity. Crops are planted on the ridges before water is applied. About 40% of irrigated land in the United States is furrow irrigated. (Source: USDA)

The disadvantages of surface irrigation include the cost of grading the land, the use of excessive water, and water loss to evaporation. One advantage is no need for high-pressure pumps to move water. Surface systems are not amenable to automation, making them more labor-intensive. A technique called *surge flow surface irrigation* delivers water intermittently and improves water efficiency of surface systems. The flow rates are larger, causing wetting to occur farther down the irrigation row but accompanied by reduced percolation at the upper end (head) of the furrow (Figure 9).

3.4 SPRINKLER IRRIGATION

Sprinkler irrigation. The method of aerial application of water through pipes fitted with sprinkling units.

Sprinkler irrigation is a technique in which water is moved under pressure through pipes and distributed through nozzles as a spray. Since water is pumped under high pressure, no grading of the land is necessary prior to installation of the system. Rolling terrain can be irrigated with this system. Further, a wide variety of soil textures (light to

FIGURE 8 Basin irrigation is a modified form of flood irrigation in which the field is divided into checks or basins by using ridges. Each tree or several trees are enclosed by a small dike. (Source: USDA)

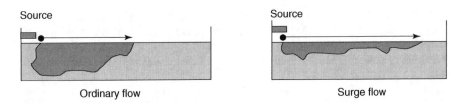

Ordinary flow   Surge flow

FIGURE 9 Surge flow improves surface irrigation efficiency by decreasing water through unnecessary depth of soil wetting at the origin. A surge flow controller may be programmed to deliver water intermittently at surge intervals of between 1 and 10 minutes or more. The smooth bursts of water allow the entire furrow to be wetted before large amounts infiltrate at the upper part of the field.

heavy) can be irrigated. The user has control of distribution and rate of delivery. The system is readily amenable to automation.

Sprinkler designs are variable. Some systems are fixed permanently in the plot where the irrigation is required (Figure 10). This involves laying pipes in the ground permanently with risers to distribute water. This design is used for high premium horticultural production. Other systems are moved periodically, either by hand (e.g., water guns and supply lines) or by automation (Figures 11 and 12). A widely used automated sprinkler system is the *center pivot* (Figure 13), which moves in a circle. Properly installed and operated, sprinklers wet the soil evenly. The water used for sprinklers should be clean to avoid clogging the sprinkler nozzles. An advantage of sprinklers is their adaptability to *chemigation* (application of chemicals such as pesticides and fertilizers through irrigation water).

There are several methods for increasing the uniformity of sprinkling. There are several causes of lack of uniformity of sprinkling, the key ones being improper irrigation pressure regulation and obstruction to water flow through the nozzles. There is new technology called *low-energy precision applicators (LEPA)* that are able to improve uniformity of distribution of irrigation water through sprinklers. Uniformity can be reduced by

(a)   (b)   (c)

FIGURE 10 Center pivot mobile sprinklers can cover areas as large as 53 hectares (130 acres) or larger in one circular sweep. (a) Water is supplied from a well located at the center pivot. The sprinkler is programmed to rotate at a specific speed. (b) Aerial photograph of irrigation by center pivot reveals the characteristic circle of green cropped land. (c) The wheel line sprinkler system does not rotate but moves in one direction on wheels.

FIGURE 11 Cable tow irrigation involves the use of a powerful spray gun connected to a long cable and mounted on wheels. The rig is moved with the cable in tow from one part of the field to another.

drift (movement of water away from intended area). This can be reduced by proper equipment adjustment and applying at wind speeds of less than 10. The boom height should be lowered and nozzles that spray larger droplets selected. High pressure of the spray causes fine droplets and increases drift.

Microirrigation

Microirrigation. A method of intentional application of water to plants in drips.

Microirrigation systems are designed to deliver water in small amounts, either in drips or sprays (hence *drip* or *trickle irrigation*). This technique offers the user the most control over the amount and placement of irrigation water. Usually, individual plants are targeted and hence this method is most suited to orchard crops. Water is delivered through

FIGURE 12 Solid set irrigation requires that irrigation pipes be permanently set in the field (buried underground). Sprinkler heads are mounted on risers of height according to the crop being irrigated.

FIGURE 13 Movable pipe irrigation is labor-intensive; it requires the irrigation pipes be moved and set up for use and dismantled after use. It is practical for use where small acreages are to be irrigated.

tubes to *emitters* (drippers or sprayers) located near individual plants (Figure 14). Only a small area (the root zone of the plant) is wetted with practically no surface flow. This system is the most water-efficient, each emitter delivering water at less than 3.7 liters per hour. The water flow is slow and at low water pressure. It is adaptable to steeper slopes. However, it requires the use of very clean water to avoid clogging the emitters. The water should not have debris, microbes, or any substance that will precipitate. Initial investment and operating costs are usually higher than for other systems. It is widely used for trees and other perennial crops, especially high-premium crops such as grapes.

Subirrigation

In both surface and sprinkler irrigation systems, water is applied over the soil surface. In **subirrigation** systems, the water table is raised to the rhizosphere. Water is pumped into a drainage system (e.g., tile or tube) laid underground. This method is effective on light soils (e.g., sandy, muck).

Subirrigation. The method of intentional application of water to plants through conduits located underground.

FIGURE 14 Drip irrigation enables water to be applied to individual plants in steady drips and minimizes evaporative losses. It is used for high-value field crops, such as grapes.

3.5 FURROW IRRIGATION IS THE MOST COMMON GRAVITY IRRIGATION METHOD USED IN U.S. CROP PRODUCTION

How important is irrigation in U.S. crop production? Where is irrigation practiced the most in the United States? What irrigation techniques are most widely used? Irrigated production areas are shown in Figure 15. The use of gravity irrigation application systems has declined by 20% since 1979 (Table 1). However, more than 50% of all irrigated cropland in the United States utilized gravity-flow systems in 1994. The practice is widely used in the arid regions of the western United States, especially in California, Nevada, Arizona, New Mexico in the Southwest; Wyoming, Colorado, and Utah in the Central Rockies; Texas and Oklahoma in the Southern Plains; and Arkansas, Louisiana, and Mississippi in the Delta Region. The most (60%) widely practiced method of irrigation is the furrow system.

Conventional systems have been improved in various states. Terrain modification and land management measures that have been implemented include improved on-farm water conveyance systems, precision field leveling, shortened water runs, alternative furrow irrigation, surge flow and cablegation, and tailwater reuse. About 60% of farms implementing the gravity-flow system utilize open-ditch systems as the main method of on-farm water conveyance. Improvements have come by way of ditch lining, ditch reorganization, and pipeline installation. Pipelines may be installed aboveground or underground. These improvements reduce percolation losses and minimize surface runoff. Producers in the Northern and Southern Plains and Delta regions lead the nation in the use of gated-pipes for water conveyance. Surge-flow and cablegation systems are concentrated in the Delta states.

The Farm and Ranch Irrigation Survey of 1994 also indicates that 20% of gravity flow users adopted alternative furrow strategies. Shortened rows were used widely in the Southwest (in Arizona and California) and in the Southern Plains regions. In 1994, 12% of gravity-irrigated farms in the Southwest, Delta, and Southeast farming regions were precision laser-leveled. Other improved water management practices adopted included

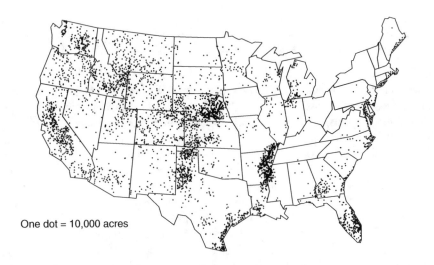

One dot = 10,000 acres

FIGURE 15 The state with the most irrigated areas is California, followed by Nebraska and Texas. The Ogallala aquifer supplies water for irrigation of lands in Colorado, Kansas, Nebraska, New Mexico, Oklahoma, South Dakota, Texas, and Wyoming. (Source: USDA)

Table 1 Changes in U.S. Irrigated Acreage According to Type of Irrigation System

System	Million Acres		Change (Percent)
	1979	1994	
All systems	50.1	46.4	−7
Gravity-flow systems	31.2	25.1	−20
Sprinkler systems	18.4	21.5	17
Center pivot	8.6	14.8	72
Mechanical move	5.1	3.7	−27
Hand move	3.7	1.9	−48
Solid set and permanent	1.0	1.0	2
Low-flow irrigation (drip/trickle)	0.3	1.8	445
Subirrigation	0.2	0.4	49

Source: USDA, ERS.

deficit irrigation techniques, such as reduced irrigation set-times, partial field irrigation, and reduced irrigation. These strategies were practiced on 10% of farms concentrated in the Northwest regions (e.g., Idaho, Oregon, and Washington). Further, 20% of farms, especially those in California, installed tailwater reuse systems.

3.6 CENTER-PIVOT IRRIGATION SYSTEMS ARE THE MOST WIDELY USED PRESSURIZED IRRIGATION SYSTEMS IN U.S. CROP PRODUCTION

Pressurized irrigation systems, including sprinkler and low-flow systems, accounted for about 46% of irrigated acreage in 1994 (Figure 16). Sprinkler irrigation is concentrated in the Northern Pacific, Northern Plains, and Northern Mountain states. They are also used for supplementary moisture supply in production of specialty crops in the humid eastern states. Self-propelled *center-pivot* systems were developed in the 1960s. Cropland on which center-pivot systems are used increased by 6.2 million acres from 1979 to

The high plains aquifer: An aquifer in trouble?

The High Plains regional aquifer system occupies a total of 174,000 square miles of underground area beneath parts of eight states—Colorado, Kansas, Nebraska, New Mexico, Oklahoma, South Dakota, Texas, and Wyoming. Elevations in this area vary between 7,800 feet on the west near the Rocky Mountains and 1,000 feet in the east near the Central Lowlands. The High Plains have gently sloping and smooth plains that are suitable for agricultural production. However, the region is dry, receiving only about 16 inches of rain in the west and about 28 inches in the east. About 54% of the land in this region is devoted to dryland and irrigated cropping, accounting for 19% of wheat, 19% of cotton, 15% of corn, and 3% of sorghum produced in the United States. Further, the High Plains region accounts for 18% of U.S. cattle production and a significant amount of swine production. These agricultural uses place a great demand on the aquifer for irrigation purposes. It is estimated that 27% of irrigated land in the United States occurs in the High Plains region.

The High Plains aquifer yields about 30% of the groundwater used for irrigation in the United States. It also provides about 82% of the domestic water needs of the over 2 million residents in the region. The High Plains aquifer is sometimes referred to as the Ogallala aquifer because the geologic unit called the Ogallala Formation forms about 80% of the aquifer. The aquifer has a saturated thickness ranging from

0 feet to more than 1,000 feet in Nebraska, with an average of about 200 feet. Depth to water ranges from 0 to 500 feet, with an average of 200 feet. Groundwater in this aquifer generally flows from east to west, discharging naturally into streams and springs. Evapotranspiration is important in areas where the water table is very shallow. In addition to these natural discharges, active pumping from wells for irrigation is a major mechanism of groundwater discharge. The primary source of recharge to the Ogallala aquifer is precipitation. Several river systems, including the Platte, Republican, Arkansas, Cimarron, and Canadian rivers, cross this aquifer and may be sources of recharge through leaks.

The High Plains aquifer is experiencing water level declines resulting from withdrawals in great excess of recharge. Drawing water for irrigation began in the 1940s. Since then, water levels in this aquifer have declined more than 100 feet in parts of Kansas, New Mexico, Oklahoma, and Texas. The declines are greater in the southern areas of the region than in the north. In certain cases, declines are severe enough to make the use of the aquifer for irrigation either impossible or cost-ineffective. Whereas most of this management has been exploitation of natural resources, the Ogallala is fossil (connate) water that cannot be recharged, at least not at rates economically feasible for irrigation. This is an example of mining groundwater.

Water-Level Changes in the Ogallala Aquifer Since 1980

State	Years: 80–88	80–89	80–90	80–91	80–92	80–93	80–94	80–95	80–96
					Change in Feet (Area-Weighted)				
Colorado	—	−1.45	−3.08	−3.15	−3.04	−3.25	−3.39	−4.20	−4.70
Kansas	—	−4.61	−4.91	−6.21	−7.39	−7.26	−6.12	−7.50	−7.00
Nebraska	—	+1.34	+0.67	+0.23	−0.27	+0.02	+1.88	+1.80	+1.60
New Mexico	—	−0.09	−0.66	−2.27	−1.86	−3.42	−2.31	−3.10	−6.20
Oklahoma	—	−0.36	−0.32	−0.11	−1.80	−0.41	−1.81	−2.80	−3.70
South Dakota	—	−2.42	−1.03	−0.74	+0.08	−0.90	+1.47	−0.60	−0.80
Texas	—	+0.55	−1.17	−1.65	−2.46	−1.96	−3.02	−4.80	−6.10
Wyoming	—	+3.12	+3.14	+2.92	+1.30	+0.63	−2.52	−3.40	−1.90
High Plains	+0.80	−0.23	−1.04	−1.41	−2.24	−2.09	−1.54	−2.40	−2.80

Source: United States Geological Service.

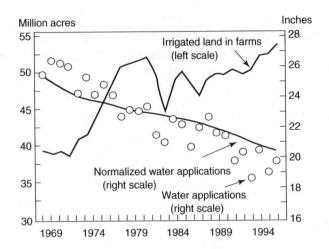

Million acres / Inches

Irrigated land in farms (left scale)

Normalized water applications (right scale)

Water applications (right scale)

1969   1974   1979   1984   1989   1994

FIGURE 16 Trends in irrigation in the United States between 1969 and 1996 indicated a general increase in the acreage irrigated. Currently, over 50 million acres of cropland are irrigated.

1994. They account for about 70% of sprinkler acreage in 1994 (Table 2). Most users were in the Northern Plains, Southern Plains, and Delta farming regions. Corn for grain and alfalfa were the two most irrigated crops in production in 1996 (Figure 17).

Center-pivot irrigation is the core technology in other new and often more efficient technologies, such as *low-pressure center pivot, low-energy precision application (LEPA),* and *linear move* systems. In 1994, 40% of center-pivot irrigated cropland was irrigated with LEPA systems. LEPA systems operate at a pressure of 30 psi, as opposed to 60 psi in conventional systems. LEPA adoption is highest in the Southern Plains. Low-flow irrigation systems (drip, trickle, or microirrigation) are used for vegetable and orchard production and occur mainly in California and Florida.

Irrigation technology continues to evolve. Advances in irrigation practices for higher efficiency are summarized in Table 3.

3.7 IRRIGATION WATER SHOULD BE WELL MANAGED FOR PROFITABILITY OF CROP PRODUCTION

The cost of water for irrigation is often high. How do irrigated crop producers use water more efficiently to increase the profitability of their enterprises? To maintain farm profitability, it is imperative that producers of irrigated crops increase water-use efficiency through proper management. Irrigation water management involves the management of water allocation and related inputs in irrigated crop production for enhanced economic returns. Whereas individuals may own separate reservoirs, in areas where irrigation is the primary source of water for crop production, producers usually draw from a common source of water (e.g., river or aquifer).

Further, the needs of farmers in a production region are similar since they tend to grow the same crops. There is the need to manage the distribution of water through a network that will ensure adequate water for all growers. This management includes drainage by which irrigation water is recycled. Producers with on-farm storage of water are able to recycle tailwater from surface irrigation. Further, the performance of irrigators is generally enhanced when the farm has its own water supply or on-farm storage to replenish it. Generally, irrigation drainage gradually declines in quality as salts and other farm chemicals leach into the water.

Table 2 Irrigation Application Systems by Type Used in the United States

System	Acres (Million)	Share of All Systems (Percent)
All systems	46.4	100.0
Gravity-flow systems	25.1	54.0
Row/furrow application	14.2	31.0
Open ditches	5.0	11.0
Aboveground pipe	7.4	16.0
Underground pipe	1.8	4.0
Border/basin application	7.5	16.0
Open ditches	5.1	11.0
Aboveground pipe	0.9	2.0
Underground pipe	1.5	3.0
Uncontrolled flooding Application	2.3	5.0
Open ditches	2.3	5.0
Aboveground pipe	0.0	0.0
Underground pipe	0.0	0.0
Sprinkler systems	21.5	46.0
Center-pivot	14.8	32.0
High-pressure	3.2	7.0
Medium-pressure	5.9	13.0
Low-pressure	5.7	12.0
Mechanical move	3.7	8.0
Linear/wheel move	3.0	7.0
All other	0.6	1.0
Hand move	1.9	4.0
Solid set and permanent	1.0	2.0
Low-flow irrigation (drip/trickle)	1.8	4.0
Subirrigation	0.4	1.0

Source: USDA, ERS, 1994. (Because of rounding and multiple systems on some irrigated acres, percents may not add up to totals.)

FIGURE 17 Corn for grain and alfalfa were the two most irrigated crops in production in 1996, with 10.9 million and 6.4 million acres, respectively. (Source: USDA)

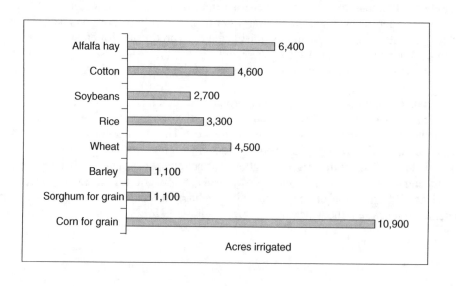

Table 3 Advances in Irrigation Technology and Water Management for Higher Water-Use Efficiency

System and Aspect	Conventional Technology or Management Practice	Improved Technology or Management Practice
On-farm conveyance	Open earthen ditches	Concrete or other ditch linings; above or below-ground pipe
Gravity-flow systems		
1. Release of water	Dirt or canvas checks with siphon tubes	Ditch portals or gates; gated pipe with surge flow or cablegation
2. Field runoff	Water allowed to move off field	Applications controlled to avoid runoff; tailwater return systems
3. Furrow management	Full furrow wetting; furrow bottoms uneven	Alternate furrow wetting; furrow bottoms smoothed and consistent
4. Field gradient	Natural field slope, often substantial; uneven surface	Land leveled to reduce and smooth field surface gradient
5. Length of irrigation run	Field length often .5 mile or more	Shorter runs of .25 mile or less
Pressurized systems		
1. Pressure required	High; typically above 60 psi	Reduced; 10–30 psi
2. Water distribution	Large water dispersal pattern	Narrower dispersal through droptubes, improved emitter spacing, and low-flow systems
3. Automation	Handmove; manually operated systems	Self-propelled systems; computer control of water applications
4. Versatility	Limited to specific crops; used only to apply irrigation water	Multiple crops; various uses—chemigation, frost protection
Water management		
1. Assessing crop needs	Judgment estimates	Soil moisture monitoring; plant tissue monitoring; weather-based computations
2. Timing of applied water	Fixed calendar schedule	Water applied as needed by crop; managed for profit (not yield); managed for improved effectiveness of rainfall
3. Measurement of water	Not metered	Measured using canal flumes, weirs, and meters; external inpipe flow meters
Drainage	Runoff to surface-water system or evaporation ponds; percolation to aquifers	Applications managed to limit drainage; reuse through tailwater pumpback; dual-use systems with subirrigation

Source: USDA, ERS.

The primary goals of irrigation water management are (1) improved farm profitability, (2) water conservation, and (3) reduction in water-quality impacts:

1. *Improved farm profitability.* Certain crop production systems depend entirely on irrigation. With the rising cost of fresh water for irrigation, the producer should avoid waste by optimizing water use.
2. *Water conservation.* Over 90% of fresh water withdrawals used in certain western states of the United States are accounted for by irrigation use. Communities have other projects (e.g., industrial use, municipal water, and recreational use) that compete with farm use for fresh water. Prospects of a new large-scale water supply are very limited, thus making the need to conserve irrigation water very compelling.

Root depth and the depth of irrigation

Irrigation must be conducted judiciously to be effective. Plants need a continuous supply of water during production. When this flow is interrupted for a significant period of time, plant growth and development are adversely affected, as is yield of economic product. Some plants are able to store water against periods of drought. Crop producers producing irrigated crops must know the water needs of their crops and select the most effective method to apply the supplemental moisture. This water should be delivered to the root zone of the crop at the time of need and in amounts that can be used without waste.

The amount and frequency of irrigation depend on several factors, including the root system of the plant (depth and distribution), the water retentive capacity of the soil, the rate of water use by the plant (consumptive use), the availability and timeliness of irrigation water, and the minimum water potential that should be maintained in the root zone to avoid moisture stress. The moisture in the soil should not be allowed to decrease to near permanent wilting point, except when the crop is in the ripening stage.

In terms of the plant root system, the depth of penetration is affected by soil physical structure. Where the soil is heavy (high clay content) or has impervious layers (pans), roots become restricted in growth. Most plant roots occur in the upper layer of the soil, and hence this zone must be kept moist. All things being equal, the recommended irrigation depth for field crops ranges from 1.5 feet for grasses to as deep as 8 feet for deeply penetrating species, such as alfalfa.

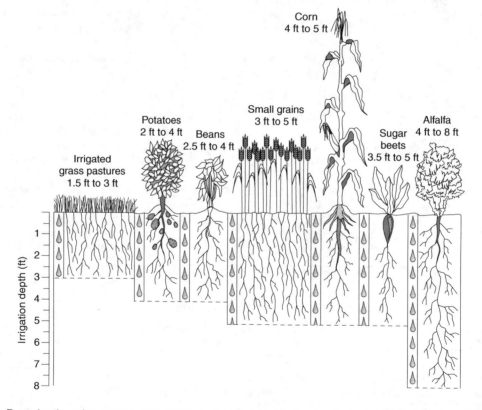

Root depth varies among crop species. Grasses are shallow-rooted, while species such as alfalfa are deeply penetrating. (Source: modified after USDA)

3. *Reduction in water-quality impacts.* Irrigated agriculture impacts off-site water quality through pollution from agrochemicals (pesticides and fertilizers) applied during crop production. Irrigation also increases field salinity and sedimentation of streams, stemming from soil erosion associated with irrigation. Irrigation-induced salinization is an important means by which cropland is lost.

Crop producers may adopt certain practices to effectively manage irrigation water, the key ones being irrigation scheduling, water-flow measurement, and irrigation drainage.

Irrigation Scheduling

Irrigation water is expensive, so farmers must determine the correct timing and quantity to avoid waste. This scheduling depends on knowledge of many factors, including evapotranspiration, the water-holding capacity of the soil, the water needs of the crop, the consequence of insufficient water on crop performance (yield), the probability of rainfall during the growing season, the available water for irrigation, and the quality of irrigation water.

There are three general categories of methods of determining irrigation schedules: (1) producer experience with the crop and production region, (2) use of simple moisture-measuring devices, and (3) detailed calculation (sometimes computerized) called the water budget method. The third method is rather involved and complex and is used mostly by irrigation professionals and consultants. Farmers may use various devices such as moisture tensiometers to determine soil moisture status. Crop water status (manifested as, for example, signs of wilting) and canopy temperature may be used as indicators of time to irrigate. It is wasteful to irrigate and have rainfall soon thereafter. As such, using fixed irrigation intervals is not a prudent irrigation strategy.

In crops such as cotton, favorable growth conditions tend to promote vegetative growth at the expense of reproductive yield. Reducing watering by the strategy of regulated deficit irrigation is known to be successful in creating a balance between the two phases of plant growth that favors economic yield.

Water–Flow Measurement

Crop producers may use water-flow measuring devices such as weirs and flumes that are installed in water conveyance systems to ensure optimal water deliveries to the field, according to the methods of irrigation scheduling.

Irrigation Drainage

Instead of allowing water to drain away, tailwater systems may be installed to recover irrigation drainage flows below the field and recycled. It may be necessary to install drainage systems to remove excess water during periods of heavy precipitation and use it during periods of drought.

SUMMARY

1. Soil water is critical to crop production. It provides the solvent for nutrients and is needed for photosynthesis and respiration.
2. Soil water is dynamic and is influenced by factors that deplete (evaporation, runoff, transpiration) or replenish (precipitation, capillary rise, irrigation) it. This is called the hydrologic cycle.
3. Water enters the soil by infiltration and moves under forces depending on whether it is saturated or unsaturated.

4. Soils differ in water-holding capacity.
5. The availability of soil moisture depends on how tightly it is held to soil particles. Too loosely held water (gravitational water) or tightly held water (hygroscopic water) is useless to crops. Capillary water is most useful for crop production.
6. Most of the water entering the plant is absorbed by passive absorption.
7. Water in the atmosphere and soil water exist in a continuum (soil-plant-atmosphere continuum).
8. Plants differ in water needs and water-use efficiency.
9. The standard method of measuring soil water is the gravimetric method. Soil water estimates are made by devices such as tensiometers.
10. Water for field crop production is stored in the soil
11. The goals of soil water management are to optimize the use of soil water while it is available, to minimize nonproductive soil water losses, and to optimize the use of supplemental moisture when applied.
12. In rainfed crop production, precipitation depended upon for all water used.
13. In terms of water depletion patterns, the variability in rainfall is more important to crop productivity than low rainfall per se.
14. In rainfed production in humid conditions, excessive rainfall may be a production problem. In dry conditions, it may be necessary to provide supplemental irrigation for the occasions in which protracted drought occurs. However, growers in dryland regions usually adopt moisture-conserving practices (e.g., catch crop, fallow) to manage soil moisture for production.
15. Water for irrigation is obtained from three primary sources: surface water, groundwater, and surface runoff.
16. Soil moisture, moisture in the atmosphere, and plant moisture occur in a soil-plant-atmosphere continuum.
17. Water quality is critical to irrigation. Sources of water may become polluted with ions, including calcium, magnesium, nitrates, sulfates, and carbonates.
18. Irrigation methods belong to one of three groups: surface (e.g., basin, furrow) sprinkler (e.g., center-pivot), or subsurface.
19. Microirrigation methods are the most water-efficient. They are not used for field crops.
20. Agricultural chemicals may be applied through sprinkler irrigation systems.

REFERENCES AND SUGGESTED READING

Brady, C. N., and R. R. Weil. 1999. *The nature and properties of soils.* 12th ed. Upper Saddle River, NJ: Prentice Hall.

CAST. 1988. *Effective use of water in irrigated agriculture.* Task Force Report no. 113. Ames, IA: Council for Agricultural Science and Technology.

Economic Research Service/USDA. 1997. *Agricultural resources and environmental indicators, 1996–97.* Agricultural handbook No. 712. Washington, DC/USDA.

Hudson, B. D. 1994. Soil organic matter and available water capacity. *J. Soil and Water Cons.* 49:189–194.

Miller, W. R., and D. T. Gardner. 1999. *Soils in our environment.* 9th ed. Upper Saddle River, NJ: Prentice Hall.

Pruitt, W. O., F. J. Lourence, and S. Von Oettingen. 1972. Water use by crops as affected by climate and plant factors. *California Agric.* 26:10–14.

Waddell, J., and R. Weil. 1996. Water distribution in soil under ridge-till and no-till corn. *Soil Sci. Soc. Amer. J.* 60:230–37.

SELECTED INTERNET SITES FOR FURTHER REVIEW

http://www.encarta.msn.com/find/MediaMax.asp?pg=3&ti=761558496&idx=461565881

Sprinkler irrigation.

http://www.encarta.msn.com/find/MediaMax.asp?pg=3&ti=761558496&idx=461530531

Furrow irrigation.

http://www.encarta.msn.com/find/MediaMax.asp?pg=3&ti=761558496&idx=461530522

Irrigation canal.

http://www.farmphoto.com/album2/html/noframe/m_P01907.asp

Aerial photo of center-pivot irrigation.

OUTCOMES ASSESSMENT

PART A

Answer the following questions true or false.

1. T F Water enters the soil by infiltration.
2. T F Under saturated conditions, soil water moves primarily by gravity.
3. T F Capillary rise occurs through macropores.
4. T F Sandy soils have higher soil infiltration rates than clays.
5. T F In crop production, evapotranspiration is higher when plants are younger.
6. T F Basin irrigation is the most water-efficient of all methods of irrigation.
7. T F Water for irrigation obtained from a well is drawn from an aquifer.
8. T F Chlorine and sodium ions are the most common sources of irrigation water pollution in humid regions.
9. T F Application of chemicals through irrigation water is called eutrophication.
10. T F Microirrigation is applicable to wheat crop production.

PART B

Answer the following questions.

1. Give the three forms of soil water.

   _____   _____   _____

2. What is field capacity? _____

3. What is the permanent wilting point? _____

4. The ability of the soil to retain water is called its _____.

5. Give three specific factors that influence water infiltration into the soil.

   _____ _____ _____

6. What is water-use efficiency?_____

7. Give the three sources of water for irrigation.

   _____ _____ _____

8. The amount of water required to produce a unit of dry matter is called _____.

9. What is an aquifer? _____

10. Give five specific ions commonly associated with water quality for irrigation.

    _____

    _____

    _____

    _____

    _____

11. Give five specific factors that affect the choice of irrigation system.

    _____

    _____

    _____

    _____

    _____

PART C

Write a brief essay on each of the following topics.

1. Describe the hydrologic cycle.

2. Describe the movement of soil water under saturated conditions.

3. Discuss evapotranspiration and its role in crop productivity.

4. Discuss the movement of water through plants.

5. Describe methods of estimating soil water content.

6. Discuss the concept of the soil-plant-atmosphere continuum.

7. Describe the use of fallow in water management for crop production.

8. What is microirrigation?

9. Describe the method of furrow irrigation.

10. Describe the method of sprinkler irrigation.

11. Discuss the importance of water quality in crop irrigation.

12. What are the general goals of managing soil water in crop production?

PART D

Discuss or explain the following topics in detail.

1. Discuss the importance of irrigation in U.S. crop production.

2. Discuss the role of the Ogallala aquifer in U.S. crop production.

3. Why is the quality of irrigation water important?

4. Discuss the importance of water-use efficiency in crop production.

Plant Nutrients and Fertilizers

From Chapter 8 of *Principles of Crop Production: Theory, Techniques, and Technology*, Second Edition, George Acquaah.
Copyright © 2005 by Pearson Education, Inc. Published by Pearson Prentice Hall. All rights reserved.

Plant Nutrients and Fertilizers

PURPOSE

The purpose of this chapter is to discuss crop nutrition and its management. The discussion includes the source of essential nutrients, their roles in plant growth and development, and how to provide supplemental nutrition for enhancing crop productivity.

EXPECTED OUTCOMES

After studying this chapter, the student should be able to:

1. List the 18 essential nutrients for plant growth and development.
2. Discuss the criteria for essentiality of an element in plant nutrition.
3. Discuss the role of essential nutrients in plant growth and development.
4. Discuss how nutrients are lost from the soil.
5. Describe plant nutrient deficiency symptoms for all essential elements.
6. Discuss the methods of diagnosing soil nutrient status.
7. Discuss fertilizers and their commercial sources.
8. Discuss methods of application of fertilizers.
9. Discuss fertilizer use in U.S. crop production.

KEY TERMS

Cholorosis

Eutrophication

Luxury consumption

Macronutrients

Micronutrients

Mineralization

Nutrient cycling

Nutrient deficiency
  symptom

Phosphorus fixation

Soil test

Necrosis

TO THE STUDENT

Plants use particular nutrient elements more than others. Thus, soil nutrients are not depleted proportionally. There are natural nutrient cycles for replenishing soil nutrients. However, these processes are often slow. In modern crop production, crop producers often supplement soil nutrients by applying inorganic fertilizers. The soil should be well managed in crop production. The goal of soil fertility management is to sustain the soil's ability to supply essential nutrients to crops. To accomplish this, there is a need to understand

1. How soil nutrients become depleted
2. How to detect nutrient deficiencies
3. How to correct nutrient deficiencies

1: ESSENTIAL ELEMENTS

Do plants absorb and utilize all of the 90 elements available? For optimal growth and development, crop plants need certain *essential elements* or *nutrients* from the soil. These elements are deemed essential because of the following reasons:

1. Plants cannot grow and develop properly without them.
2. They play critical roles in plant metabolism.
3. Their roles cannot be replaced by another element.
4. Deficiency symptoms can be corrected only by supplying that deficient element.

There are 18 essential elements that are required by most plants. Even though silicon is not universally accepted as essential, it occurs in the tissues of most plants. Selenium is referred by some range plants. Essential plant nutrients may be placed into two general categories according to source as either *non-mineral* or *mineral,* of which there are 3 and 15, respectively. The non-mineral elements are carbon (C), hydrogen (H), and oxygen (O). Carbon, hydrogen, and oxygen are present in the largest amounts in the plant. Carbon is fixed in the plant by the process of photosynthesis from CO_2 derived from the atmosphere to produce organic compounds. Hydrogen and oxygen enter the roots as water through root hairs. The mineral elements may be subdivided into three groups according to quantities used by the plant, as **macronutrients** (or major elements), secondary nutrients, and **micronutrients** (or trace elements) (Table 1).

Macronutrients are used by plants in large amounts, while micronutrients are needed in minute amounts. Further, calcium, magnesium, and sulfur are sometimes

Macronutrients. Chemical elements needed in large amounts for plant growth.

Micronutrients. Chemical elements required in small amounts for plant growth.

Table 1 The 18 Soil Mineral Elements Essential for Plant Growth and Development

Macronutrients	Secondary nutrients	Micronutrients
Nitrogen	Calcium	Boron
Phosphorus	Magnesium	Iron
Potassium	Sulfur	Molybdenum
		Manganese
		Zinc
		Copper
		Chlorine
		Cobalt
		Nickel

classified as *secondary nutrients* because they are utilized in larger quantities than the other micronutrients.

A plant requires all these essential elements in proper amounts and proper ratios to each other for development and crop productivity. Deficiency of one element may result in improper development of the plant. The severity of response to deficiency differs among plant species. Certain characteristic symptoms accompany deficiency of each of these elements. Plant species differ in their need and use of these essential elements. Each element has a specific role in plant growth and development. Certain elements promote vegetative growth and development, while others promote reproductive functions and root development, among other roles.

Do plants know when to stop absorbing nutrients? When the nutrients are present in non-limiting amounts, plants have a tendency to use more than they need. Up to a certain point, uptake of nutrients does not translate into increased biomass (or productivity). At this level, the use of nutrients is described as **luxury consumption.** If consumption continues, it might reach a toxic level (Figure 1).

Luxury consumption. The intake by a plant of an essential nutrient in amounts in excess of what it needs.

Nutrient deficiency symptom. A visible change in plant morphology or appearance associated with the deficiency of a specific plant nutrient.

FIGURE 1 Plants vary in their need for and use of nutrients. Nutrients accumulate in plants and may be economically used up to a certain concentration. At low concentrations, plants start to display **nutrient deficiency symptoms**. This stage is followed by the hidden hunger stage, at which time the nutrient concentrations are less than optimal but not low enough to cause deficiency symptoms to be observed. The critical nutrient range or the threshold level is the level below which an essential element is deemed to be deficient in the plant. Sufficiency occurs when the nutrient is present in the plant in an adequate amount and proper balance with other nutrient elements. After this stage, accumulation of nutrient elements may become toxic to the plant. This curve may be interpreted in another light, as in Figure 1b. Soil nutrients may accumulate in plants in four main categories. At the deficiency level, plant growth is hampered. When nutrients are present in adequate amounts, the plant can use them for economic production. After this level, additional amounts of nutrients are wasteful and will not result in economic use. Finally, higher levels may become toxic to plants, causing a decline in growth and yield of the economic product.

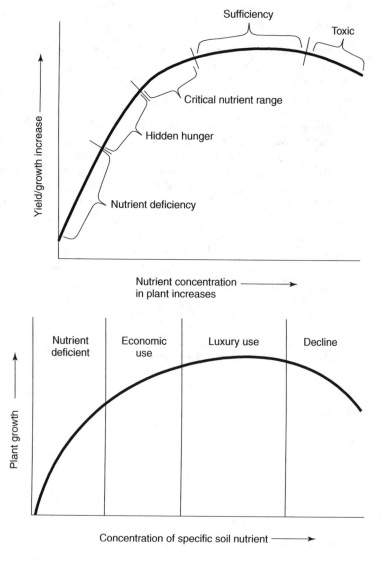

In crop production, the grower may increase certain nutrients in the general nutrition for enhanced productivity according to the yield objective. This may be accomplished in a variety of ways, using inorganic (artificial) or organic (natural) fertilizers.

2: NITROGEN

Nitrogen is the key nutrient in plant growth and productivity. It is often the limiting nutrient in plant growth and the soil nutrient required in the greatest amount. It is a constituent of nucleic acids and therefore plays a role in plant heredity. Nitrogen is also a constituent of proteins and chlorophyll, the primary pigment in photosynthesis. It promotes vegetative growth, making tissues more tender and succulent and plants larger. Crop yields are adversely affected when nitrogen is deficient.

Nitrogen uptake by plants is in the form of NO_3^- and NO_4^+ ions. The dinitrogen (N_2) form, though most abundant in the atmosphere, is unusable directly by plants. Nitrogen is very mobile in the plant. As such, when deficient in nutrition, it is translocated from older leaves to younger ones, where it is most needed. The older leaves lose color (**chlorosis**) and become yellowish.

Soil nitrogen derives from mineral, atmospheric, and organic sources. Weathering of minerals adds to soil nitrogen as rocks decompose and interact with other chemicals in the soil environment. The decomposition of organic remains of plants and animals by soil microbes releases the organic nitrogen (*immobilized nitrogen*) into inorganic forms. This conversion process is called **mineralization.** Soil microbes also convert atmospheric dinitrogen into usable forms through the process of nitrogen fixation. This can happen independently when bacteria fix nitrogen in the soil (non-symbiotic) or in association with plant roots (symbiotic).

Nitrogen is released into the soil when organic matter decomposes by the process of mineralization. Organic matter decomposition is accelerated by increased temperature. Thus, it occurs fastest in moist, sandy soils (especially in summer), which are well aerated and warmer, and slower in clay and silts in cool spring.

Even though plants can absorb nitrogen as either NO_3^- or NO_4^+, the latter ion is subject to microbial transformation into the former. *Nitrosomonas* oxidizes NO_4^+ to nitrite (NO_2^-) before *Nitrobacter* converts the product to nitrates (NO_3^-). Nitrates are readily leached from the soil. The positively charged NO_4^+, though soluble in water, is more resistant to leaching. Instead, it is readily rendered unexchangeable and unavailable to plants by the process of *ammonium fixation.* Nitrogen is also lost in gaseous form through the process of denitrification, another bacterial process. This rapid process occurs under warm anaerobic conditions when bacteria are compelled to use an alternative source (NO_3^-) as a source of oxygen. Nitrate ions are changed to N_2 and N_2O and lost through volatilization as gas into the atmosphere. For this reason, it is best to use the ammonium form of fertilizer as a source of nitrogen under paddy rice cultivation so as to eliminate waste due to denitrification. It may also be lost through ammonium volatilization when ammonium or urea fertilizer is applied to the soil surface. To reduce ammonium volatilization, the fertilizer should be covered immediately after application or watered. Broadcast application should be avoided when using these materials for fertilization. When deficiency occurs in the soil, leaves become yellow (chlorosis). Chlorosis starts with older leaves, since nitrogen is a mobile element in the plant.

Chlorosis. A condition in which a plant or a plant part is light green or greenish yellow because of poor chlorophyll development or the destruction of chlorophyll resulting from a pathogen or a mineral deficiency.

Mineralization. The conversion of an element from an organic form to an inorganic form as a result of microbial decomposition.

3: PHOSPHORUS

Phosphorus is second to nitrogen in importance in plant nutrition. Plants utilize about 1/10 as much phosphorus as nitrogen. It is part of plant nucleoprotein and hence important in plant heredity. Phosphorus also plays a role in cell division, stimulates root growth, and hastens plant maturity. One of the notable physiological roles of phosphorus is in the energy storage and transfer bonds of ATP (adenosine triophosphate) and ADP (adenosine diphosphate). Phosphorus deficiency shows up as purpling of plant parts.

Soil phosphorus, unfortunately, is largely of very low solubility and therefore not readily available to plants. It is very reactive to both the soil solution and solids, and hence very immobile, except in organic soils or soils with very high CEC. The original source of phosphorus is rock phosphate (apatite). Plants absorb phosphorus in the soluble ions of $H_2PO_4^-$ and HPO_4^{2+}. The orthophosphate form, however, is readily precipitated and adsorbed to soil particles (a process called **phosphorus fixation**). At low pH, iron and aluminum ions are very soluble and react with phosphorus to form precipitates. At high pH, calcium precipitates phosphorus. Phosphorus is most available at pH of 6.5. It is more soluble under anaerobic conditions than aerobic. Phosphorus is lost through surface runoff into surface water, where it is implicated in **eutrophication** (nutrient enrichment of surface water, leading to excessive plant growth and oxygen deficit). Clay soils fix more phosphorus, fixation being higher in expanding clays than kaolinites.

When deficient, leaves become dark green and plants stunted. This deepening in color is attributed to increase in nitrates in the leaves. Purplish color may also develop, especially in older leaves. Phosphorus is mobile and thus symptoms appear first in older leaves.

Phosphorus fixation. The rendering of phosphorus unavailable to plants through the formation of insoluble complexes in the soil.

Eutrophication. Nutrient enrichment of surface waters such as lakes and ponds resulting in the stimulation of growth of aquatic organisms, and leading eventually to oxygen deficiency in the water.

4: POTASSIUM

Potassium is a very soluble cation. However, its common natural forms (micas and orthoclase feldspar) are very slowly soluble. However, it is not an integral part of any specific cell compound. It is required by many enzymes for activation and plays a role in cell division, formation of carbohydrates, and translocation of sugars. Potassium is also known to enhance the resistance of certain plants to certain diseases. It is a key factor in the regulation of osmosis (water control) in plants.

Potassium can be adsorbed between clay layers *(potassium fixation)*. Further, both soluble and exchangeable potassium can be adsorbed in excessive amounts by plants with little or no consequence (luxury consumption). Sometimes, excess potassium can hinder the adsorption of magnesium. Potassium is also immobile in the soil, even though less so than phosphorus. It is lost through erosion.

Potassium deficiency symptoms include marginal leaf burn *(marginal necrosis)*, speckled or mottled leaf, and lodging.

5: CALCIUM, MAGNESIUM, AND SULFUR

5.1 CALCIUM

Calcium is important for cell growth, cell division, cell wall formation, and nitrogen accumulation. Apart from being directly used by plants, calcium is used to make other nutrients more available to plants. Calcium is used in soil amendment to correct soil acidity (liming). Calcium also forms organic salts (e.g., calcium oxalate) with certain organic acids in the plant that cause irritations to humans when ingested. Calcium is absorbed as Ca^+ ions by plants. Its deficiency in plant nutrition causes a variety of symptoms such as strap leaf, poor root development, and defective terminal bud development (blunt end).

5.2 MAGNESIUM

Magnesium is absorbed by plants as Mg^{2+} ions. It is the central atom in the structure of a chlorophyll molecule. It is essential in the formation of fats and sugars. Large amounts of potassium may interfere with the uptake of magnesium. Magnesium is mobile in plants and, as such, deficiency symptoms first appear in older leaves as chlorosis.

5.3 SULFUR

Sulfur is a constituent of many amino acids and many vitamins. The oils of plants in the mustard families contain sulfur, which is responsible for the characteristic flavors of onion, cabbage, and other cruciferous plants. When organic matter is incinerated, the sulfur oxides are washed down in rain. This rainwater can be acidic (acid rain). It is absorbed by plants as SO_4^{2+} ions. When deficient, plants become chlorotic.

6: MICRONUTRIENTS (TRACE ELEMENTS)

Plants require micronutrients in minute amounts but are by no means less important. They are predominantly involved in plant physiology as activators of many enzyme systems.

6.1 BORON

Boron is one of the most commonly deficient of the trace elements. Boron is absorbed by plants BO_4^{2+}. It affects flowering, fruiting, cell division, and water relations (translocation of sugars) in the plant. When deficient, symptoms appear first at the top. The terminal bud produces growth described as *witches' broom*. Lateral branches form rosettes while young leaves thicken.

6.2 IRON

Iron is abundant in the soil. It can be absorbed through the leaves or roots as Fe^{2+} and sometimes as Fe^{3+} ions. It is a compound in many enzymes and a catalyst in the synthesis of chlorophyll. Its deficiency shows up as *interveinal chlorosis* (yellowing between the veins) of young leaves. The symptoms appear first in younger leaves, since iron is immobile.

6.3 MOLYBDENUM

Molybdenum is involved in protein synthesis. It is also required by certain enzymes that reduce nitrogen. Vegetables, cereals, and forage crops are among a number of plant species that are known to show very visible symptoms when the element is deficient in the soil. A classic symptom in cauliflower and other crucifers is narrowing of leaves *(whiptail)*. Plant leaves may also become pale green and roll up.

6.4 MANGANESE

Manganese has an antagonism reaction with iron (i.e., as one increases the other decreases). Deficiencies are common on sandy soils. Manganese is absorbed as Mn^{2+} ions.

It is crucial to photosynthesis because of its role in chlorophyll synthesis. It is also important in phosphorylation, activation of enzymes, and carbohydrate metabolism. When deficient, plants develop interveinal chlorosis in younger leaves.

6.5   ZINC

Zinc is absorbed as Zn^{2+} ions. It is an enzyme activator that tends to be deficient in calcareous soil with high phosphorus. When deficient, plant leaves become drastically reduced in size, while internodes shorten to give a rosette appearance. Leaves may also become mottled.

6.6   COPPER

Copper is absorbed mainly as Cu^{2+} ions. Copper deficiency is common in soils that are high in organic matter. The element is important in chlorophyll synthesis and acts as a catalyst for respiration and carbohydrate and protein metabolism. When copper is deficient, terminal buds die and the plant becomes stunted. Younger leaves may show interveinal chlorosis, while the leaf tip remains green.

6.7   CHLORINE

Chlorine deficiency is rare. Excessive levels of chlorine are a more common problem. It is absorbed at Cl^- ions. When deficient, plants may be stunted and appear chlorotic with some necrosis.

6.8   COBALT

Cobalt is essential for the symbiotic fixation of nitrogen. However, some plant species have non-symbiotic nitrogen fixation-associated need of cobalt. It is found in vitamin B_{12}.

6.9   NICKEL

Nickel is essential for the functioning of enzymes, such as urease, hydrogenase, and methyl reductase. It is essential for grain filling, seed viability, iron absorption, and urea and ureide metabolism. When nickel is deficient, legumes accumulate toxic amounts of urea in their leaves. Also, the seeds of cereal plants that are deficient in nickel are not viable and fail to germinate.

7: NEED FOR NUTRIENT BALANCE

Plants need all of the 18 essential nutrients in the proper quantities and balance in order to grow and develop properly. An imbalance may result in the improper use of nutrients or even toxicity of the one(s) present in excessive amounts. According to the concept first proposed by Liebig, plant production can be no greater than the level allowed by the growth factor present in the lowest amount (limiting factor) relative to the optimum amount for that factor. In other words, if a factor (e.g., temperature, nitrogen, water) is not the limiting factor, increasing it will hardly enhance plant growth. On the contrary, increasing the non-limiting factor may cause an imbalance in the growth factors in the plant environment. For example, increasing nitrogen in a situation where phosphorus is the limiting factor may actually intensify the deficiency of phosphorus. On the other hand, increasing phosphorus (the limiting factor) may cause the plant to respond better to an increase in nitrogen. This synergistic effect is desirable in fertilization. By the same token, antagonistic effects occur when certain nutrient elements compete with or cause a reduction in the uptake of other nutrients. Antagonism may be used to reduce the toxicity of certain elements in the soil. For example, adding sulfur to calcareous soils that contain toxic quantities of soluble molybdenum may reduce the availability and hence the toxicity of molybdenum.

The most modern precision application of fertilizers for proper balance is *precision agriculture*, the application of fertilizers and other agronomic inputs using geospatial technology. This technology is discussed later in the chapter.

8: SOIL NUTRIENT STATUS DETERMINATION

How can a producer tell if the soil is deficient in an essential element for plant nutrition? Soil nutrient status can be diagnosed visually or by chemical analysis. In order to determine the fertilizer needs during crop production, the producer should first determine what nutrients are deficient. Two general methods are used for this purpose: *visual examination* of plants and *chemical analysis*. Dark color of soils indicates high organic matter content. Color is used to identify the presence of certain elements in the soil. Just as plants respond to fertilizers, they also respond adversely, and sometimes readily visibly, to nutrient deficiency.

8.1 VISUAL EXAMINATION

Plants growing in soils that are deficient in essential nutrients may display certain tell-tale symptoms (called nutrient deficiency symptoms). How easy are these symptoms to spot and how reliable an indicator of nutrient deficiency are they? These visible signs are frequently ambiguous; thus, their use requires skill and experience. The general symptoms are change in growth (e.g., stunting), change in color (e.g., chlorosis, purpling, deepening of green color, a whitish appearance), and tissue death.

The symptoms manifest to different intensities, depending on the severity of the deficiency and the age of the plant part. As stated previously, certain nutrient elements such as potassium, magnesium, sodium, and sulfur are mobile and hence translocated from older tissues to younger ones. When these elements are deficient, the symptoms for these elements appear first in older leaves. On the other hand, relatively immobile elements such as iron, manganese, zinc, and boron, exhibit deficiency symptoms first in younger leaves. Further, nutrients that affect chlorophyll formation produce color abnormalities (especially yellowing) when they are deficient.

The major visual symptoms associated with nutrient deficiency are

1. *Chlorosis.* When older leaves are affected, nitrogen deficiency is suspected. In this case, the yellowing is also uniform over the entire leaf. When both young and older leaves are chlorotic, sulfur deficiency is more likely. Sometimes, the yellowing does not occur over the entire leaf but is restricted to between the veins. When only older or recently mature leaves are involved, magnesium deficiency is suspected. However, if younger leaves are affected, iron, magnesium, copper, and zinc may be implicated.

2. *Purpling.* When phosphorus is deficient in plant nutrition, leaves may appear dark green with a tint of purple (or sometimes blue or red). This purpling is caused by an accumulation of anthocyanin pigments.

3. *Necrosis.* **Necrosis,** or tissue death, may occur as patches or spots on leaves, or as marginal or leaf tip necrosis (also called leaf scorch or tip burn). This damage is also symptomatic of severe weather (e.g., drought or frost) damage.

Necrosis. Tissue death associated with discoloration and dehydration of all or some parts of plant organs.

4. *Stunted growth and other growth abnormalities.* Generally, deficiency symptoms include some growth abnormality, especially stunting of growth. Zinc deficiency causes young leaves to be severely reduced in size. Short and thick roots and the cessation of growing points of plants indicate calcium deficiency. If boron is deficient, the terminal buds usually die, while the leaves become thickened and chlorotic.

8.2 CONCEPTS IN SOIL TESTING

Purpose of a Soil Test

Soil test. A chemical, physical, or microbial operation that estimates a property of the soil.

A **soil test** is key to the development of an effective nutrient management plan for crop production. Its purpose is to allow the crop producer to assess the nutritional status of the soil in order to develop and implement a cost-effective and environmentally sound lime and fertilizer practice. Producers may use soil testing kits to determine the general fertility status of their field. However, commercial crop producers normally farm large acreages and usually submit soil samples to professional labs for analysis and recommendations.

Philosophies of Soil Testing

Soil fertility testing is not an exact science. There are general steps that are followed by soil testing labs: analysis, calibration, interpretation, and recommendation. However, there is no consensus on that approach to use to make recommendations from lab results. Three of the common approaches are basic cation saturation ratio, nutrient maintenance, and sufficiency level concept:

1. *Basic cation saturation ratio.* This approach assumes that a certain ideal ratio of exchangeable bases exists in the soil that will optimize plant nutrient use for optimal crop yields. The benchmark used is 60% Ca, 10% Mg, and 5% saturation of 80%), corresponding to Ca/Mg ratio of 6.5, Ca/K ratio of 13, and Mg/K ratio of 2.0. A departure from these ideal ratios indicates the deficiency of one or the other elements. The approach does not address P, S, and trace elements. The assumption is valid in soils with fairly high CEC and high natural pH. Some experts argue that cation balance is not useful for estimating the nutrient needs of most crops.

2. *Nutrient maintenance.* This is a more liberal philosophy in the sense that it assumes that a level of nutrient sufficiency to replace what was removed during previous crop production should be added, notwithstanding the soil levels of nutrients. In other words, it does not matter if nutrient levels are high and capable of supporting one or two production cycles without fertilization. Nutrients removed by plants must be replaced, nonetheless, even if it may be at the risk of toxicity to plants.

3. *Sufficiency level concept.* This conservative philosophy simply states that when a soil test calibration indicates that the nutrient levels are adequately high, there is no need to add fertilizers to the soil. This is common with many state-run testing labs. It has the greatest potential for producing the highest economic yield in the least environmentally intrusive way. An underlying principle of this philosophy is that the goal of fertilization is to fertilize the crop, not the soil.

8.3 SOIL SAMPLING

How useful is a soil test? The usefulness of a soil test depends on the soil material submitted for testing. The key to success is to sample the field such that the composite sample represents what it is supposed to represent. Since soil is heterogeneous, sampling for soil analysis is a more critical step than the method used for the analysis. Soils vary in two dimensions (vertically and horizontally). The depth of sampling is important to a soil test. Most testing labs recommend a depth of 30 centimeters (13.3 inches). The nutrients to be tested also affect the depth of sampling, being deeper (at least 60 centimeters, or 23.6 inches) for nitrogen, and shallower (15 to 20 centimeters, or 5.9 to 7.9 inches) for phosphorus and potassium. Even though it is recommended to sample 15 to 20 cores that are then mixed to obtain a composite sample, fewer samples are taken in practice. More samples (about 25) are needed for a phosphorus test and fewer (about 5) for potassium.

Depth of sampling

For mobile elements, it may be helpful to sample at different depths to determine their relative positions in the soil profile. Sampling depth is deeper (24–48 inches) for sugar beet and malting barley than for most crops. Once collected, soil samples should be immediately air-dried to avoid changes in NO_3^-N as a result of microbial activity.

The best time to sample a soil for analysis is as close as possible to the planting time. This way, the nutrients that the soil can supply on its own to the crop are best estimated. An established producer may sample his or her field every 2 to 3 years. Samples should be obtained from the areas between rows, making sure to avoid sampling soils from previous fertilizer bands. Unique spots should also be avoided.

Another key consideration in sampling is uniformity. Areas that differ in topography (flat, slope, valley), soil texture (clay, sandy), soil structure, depth, color, productivity, and previous management (e.g., liming, fertilizing), should be sampled separately. The land user should delineate these areas prior to sampling. Factors to consider in sampling are depth, number of samples, frequency, time, location, and uniformity.

Time to sample

Whereas a soil may be sampled at any time of the year for the determination of pH, salt content, Zn, and P levels, sampling when the soil is frozen may give higher than actual K value. Similarly, because NO_3^-N, S, and Cl are mobile, they are best tested by sampling the soil in fall or spring. In addition to the method of composite soil sampling described so far, there are other sophisticated procedures that provide more accurate assessment of total nutrient levels that are more compatible with the needs of precision or site-specific farming. These other methods, grid sampling and directed sampling, may involve the use of GPS technology or prior knowledge about the field. Satellite imagery and aerial photography, as well as data from yield monitoring, may be used to guide sampling for within-field nutrient levels determination.

8.4 SOIL TEST COMPONENTS AND THEIR IMPORTANCE

Soil analysis labs differ in the specific tests they conduct as standard and the methods used, as well as the units in which results are reported. Some of the important soil test components are as follows:

1. *Humic matter content.* The importance of soil organic matter is discussed elsewhere in this book. The relatively stable fraction of organic matter is called the humic matter (humus), which comprises 60 to 80% of the actual organic

matter status of the soil. A conversion formula is used to convert humic matter to organic matter percent. The soil component is used to provide guidance for adjusting lime, P, and micronutrient recommendations and for safe use of pesticides. Manufacturers of pesticides may restrict application to soil with a minimum humic matter percentage to prevent groundwater contamination. On the other hand, a high humic matter may prevent the effectiveness of certain pesticides because the latter becomes trapped in the former through strong binding.

2. *Weight per volume.* Measured in gm/cm^3, this determination is used for assigning the soil testing class of the soil. A value of 1.5 or higher indicates a soil that is high in sand, while silt and clay loams have a weight/volume ratio of about 1.0. Soils that are high in organism matter have values of about 0.4. Soil textural class helps to make proper recommendations for liming and application of fertilizers, especially regarding P_2O_5, Cu, and Zn rates.

3. *Cation exchange capacity.* Soils that are rich in colloids (organic matter, clay) have a high CEC (hold more cations, especially, Ca^{2+}, K^+, Mg^{2+}). Soils with low CEC are susceptible to leaching. Split application of fertilizers is recommended to minimize leaching losses.

4. *Base saturation percent.* Calcium is usually the most dominant cation in the CEC determination. This ion is also the principal component of aglime. When a crop production enterprise requires high availability of CA, the producer may use gypsum ($CaSO_4 \cdot 2H_2O$).

5. *Mg saturation.* This determination of the proportion of total CEC represented by Mg is used to determine the type of lime or the need to include Mg in fertilizers. If a test indicates a deficiency of Mg (extractable Mg CEC of < 0.5) and liming is recommended, dolomitic lime should be used.

6. *pH.* A soil pH test is used mainly to determine the lime requirements.

Nutrients Reported as Index Values

For trace elements and sometimes for P and K, the index system of reporting soil nutrient levels is used for ease of interpretation of the results. Specific critical values are not reported for these elements. Rather, a range is provided to indicate the likelihood of the crop's response to supplemental application of an element. A soil test may be reported as follows: a range of 0–25 = low, 26–50 = medium, 51–1,000 = high, and $1,000^+$ = very high presence of the element. A rating of low normally means a crop would benefit from a supplemental application of the element. A medium rating indicates a likelihood of response for P and K. However, crops would seldom respond to added nutrients if the soil test rating were high or very high.

Soluble Salt Index

The soil accumulates soluble salts from fertilizers, manures, and irrigation water. A moderate amount of soluble salts is desirable. The soluble salt index indicates the amount of fertilizer elements that are soluble in the soil. An excessive amount of soluble salts is injurious to sensitive plants. The injury level depends on the soil type, the soil moisture content, and the species.

8.5 CALIBRATION OF A SOIL TEST

The ultimate goal of soil testing is to provide actual fertilizer recommendations from the results and interpretations made (Figure 2). As a service to growers, state extension services and soil analysis labs usually develop practical ratings to indicate the likelihood of

Agricultural Testing Services

The Samuel Roberts Noble Foundation, Inc.

2510 Sam Noble Parkway   P.O. Box 2180
Ardmore, Oklahoma 73402   Telephone (580) 223-5810

Field Name:	10 Very S Field	Howard Sheep & Cattle	Intended Crop: Wheat
Lab Number:	55572 Date: 8/18/03	Ranch	Yield Goal:
County:	OK-Jefferson	Route 2 Box 129A	Test Run: Test A
		Waurika, OK 73573	

Sample Depth	pH	Buffer Index	Nitrogen NO3	Phosphorus P	Potassium K	Calcium Ca	Magnesium Mg	Sodium Na	Sulfur SO4	Soluble Salts (ppm)	Organic Matter %	Cation Exchange Capacity Meg/100 gms	Iron Fe	Zinc Zn	Manganese Mn	Copper Cu	Boron B
				Pounds per Acre Extractable Nutrient										*Parts Per Million Extractable Nutrient*			
0-6" TOP	4.30 Strongly Acid	6.30	80	146 Sufficient	398 Sufficient	706 Adequate	162 Adequate	32 Normal			1.5	10.0					

Fertilizer Recommendations
(Pounds per Acre Actual Nutrient)

N Nitrogen	P2O5 Phosphorus	K2O Potassium
70	0	0

Tons Lime per Acre   0.0
100% ECCE

Recommendations and Comments:

pH is below the optimum for wheat. You may wish to re-sample this field this year or next to make sure you need to lime. If you want to go ahead and lime, you would need to apply 2.0 ton ECCE lime/ac to raise pH to 6.4.

Phosphorus is adequate.

Potassium is adequate.

Nitrogen is based on yield goal. It takes about 60 lb N/ac to produce one ton of winter forage minus soil carryover, so if you want to produce 2 ton/ac forage, you need to apply 40 lb N/ac. If you plan to combine wheat as well, you should add another 30 lb/ac Nitrogen. I recommend splitting this application with some at planting and some as a spring topdress.

Laboratory Analysis by Ward Laboratory Inc., Kearney, NE
Recommendations by Noble Foundation Specialist

Wade Thomason

FIGURE 2 Soil test results of a farmer's field. (Source: Courtesy of Dennis Howard)

crop response with reference to specific soil test outcomes. These ratings are not only crop-specific but also cultivar-specific, and hence the labs must constantly calibrate new cultivars as they are produced by plant breeders. Calibrations are based on replicated field trials over time and locations.

8.6 NUTRIENT AVAILABILITY

Plant nutrient availability depends on the pH of the soil solution. As pH decreases (increasing acidity), elements such as Mn, Zn, Cu, and Fe become more available. When pH decreases below 5.5., toxicity of Mn, Zn, and Al start to be a problem in crop production. On the other hand, increasing soil acidity (low pH) inhibits the availability of N, K, Ca, Mg, and S. The availability of P and B is decreased at both very low and very high pH, being most available at between pH 5.5 and 7.0.

8.7 FACTORS AFFECTING ACCURACY OF SOIL TEST

A soil test is conducted for the purpose of recommending appropriate fertilizer application. A good recommendation depends on several factors.

1. *Crop producer.* What can the producer do to improve the usefulness of a soil test? The role of the producer is to provide the following information and materials to the testing laboratory:
   a. Accurate and representative soil samples
   b. Accurate cropping history of the land
   c. Accurate projection of expected yield; a recommendation is based on the yield goals of the producer
2. *Laboratory analysis.* The technicians at the laboratory should have the skills and expertise to conduct a correct soil analysis. Further, the laboratory should have an up-to-date good correlation to field plot data. Without correlation of results to crop responses to different fertilizer levels in field plot trials, the laboratory results are meaningless. The laboratory should continually test new cultivars and fertilizers as well as new crop improvement systems.
3. *Evaluator.* The scientists who evaluate soil test results should be well trained in the science and art of evaluation and should be familiar with the production area and the plants for which the predictions or recommendations would be applied. The evaluator should know the plant and its nutritional needs, the rainfall regime of the area, and other natural nutrient cycling activities in the soils of the area.

    After a recommendation has been made, the successful implementation depends on several factors:
   a. *The producer.* Crop production depends to a large extent on the producer's ability as a decision maker. The soil test recommendation should be properly implemented. The evaluators usually recommend that the crop producer amend the recommendations according to his or her experience and management skills, rather than following them to the letter. In addition, the producer should select the best planting materials, plant on time and at proper density, control pests, and implement other appropriate management practices.
   b. *Weather.* Crop productivity is weather-dependent. Inclement weather, such as prolonged drought, excessive rain, and hail, is destructive to crops and will erode the benefits of implementing the soil test recommendations.

8.8 TISSUE TEST

An indication that nutrients are available in adequate amounts in the soil does not necessarily mean that the plants will absorb nutrients. Analyzing plant tissue (*tissue test*) is the only way to ascertain that the soil nutrients are available to plants. However, plant analysis has shortcomings:

1. Plants cannot be tested until they are growing.
2. The purpose of a soil test is to obtain information for application to crop production. Unfortunately, plant analysis results are not available for preplanting decision making.
3. Sometimes, when plants show deficiency symptoms, it is too late to salvage the crop.

Plant analysis, however, is useful for predicting fertilizer needs of perennial crops such as sugarcane, fruit trees, permanent pastures, and forest trees that remain in the field for long periods in the growing season.

Plant tissue analysis is performed on samples obtained with care, taking into account the physiological status, age, health, and representativeness of the plant population. Differences in results have been obtained between different portions of even a single leaf. Like soil testing, the laboratory performing the tests should have a database of results from analysis using tissue from the same plant parts sampled.

Plant Tissue Sampling

The time of tissue sampling varies with the crop. For example, tobacco is best sampled before bloom, taking the uppermost leaf. In corn, the ear leaf should be sampled when about 50% of plants are at the stage where the silk is just beginning to appear. Soybeans and other legumes should be sampled when 10% of the plants are in bloom. The uppermost leaf of soybean is picked, while in the case of leguminous forage species (e.g., alfalfa, red clover), the upper one-third of the plant is picked. In wheat and barley, the flag leaf is sampled when about 25% of the plants have headed. The top 6 inches of forage grasses constitute the best sample to take for plant tissue analysis.

The parts of the plant sampled for effectiveness depends on the species. For crops such as cassava, the bark of the plant is most reliable for analysis, while the whole seedling is most effective for annual crops such as corn and beans.

These plant samples should be washed to remove contaminants such as soil and chemicals sprayed by the producer or accumulated from pollutants in the environment. The producer should provide the name of the plant cultivar, the planting density, and other meteorological pieces of information.

In interpreting plant analysis, there is a threshold (critical) nutrient level against which the results are compared. An element is declared deficient when it is present in the tissue at a level lower than the threshold value. Unfortunately, the critical nutrient levels vary readily with growth environment (e.g., pH, moisture, and soil nutrients), cultural conditions, plant health, and other factors. It is difficult to prescribe threshold values, thus making interpretation of plant tissue analyses problematic.

9: ANTAGONISM AND SYNERGISM

Plant nutrients, especially micronutrients or trace elements, interact in the soil either to enhance or to hinder their absorption by plants. This emphasizes the need for nutrient balance, so that no particular one is present in excess amounts. Nutrient interaction may be *antagonistic* (negative) or *synergistic* (positive). Antagonism is when one substance reduces the detrimental effects of a second substance. Synergism, on the other hand, is when two factors interact to cause a greater effect than the sum of the two substances separately. Antagonistic effects may be used to reduce the toxicities of certain trace elements in the soil. For example, adding sulfur to calcareous soils containing toxic quantities of Mo may reduce the availability of Mo and thereby avoid toxicity of the element. Similarly, adding Mn or Zn reduces the availability of Fe. Examples of synergistic effects include the increase in Mo utilization as a result of increasing P in the soil and the enhanced utilization of Zn by increasing N application.

10: LIMING

High soil acidity is corrected (decreased) by liming to raise soil pH. However, the main goal of liming is to neutralize the toxic elements that occur under high acidity (especially Al and Mn) while improving the availability of desired elements. The effect of liming is to add hydroxide (OH^-) ions to the soil solution to decrease the solubility of Al^{3+}, Mn^{2+}, Fe^{3+}, Zn^{2+}, and Cu^{2+} ions. Liming causes these ions to precipitate out of the soil solution while supplying basic elements (Ca, Mg, depending on the type of liming material). Liming also increases the availability of P, Mo, and B and promotes microbial growth, development, and processes (e.g., biological nitrogen fixation, nitrification). Overliming is undesirable, since it can result in the deficiency of some elements—for example, Zn, Fe, Mn, and Ca.

10.1   LIMING REACTION

Liming materials contain mainly carbonates of Ca and Mg that are generally sparingly soluble. The oxides and hydroxides of Ca are more soluble in water. Soil acidity is neutralized as follows:

1. $CaCO_3 + H_2O \rightarrow Ca^{2+} + HCO^{3-} + OH^-$
    $CaO + H_2O \rightarrow Ca^{2+} + 2OH^-$
2. $H^+ + OH^- \rightarrow H_2O$

10.2   SOURCES OF LIMING MATERIALS

Limestone varies in purity. Limestone consists of sedimentary rocks that are rich in calcite ($CaCO_3$) or dolomite [$CaMg(CO_3)_2$]. When the rock is relatively pure in calcite, it is called *calcitic limestone*. Similarly, when magnesium predominates in the rock, it is called *dolomitic limestone*. The CEC percentage (or total neutralizing power) is a measure of the acid neutralizing value of the liming materials. This value is calculated by using pure calcite ($CaCO_3$) as a standard. Values greater than 100 (e.g., 110) indicate that the source is higher (10%) than pure calcite in neutralizing power (Table 2).

Slaked or hydrated lime [$Ca(OH)_2$] is difficult to handle because it is very reactive and caustic. It produces quick results and may be applied when there is a need to rapidly raise soil pH.

10.3   CALCULATING LIME REQUIREMENT

Soil pH measures the relative intensity or the ratio of the base cation saturation of the exchange complex. It does not provide information on the total amount of acidity that must be neutralized. To be able to calculate the amount of lime to apply, the pH requirement of the crop, the current actual pH of the untreated soil, and the CEC should be known (i.e., the soluble and exchangeable acidity). The amount of lime required depends on (1) the change in pH required, (2) the CEC, (3) the chemical composition of the liming material, and (4) the fineness of the lime. Calculations and recommendations are best done by the soil-testing lab than by producers because of the chemistry involved. However, as previously indicated, field testing kits may be used by producers for estimating soil nutritional status.

Particle size is determined by passing the ground material through a series of mesh screens. The sieve number is the number of holes per square inch (e.g., a 20 mesh has $20 \times 20 = 400$ holes). States have laws regarding the fineness of liming materials. The beneficial effects of liming are achieved only when the material is in contact with the soil.

Table 2   Sources of Lime Materials, Their Chemical Formulas, and Their Calcium Carbonate Neutralizing Equivalents (CCE)

Source	Formula	CCE%
Calcitic limestone	$CaCO_3$	85–100
Dolomitic lime	$Ca/Mg(CO_3)_2$	95–108
Hydrated lime	$Ca(OH)_2$	110–135
Burnt lime	CaO	150–175
Marl	$CaCO_3$	50–90
Basic slag	$CaSiO_3, CaO$	50–70

Liming materials are relatively insoluble in water and immobile in the soil. When applied, they affect only the top 2 to 3 inches. It is desirable to mix the liming material into the soil in order to have soil pH modified in the root zone.

The amount of lime needed to increase the pH of a sandy soil by a certain degree is generally less than the amount needed to cause the same change in a clay soil. This is because the sandy soil has less residual or reserve acidy (buffering capacity).

11: CONCEPT OF REALISTIC YIELD

The crop producer should manage his or her production enterprise to obtain an optimum economic yield rather than maximizing yield. Optimizing economic yield implies that a producer is careful not to waste resources (i.e., uses cost-effective management practices). As management and inputs increase, the cost of production also increases. At a certain critical point, profits are maximized. Adding inputs after this point only increases production cost without increasing profits, since the added yield gain is not cost-effective. A producer can eliminate unnecessary costs from production inputs by practices such as periodic soil testing to determine if added fertilizers would be economically beneficial.

Application of fertilizers should be based on the realistic yield expectation (RYE) of the producer's field. Determining a RYE is not an exact science. Averaging the crop yield on the producer's farm over 5 years, and using the yield from the three most productive years, is generally the common method of estimating RYE for agronomic crops. The challenge is finding such historic records for the farm. Once a RYE for a farm has been determined, the appropriate rate of nitrogen to be applied is calculated by multiplying the RYE by the rate of nitrogen suggested by soil analysts from the soil test.

RYE is influenced by a host of soil-related factors, including depth of subsoil, soil texture and structure, organic matter content, permeability, drainage, slope, and local climate. The amount of nutrients needed to optimize crop yield and economic return while minimizing undesirable effects on the environment is called the agronomic rate. Excessive amounts of nutrients can adversely impact both yield and the environment, while insufficient amounts can cause yield reducing nutrient deficiency symptoms in plants.

Commonly, agronomic rates are determined by the RYE of a site and the amount of nitrogen (often the priority element—the nutrient element most likely to have adverse effects on crop yield or the environment) and the amount of nitrogen required to produce a unit of a specific crop. For example, if it takes 1.0 to 1.20 lb of nitrogen to produce a bushel of corn, and the RYE is determined to be 100 bushels per acre, the agronomic rate is between 100 and 120 lb/acre of nitrogen (obtained as 100 bu/acre × 1.0 lb/acre = 100 lb/acre, and 100 bu/acre × 1.2 lb/acre = 120 lb/acre).

12: SOIL NUTRIENTS CAN BE SUPPLEMENTED THROUGH NATURAL PROCESSES AND ARTIFICIAL METHODS

12.1 CERTAIN ESSENTIAL NUTRIENTS MAINTAIN NATURAL CYCLES

Through a combination of physical, chemical, and microbial interactions, certain essential nutrients maintain natural cycles. The major cycles include the nitrogen, phosphorus,

FIGURE 3 Nutrient cycling in nature is characterized by changes, additions, and losses in nutrients. Enrichment of the soil nutrients comes through application of fertilizers as well as naturally through microbial decomposition of organic matter and weathering of minerals. Depletion of soil nutrients may be wasteful and occurs through avenues such as leaching, soil erosion, and microbial activities. Crop production is a means of economic depletion of soil nutrients.

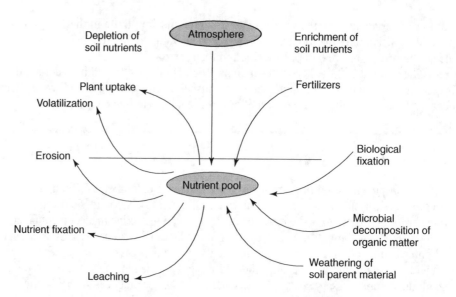

Nutrient cycling. The absorption of inorganic forms of elements, their conversion into organic forms, and their subsequent conversion back to inorganic forms through microbial decomposition.

and potassium cycles. These elements change state from organic to inorganic, existing for varying periods of time in various nutrient pools. Natural **nutrient cycling** plays a significant role in the sustainability of the ecosystem. The cycles differ in complexity. Nutrient cycling consists of processes that can be categorized into three: *addition, fixation,* and *loss* (Figure 3).

In nutrient cycling, certain factors increase the status of various nutrient elements in the soil. Some of these are natural processes, while others are human-made. Certain atmospheric phenomena (e.g., lightning) cause chemical reactions to occur. In the nitrogen cycle, dinitrogen gas is converted to NO_4^+, while fires produce oxides of nitrogen such as NO_2. Similarly, atmospheric sulfur in various compounds [SO_2, SO_3, H_2S, $(CH_3)_2S$, etc.] are washed down to the soil as acid rain. Atmospheric sources of phosphorus are minimal. A large amount of dinitrogen gas is fixed by microbial activity into the soil (e.g., symbiotic and non-symbiotic nitrogen fixation).

These natural processes are untargeted in the sense that they occur in both agricultural and non-agricultural areas. Crop producers, however, deliberately add large amounts of selected nutrients in desired amounts to specific cropping lands to boost crop productivity. These are in the forms of organic manure or industrial chemicals (inorganic fertilizers). Nutrients removed by plants (immobilized) are reconverted by microbial actions into inorganic nutrients by mineralization, when plants are deliberately incorporated into soil.

12.2 SOIL NUTRIENTS ARE DEPLETED IN A VARIETY OF WAYS SOME BENEFICIAL, OTHERS WASTEFUL

Nutrient cycles are also leaky, and hence the nutrients that enter the soil can be lost. In crop production, the producer should adopt practices that minimize the losses. Losses occur through the following main avenues: *soil erosion, volatilization of gases, leaching, removal by crops,* and *fixation*. These mechanisms vary in importance from one nutrient element to another.

1. Soil erosion is a process of removal and translocation of soil. Soil is the medium that supports agricultural crop production. Soil erosion depletes the soil, especially of nitrogen and phosphorus. The nutrients may end up in bodies of water and cause eutrophication.

2. Volatilization entails the loss of nutrients in gaseous forms into the atmosphere. The most affected elements are nitrogen and sulfur. The forms of these nutrients, such as N_2O, NO_2, and SO_2, occur when plant material is burned. Some nitrogen can be lost directly from applied fertilizer under improper environment. For example, ammonia gas applied as a source of nitrogen can be lost if the soil is dry or alkaline. Soil microbes can also cause loss of nitrogen through the process of denitrification that involves the reduction of NO_3 to N_2 and N_2O. Sulfur is also volatilized through reduction to SO_4 or H_2S.

3. Leaching is the loss of nutrients in soluble form. The mechanism is important in the loss of nitrogen, potassium, and sulfur in the nitrate or sulfate forms.

4. Crop use of nutrients through absorption from the soil is the fourth mechanism. Crops are cultivated to exploit the soil nutrients for economic yield. Crops vary in amounts of nutrients removed. Alfalfa and corn are heavy feeders of all macronutrients, while rice and cotton remove small amounts of nutrients.

5. Ammonium ions may become highly bonded to clay mineral lattices such that they are unavailable to plants (*ammonium fixation*). Similarly, soluble phosphate ions ($H_2PO_4^-$) may react with other soil chemicals to become insoluble (*phosphate fixation*). Some of these fixed nutrients can become available at the appropriate pH.

12.3 FERTILIZER TERMINOLOGY

If a fertilizer recommendation is made following a soil test, what does a producer use to supply the needed supplement? Commercial fertilizers are formulated as either liquids or solids. The nutrient composition of a fertilizer is displayed on the container or bag in a certain standard format. The label indicates the *fertilizer grade* and the minimum guaranteed percentage of nitrogen, phosphorus, and potassium (NPK), in that order. The remainder of the content consists of an inert material called a *filler* (used to bring the formulation up to the desired weight or volume) that is used as a carrier of the active ingredients. The fertilizer grade information is presented as

1. Percent total nitrogen (measured as elemental nitrogen, N)
2. Percent available phosphorus (measured as phosphorus that is soluble in ammonium citrate solution and calculated in practice as phosphorus pentoxide, P_2O_5)
3. Percent water-soluble potassium (calculated as potassium oxide, K_2O)

A fertilizer grade of 10-40-5 means the material contains 10% nitrogen, 40% phosphorus, and 5% potassium. Why not revise the convention to say exactly what is in the bag? Efforts have been made to change the nomenclature to a simplified elemental format of N-P-K, instead of N-P_2O_5-K_2O. It is believed that resistance to change by the fertilizer industry is because an elemental format will produce smaller equivalent numbers. This may seem to indicate that the fertilizer has a lower grade than it really does. For example, a conventional fertilizer grade of 0-45-0 is equivalent to 0-19-0 in elemental form (P). A fertilizer may also be described according to the concentration of the nutrients present. For example, a fertilizer grade of 10-10-10 is described as *low analysis* as compared with a grade of 30-25-25 (high analysis). In applying fertilizer, the producer will need more bags of a low analysis fertilizer than a high analysis one to provide the appropriate rate.

Certain fertilizers leave residual acidity in the soil when applied. Most nitrogen fertilizers, all ammonium materials, and many organic nitrogen fertilizers are acid forming. On the other hand, fertilizers such as urea, diammonium phosphate, and anhydrous ammonia, initially produce soil alkalinity. All potassium fertilizers, except potassium nitrate, produce neutral residual soil reaction.

12.4   FERTILIZER SOURCES AND THEIR USE

Nitrogen Fertilizers

The major fertilizer sources of nitrogen and their characteristics are summarized in Table 3.

Anhydrous ammonia has the highest available nitrogen per unit source (82%). It is applied by special equipment used to inject it into the soil. To reduce losses (by volatilization), it should be sealed into the soil immediately after application. The equipment usually has an attachment for this purpose. Sandy and dry soils are susceptible to high losses. This source of nitrogen is applied between rows. Urea is also susceptible to volatilization losses and hence is not suitable for surface applications (e.g., in pastures, no-till systems). Ammonium nitrate is easy to apply but can cause fertilizer burn. UAN solutions are commonly applied to winter wheat. These may be injected into the soil in no-till production systems or surface-applied with the aid of streamer bars to reduce fertilizer burn. Ammonium sulfate is recommended where sulfur deficiency occurs along with low nitrogen.

Phosphorus

The major commercial sources of phosphorus and their characteristics are summarized in Table 4. Diammonium phosphate (DAP) produces alkalinity in the soil and hence is suitable for application when soil acidity needs to be reduced. It is best applied in concentrated bands. Triple superphosphate (TSP), on the other hand, produces acid residues and hence is suitable where soil alkalinity needs to be reduced. It is more readily available than single superphosphate (or ordinary superphosphate) (SSP). SSP contains gyp-

Table 3   Commonly Used Nitrogen Fertilizer Materials

Fertilizer	Formula/Symbol	Percent by Weight Nitrogen
Anhydrous ammonia	NH_3	82
Urea	$CO(NH_2)_2$	45
Ammonium nitrate	NH_4NO_3	33
Sulfur-coated urea		30–40 (plus 13–16 sulfur)
Ureaformaldehyde	UF	30–40
UAN solution		30
Isobutylidene diurea	IBDU	30
Ammonium sulfate	$(NH_4)_2SO_4$	21 (plus 24 sulfur)
Sodium nitrate	$NaNO_3$	16
Potassium nitrate	KNO_3	13 (plus 36 phosphorus)

Table 4   Commonly Used Phosphorus Fertilizer Materials

Fertilizer	Formula	Percent by Weight P
Monoammonium phosphate	$NH_4H_2PO_4$	21–23 (plus 11 N)
Diammonium phosphate	$(NH_4)_2HPO_4$	20–23 (plus 18–21 N)
Triple superphosphate		19–22 (plus 1–3 S)
Phosphate rock	$Ca_3(PO_4)_2 \cdot CaX$	8–18 (plus 30 Ca)
Single superphosphate		7–9 (plus 11 S, 20 Mg)
Bone meal		

Table 5 Commonly Used Potassium Fertilizer Materials

Fertilizer	Fertilizer	Percent by Weight K
Potassium chloride (muriate of potash)	KCl	56
Potassium sulfate	K_2SO_4	42
Magnesium sulfate	$MgSO_4$	18 (plus 9 Mg, 18 S)
Potassium nitrate	KNO_3	37 (plus 11 N)

sum. Ammonium polyphosphate is used primarily in fertigation and for weed-and-feed and seed placement applications. It can be surface applied without incorporation into the soil. Surface application of phosphorus is the least efficient method. Hence, it is best to build up soil P before initiating a no-till system.

Even though nitrates are more soluble than phosphates, eutrophication is attributed to P, the element that is often the limiting factor in surface water because of its relatively high insolubility. Hence, an entry of relatively small amounts of P into the body of water is enough to stimulate accelerated growth of algae and other water plants, leading to reduced oxygen.

Potassium

Some of the most commonly used commercial sources of K are presented in Table 5. KCl is a commonly used source of K. The sources presented in the table usually have a high salt index and hence should not be applied close to crop seeds. Further, each of these sources provides more than one of the essential plant nutrients. Crops that are responsive to K fertility include soybean, alfalfa, and corn. The chlorine in KCl makes it unsuitable for fertilizing tobacco because it leads to an elevated Cl level in the leaves and poor product quality.

Secondary Nutrients

Numerous materials are used as sources of secondary nutrients (Ca, Mg, S) in crop production. Calcium and magnesium are relatively low in mobility in the soil. When fertilizers such as SSP are applied, they supply significant amounts of S. Fertilizer materials containing sulfate (SO_4^{2-}) do not impact soil acidity in the short run, but over time the pH may decrease with use. Elemental sulfur needs to be converted to sulfate through biological oxidation involving the bacterium *Thiobacillus*.

12.5   METHODS OF FERTILIZER APPLICATION

How is fertilizer applied in the field? There are several techniques of applying fertilizers in crop production. The common methods are *starter, broadcast, deep banding, split, side dress, top dress, injection, fertigation,* and *foliar.*

Starter Application

Also called *pop-up application, starter application* is the application of fertilizer at the time of seeding. Depending upon the implement used, the fertilizer may be dribbled in the soil near the seed or placed in a band near it. This application is generally at a low rate and is more suited to phosphorus and potassium than nitrogen. It is desirable for plants that grow rapidly, or when a soil test indicates a very low nutritional level.

Some species are sensitive to salt damage and hence no more than 10 kg/ha nitrogen and potassium should be applied, and contact with seed should be avoided. Phosphorus is

---

Fertilizer calculations

Following a soil test, recommendations are made as to the type and amount of fertilizer the producer may apply. An amount of a certain nutrient may be prescribed. However, the weight of fertilizer applied depends on the source, since fertilizers come in all kinds of grades. The three common calculations involving dry fertilizer formulations are nutrient percentage, the amount or weight of source (commercial) fertilizer to apply, and the amount (weight) of component materials to use in preparing a bulk of mixed fertilizer.

a. Nutrient percentage

Problem: What is the percentage of nitrogen in the fertilizer urea?

Solution: Urea has a formula of $(NH_2)_2CO$ and a molecular weight of 60.056 g
Molecular weight of nitrogen (N_2) = 28.014 g
Percentage of nitrogen = $[28.014/60.056] \times 100$ = 46.6, or 46%
approximately (round down to nearest whole number)

b. Simple fertilizer mixture

Problem: Given ammonium nitrate (34-0-0) and treble superphosphate (0-45-0), prepare 1,000 kg of fertilizer of grade 15-10-0.

Solution: Final mixture will contain 150 kg of nitrogen (i.e., 15% of 1,000 kg).
It will also contain 100 kg P_2O_5 (i.e., 10% of 1,000 kg).
Amount of ammonium nitrate needed (note: it contains 34 kg of N per 100 kg of ammonium nitrate):

$[100 \times 150]/34$
= 441 kg of 34-0-0

Similarly, for phosphorus (contains 45 kg of P_2O_5 per 100 kg)

$[100 \times 100]/45$
= 222 kg of 0-45-0

---

less mobile and less likely to cause salt damage. As the rates of application of fertilizer increase, the distance between seed and fertilizer should be increased.

Broadcast Application

In broadcast application, the fertilizer is spread over the soil surface in no particular pattern, making this method the one with the lowest *fertilizer efficiency* (the percentage of fertilizer added that is actually used by the plant). It may be left on the soil surface or later incorporated by, for example, disking. This method is desirable for paddy rice fields and established pastures. It is easy to apply. Further, large amounts (a high rate) of fertilizer may be applied by this method. Certain fertilizers may volatilize unless disked. Watering after application also helps to move nutrients down more quickly to the root zone.

Sometimes, as in pastures, broadcasting is the only method for applying fertilizer. Broadcast efficiency is increased if the fertilizer is incorporated into the soil or if the soil remains moist (e.g., from shading).

Deep Band Application

The goal of deep band application is to place most of the fertilizer where plant roots have most access. Phosphorus fertilizers have low mobility and hence are best placed near the roots. Further, by concentrating phosphorus this way, the danger of fixation is

Total nutrients = 441 + 222 = 663 kg (leaving 337 balance of the desired 1,000 kg)
The balance is satisfied by adding a filler (inert material) or lime. The procedure is the same for compounding a mixture of three components (i.e., N-P-K).

What if calculated proportions of nutrient components add up to more than total desired weight? In this example, what if the two amounts exceeded 1,000 kg? The component amounts cannot exceed the total desired weight. If that happens, the desired grade should be lowered or a source with higher analysis (e.g., for nitrogen, use urea with 46% N) should be used.

c. Amount (weight) of sources (fertilizers) to apply

Problem: It has been recommended that a producer apply 80 kg of nitrogen and 40 kg of phosphorus per acre to the field. How much of ammonium nitrate and treble superphosphate should be applied to achieve the recommended rate?

Solution: Ammonium nitrate contains 34% N; treble superphosphate contains 45% P_2O_5.
From example (b), the amount of source to be added to provide 80 kg of N

$$= [80 \times 100]/34$$
$$= 235 \text{ kg of 34-0-0 per hectare}$$

Similarly, for 40 kg of P_2O_5

$$= [40 \times 100]/45$$
$$= 88.9 \text{ kg of 0-45-0 kg per hectare}$$

Total of mixture = 235 + 89 = 324 kg per hectare

To convert from kg per hectare to pounds per acre, multiply by 0.89.

minimized. Anhydrous ammonia gas is applied by this technique, using equipment under high pressure.

Deep banding is expensive to conduct because of the specialized stronger equipment and the energy needed to apply at lower soil depth.

Split Application

Split application is the technique of dividing the recommended fertilizer rate into several portions and applying at various stages in the growth and development of the crop. Split application may be accomplished by more than one technique of fertilizer application (e.g., starter application, followed by side dressing). The advantage of this technique is that waste of especially highly mobile nitrogen fertilizers is reduced. By timing the application, the producer is able to provide the appropriate amount of nutrients at times when the plant needs it the most. Split application helps to control vegetative growth of the plant. Fertilizer efficiency is increased especially for nitrogen. However, multiple applications add additional cost to crop production operations.

Side Dressing

Side dressing is undertaken after the crop is growing in the field. Usually, it is done as part of a split application. The fertilizer may be broadcast to the soil surface or applied as a shallow band application in rows along the row of plants or around individual plants. This method is not very effective for phosphorus and potassium fertilizers. This method is applied to row crops.

Top Dressing

This post emergence application is usually applied to small grains and pastures.

Fertigation

Liquid fertilizer may be applied through fertigation. It is very commonly used in greenhouse production. It is most effective where soils have low nutrient retention and for mobile nutrients such as nitrates and sulfates. It allows a quick and convenient way of applying fertilizer, especially where nutrients are needed immediately.

Foliar Application

Foliar application is the application of fertilizers to the leaf as a liquid spray. The nutrients are absorbed through stomata. The technique is adapted to very low rates of fertilizer application. Further, it is commonly used for applying micronutrients. For example, iron chelates are readily mobilized in the soil and thus are best applied to leaves.

13: Soil Fertility Versus Soil Productivity

Soil fertility is the capacity of a soil to provide the essential plant nutrients in adequate amounts and proportions for plant growth and development. The productivity of soil, on the other hand, is the capacity of a fertile soil to perform under a set of environmental conditions. A fertile soil is not necessarily productive, but a productive soil must be fertile. This is so because a soil can have all the essential nutrients in the right amounts and proportions but is useless for crop production unless there is adequate moisture and appropriate temperature as well as other essential growth factors. For practical purposes, two kinds of fertility may be identified—general fertility and enterprise-specific fertility. Some soils are naturally fertile and suitable for producing a wide variety of crops. Other soils lack such all-around fertility but are nonetheless ideal for specific crop production enterprises.

14: Not All Applied Fertilizer Is Used by Plants

How much of the fertilizer applied to crops is actually used by plants? The percentage of added fertilizer that is actually used by the plants is called the *fertilizer efficiency*. The efficiency differs for various fertilizer elements. It is estimated that about 30 to 70% of added nitrogen is used, while 5 to 30% of phosphorus and 50 to 80% of potassium are utilized by plants. Fertilizer efficiency is influenced by several factors, including the operator's technique of application, the weather conditions, the soil type, and the crop. Plants differ in the ionic form of nutrients preferred. For example, legumes are known to prefer divalent cations such as Ca^{2+}, while grasses prefer monovalent ones such as K^+. Soil impediments such as rocks and hard pans restrict root growth and development and subsequently nutrient absorption.

The technologies of precision farming

Fields are seldom homogeneous, or uniform. They vary in their physical and chemical characteristics. A farmer growing a large field is likely to have several soil areas in the field that react differently with respect to their ability to grow plants under a particular management. In such a case, it is not prudent to treat them all alike and apply the same rate of fertilizer to the whole area. Certain portions may be overfertilized and wasteful in terms of resources, whereas other areas would be underfertilized.

Precision agriculture (or *high-tech agriculture, spatial variability management*) is a *site-specific management* approach in modern crop production for applying agrochemicals to the field in an economic and environmentally sound fashion.

Precision farming entails the collection and management of a wide variety of agronomic information with the purpose of identifying and meeting the *real* needs of variable parts of a field, through supplying what is *actually* needed rather than the *average* needs of the whole field, as is the case in conventional management. The key objective of a variable rate technology (VRT) strategy is to develop an accurate application map for the field to be used as the blueprint for determining the level and location of agronomic inputs applied to the field. This technology is applicable to a wide variety of agronomic production operations, including fertilizer application, liming, seeding rate, pesticide application, irrigation, and tillage operation. To be effective, each application requires a clearly developed and accurate guide.

Conventional ways of variable application of agronomic inputs are based on operator intuition, soil survey maps, soil data from sparsely spaced grid samples, and visual observation of variations in the field by the operator while traversing it. Grid soil sampling is unguided and has serious limitations. Conventional applications are not usually automated and often subjective. Modern strategies used in site-specific applications involve dividing the field into smaller, homogeneous *management zones*. A precision farming management zone is a subregion of a field that expresses a functionally homogenous combination of yield-limiting factors for which a single rate of a specific cropping input is appropriate. A good management zone strategy will maximize economic return by optimizing rates of yield-limiting inputs and controlling the adverse effects of weeds and other crop pests.

Accurate delineation and classification of spatial variability should take into account four categories of site characteristics: (1) quantitative and stable (e.g., relief, pH, and soil organic matter), (2) quantitative and dynamic (e.g., crop yield and weed density and distribution), (3) qualitative and stable (e.g., soil color, immobile nutrients like phosphorus and potassium, and soil drainage), and (4) intuitive or historical (e.g., grower past experience of field characteristics, history of cultural practices, soil tilth and quality, and crop rotations).

This modern production method depends on two technologies—*geographic information systems* and *global positioning systems*.

Geographic information systems

A geographic information system (GIS) is a computer-based system for storing very large amounts of data (collected based on spatial location) and retrieving, manipulating, and displaying them for easy interpretation. The term *geographic* should be interpreted to mean "space" or "spatial." For crop production, some of the data of importance are soils, land use, vegetation, fertility, hydrology, and rainfall averages. Spatial analysis is concerned with analyzing data involved with changes with space or location within an area. GIS has the capability of linking multiples sets of data (in layers) to study relationships among various attributes and creating new relationships.

GIS is an aid for decision making. It can be used to answer the location question "What is there?" or "Where is it?" It can also be used to study trends—that is, to answer the question "What has changed since a certain point in time?" Another application of GIS is in the area of prediction of change or modeling.

The success of GIS analysis depends on the availability of accurate and reliable data. These databases are created by various private and public entities and are available for a fee or freely accessible via the Internet or other means. One of the leading suppliers of GIS products is the Environmental Systems Research Institute (ESRI), makers of ArcView® and ArcInfo® software and various accessories. In view of the enormity of data routinely involved in GIS applications, one

continued

needs to have access to a computer with appropriate capabilities and speed, in order not to make use of the technology cumbersome to apply.

Global positioning systems

A global positioning system (GPS) is another of the cutting edge technologies of the information age. Whereas GIS basically asks the question "What is it?" GPS asks the basic question "Where is it?" It is a versatile navigational aid. Also computer-based, the key components in this technology are satellites. GPS depends on 24 satellites (courtesy of the U.S. Department of Defense) that are strategically positioned in orbits such that, at any given time and place on earth, one can have a line of sight to at least four of these satellites. Using the technique of *trilateration,* a user is able to access at least three satellite signals, each producing a surface that will overlap each other to locate the site in question, providing both longitude and latitude. A fourth satellite signal allows the elevation of the site to be calculated.

Satellite signals can be clearly received even under inclement weather conditions. However, tall building, dense forests, mountains and hills, and other such structures can obstruct clear signal communications. The GPS technology is used in everyday life as navigational aids in automobiles, in tracking sites of breakdown, in routing emergency response crew, and in other applications. Individuals can purchase handheld units of varying resolution.

Implementing a precision agricultural production operation

There are two basic methods for implementing a precision farming strategy.

1. *Map-based technologies.* This is currently the most widely used method. It may involve a GIS-based method of pre-sampling and mapping of the field. This is effective for quantitative stable characteristics of the field. The computer-

generated maps are then converted into a form that can be used by the variable rate applicator. The applicator's controller then calculates the desired amount of an agronomic input to apply at each moment in time as the equipment traverses the field. The farmer knows how much of the agronomic input is needed before starting the application. A DGPS (differential global positioning system) must be used to constantly evaluate the location in the field with a coordinate on the map and the desired application rate for that coordinate.

Nutrients are not absorbed effectively unless there is adequate soil moisture because mineral nutrients must go into solution (for/solution) to be absorbed. However, excessive moisture causes leaching of nutrients. Nutrient efficiency is also reduced when timing is improper. Nutrients should be applied when the plant needs them the most and can absorb them effectively. Ammonia fertilizers are prone to volatilization and should be applied

2. *Sensor-based technologies.* This method offers real-time sensing and variable rate control. The strategies provide on-the-go sensing of field characteristics, thereby eliminating the need for a positioning system. The sensors must be mounted strategically (e.g., at the front of the tractor) to allow the variable rate applicator's controller adequate time to adjust the rate of the agronomic input accordingly before it passes the sensed location. More sensing packages need to be developed for the various agronomic applications.

Sensed yield data should be interpreted carefully. Variable yield data by themselves are not informative. If the monitor records that grain yield varies 50 bushels per acre from one location in the field to another, there is no clue to the causes of this variation. A field is influenced by many factors such that, if the sensor records identical low yields for two different locations, the causes could be very different. To increase utility of yield monitoring, it should be coupled with walking the field to record site-specific variations.

The area to be cultivated is first delineated into portions according to soil differences (i.e., the soil special variation is delineated). This may be done by inspection or use of computer programs. A map is made to show the variations in the levels of fertility. The soil is then sampled on a grid pattern. Plant health data from previous cropping may also be used to assist in delineating the field. Record keeping is critical to success in precision farming. All data must be tied to locations in the field (i.e., *georeferenced*). *Ground control points* should be set up using the DGPS. All sampling is done with reference to the ground control points and entered into a GIS for processing. The data are then processed to determine the variable rates of application to use. Precision farming requires specialized equipment with sensors. The tractor or other vehicle being used should have an onboard computer and GPS receiver. The GIS information is coupled to the guidance system of the

GPS receivers to dispense variable treatment as the tractor or other vehicle moves over the field.

Cost and profitability

Information gathering and analysis for precision farming is expensive. Precision farming requires a significant initial investment into equipment. Variable rate management does not necessarily increase yield all over the field. In some cases, yield increase is observed in lower-yielding parts of the field. The value of yield gains is more important than savings from reduced application of the agronomic input. Generally, in cases of variable rate fertilization, high-value crops that are responsive to the technology tend to be more profitable than low-value crops, because the yield gains are worth more.

Farmers should adopt this technology only after careful consideration. It is not the "golden egg" to financial security, as some think. Producers with weaker financial standing should be more cautious about adoption of this technology.

with care. If the soil pH is not at the proper reaction, certain nutrients may be rendered immobile and unavailable through fixation.

To improve fertilizer efficiency, the producer should avoid adding a large amount of fertilizers, especially nitrogen and potassium, at one time. It should be borne in mind that Liebig's law of the minimum (i.e., a growth factor in the least relative amount will limit the growth of the plant) is operational in the case of fertilizer application to plants. Regular soil tests will aid in discovering any improper pH levels and lack of nutrient balance that can cause nutrient deficiency symptoms in plants.

15: U.S. Agriculture Is a Big User of Fertilizers, Especially in Areas Such as the Corn Belt

The application of fertilizers played a significant role in the dramatic rise in yield per unit land area for major crops in the United States. For example, corn yield rose from 55 bushels per acre in 1960 to 139 bushels per acre in 1994. Nutrient sources used in U.S. crop production are primarily commercial fertilizer and to a lesser extent animal waste.

Of the major nutrients, nitrogen is by far the most widely used nutrient supplement in crop production (Figure 4). In 1960, nitrogen use constituted about 37% of total commercial nutrient use. By 1981, the proportion had reached over 50%. In 1995, 55.2% of total commercial nutrients used in crop production in the U.S. was nitrogen, a total of 11.7 million tons of the element. On the other hand, the use of phosphate commercial fertilizers declined from its share of 34.5% of total nutrients used in 1960 to 20.8% in 1995. Potash use exceeded that of phosphorus in 1977. In 1995, it accounted for 24.0% of total commercial fertilizer used in the United States. Most (63%) of the fertilizers used in 1995 were mixed (i.e., supplied more than one major nutrient).

Most of the commercial fertilizers in the United States are used by producers in the Corn Belt (i.e., Ohio, Indiana, Illinois, Iowa, and Missouri). This is because corn is the most fertilizer-using crop. The Northern Plains region (North Dakota, South Dakota, Nebraska, and Kansas) is second after the Corn Belt in the use of commercial fertilizers. Though the most frequently fertilized crop in the United States is corn, the rate of application of nitrogen, the most frequently used fertilizer for corn, is normally highest for fall potatoes, averaging 221 pounds per acre in 1995 (Figure 5). The average application rates of nitrogen in

FIGURE 4 Primary fertilizer nutrients applied in U.S. crop production. Nitrogen accounts for more than 50% of fertilizer consumption. In 1997, it was applied to 71% of cropland. Only 29% of cropland was not treated with nitrogen. Similarly, 60% and 56% of cropland were treated with phosphorus and potassium fertilizers, respectively. (Source: USDA)

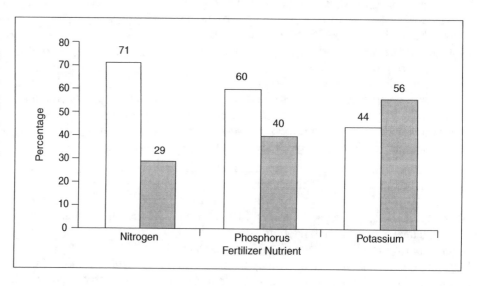

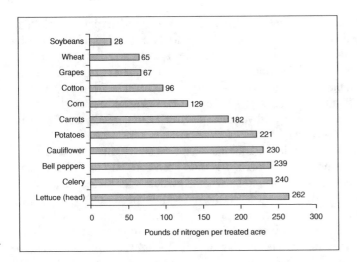

FIGURE 5 Nutrient application rates are higher for vegetables than field crops. In 1997, potatoes received the highest rates of all the three primary nutrients applied to field crops. After potatoes, corn received the next highest rates of fertilizer nutrients, receiving 129 lb/acre of nitrogen, 57 lb/acre of phosphorus, and 51 lb/acre of potassium. Wheat generally receives moderate amounts of NPK. (Source: USDA)

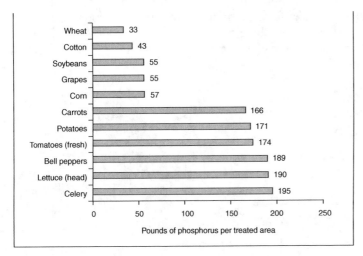

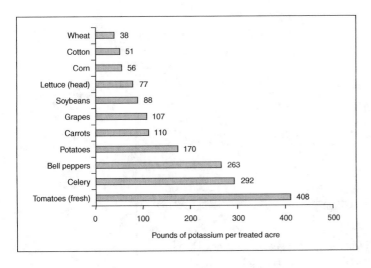

corn production dropped from 132 pounds per acre in 1986 to 129 pounds per acre in 1995. Similarly, fall potatoes receive the highest application rate for both phosphorus and potash, two to three times higher than other major crops. Potatoes also receive large amounts of sulfur (82 pounds per acre in 1994) and micronutrients. About 75% of nitrogen fertilizers used is applied before or at planting (Figure 6). The fertilizer use is influenced by the cropping practice. Producers adopting conventional tillage tend to use less nitrogen fertilizer but often supplement with manure. However, livestock manures are not widely used in crop production in the United States (Figure 7).

The amount of fertilizer used depends on acreage farmed, fertilizer prices, commodity programs, and nutrient management. As more acreages of major crops are farmed, the use of fertilizer increases, especially when corn and wheat acreages increase (since they account for 45% and 16% of total fertilizer used, respectively). Larger crop acreages will be planted if crop prices are favorable. Fertilizers constitute about 6% of crop production cost. Generally, fertilizer use is unresponsive to changes in fertilizer prices, at least in the short term. Events such as the oil embargo brought about sharp rises in fertilizer prices. Also, increased demand for fertilizers (e.g., after the floods of 1993 and export demand) increases fertilizer prices. Government programs such as the commodity programs tend to create a stable farm economy that engenders the use of fertilizers. As producers incorporate more effective nutrient management practices such as

FIGURE 6 About 75% of nitrogen fertilizer is applied before or at planting in the production of most of the major field crops, including corn, soybeans, wheat, cotton, and potatoes. (Source: USDA)

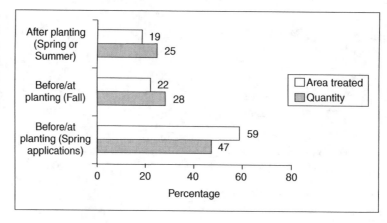

FIGURE 7 Livestock manures are not widely used in crop production in the United States. Corn received the most amount of livestock manure. About 17% of all corn acreage was treated with livestock manure between 1994 and 1996. (Source: USDA)

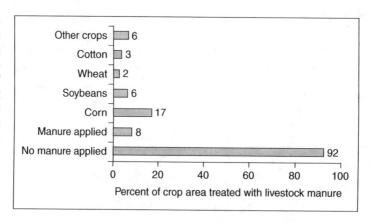

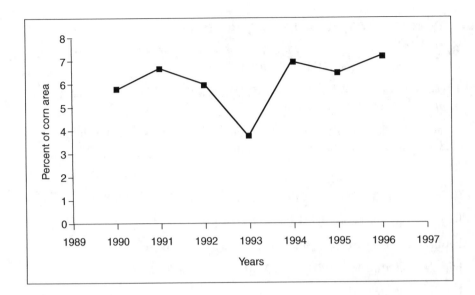

FIGURE 8 The use of nitrogen stabilizers reduces the leaching loss of applied nitrogen fertilizers. In 1993, soils in the Corn Belt were extremely wet from the heavy rains, thus delaying the normal application of fertilizers, resulting in a reduction in the use of nitrogen stabilizers. (Source: USDA)

split application, nitrogen stabilizers, and timing of application, loss of nutrients through leaching and other avenues is decreased (Figure 8). Lower rates of fertilizer use can then be practiced. Modern technologies such as precision farming further reduce the amounts of fertilizers used in crop production through more effective application.

Soil fertility management in crop production should be conducted as part of the general soil management practice that includes managing soil physical properties (through tillage, drainage, and control of erosion).

SUMMARY

1. The goal of soil fertility management is to sustain the soil's ability to supply essential nutrients to crops.
2. The nutrients required by plants are called essential nutrients. There are 18 essential nutrients. These are categorized into three according to quantities absorbed. Major or macronutrients (required in large amounts—nitrogen, phosphorus, and potassium), secondary nutrients (required in medium amounts), and minor nutrients, or micronutrients (required in minute or trace amounts).
3. Soils lose nutrients through leaching, erosion, volatilization, and crop removal.
4. A soil test is used to determine the nutritional status of the soil. Based on the tests, fertilizer recommendations for amendment are made for application by the farmer.
5. Plant tissue may also be analyzed to detect soil nutritional deficiency.
6. Nutrient availability is influenced by the soil pH.
7. There are natural cycles (e.g., N, P, S) in nature that return nutrients absorbed and used by plants into the soil upon decay.
8. Fertilizers are used to supply supplemental nutrition to the soil for crop production.
9. There are several ways of applying fertilizer to crop plants: starter, split, top, broadcast, banding, foliar, and fertigation.
10. Not all of the applied fertilizer is actually utilized by plants. Some of it is lost to leaching, fixation, and other causes.

REFERENCES AND SUGGESTED READING

Brady, C. N., and R. R. Weil. 1999. *The nature and properties of soils.* 12th ed. Upper Saddle River, NJ: Prentice Hall.

Burns, R. C., and R. W. F. Hardy. 1975. *Nitrogen fixation in bacteria and higher plants.* Berlin: Springer-Verlag.

Mengel, K., and E. A. Kirby. 1987. *Principles of plant nutrition.* 4th ed. Bern, Switzerland: International Potash Institute.

SELECTED INTERNET SITES FOR FURTHER REVIEW

http://www.fertilizer.org/PUBLISH/PUBMAN/introdc.htm

Fertilizer use/abuse, types, pollution, pH, diagnosis of deficiency.

http://www.fertilizer.org/PUBLISH/PUBMAN/manual.htm

Fertilizer recommendations for various crops.

OUTCOMES ASSESSMENT

PART A

Answer the following questions true or false.

1. T F Nitrogen is a micronutrient in plant nutrition.
2. T F Nitrogen is associated with vegetative plant growth.
3. T F Purpling is associated with potassium deficiency.
4. T F Necrosis is tissue death.
5. T F An established farmer should conduct a soil test every year.

PART B

Answer the following questions.

1. Give the three macronutrients or major nutrients in plant nutrition.

   _____

   _____

   _____

2. Soil nutrient diagnosis is also called _____.

3. Give a function of nitrogen in plant nutrition.

   _____

4. Give a list of the secondary nutrients in plant nutrition.

_____

_____

_____

_____

_____

5. Give two examples each of the commercial fertilizers used to supply
   a. Phosphorus

_____

_____

   b. Nitrogen

_____

_____

PART C

Write a brief essay on each of the following topics.

1. Discuss chlorosis as a symptom of nutrient deficiency in plant nutrition.
2. Discuss the criteria for declaring a nutrient as essential in plant nutrition.
3. What is phosphorus fixation?
4. Discuss nutrient cycling.
5. What is eutrophication?
6. Discuss the methods of fertilizer application.
7. Discuss the factors that affect a soil test.
8. Discuss the factors that affect the implementation of recommendations from a soil test.

PART D

Discuss or explain the following topics in detail.

1. A fertile soil is not necessarily productive. Explain.
2. What can be done to improve fertilizer efficiency?
3. Discuss the role of fertilizers in boosting crop productivity in U.S. agriculture.
4. Discuss the impact of leached fertilizer on the environment.

Pests in Crop Production

From Chapter 10 of *Principles of Crop Production: Theory, Techniques, and Technology*, Second Edition, George Acquaah.
Copyright © 2005 by Pearson Education, Inc. Published by Pearson Prentice Hall. All rights reserved.

Pests in Crop Production

PURPOSE

This chapter explores the living organisms in the environment and the non-living environmental factors that cause diseases and other forms of damage to crop plants, as well as how they are managed in crop production.

EXPECTED OUTCOMES

After studying this chapter, the student should be able to:

1. List and describe the categories of organisms that cause disease.
2. Discuss the factors that cause disease.
3. Describe the disease cycle.
4. Discuss the strategies and mechanisms plants adopt to resist disease.
5. Discuss the genetic basis of disease resistance.
6. Discuss how pathogens affect crop productivity.
7. Describe insect pests, their classification, and their economic importance.
8. Describe weeds, their classification, and their economic importance.
9. Discuss abiotic disease agents.
10. List and describe important crop pests.
11. Discuss the principles of pest management.
12. Describe how pest attacks can be prevented.
13. List and discuss the methods of pest management.
14. Describe the steps in selecting and applying pesticides safely.
15. Discuss the impact of pesticides on the environment.

KEY TERMS

Active ingredient	Annual weeds	Biological pest
Aerosol	Biennial weeds	management (control)

Complete metamorphosis	Integrated pest management (IPM)	Overwintering
Cultural pest management (control)	Legislative pest management (control)	Pathogenicity
Disease triangle	Lethal dose (LD_{50})	Perennial weeds
Economic injury	Lifecycle	Pesticides
Formulation	Mechanical pest management (control)	Phytoallexins
Horizontal resistance	Obligate parasites	Plant quarantine
Host range	Organochlorines	Postemergence herbicides
Hypersensitive reaction	Organophosphates	Preemergence herbicides
Incomplete metamorphosis		Surfactants
		Toxicity
		Vertical resistance

TO THE STUDENT

Plants, as primary producers, are the main sources of energy that support life on earth. Plants are hence preyed upon by a wide variety of consumers, from microbes to mammals. Obtaining the crop potential or maximum yield in production is elusive for the reason that crop production is subject to physical, chemical, and biological factors in the environment that impact crop productivity. Yield reduction from biological sources alone is estimated at about 30% or more of the potential yield. These yield losses occur at various stages in the production operation, from seedling establishment, to crop growth and development, to harvesting and storage. Some of the organisms in the plant's environment are beneficial to the plant, while others are destructive. In order to manage the plant biotic environment effectively, there is the need to understand how these organisms fit into the ecosystem, their nature, and their behavior. It is important to know the lifecycle of an organism in order to know the stage in which it is most vulnerable to be effectively controlled. This chapter focuses on the biology of the organisms. The term *pest* is all-inclusive for organisms that are bothersome or annoying and undesirable to humans. In this chapter, emphasis is placed on economic loss caused to crops by pests. Pests and adverse environmental conditions cause diseases.

Agricultural production occurs within an ecosystem (i.e., an agroecosystem) in which biotic and abiotic components interact. Agriculture is a "managed ecosystem," as opposed to a natural ecosystem. The producer manages resources, making decisions that are influenced by nature, economic factors, and political factors. Since crop production is goal-oriented, the producer deliberately restricts interaction among organisms in the agroecosystem in order to favor the crop being grown for maximum productivity. Agricultural pests reduce crop productivity. The crop producer must therefore adopt appropriate strategies to exclude harmful associations without endangering the environment. The methods used should also be economical. You will learn that the mere sight of a pest does not warrant the implementation of a control measure. Since pest management can be expensive, the pest population should be at a critical threshold, beyond which economic yield is jeopardized, before pest control is essential. You will also learn that, whereas modern crop production technology enables producers to use chemicals in pest management, there are non-chemical strategies that can be used. Chemicals pollute the environment and must be used judiciously.

Some prefer the term *management* rather than *control* of pests because, in practice, producers rarely control or eliminate any pest. Rather, pest populations are reduced to levels at which they cause no economic loss.

1: CONCEPT OF DISEASE

Pathogens and improper physiological environment may cause plants to malfunction. The biotic factors that cause yield reduction are of both plant and animal origins. They may be placed into four general categories:

1. Disease-causing organisms
2. Plants as pests (weeds)
3. Insect pests
4. Non-insect invertebrate or vertebrate pests

A plant is said to be diseased when it deviates from one or more of its normal physiological functions (e.g., cell division, absorption of water and minerals, photosynthesis, and reproduction). The deviation is caused by an agent of disease, which may be either a living pathogenic organism (called a *pathogen*) or some physical environmental factor. The affected plant is unable to perform certain physiological functions to the best of its genetic potential. A disease may be defined as the malfunctioning of afflicted cells and tissues attributed to the presence of a causal agent and which produces a symptom (e.g., change in form, physiology, integrity, or behavior).

The extent of incapacitation is dependent upon the causal agent as well as the plant. Further, the kind of cells and tissues infected will determine the kind of physiological function to be affected first. The first effect will then trigger other effects that may eventually result in the death of the plant. For example, if the root becomes afflicted by root rot, the conducting vessels may be damaged (as is the case in vascular wilt), translocation of water and minerals is interrupted, photosynthesis is adversely impacted, plant growth is reduced, and yield is reduced. Infections involving the foliage leaf (e.g., blight and leaf spot) reduce photosynthetic area and hence photosynthetic output which, in turn, reduces growth and yield. Diseases do not always weaken or destroy afflicted cells. On the contrary, certain diseases stimulate cell division (*hyperplasia*) or cell enlargement (*hypertrophy*). These abnormal events lead to tissue proliferation, resulting in amorphous overgrowths (e.g., tumors).

There are tens of thousands of crop plant diseases that must be classified to facilitate their study, identification, and management. Just like classification of plants, there are several ways to classify plant diseases, operationally or scientifically.

Operational categories of plant disease include the following:

1. *Symptoms caused.* Diseases cause numerous symptoms, such as rots (root rot), canker, blights, rusts, smut, mosaic, and yellows.
2. *Plant organ afflicted.* General categories of plant disease by this classification include root diseases, foliage diseases, fruit diseases, and stem diseases.
3. *Plant category.* Certain diseases are associated with field crops, ornamentals, trees, vegetables, fruit trees, and turf.
4. *Causal organism or factor.* This system of classification is one of the most useful and widely used. The specific mechanisms by which diseases are produced depend on the causal agent. By knowing and studying the causal agent, as well as its nature, functioning, and behavior, scientists are more readily able to develop effective strategies to control the agents. On the basis of causal agent, plant diseases may be classified into two broad groups: *biotic* (infectious) and *abiotic* (non-infectious):
   a. *Biotic (infectious) diseases.* These diseases are caused by pathogens and can be transmitted from one victim plant to another. The organisms are fungi,

viruses and viroids, parasitic higher plants, prokaryotes (bacteria and my-coplasmas), nematodes, and protozoa.

   b. *Abiotic (non-infectious) diseases.* These diseases are caused by environmental factors and thus not infectious. They include abnormal levels of growth requirements (e.g., extreme high or low temperature, moisture excess or deficit, low or intense light, nutrient deficiency, nutrient toxicity, lack of oxygen), improper cultural practices, pollution, and improper pH.

2: CLASSIFICATION OF PLANT DISEASES

What microorganisms are responsible for plant diseases? What is the relative economic importance of the diseases they cause? A variety of microorganisms are pathogenic on plants. Plant pathogens may be grouped into the following main categories:

1. Viruses and viroids
2. Bacteria
3. Fungi
4. Mycoplasma-like organisms
5. Protozoa
6. Nematodes
7. Parasitic higher plants

2.1 *VIRUSES ARE OBLIGATE PARASITES*

Viruses need a host tissue to stay alive (i.e., obligate parasites). They are not cells and do not consist of cells. They are not true animals and are incapable of digestion and respiration. They consist of a core of nucleic acid that may be RNA or DNA encased in a protein or lipoprotein coat (called a capsid). They are variable in shape and size. Most plant viruses are RNA viruses.

Viroids are small, naked, single-stranded, circular RNAs. Plant viruses enter plants through mechanical wounds or vectors (carriers). Sometimes, an infected pollen grain carries a virus into an ovule. Viruses are primarily systemic, occurring in the host's vascular (phloem) fluids. Once in the phloem, the virus moves towards the apical meristem. As such, sucking insects (especially aphids) and chewing insects (e.g., thrips) transfer viral diseases from infected plants to healthy ones through feeding. Viruses may be seed-transmitted (though the ovule of infected plants). Certain nematodes, mites, and fungi also transmit viruses.

Viral disease symptoms include *mosaics* (light-green, yellow, or white patches mingled with normal green) and especially the stunting of growth. The pattern of discoloration is variable and may be described accordingly as mottling, streak, ring, line, vein clearing, vein banding, or chlorosis. Viruses seldom kill their plant hosts. Why do you think this is advantageous to the pathogen? Viruses instead diminish plant growth and development, resulting in stunted growth and consequently reduced productivity. Some infected plants can show no symptoms *(asymptomatic).* In fact, these pathogens (latent viruses) can remain in the host for as long as the host remains alive. Stunted growth is caused by a reduction in growth regulatory substances.

Viral infections are customarily described in a variety of ways, but especially according to the host (host specificity) (e.g., tobacco mosaic virus, or TMV; maize dwarf mosaic virus, or MDMV) and the most visible symptoms caused. They are also described by the type of nucleic acid (e.g., DNA or RNA), morphology, mode(s) of transmission, and others.

Viral diseases are not controlled by the use of pesticides (chemicals that are used to control plant pests). The most effective control is prevention from entry through quarantine, inspection, and certification. Resistant cultivars are commonly used to control viral diseases. Another method of control is to expose infected tissue to high heat (38°C or 100°F) for 2 to 4 weeks (called *heat therapy*) in order to inactivate the virus. Growing tips of infected plants are free of viruses. These tips may be retrieved and propagated by tissue culture.

2.2   ALMOST ALL PATHOGENIC PLANT BACTERIA ARE ROD-SHAPED (BACILLI)

There are two kinds of prokaryotes that cause disease in plants: *bacteria* and *mycoplasma-like organisms*. Ubiquitous in the environment, these unicellular organisms occur in one of four forms: spherical *(cocci),* rod-shaped *(bacilli),* spiral *(spirilli),* and filament *(filamentous).* They may also be classified according to their reaction to the Gram's stain as either *Gram positive* (violet) or *Gram negative* (pink-red). Bacteria multiply by *binary fission* (divide into two parts). Most bacteria are facultative saprophytes and hence useful in decomposing organic wastes. Many species have numerous pathovars (strains that differ in the plant species they infect). Plant pathogenic bacteria occur in places where it is moist and warm. Bacteria contain small, circular DNA that is used in biotechnological research. One genus of importance to biotechnology is the *Agrobacterium.* Some bacteria thrive in plant hosts but many (e.g., common scab of potato or *Streptomyces scabies*) are soil inhabitors.

Bacteria are spread by a variety of means, including wind, splashing from irrigation or rain, and use of infected seed or other propagation material. They gain entry into the host through natural pores (e.g., stomata) or wounds. Bacterial diseases include soft rots, bacterial cankers, wilts, overgrowth, scabs, and rots. These usually affect the stem and roots of the plant.

Bacteria are generally intolerant of temperatures above 125°F (51.7°C). Since they spread through wounds, pruning tools should be properly cleaned between plants. Sanitation should be observed during crop production so as to destroy sources of disease and protect wounds. Like viral diseases, the best control is to use resistant cultivars.

Not all bacteria are pathogenic. Leguminous crop plants (e.g., soybean) benefit from symbiosis (the mutually beneficial plant-bacteria association that fixes atmospheric nitrogen for plant use). In commercial production, soybean seeds may be treated with artificially cultured *Rhizobia* inoculant.

2.3   MYCOPLASMA-LIKE ORGANISMS

Mycoplasma-like organisms are wall-less microbes that occur in the phloem tissue. They are capable of reproducing themselves, have both DNA and RNA, but lack a cell wall. Mycoplasma-like diseases have been identified in vegetables and field crops.

Mycoplasma-like organisms are systemic and transmitted by vectors such as grasshoppers and aphids. Spraying is used to control the insect vectors. Tetracycline application has proved successful in the control of pear decline disease.

2.4   FUNGI CAUSE MOST OF THE IMPORTANT INFECTIOUS DISEASES OF CROP PLANTS

Over 100,000 fungal species have been identified, most of which are saprophytic (live on dead organic matter). About 8,000 of these cause diseases in plants. They have been responsible for a number of crop destruction episodes that have led to famines.

Fungi attack flowers, seeds, leaves, stems, and roots. Most are multicellular (even though some are unicellular) and have no chlorophyll. Unable to photosynthesize, fungi live parasitically. They may be classified into four categories. Usually, each plant fungal disease is caused by only one fungus.

1. *Obligate saprophytes.* These live only on dead plant and animal tissue.
2. **Obligate parasites.** These live only on living plant tissue.
3. *Facultative saprophytes.* These usually live on living tissue but can also live on dead tissues under certain conditions.
4. *Facultative parasites.* These are normally saprophytic but occasionally parasitic.

Obligate parasites. Organisms that must live as a parasite and cannot otherwise survive.

Fungi are spread primarily by bodies called *spores* (with a few exceptions) that vary in shape, size, and color. Upon germination, spores produce structures called *hyphae* (singular is *hypha*) that grow and branch to produce other structures called *mycellia* (singular is *mycellium)* or fungal bodies. Spores spread by wind, water, insects, and other agents. They infect through wounds, through natural openings, or by direct penetration of the epidermis. Nearly all the pathogenic fungi spend part of their lifecycles on the plant host and part on plant debris or soil. Their survival depends on the temperature conditions that prevail.

Fungal diseases include leaf spots, blights, mildews, rusts, and wilts. Some spores grow on the leaf surface as molds (e.g., *Helminthosporium* diseases). Other fungi, such as *Septoria* and *Ascochyta,* live embedded in plant tissue. Key symptoms of fungal diseases are *necrosis* (tissue death), *hypotrophy* (stunted growth), and *hypoplasia* (excessive growth):

1. *Necrotic symptoms.* The common necrotic symptoms include leaf spot (localized lesions), blight (rapid browning leading to death of organ), die back (necrosis starting at the tip of the organ), canker (localized wound that is usually sunken), anthracnose (necrotic and sunken ulcerlike lesions), damping off (rapid collapse and death of young seedlings), and scab (localized usually raised lesions).
2. *Symptoms involving growth.* The key symptoms involving hypertrophy or hyperplasia include clubfoot (enlarged wilts), gall (enlarged plant part), witches' broom (profuse upward branching), and leaf curl (curling of leaves).
3. *Other symptoms.* Other common symptoms associated with fungal diseases are wilts (vascular system collapse), rust (numerous small lesions that appear as rusty color), and mildew (covering of mycelium and fructification of the fungus).

Fungal diseases are relatively easy to control. Control measures include the use of chemicals, diseased seed, and resistant cultivars. There are protective pesticides that are commonly used as seed treatment or are applied to the surface of plants. Chemical control is the most effective control measure of the disease. A new generation of systemic fungicides is in use. Sanitation also helps to keep fungi under control. Plant remains should be destroyed, especially those infested.

Like bacteria, some fungi are beneficial to humans. These include *Penicillium* (from which the antibiotic penicillin is produced), edible mushrooms, and yeast (used in fermentation of alcoholic beverages such as beer and for leavening bread and other foods). Like symbiosis in legumes, fungi-plant associations called michorrhizae occur in species such as corn, cotton, soybean, and tobacco, aiding in the absorption of phosphorus.

2.5 NEMATODES

Nematodes or eelworms may live parasitically on living plants and animals. Plant-parasitic nematodes are microscopic and mostly inhabit the soil. Some of them are ectoparasites (remain in the soil), while others are endoparasites (enter the plant roots, tubers, bulbs, etc.). A few nematodes are able to infest the leaf (foliar nematodes). Infected roots appear knotted or with galls. Tubers and roots of root crops are malformed. Root knotting interrupts the uptake of soil nutrients and water. Infested plants may, therefore, show symptoms of moisture stress or nutrient deficiency as well as reduced crop yield. Using chemicals or resistant cultivars controls nematodes.

Important nematodes of economic importance in crop production include the root knot and cyst nematodes.

Root Knot Nematodes

Almost all cultivated plants are susceptible to root knot nematodes (*Meloidogyne* spp.). Affected plants develop knots or galls at the points of infection. These swellings are irregular and easily distinguished from the roundish nodules developed from *Rhizobia* infection of legume roots. When root or tuber crops are infected, the roots or tubers are deformed. The development of infection by other soil pathogens such as *Pythium* and *Rhizoctonia* are found to be accelerated through galls formed by nematodes.

Cyst Nematodes

Cyst nematodes cause cysts on the roots and cause root proliferation. The cyst nematodes of importance in crop production are the *Glabodera* and *Heterodera*. *G. rostochiensis* affects potato especially, as well as tomato and egg plant. *H. glycines* affects soybean, while *H. avenae* and *H. trifolii* affect cereals and clover, respectively.

2.6 PARASITIC PLANTS

Of the more than 2,500 species of higher plants known to be parasitic on other plants, few are economic pests of cultivated crops.

Dodders

Dodders (*Cuscuta* spp.) infest alfalfa, sugar beet, potato, and other species. They are composed of orange or yellow vine strands that smother above-ground parts of plants. The plant produces seed in summer that overwinters in the field or in harvested produce. Chemical control is effective.

Witchweed

Witchweed (*Striga* spp.) is a parasite of corn, tobacco, rice, sugarcane, and some small grain. Infected plants are stunted and chlorotic, followed by wilting and death in cases of severe infestation. The parasite has attractive features. It grows at the base of the infected plant, where it parasitizes the roots of cultivated plants.

Broomrapes

The causal parasite is *Orobanche* spp. It is a whitish-to-yellow annual plant. It infests herbaceous crop plants, including tobacco, potato, clover, and alfalfa. It produces seeds that overwinter and can persist in the soil for many years. When a susceptible root grows near the seed, germination is induced, followed by penetration of the host roots.

3: NATURE OF DISEASE

Disease is the product of the interaction among the causal organism, host, and certain factors within the environment. The capacity of a pathogen to cause disease is called its **pathogenicity**. The variety of plants a pathogen can grow on is its **host range**. Obligate parasites tend to be limited to one host *(host-specific),* while non-obligate parasites can cause diseases in various plant species. What are the essential requirements for disease conditions to develop? In order for disease to occur, three factors are essential:

1. Pathogen (causal organism)
2. Susceptible host (e.g., plant)
3. Favorable environment

These three factors form what is called the **disease triangle** (Figure 1). The degree of disease occurrence depends on the nature of these factors. A little amount of disease agent may multiply rapidly and become established if the host is very susceptible and the environment ideal. On the other hand, a large amount of pathogen inoculant on a plant in an unfavorable environment may not cause any pathogenic effect at all, or only mildly so.

Each pathogen has its biological lifecycle. The disease cycle is the series of events that leads to disease development and perpetuation in a host. There are several general stages in disease development:

1. Inoculation
2. Penetration
3. Infection
4. Dissemination
5. Overwintering/oversummering

3.1 INOCULATION

The contact between host and pathogen is called *inoculation.* The pathogen or part of it that is involved in the inoculation is called the *inoculum.* This may be spores, viruses, bacteria, or other microorganisms. The initial unit of inoculum that comes into contact with the host is called the *primary inoculum.* It produces the *primary infection.* As indicated previously, the inoculum may be spread by vectors or other agents such as water and air.

Pathogenicity. The capacity of a pathogen to cause disease in a host.

Host range. The variety of plant species a pathogen can successfully invade and grow on.

Disease triangle. The concept that disease occurs only when three factors, namely pathogen, susceptible host, and favorable environment, occur at the same time.

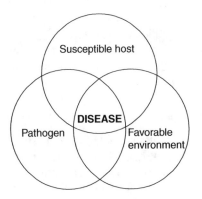

FIGURE 1 The disease triangle. Disease will occur only when the pathogen interacts with a susceptible host under favorable conditions. The presence of a pathogen alone is not sufficient to cause disease.

3.2 PENETRATION

Penetration is the stage at which the pathogen enters the host tissue. This occurs as germination of spores in fungi. Some pathogens (e.g., fungi and nematodes) and parasitic plants exert mechanical pressure to gain entry into plants. Other pathogens secrete enzymes and other chemical compounds that soften the cell wall to facilitate entry. Penetration may also occur through natural pores (e.g., stomata), wounds (caused by equipment damage during cultivation, hail damage, and other/causes), or directly through the cuticle by a growth called *penetration peg*. Penetration may trigger a defense mechanism to resist the entry of the pathogen, thereby curtailing disease development.

3.3 INFECTION

Infection is the process whereby the pathogen establishes contact with host cells or tissues to be nourished for growth and multiplication. For infection to occur, the host must be susceptible to the race of the pathogen (i.e., the pathogen must be virulent on the host). Once entry into the host has been gained, the pathogen starts to invade the cells and tissues to colonize them. This may result in visible signs or symptoms. Colonization (growth and reproduction) may occur primarily on the surface, as in powdery mildew, or the vascular system, as in wilts. Sometimes, only one or a few cells are colonized (called *localized infection*). Viruses, on the other hand, invade the entire plant (called *systemic infection*). Symptoms may appear almost immediately after entry of the pathogen. However, some infections may remain *latent* and undetectable for a period. The time between inoculation and symptom development is called the *incubation period*.

How do plants react to invasion by pathogens? There are three general responses:

Hypersensitive reaction. A strategy adopted by a host plant to contain the invasion of a pathogen by self-induced death of the tissue around the site of invasion.

1. *Overdevelopment of tissue.* Affected tissue overdevelops, resulting in symptoms such as curling or galls.
2. *Underdevelopment of tissue.* Plant organs and the whole plant may become stunted, as occurs in viral infections.
3. **Hypersensitive reaction**. The pathogen is contained through drastic measures that result in tissue death around the site of invasion (necrosis), as occurs in leaf spots and blights, or rots, as in canker and soft rot.

3.4 DISSEMINATION

Disease-causing organisms are spread by vectors and other agents to new hosts. Nematodes, fungal zoospores, and bacteria move only short distances. Consequently, they spread slowly from one plant to another. Spores, on the other hand, can be carried long distances by air. Bacteria, spores, and nematodes are also disseminated by water (e.g., rain, splashing of irrigation water). Insect vectors include aphids and leafhoppers (for viral infections). Activities of humans (handling of plants) also contribute to the spread of disease. Humans are blamed for introducing pathogens such as powdery mildews and downy mildews of grapes.

3.5 OVERWINTERING OR OVERSUMMERING

Overwintering. Strategy by which field pests survive the winter.

Pathogens persist in the environment, in the ground, or on plant material in a certain stage in the lifecycle until the next crop growing season arrives. When a host dies in winter, the pathogen must be able to survive the harsh winter conditions (called **overwintering**). On the other hand, if the host dies in summer, the pathogen must *oversummer* in order to survive. Some pathogens are soil inhabitants (e.g., *Pithium* and *Fusarium*), while others are soil transients, living most of their lifecycles on the host. Viruses and mycoplasmas survive only in living tissue.

4: PLANTS HAVE CERTAIN DEFENSE MECHANISMS TO WARD OFF PATHOGENIC INVASION

How do plants defend themselves against attack from pathogens? Upon inoculation, the host plant may resist further development of the disease cycle by either *active* (preexisting) or *passive* (induced) resistance strategies. These strategies involve *structural* and *biochemical defense mechanisms:*

1. *Structural defense.* Plants have structural features such as water-repellent waxy deposition on the epidermis or a thick cuticle that hinders penetration by pathogens. Some plants also have pubescence (hairlike structures) on the leaf and other parts that interfere with the pest organism's lifecycle.

   Should the pathogen succeed in penetrating the host tissue, structural degradation of tissue (e.g., necrosis in hypersensitive reaction) restricts the spread of the disease. In some species, a cork layer forms to contain the invasion.

2. *Biochemical defense.* Certain species produce fungitoxic exudates when invaded by pathogens. Red onions resist onion smudge fungus by exuding toxins called protocatechaic acid and catechol. White onions do not produce these toxins and are thus susceptible to the fungal attack.

   Similarly, potato cultivars that are low in reducing sugars are less susceptible to bacterial soft rot caused by *Erwinia carotova* var *atroseptica* than those that are high in reducing sugars.

   Injured plants exude certain chemicals called **phytoallexins**. For example, injured bean plants exude phaseolin, while potato and pepper exude rishitin and capsidol, respectively.

Phytoallexins. Chemicals exuded by certain plants upon injury to ward off pest attack.

4.1 SOME PLANTS ARE GENETICALLY EQUIPPED TO RESIST CERTAIN DISEASES

Crop plants may resist disease through several types of resistance:

1. *Non-host resistance.* Plants that are taxonomically outside the host range of the pathogen will not be infected by the pathogen. Certain diseases occur only in certain taxonomic groups. As such, a certain corn disease may not affect potatoes even if the most favorable conditions prevail.

2. *Genetic or true resistance.* The plant with true genetic resistance possesses a certain gene (or genes) that is able to resist the virulence gene(s) of the pathogen.

3. *Apparent resistance.* The plant, through other strategies or mechanisms, is able to avoid the disease.

Vertical resistance. The genetic resistance in a host that is conditioned by one or a few genes.

Genetic (True) Resistance

True resistance to pathogens is genetically controlled, enabling plant breeders to breed cultivars with resistance to certain diseases. According to the origin of control, there are two forms of genetic resistance: *nuclear* and *cytoplasmic*. Further, there are two kinds of nuclear resistance: **vertical resistance** and **horizontal resistance**. Is one of these more advantageous in crop production than the other?

Horizontal resistance. Genetic resistance of a plant host to disease that is conditioned by several to numerous genes.

Nuclear Resistance   This form can be either vertical or horizontal.

1. **Vertical Resistance**   Also called *major gene, oligogenic, monogenic, qualitative, race-specific,* or *differential resistance,* vertical resistance is controlled by one or a few genes. Thus, it is simply inherited and relatively easy to breed into cultivars. Cultivars protected by major gene resistance usually have race-specific resistance. They show complete resistance to a particular pathogen under a wide variety of environmental conditions. However, a simple mutation in the gene (new race) abolishes the host resistance to the disease. This resistance is also described as not durable. The host and pathogen are not compatible. Consequently, the host exhibits a hypersensitive response to invasion. Even though a crop cultivar may have one or two resistance genes, a single species may have over 20 resistance genes against a single pathogen (e.g., wheat has 20 to 40 genes for resistance against Puccinia recondita).

2. **Horizontal Resistance**   Horizontal resistance is controlled by several to numerous genes, each contributing to the total resistance. It is also described as *minor gene, non-specific, general, quantitative, adult plant, field, polygenic, multigenic,* or *non-differential resistance.* This resistance is usually not complete. It reduces certain aspects of the disease (e.g., sporulation, infection frequency, spread of the disease in the field). It is more difficult to incorporate into a breeding program but is more durable than vertical resistance (i.e., mutation effects do not easily overcome it). It is environmentally labile, and hence resistance is variable from one environment to another. All plants have some degree of horizontal resistance. It does not protect the crop plant from infection but, rather, slows down the development and spread of the disease.

Cytoplasmic Resistance   The genes involved in vertical resistance and horizontal resistance are nuclear in origin and hence subject to Mendelian laws of inheritance. However, certain diseases are controlled by genes that are extranuclear or extra-chromosomal, occurring in organelles in the cytoplasm. Examples of diseases under cytoplasmic control are the southern corn leaf blight *(Bipolaris Helminthosprium maydis)* and yellow leaf blight *(Phyllosticta maydis).* The normal cytoplasm has genes for resistance while the genes are suppressed in hybrids with the Texas (T) male-sterile cytoplasm.

Apparent Resistance

Certain plants without resistance genes are able to avoid diseases through two kinds of mechanisms: *escape* and *tolerance.*

1. *Escape*   As described previously, the balance among three factors (pathogen, host, and environment) determines the severity of a potential outbreak of disease. Even though a pathogen may be present on the crop plant, absence of the appropriate environment may cause the plants to escape the infection. Some plants are susceptible to a disease only at a certain stage in growth. For example, younger tissues are more susceptible to certain diseases such as powdery mildew *(Phytium)* and viral infection than older tissues. The producer may also vary the cultural conditions (e.g., spacing, rate of planting, fertilization, sanitation, rouging, use of vigorous seeds) to prevent or reduce disease incidence in the crop. Monoculture favors the buildup of disease inoculum, while mixed cropping or crop rotation lowers the pathogen population. Many plants escape diseases due to lack of moisture and low humidity. In potato production, a low soil pH prevents potato scab *(Streptomyces scabies).*

2. *Tolerance* Certain plants can be productive while harboring pathogens and are said to be tolerant to the disease. Viral infections usually do not kill the host plants but cause reduced productivity through stunting of plants. Tolerant plants have certain specific heritable characteristics that enable them to allow the pathogen to multiply without any adverse effects. The host plants are either able to inactivate toxins or are able to compensate for any dysfunctional effects and still be productive.

Genetic Basis of Disease Incidence

Disease infection depends on the host and pathogen (and environment), each with its separate genetic properties. The *degree of susceptibility* or *resistance* of the host to infection is called the *host reaction.* The degree of pathogenicity of a pathogen is called its *virulence.* There are genes for resistance (in the host) and virulence (in the pathogen). These two sets of genes are thought to be closely related to the extent that, for each resistance gene in the host, there is a corresponding virulence gene in the pathogen. This is called the *gene-for-gene hypothesis.* The genes for resistance are dominant *(R),* while susceptibility is controlled by a recessive gene *(r).* In the pathogen, *avirulence* (inability to infect) is under dominant gene control *(A),* while virulence is recessive *(a).* A host is resistant to a disease only when it has the resistant gene *(R),* while the pathogen lacks the gene for virulence *(A)* (that is, a host × pathogen gene combination of *AR*). Disease will occur if the host is susceptible *(r)* or if the pathogen is virulent *(a).* In the *Ar* combination, disease occurs because the pathogen, though lacking the specific virulent gene, has other genes for virulence.

5: HOW PATHOGENS AFFECT
CROP PRODUCTIVITY

What is the economic importance of plant disease? In what specific ways are crop plants affected by disease? Disease adversely affects plant physiology and hence metabolism. Disease may result in the death of plants or their parts. The major physiological processes affected are photosynthesis, respiration, translocation, growth, death, and economic product.

5.1 PHOTOSYNTHESIS

Foliar pathogens (pathogens that attack plant leaves, such as blight) reduce the photosynthetic surface, or leaf area. The effect of photosynthesis on plant growth and subsequently on yield depends on the severity of reduction in leaf area. It has been found that certain species (e.g., broad bean) are able to grow normally while suffering about 30 to 40% leaf loss. The remaining leaves somehow increase photosynthetic efficiency to compensate for decreased leaf area. In addition to leaf loss, pathogenic infections may degrade chlorophyll, producing chlorosis (yellowing of leaves). The total amount and the efficiency of chlorophyll may both be reduced as a result of viral infections that produce chlorosis. Starch metabolism is adversely affected by disease. Carbon dioxide fixation is also decreased. Thus, there are less assimilates for plant use and biological and economic yield. Leaf spots are particularly known for reducing leaf area. Shoot blights also cause such an effect.

5.2 RESPIRATION

Plants under pathogenic attack have been known to have increased respiration. In fact, where the infection is caused by biotrophic pathogens or obligate parasites (parasites that depend solely on living tissue for nutrients), host plant respiration has been observed to double. The host's metabolism is generally stimulated. Synthesis (or anabolism) is increased to meet the demand for nutrients under infection. Diseased plants also appear to have a shift in respiratory balance from glycolysis to the pentose phosphate pathway. Infected tissue frequently has low ATP.

5.3 TRANSLOCATION

Plants infected by obligate parasites tend to experience translocation of photosynthates to regions of infection. Pathogens called *vascular wilts* (caused by *Fusarium, Verticilium,* and *Ceratocytis*) invade the vascular system of the host, blocking the transpiration stream and producing wilting of the plant. *Necrotrophs* (parasites that cause immediate death of the tissue through which they pass) are also capable of directly affecting vascular transport by killing the plant tissue. Root and stem rots affect uptake of nutrients.

5.4 GROWTH

The adverse effect of disease on plant physiological processes (photosynthesis, respiration, and translocation) results in reduced biomass accumulation. Growth hormone levels, and hence growth regulation, adversely affect plant growth. Viral infections are noted for stunting plants rather than killing them.

5.5 PLANT DEATH

While certain diseases reduce growth, others are capable of completely destroying the entire plant or the part of economic importance to the producer. Damping off disease kills plant seedlings (reduces biomass), leading to an incomplete crop plant stand and reduced economic yield. In the case of grain pathogens, an important disease of field crops that destroys grain, thus leading to reduced economic yield, is the ergot fungus *(Claviceps purpurea).*

5.6 ECONOMIC PRODUCT

Whereas all the previously discussed effects of pathogens eventually adversely impact crop yield, some diseases directly affect the marketable plant part (e.g., fruit rot).

6: INSECT PESTS

Insect pests are widely adapted. Insects belong to the phylum Arthropoda (have jointed legs, exoskeleton, segmentation, bilateral symmetry) and class Insecta (true insects). Class Arachnida (spiders and mites) along with true insects constitute the source of most pests of plants in production. A majority (about 80%) of animal life consists of insects. Insects are widely adapted and distributed all over the world. They may cause direct damage to crop plants or be carriers (vectors) of pathogens. About 600 species of insects are considered crop pests.

The insect orders that are important to crop production are Lepidoptera, Coleoptera, Hymenoptera, Diptera, Thysanoptera, Aphididae, Pseudococcidae, and Cicadellidae. Examples of important pests in these orders are presented in Table 1.

Insects may be classified in various ways, for example, according to their lifecycle or feeding habit.

Table 1 Insect Orders of Importance to Crop Production

Order	Examples
Thysanura	Silverfish
Collembola	Springtails
	Several families damage seedlings and succulent stems.
Othoptera	Crickets, grasshoppers, and locusts
	Destroy roots or leaves
Phasmida	Stick insects
	Defoliate plants
Isoptera	Termites
	Destroy roots
Suborder Homoptera	Leafhoppers, whiteflies, aphids, mealy bugs, soft scale, and armored scale
	All are sap-sucking insects.
Suborder Heteroptera	Capsid/mosquito bugs, stink bugs, and shield bugs
	All are sap-sucking insects.
Thysanoptera	Thrips
	Cause leaf rolling and folding
Coleoptera	Beetles
	Biting and chewing mouthparts
Diptera	Flies, gall midges, shoot flies, fruit flies
	Larvae (never adults) are pests, destroying plant parts.
Lepidoptera	Leaf miner, stem borer, stinging/slug caterpillars, loopers, moths, armyworms, cutworms, butterflies, swallowtails
	Only larvae are destructive to plants, destroying leaves, stems, and other parts.
Hymenoptera	Sawflies, ants
	Larvae destroy leaves.
Acarina	Mites
	Piercing and sucking insects

Source: Extracted from list by Dennis, S. H., and J. D. Hill. 1994. *Agricultural Entomology.* Portland, OR: Timber Press.

6.1 LIFECYCLE

Based upon metamorphosis (the process of change an insect passes through), insects may be classified into four categories (Figure 2):

1. *No metamorphosis.* These insects are hatched as miniature adults. The young look like small versions of adult insects. This type of change occurs in Thysanura and Collembola.
2. *Gradual metamorphosis.* The young of such insects are called nymphs, and do not have all adult features. Insect orders with this type of metamorphosis include Homoptera, Isoptera, and Orthoptera (e.g., grasshopper, aphid).
3. **Incomplete metamorphosis.** The young change shape gradually from a naiad to an adult, as found in Odonata.
4. **Complete metamorphosis.** The **lifecycle** of insects with this type of metamorphosis consists of four distinct stages, namely egg, larva, pupa, and adult. Examples of insect orders with this type of metamorphosis include Hymenoptera, Lepidoptera, and Diptera (e.g., butterfly, housefly, bee). The most destructive stages are the larva (caterpillar) and adult.

Lifecycle. The set of stages an organism goes through from birth or germination, through maturity, and eventually death.

Incomplete metamorphosis. The insect lifecycle in which the young changes shape gradually to adult.

Complete metamorphosis. An insect lifecycle that is characterized by stages that are morphologically different from each other.

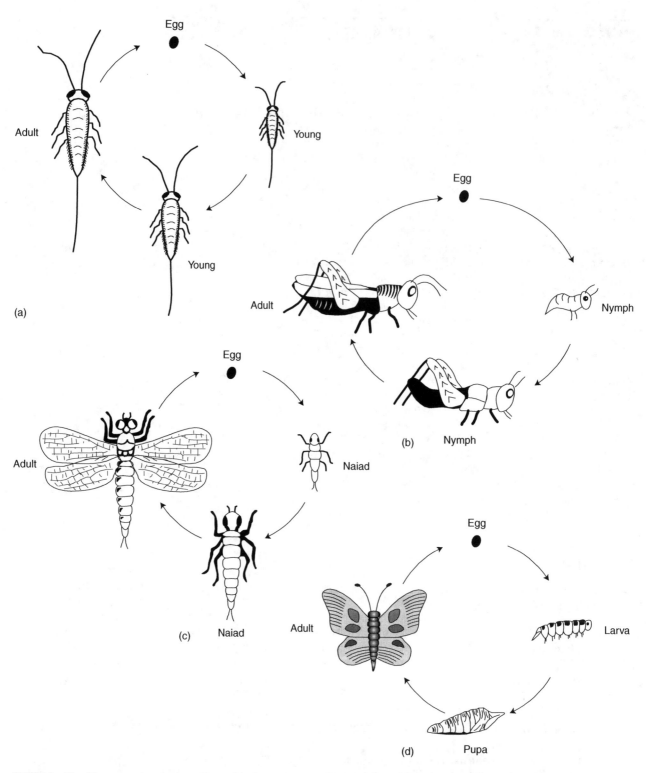

FIGURE 2 The lifecycle of insects consists of several stages of growth and development, starting from egg to adult. (a) Some insects have no metamorphosis, their young being miniature adults. (b) Some insects have gradual metamorphosis, their young lacking adult features. (c) In insects with incomplete metamorphosis, the young change shape gradually through the maturation process. (d) Some insects have complete metamorphosis, whereby there are four distinct stages.

The lifecycle of an organism plays a major role in pest management. A pest with one generation per year (e.g., alfalfa weevil) is relatively much easier to manage than a pest with several generations per year (e.g., tobacco aphids). Similarly, an insect pest with complete metamorphosis presents different management challenges than one with no metamorphosis. In the case of complete metamorphosing insects, the grower should target the appropriate management intervention to the most vulnerable stage in the life-cycle, and before the stage in which it causes economic damage. For example, the alfalfa weevil is more vulnerable in the larval stage than in the adult stage. As previously indicated, the larvae are most destructive to plants.

6.2   MOUTHPARTS AND FEEDING HABITS

Based on mouth parts and feeding habits, insect pests may be classified as *chewing* or *sucking and piercing*:

1. *Chewing insects.* Chewing insects have chewing mouthparts and chew during feeding. Larval stage of insects, adult beetles, and boring insects is chewing insects. The symptoms of chewing insect attack include defoliation, boring, leaf mining, and root feeding.
2. *Sucking and piercing insects.* These insects puncture plant tissue and suck fluids during feeding. Examples include aphids, scales, mealybugs, thrips, and leaf hoppers. These insects are usually small, sometimes even microscopic. During the feeding process, they may inject poisons into the plant. Sucking and piercing insect attack produces symptoms such as leaf curling or puckering and abnormal growth (gall).

Chewing insects are susceptible to foliar sprays that have either contact (effective on physical contact) or stomach (effective upon ingestion) mode of action. In cases where the pest starts its destructive activities from within the whorl of leaves (e.g., in corn borer), it is important that the pest be controlled before it gains access to the whorl. Insects with sucking and piercing mouthparts suck the food from the plant vessels and hence are best controlled by systemic insecticides (that are distributed throughout the entire plant in its vessels). Some insects have nocturnal feeding habits (e.g., moths). They hide during the daytime and evade direct contact with pesticides. The grower should know where such insects hide in order to be able to spray effectively to kill them.

6.3   INSECTS DAMAGE VARIES WITH PLANT
GROWTH STAGE

Insects indirectly affect photosynthesis by reducing leaf area through defoliation. Photosynthates are reduced as are, subsequently, growth and yield. Chewing insects such as cutworms reduce crop stand by killing plants and thus reducing the number of established plants and yield. Insects may bore through fruits and tubers in the field, reducing harvestable yield. In the storehouse, insects continue their devastation through the damage they inflict on grain and other crop products. Root-feeding insects (e.g., wire worms and white grub) can kill plants from below the ground level. Insects act as vectors of disease.

The damage caused depends on the crop growth cycle. Seed maggots and cutworms are effective in the very early stages of plant growth but cannot damage larger plants. The economic loss depends on the plant part attacked by the pest. An attack at the vegetative stage is less economically injurious than at the reproductive stage. For example, whereas soybean can tolerate a relatively large amount of leaf damage, the presence of a small number of stinkbugs is a greater cause for concern.

6.4 TYPES OF INSECT DAMAGE AND THEIR IMPACT ON PLANT ECONOMIC PRODUCTS

The type of insect damage determines the justification for control and when and how to implement pest management intervention. There are four general types of economic insect damage:

1. *Direct damage.* The insect pest may damage the economic product for which the crop is grown (e.g., an attack on the grain in cereals or leaves of salad crops or greens). The primary effect is reduction in product quality. For example, the earworm destroys the corn kernels, while the cabbage worm destroys the cabbage head by boring holes through the wrapped leaves.
2. *Indirect damage.* Insects that cause indirect damage to crops attack either vegetative or reproductive parts of plants that are not the economic plant parts. Their primary effect is overall yield loss.
3. *Product contamination.* Insects may not attack plant parts, but they decrease crop product value by contaminating the harvested product with their presence as living organisms, dead bodies or parts, or the byproducts of their metabolism (e.g., wastes). These foreign materials in economic products diminish their quality and consequently economic value.
4. *Insects as vectors for diseases.* Some insects may not attack the economic plants (i.e., they are not pests of plants). However, they may serve as vectors, acquiring a pathogen from an infected host and transmitting it to another host. Leafhoppers and aphids are vectors for various viral diseases (e.g., maize dwarf mosaic virus [MDMV] and barley yellow dwarf virus [BYDV]).

7: OTHER CROP PESTS

Other pests that plague crops during production include a variety of mites, vertebrates, and storehouse pests.

7.1 MITES

Mites belong to the order Acrina. They reproduce very rapidly and frequently. Spider mites (*Bryobia praetiosa, Tetranychus urticae,* and *Panomychus ulmi*) are important pests of both field crops and indoor-produced crops.

7.2 VERTEBRATES

Two groups of vertebrates, birds and mammals, are important pests of crop plants. Birds are important pests of cereal grains, wreaking havoc toward the end of the crop production cycle. Birds may eat both mature and immature grains. Small mammals (rodents) destroy field crops by either removing planted seeds or destroying mature grain or herbage and other products.

7.3 STORAGE PESTS

8: WEEDS

When a plant grows where it should not, it is deemed a pest. A *weed* is a plant growing where it is not wanted (i.e., a plant out of place). This broad definition notwithstanding, the term is normally reserved for certain specific plant species that perpetually are unwanted in crop production. Weeds are more aggressive than cultivated plants and outcompete them in production. They can thrive on marginal soils and have characteristics associated with the wild. Weed management is a major concern in crop production. More than 50% of all agricultural chemicals consists of those designed to control weeds (called herbicides).

8.1 ECONOMIC IMPORTANCE OF WEEDS

What is the economic importance of weeds in crop production? Weeds are undesirable in crop production for several reasons:

1. Weeds compete with cultivated plants for growth factors (light, water, nutrients). They are usually better competitors and thus cause reduced crop productivity.
2. They harbor pests such as rodents, snakes, insects, and pathogens.
3. Weeds increase crop production costs. This is so because the producer controls weeds at additional cost through weeding, mechanical cultivation, or use of herbicides.
4. When harvested grain becomes contaminated with weed seeds, cleaning the grain poses another additional production expenditure. Further, the seed quality, and subsequently the market value, is reduced.
5. Some weed species are poisonous or injurious to humans and animals (e.g., ragweed causes hay fever, locoweed causes "blind staggers" in animals).
6. Weeds reduce the aesthetic value of the area. A weed-infested farm is an eyesore.

Weeds may be classified according to plant lifecycle or leaf characteristics.

8.2 USEFUL ROLE OF WEEDS IN AN AGROECOSYSTEM

Weeds may be plants out of place, but they arise where they are most at home. They are the most adapted to the conditions under which they grow to maturity. Weeds are hardy plants and a part of the ecosystem. Weeds can have useful roles in crop production. They can serve as indicators of soil fertility, and also protect the soil from erosion.

1. Bare land is susceptible to soil erosion. When crops are not being grown on the land, it is best to have some plants growing on it rather than leaving it bare, especially where the land is erosion-prone.
2. Weeds can be plowed under the soil to improve soil organic matter.
3. A piece of land on which a good population of goosegrass, thistles, chickweed, and yarrow is found usually indicates that the soil is fertile and nutritionally balanced.
4. When dandelions, poppy, bramble, shepherd's purse, bulbous buttercup, and stinging nettle occur in dense populations, the soil is likely to be light and dry.
5. Sedge, buttercup, primrose, thistle, dock, comfrey, and cuckoo flower are found in wet soils.

6. Acid soils support acid-loving plants, such as cinquefoil, cornflower, pansy, daisy, foxglove, and black bindweed.
7. White mustard, bellflower, wild carrot, goatsbeard, pennycress, and horseshoe vetch are found in alkaline soil.
8. Clay or heavy soils hold moisture and favor crops such as plantain, goosegrass, annual meadow grass, and creeping buttercup.

Large populations of mixtures of several of the associated species listed should occur in order for the diagnosis to be reliable.

8.3   CLASSIFICATION OF WEEDS

Weeds may be described, according to lifecycle, in three ways:

Annual weeds. Weeds that are seasonal, appearing and completing their lifecycles either in summer or winter.

Biennial weeds. Weeds that complete their lifecycles in two seasons, the first involving vegetative growth and the second flowering and death.

Perennial weeds. Weeds with perpetual lifecycles that reappear without reseeding.

1. **Annual weeds** complete their lifecycle in one year or growing season. Most weeds are annuals. They are relatively easy to control. Many annual weed seeds can remain dormant in the soil for many years. There are two types of annual weeds, *summer annuals* and *winter annuals.* Summer annuals (warm season) germinate in spring and grow through summer. They include foxtail, crab grass, and lamb's quarter. Winter annuals (cool season) germinate in fall, live through winter, and produce seed in spring. Examples are chickweed, broadleaves like shepherd's purse, and grasses such as cheat and ryegrass.
2. **Biennial weeds** germinate in the spring of one year, live vegetatively through winter, and flower the next spring. Examples are pigweed and musk thistle.
3. **Perennial weeds** are difficult to control once they are established. They consist of many grass and non-grass species such as johnsongrass, nutsedge, and bindweed. They may be warm season (e.g., johnsongrass, yellow milksedge, morning glory, milkweed) or cool season species (e.g. wild garlic, curly dock).

Grass Versus Broadleaf

Weeds may be generally classified as either *broadleaf* or *grass weeds.* Grass weeds are very difficult to control. Most noxious weeds are grasses. Grass weeds include nutgrass, quackgrass, and bermudagrass. Broadleaf weeds include milkweed and dandelion.

Other Operational Classifications of Weeds

Weeds differ also in their impact on crop productivity and how difficult they are to control. In seed purity analysis (which provides information on the physical condition of the seed and the presence of unwanted material), evaluators check for the presence of weed seed. Seeds of weeds classified as *common restricted* or *secondary* are relatively less important to crop production in a particular production region and hence can be allowed in minimal amounts in the crop seed. However, weeds classified as *primary, prohibited,* or *noxious* are very difficult to control and are more undesirable. Consequently, crop seed cannot be contaminated by certain noxious weeds and cannot be marketed in a production region where such weeds are of economic importance.

8.4   WEED SPECIES ARE PERSISTENT IN THE LANDSCAPE

Adaptive Properties of Weeds

Why are weeds so competitive in the field and difficult to control? Weeds have specific properties that increase their survivability and make it difficult to control them in production. They produce numerous seeds (e.g., corn produces 400 seeds per plant, while a weed such as pigweed produces about 20,000 seeds per plant).

1. Weed seeds have dormancy mechanisms that enable them to avoid adverse weather conditions.
2. Weeds are more resistant to adverse environmental conditions (heat, drought, low light, pests) than are cultivated plants.
3. Certain weeds have features that are similar to the cultivated plants with which they are associated. For example, wheat is similar in growth habit to cheat and both are winter annuals, while sorghum and johnsongrass are both warm season grasses. Similarly, dodder is similar in size to alfalfa seeds and blends in readily.
4. Weeds are very competitive and spread quickly in multiple ways. When clipped, they regrow quickly and produce seed rapidly.
5. Many weeds have adaptive features that make them persist in the soil. Most noxious weeds have rhizomes or stolons.

Succession is an ecological event that describes the natural and directional changes in plant community structure over time. The phenomenon occurs when land is disturbed. The disturbance modifies the environment, destroying existing ecological niches. As new niches form, the first species to colonize the disturbed field are short-lived, have high reproductive rates, and are generally controlled by density-independent factors (these are the so-called r-selected species and differ from the k-selected species, which follow r and have opposite characteristics). In an agroecosystem, the field is often disturbed (by tillage) for planting. This activity promotes the growth of weeds (from the stirring up of weed seeds stored in the ground). Weeds are r-selected species. The frequency of tillage will determine the kinds of weeds that will arise in the field. However, cultivated crops are mostly r-selected species. Since both weeds and crop plants are r-selected species, they compete to the detriment of crop plants.

Weed–Crop Interaction

Weeds and crop plants interact in a competitive fashion, the outcome of the competition depending on such factors as weed density, time of weed appearance in the crop field, weed plant biology, and prevailing environment.

Weed Density   Generally, the more weeds there are in a cultivated field, the greater the competition for growth factors and, consequently, the greater the yield reduction. However, a few large weeds can have a greater adverse effect than many small weeds. Similarly, a high crop density is more effective in suppressing weeds.

Timing of Weeds' Appearance   There are certain times in the lifecycle of cultivated crops at which they are most adversely impacted by competition from weeds. Generally, the period of crop establishment should be weed-free, since the seedlings are most vulnerable. Fast-growing species such as corn and soybean are able to establish sooner and compete well with weeds, while slow-growing species can be devastated when weeds appear early in the growing season.

Plant Biology   The photosynthetic pathway employed by a plant to fix carbon dioxide plays a significant role in how some cultivated crops and weeds compete. C_4 plants have a higher photosynthetic rate than C_3 plants and can continue to photosynthesize under high temperature and high light intensity conditions. C_3 plants, under these conditions, photorespire. Consequently, C_4 weeds are more aggressive and difficult to control in summer when they occur in a field of C_3 crop plants. Corn is a C_4 plant and thus can compete well with many weeds in summer. In cooler periods of early spring, C_3 weeds may be better competitors.

Most weed species reproduce mainly by seed. Hence, it is an effective weed management practice to prevent weeds from flowering and producing seed (i.e., prevent buildup of weed bank in the soil).

Environment Indigenous weeds are better adapted to the locality and hence more competitive than introduced crop plants.

8.5 TROUBLESOME WEEDS

Some of the most troublesome weeds in the world are purple nutsedge *(Cyperus rotundus)*, yellow nutsedge *(Cyperus esculentus)*, bermudagrass *(Cynodon dactylon)*, barnyardgrass *(Echinochloa crusgalli)*, jungle rice *(Echinolchloa colonum)*, goosegrass *(Elensine indica)*, johnsongrass *(Sorghum halepense)*, congograss *(Imperata cylindrical)*, common purselane *(Portulaca oleracea)*, lamb's quarter *(Chenopodium album)*, large crabgrass *(Digitaria sanguinalis)*, and field bindweed *(Convolvulus arvensis)*.

Other common weeds are described in Appendix G.

8.6 MANAGING WEEDS IN CROP PRODUCTION

Weeds always occur in field cultivation. Producers can manage weeds for economic crop production by exploiting crop-weed competition to the advantage of crops, using various tactics:

1. *Mechanical/physical weed control.* Weeds may be controlled by weeding with hand tools (e.g., hoes) or inter-row cultivation (tillage) with tractor-drawn implements. Other methods include burning, flaming, mulching, mowing, solarization (heating the soil in the sun under clear plastic), and flooding (e.g., in rice fields to control red rice).
2. *Biological control.* One of the oldest methods of biological weed control is the selective grazing of plants using domestic animals (e.g., goats, sheep). The use of mycoherbicides (herbicides consisting of specially formulated disease-causing fungi) have been tried in some crop production systems.
3. *Cultural control.* Various crop production practices that improve crop compaction or reduce weed numbers are useful in controlling weeds. Tactics for increasing crop competition against weeds include
    a. Using narrow row spacing and high seeding rates to reduce open space in the field after crop establishment.
    b. Using transplants, where feasible, for a quick establishment of the crop to provide a quick ground cover.
    c. Selecting a cultivar that is able to establish an effective canopy quickly to shade out weeds.
    d. Timing of planting such that it quickly follows land preparation to avoid giving weeds a head start over the crop. Seeding at a time when germination conditions are not ideal (e.g., low temperature, low moisture) would allow the more adapted weed seeds to have a competitive advantage over the crop seed to become established ahead of the crop.
    e. Using a high enough crop density to provide an effective ground cover to shade out weeds. However, it is important that the crop density selected is not extreme, since this can promote competition within the crop itself.

Tactics for reducing weed number include the following:

    a. Planting cover crops and using crop rotations to break the cycle of weeds with the competitive crop

    b. Intercropping to fill open spaces in the field

    c. Mulching to suppress weeds

    d. Planting a living mulch to provide a good ground cover

4. *Chemical control.* Herbicides are pesticides used for controlling weeds. They are the most heavily used pesticides in U.S. agriculture. These are discussed in detail later in the chapter. Herbicides may be applied as preplant (before seeding), preemergence (before seedling emergence), or postemergence (after seedling emergence). In the production of crops such as cotton and potato, producers may facilitate harvesting by applying desiccants (to kill the foliage).

5. *Preventive measures.* Quarantine measures may be used to reduce the spread of weeds. States have their own laws restricting the spread of weed seeds through seed inspection that forbid the sale of seeds with certain weed seeds. Seed analysis includes a test for the presence of weed seeds. The producer can also reduce the spread of weed seeds by adopting certain sanitary observances on the farm (e.g., cleaning equipment), purchasing quality seeds, and composting manure before using it (fresh cow manure may contain weed seeds that are killed during composting).

9: NON-PATHOGENIC CAUSES OF PLANT DISEASE

How does an adverse environment impact the crop physiology and consequently crop production? Some disease symptoms are not caused by pathogens but by physical factors in the environment. Plants in the wild grow in regions to which they are best adapted. Modern crop production entails growing crops under cultural conditions that are significantly artificial. Because growers are able to manipulate the growing environment through the adoption of various kinds of technology (e.g., irrigation, fertilization, mulching, tillage, pesticides), crops are often cultivated in areas that are less than ideal. Consequently, modern crops are more prone to the vagaries of the weather than wild species. Improper levels of any of the environmental factors required for plant growth and development (temperature, water, light, nutrients, etc.) can produce disease symptoms in plants. Unlike pathogenic diseases, diseases caused by environmental factors are non-infectious and not transmissible.

9.1 TEMPERATURE

The best temperature range for plant production is 15° to 30°C. Perennial plants and overwintering or oversummering materials can, however, endure much lower or higher temperatures than indicated. Plant species differ in the temperature extremes they can tolerate. Further, the age of the plant (seedling or adult) also affects plant response to adverse temperature. In addition, plant parts or organs differ in their sensitivity to adverse environment. Buds and flowers are more affected than other plant parts.

High temperature induces plant diseases such as *sunscald* injuries, in which the plant parts (e.g., leaves, fruits) exposed to high sunlight intensity may become discolored, become desiccated, or develop a water-soaked appearance and blisters. Blackheart of potato is associated with excessive temperature. Warm-season crops (e.g., corn, beans) are susceptible to low temperatures. In potato, low temperature causes hydrolysis of starch to sugars that leads to caramelization and excessive sweetening of the root product. Freezing temperatures cause various kinds of frost damage. Young growth, flowers, buds, and meristematic tips are prone to frost-killing.

9.2   MOISTURE

Inadequate soil moisture, as well as atmospheric moisture, is detrimental to crop plant growth. Low soil moisture predisposes plant leaves to wilting. Nutrient uptake is also reduced under drought. Plant leaves may drop eventually or die back, reducing the photosynthetic surface. Filling of grain or fruits is adversely affected. Plants grow slowly and become stunted.

Low atmospheric moisture (i.e., low relative humidity) encourages increased transpiration and moisture loss from fruits. Plants may wilt, while fruits dehydrate and shrivel from a dry atmosphere. Low humidity is often a transient event, just as much as excessive soil moisture is infrequent. When flooding occurs, often the whole crop is lost. Poor drainage may cause flooding more frequently even from normal amounts of rain. Waterlogging creates anaerobic conditions in the soil, causing root decay in some cases.

9.3   AIR

Waterlogging, as indicated previously, reduces soil air. Blackheart of potato is a storage disease caused by excessive respiration at high temperature (leading to oxygen deficit and abnormal physiology). Air pollution from industrial sources, automobiles, and other sources is injurious to plants. Ozone injury is found in potato, soybean, tobacco, wheat, and many others. Common symptoms of pollution damage include bleaching of leaves, chlorosis, mottling, and bronzing.

9.4   NUTRITIONAL DEFICIENCY AND TOXICITY

9.5   HERBICIDE INJURY

Herbicide injury results from improper use of herbicides (e.g., improper choices, improper rate and timing of application) or collateral damage caused by drift. Crops may be accidentally killed or scorched by unintended application of herbicides.

10: PRINCIPLES OF PEST MANAGEMENT

How can crop producers manage pests in crop production so their enterprise becomes profitable? Agricultural pest management uses various methods either separately or in combination (integration). These methods may be biological, chemical, physical/ mechanical, or cultural. A pest management plan or method includes one or more of these methods.

The methods of pest management in an agroecosystem may be described as *exclusion, eradication, protection, resistance,* or *no action.*

1. *Exclusion.* This is the strategy of preventing the causal organism (pathogen, insect, etc.) from being introduced in the area in the first place. If already present, the

organism should be prevented from establishing itself. One method of exclusion is *quarantine,* the use of laws to restrict import-export of living materials. Observance of certain sanitary regulations also helps prevent entry of pests into the field. The grower should use healthy, clean seed for planting the crop.

2. *Eradication.* An established causal organism can be prevented from spreading and its population reduced, eventually eliminating it from the locality. Previous success of significance to crop production includes the eradication of the screw-worm from the southern United States and the medfly from Florida.

3. *Protection.* It takes a pathogen and a susceptible host (plus a favorable environment) for disease to occur. One approach of pest management is to prevent pathogen-host contact. This can be done by physical methods or chemicals (pesticides). This is a preemptive approach to reduce a pest population.

4. *Resistance.* Since disease resistance has a genetic basis, plant breeders can breed cultivars with resistance to important diseases and insect pests. This is also a preemptive approach for reducing pest population.

5. *No action.* Just because a pest is observed does not warrant the implementation of a management approach. Based on knowledge about the biology of the pest and other factors, the producer may be better off ignoring the pest for the time being. This is usually the case for minor pests (i.e., pests that are not economic pests of the crop being produced).

10.1 PEST ATTACK MAY BE PREVENTED BY EMPLOYING CERTAIN METHODS

Prevention is better than cure. Since pest control increases production cost, it is better to prevent pest attack from occurring in the first place. Some of the effective preventive methods are as follows:

1. *Use adapted cultivars.* Climate determines crop plant adaptation. Adapted plants have less likelihood of succumbing to disease and insect pests.

2. *Use resistant cultivars.* Where a disease or insect pest is a problem, using cultivars that are resistant to the pest will eliminate the effect of the pest on crop production.

3. *Plant high-quality seed.* The producer should always purchase seed from reputable suppliers. Good-quality seed promotes rapid seed establishment. It should have no noxious weed contamination or diseased seeds.

4. *Prepare seedbed or growing medium properly.* In field production, tillage operations should remove weeds that can jeopardize seedlings in early stages of establishment. In greenhouse production, the soil or growing medium should be sterilized against soil-borne pests.

5. *Plant at the best time.* The soil temperature should be right for seeding in order to avoid seed rot. The producer can plant early or late to make the crop escape disease.

6. *Provide adequate nutrition.* Healthy plants are able to resist pest attack much better than malnourished plants.

7. *Observe good sanitation.* Good sanitation during production reduces plant debris left on the soil after harvest. In the greenhouse, sterilizing soil, cleaning and disinfecting tools, hosing the floor, and hanging the watering hose after use are strategies for reducing disease incidence.

8. *Remove weeds.* Weeds compete directly with crop plants for crop growth factors and may harbor pests.

9. *Avoid conditions that create microclimates that are conducive to disease.* Such conditions include high humidity, improper lighting, poor aeration, and high temperature.

10.2 DESIGNING A PEST MANAGEMENT STRATEGY INVOLVES CERTAIN CONSIDERATIONS

There are certain considerations and management decisions involved in designing a management strategy. A good pest management strategy should be effective, inexpensive, and safe to the plant, environment, applicator, and consumers of the product. It should be kept in mind that disease occurrence depends on three factors—causal organism, environment, and susceptible host. The producer should exploit the lifecycle of the causal organism in pest control. The pest management strategy should attack the pest at its most vulnerable stage in the lifecycle and before it is destructive to the crop plant. The management strategy should also take into account the feeding habits of the organism (e.g., sucking or chewing).

From the plant's perspective, the management strategy should consider the stage (young or adult) when it is most vulnerable to the pest. The plant product of economic importance should also be considered. The pathogen or insect may or may not affect the product of interest directly.

The environment under which a management method measure is to be implemented is important. Certain methods of management work best under enclosed conditions. Weather conditions (wind, rain, and temperature) affect the success and effectiveness of the method of management. The pest management decision-making process is a dynamic one. In the management cycle, the farmer or producer makes a decision based on various pertinent information, implements the appropriate management strategy, monitors the crop and the pest status, and then revisits the original decision. The producer must be familiar with pest management strategies. He or she must decide when to manage pests. To do this, the following pieces of information are needed.

Density of Pest Population

Pest population density is determined by sampling methods. Sampling of pests is challenging because their dispersal pattern is not uniform but clumped. This is so because pests tend to lay eggs in clumps or clusters and tend to gather in microhabitats of ideal conditions in the field. In microbes, bioassays may be needed to identify specific strains. Sometimes (in the case of large insects), the pests can be counted. On other occasions, the surface of the plant covered or damaged is the basis of estimating pest population density.

Estimate of Expected Crop Damage

Generally, yield decreases as pest population density increases. There is a level of pest population below which yield loss is negligible. This is the crop *damage threshold.* The amount of damage that can be tolerated differs among crops. Where the economic part is the leaf (e.g., tobacco), leaf damage and defoliation are intolerable. However, in a grain crop such as soybean, even 20% defoliation or more may be inconsequential to crop yield.

Economic injury. The level of pest incidence at which the producer would experience an economic loss of product.

Economics of Management Strategy Being Considered

The producer needs to estimate the cost of implementing the management strategy against the expected return (i.e., price expected from the yield). Cost/benefit analysis is critical in pest management. The **economic injury** level is an estimate of the pest popu-

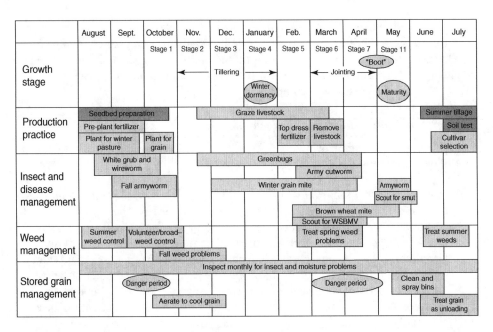

	August	Sept.	October	Nov.	Dec.	January	Feb.	March	April	May	June	July
Growth stage			Stage 1	Stage 2	Stage 3 ← Tillering →	Stage 4 Winter dormancy	Stage 5	Stage 6 ← Jointing →	Stage 7	Stage 11 "Boot" Maturity		
Production practice	Seedbed preparation Pre-plant fertilizer Plant for winter pasture			Plant for grain	Graze livestock		Top dress fertilizer	Remove livestock		Summer tillage Soil test Cultivar selection		
Insect and disease management	White grub and wireworm		Fall armyworm		Greenbugs Army cutworm Winter grain mite Brown wheat mite Scout for WSBMV				Armyworm Scout for smut			
Weed management	Summer weed control	Volunteer/broad– weed control	Fall weed problems				Treat spring weed problems			Treat summer weeds		
Stored grain management	Inspect monthly for insect and moisture problems		Danger period	Aerate to cool grain				Danger period		Clean and spray bins	Treat grain as unloading	

FIGURE 3 The different stages in the growth of a crop plant may be plagued by different kinds of pests. A crop producer should have a detailed schedule of pest control for a particular crop. The strategy should include preventive measures as well as control measures. (Source: Adapted and modified from Oklahoma State University Fact Sheet.)

lation density at which the value of the crop yield loss prevented is equal to the cost of implementing a treatment. The *action threshold* is defined as the pest population density at which treatment is necessary to prevent economic injury or prevent the pest population from reaching the economic injury level. It is best to implement a treatment program at a pest density that is slightly below the economic injury level, so that the possibility of exceeding this level is prevented. Further, pests develop at different rates such that in certain cases the window of opportunity between sampling and the attainment of economic injury level by the pest is very narrow.

Frequently, the crop producer is confronted with more than one pest that may occur simultaneously or in succession. These pests may have different biological and ecological characteristics. The management schedule of pests in wheat production in Oklahoma is summarized in Figure 3.

11: METHODS OF PEST MANAGEMENT

Pests in crop production are managed by one of five major methods: *biological, cultural, legislative, physical/mechanical,* and *chemical.*

11.1 BIOLOGICAL PEST MANAGEMENT

Biological pest management (or *biological pest*) **control** is the use of one organism to manage the population of another organism. This is the oldest method of pest management. Biological pest management is based on the ecological principles of parasitism and predation. Every organism has its natural enemies. This design of nature ensures that no

Biological pest management control. The use of a natural enemy to control a pest.

one organism dominates nature through overpopulation. Natural disasters (e.g., drought) can offset this equilibrium, jeopardizing certain organisms. The goal of ecological pest management is to manipulate various biotic factors in the production environment to maintain pest populations at levels below the economic threshold (above which the crop being produced suffers economic injury).

Strategies of Biological Pest Management

Crop producers may exploit and manage certain natural defense mechanisms of plants to control pests. Some of these strategies are

1. *Parasitism.* The alfalfa weevil is a host for the stingless wasp *(Microstomus aethipoides),* which hatches inside and eventually destroys the weevil. The cyst nematode *(Heterodera)* is parasitized by fungi (e.g., *Catenaria auxilianis).*
2. *Prey-predator relationships.* Predators feed on other living organisms (prey). Certain birds prey on insects and rodents. *Carabid* beetles prey on aphids and caterpillars, while lacewings *(Chryosopa)* prey on spiders and other insects.
3. *Structural.* Certain plant anatomical features (e.g., thick cuticle, pubescence) interfere with feeding and spread of pathogens and insect pests. Sucking insects are unable to penetrate thick cuticles, while pubescence interferes with oviposition of certain insects.
4. *Chemicals.* Certain plant extracts have insecticidal action—for example, pyrethrum from chrysanthemum and nicotine from tobacco. These toxins discourage feeding by susceptible insects.
5. *Phytoallexins.* Phytoallexins are chemicals exuded by certain plants when they become injured. These chemicals are toxic to the invading insects or pathogen.
6. *Repellents.* Plants such as onion and garlic have strong scents that repel aphids. Similarly, marigold repels nematodes.
7. *Trap plants (alternative host).* Pests have preferences for host plants. For example, slugs prefer lettuce to chrysanthemum. Thus, in the production of chrysanthemum, lettuce may be planted in the field as "decoy" plants, or trap plants. In bean and squash production, planting of corn around the field attracts aphids away from these crops. By the time the aphids reach the bean plants, they would have lost much of the viral infection that they are carrying. Trap crops are also used to control nematodes. For example, *Clotalaria* plants trap the larvae of root-knot nematodes.
8. *Biocontrol.* Prior to storage, fruits may be treated with a suspension of the bacterium *Bacillus subtilis* to delay brown rot caused by the fungus *Monilinia fruiticola.*
9. *Microbial sprays (biopesticides).* Artificially cultured *Bacillus thuringiensis* is prepared as a spray application for controlling cutworms, corn borers, and other caterpillars.
10. *Resistant cultivars.* Crop producers may use cultivars with resistance against diseases and other pests of agronomic importance.

Advantages of Biological Pest Management

The advantages of biological pest management include the following:

1. They are safer to apply.
2. Resistant cultivars are cheaper than pesticides.
3. Chemicals are harmful to the user and the general environment.

Disadvantages of Biological Pest Management

The major disadvantages of biological pest management include the following:

1. Handling of living organisms is more difficult than chemicals.
2. Availability and application are limited to relatively few crop plants.

11.2 CULTURAL PEST MANAGEMENT

Crop producers may manipulate the way in which plants are cultivated to manage pests in the field. This can be accomplished in several ways:

1. *Crop rotation.* Crop rotation is the production plan of growing different crops on sections of the same piece of land or plot in a predetermined cycle, such that the same crop is not planted in the same section in successive seasons. Specific pests attack crops. Planting the same crop in the same location season after season leads to a buildup of certain pests, especially soil-borne pests such as nematodes. Crop rotation reduces pest buildup.
2. *Sanitation.* Pathogens and other pests overwinter or oversummer in plant remains from harvesting and other debris. Diseased plant materials should be incinerated.
3. *Resistant cultivars (genetics).* Plant breeders have bred cultivars that are resistant to many crop pests. One of the early successes of agbiotechnology is the development of pest-resistant crop varieties—specifically, herbicide-resistant and insect-resistant crop varieties. The use of genetic resistance in crop production eliminates or reduces the use of pesticides in crop production. There are limitations to the use of pest-resistant varieties in production. Disease-resistant varieties are not available in most crops. Furthermore, the resistance is not indefinite because pathogens may adapt to overcome the resistance. Sometimes, having disease resistance in a crop variety causes a reduction in overall productivity because of a possible linkage of the resistance genes to undesirable agronomic genes.
4. *Mulching.* The application of a plastic mulch traps heat in the soil. This may be used to sterilize field soil (solarization). The heat kills soil pathogens and weeds. Certain mulches may leach out phytoallexins that inhibit the growth and development of plants.
5. *Host eradication.* This strategy is employed to preempt the spread of disease. On a small scale, infected plants may be rogued (removed) from the field. On a more drastic scale, a disease outbreak is curtailed by destroying all the crops in the region that are susceptible.
6. *Planting date.* Certain pests appear late in the growing season. Early planting enables a crop to escape infection. On the other hand, aphids that transmit barley yellow dwarf virus (BYDV) are more active before the first hard frost. Hence, planting wheat before the tessian fly free date makes it more susceptible to BYDY than wheat planted later.
7. *Soil reaction.* Liming to increase pH helps to control certain fungal pathogens, while lower pH controls potato scab.
8. *Drainage.* Certain pests (e.g., nematode) prefer moist conditions. Drainage improves aeration and prevents non-pathogenic diseases induced by oxygen deficiency.
9. *Wider spacing (crop density).* Wider spacing improves air circulation around the plants and reduces the occurrence of humid microclimates that support pathogens.

Cultural pest management (control). The manipulation of crop growth environment and cultural practices to control a pest.

10. *Tillage.* No-till methods decrease soil temperature and increase soil moisture. This condition favors certain pests. Soybean cyst nematode may be spread in the direction of tillage.

11.3 LEGISLATIVE PEST MANAGEMENT

Legislative pest management (control). The pest management strategy that depends on government regulations to curtail the spread of disease by monitoring and restricting transfer of biological materials across borders.

Plant quarantine is the use of legislation to control the movement (import-export) of plants across certain designated borders. This preemptive and preventive action is aimed at reducing the spread of disease. In the United States, government intervention in movement of biological materials was formally introduced with the enactment of the *Plant Quarantine Act of 1912*. These laws are developed for local, regional, and international scenarios. For example, if a country's primary agricultural crop is wheat, quarantine laws will be very strictly enforced to avoid the introduction of wheat germplasm from parts of the world that are known to be infested with pests. Whereas the laws may be enforced, the success and effectiveness of plant quarantine depend on the experience of the inspector in detecting pathogens when they occur. Certification programs (e.g., seed certification) are also used to ensure that disease-free seeds and plant materials are sold to growers. What other factors can you suggest that are critical in the success of implementing a quarantine measure?

Plant quarantine. The use of specific laws to control the movement of infected organisms.

11.4 PHYSICAL/MECHANICAL PEST MANAGEMENT

A variety of **physical and mechanical management methods** may be implemented to effect this method of pest control:

Mechanical pest management (control). The pest management method in which mechanical devices or physical agents are used to trap and destroy pests.

1. *Mechanical traps.* Traps may be set to catch large vertebrates such as rodents, while flycatchers are used in the greenhouse to trap insects.
2. *Handpicking.* In small-scale crop production operations, caterpillars and larger bugs may be physically picked up from plants and destroyed.
3. *Barriers.* Mechanical barriers such as fences and tree wraps are used to keep certain pests away from plants.
4. *Tillage.* Tillage operations may be used to reduce weed populations to some extent. The operation brings soil pests to the soil surface, where they are subjected to desiccation. However, disturbance of soil may also favor new weeds that otherwise were buried and lay dormant.
5. *Heat treatment.* Solarization (in the field) and sterilization (in the greenhouse) use heat to control pathogens in the soil.
6. *Radiation.* Ultraviolet radiation is used to sterilize the greenhouse and other enclosures. Gamma radiation is used to prolong the shelf life of produce in storage.

11.5 CHEMICAL PEST MANAGEMENT

Chemicals used to manage pests are called **pesticides**. They are designed to kill, hence the suffix *cide* in their names.

Pesticides. Chemicals designed to destroy, prevent, repel, or mitigate any form of life declared to be a pest.

General Classification of Pesticides

Pesticides may be classified in several ways: target pest, type of material, chemical structure, mode of action, and formulation.

1. *Target pest.* On the basis of the type of organisms on which they are used, pesticides may be grouped into two broad groups: those used to manage unwanted plants

Table 2 General Groups of Pesticides

Pesticides Used to Manage Unwanted Plants
1. Herbicides: used to manage weeds (unwanted plants)
   a. Preemergence: applied before the appearance of a specified weed or crop
   b. Postemergence: applied after the appearance of a specified weed or crop
2. Defoliants: used to cause premature leafdrop to facilitate harvesting (e.g., of soybean, cotton, and tomatoes)
3. Dessicants: used to cause preharvest drying of plants that do not normally shed their leaves (e.g., rice, corn, small grains) or drying of actively growing plant parts when seed or other plant parts are developed but only partially mature

Pesticides Used to Manage Unwanted Animals
1. Those used to manage insects: insecticides
2. Those used to manage vertebrate pests
   a. Small animals
   b. Large animals
   c. Birds
   d. Reptiles
3. Pathogens: cause diseases
   a. Fungi
   b. Bacteria
   c. Viruses
   d. Mycoplasmas
   e. Nematodes

(weeds) and those used to manage unwanted animals (Table 2). Pesticides used to manage unwanted plants are generally called *herbicides.* Pesticides used to manage animal pests are usually classified to reflect the category of animal targeted:

Insecticides: for insects

Fungicides: for fungi

Nematicides: for nematodes

Rodenticides: for rodents

Molluscides: for mollusks

Miticides: for mites

Aviacides: for birds

Bacteriacides: for bacteria

2. *Type of material.* Pesticides may be developed from *natural products* isolated from plants (e.g., pyrethrum and nicotine) or other living organisms, or they may be developed from *artificial compounds* or *synthetic products.*
3. *Chemical structure of the compound.* Based on the *active ingredient* (the chemical compound responsible for the killing action of the pesticide), pesticides may be classified as either *inorganic* or *organic* (Table 3). Inorganic pesticides (e.g., Bordeaux mixture) are on the decline. Natural organic compounds, also called *botanicals,* are derived from plants. Examples are pyrethrum, nicotine, and rotenone. *Synthetic organic compounds* are effective against a wide variety of insects and other pests. **Organochlorines** (or

Organochlorines.
Pesticides containing chlorinated hydrocarbons as the active ingredient.

Table 3 Classification of Herbicides Based on Chemistry of Active Ingredients

Inorganic compounds (inorganics)
Organic compounds (organics)
  1. Natural (botanicals)
  2. Synthetics
     a. Organochlorines (chlorinated hydrocarbons)
     b. Organophosphates
     c. Carbamates
     d. Pyrethroids
  3. Fumigants
  4. Spray oils
  5. Biologicals (microbial insecticides)

Organophosphates.
Pesticides containing phosphorus in organic compounds.

chlorinated hydrocarbons) are not readily biodegradable and persist in the food chain. Examples are DDT (dichlorodiphenyl trichloroethane), chlordane, and lindane. **Organophosphates** have shorter residual action in the environment and are safer to use. Examples are malathion and diazinon. Organic pesticides are more selective and pose less environmental danger. Other classes of pesticides are *carbamates* (e.g., carbaryl), *formamidines* (e.g., amitraz), *organotins* (e.g., fenbutatin), *biologicals* (living organisms, such as *Bacillus thuringiensis* spores) and *pyrethroids* (or synthetic pyrethrins, such as permethrin).

4. *Mode of entry and action.* Pesticides kill pests in a variety of ways:
  a. *Contact action.* They are applied before the infection occurs. Hence, they are less efficacious than systemic pesticides. They are easily washed by rain or sprinkler irrigation. Contact insecticides kill upon making physical contact with the target organism. Examples are malathion, manconeb, captan, and thiram.
  b. *Stomach action (stomach poison).* This kind of insecticide kills upon ingestion. It is effective against chewing insects such as caterpillars and beetles.
  c. *Systemic action.* Systemic insecticides are effective at controlling sucking and chewing insects. Once ingested, the poison moves through the entire organism. They can be applied after the infection. They are absorbed and translocated throughout the plant. Examples are benomyl and metalaxyl.
  d. *Repellent action.* Some pesticides do not kill pests but repel them with strong odors.
  e. *Fumigants.* These pesticides attack the respiratory system of the target organism.

Formulation. The chemical state (solid, liquid, or gas) in which a pesticide is manufactured for use.

5. **Formulation**. Pesticides contain *active ingredients* (a.i.) that are responsible for the killing of target pests. These ingredients are mixed with inert substances to create preparations that facilitate the application or use of pesticides. The inert substances also reduce the toxicity of the pesticides and make them safer to handle. Pesticides may be formulated as *liquid* or *dry* formulations.
  a. *Liquid formulations.* The common liquid formulations of pesticides include the following:
    1. Aerosols. These have low concentrations of active ingredients and are propelled by an inert pressurized gas. They are commonly used indoors.

Aerosol. A chemical that is applied by propelling it through pressurized gas.

    2. *Emulsifiable concentrates.* The pesticide contains an active ingredient and an emulsifier that are dissolved in petroleum solvents and prepared in high concentration. They are diluted (e.g., by mixing with water) before use and applied with a sprayer.
    3. *Flowables.* These chemicals are fine suspensions of active ingredients.

4. *Fumigants.* The active ingredient is carried in a volatile liquid. Fumigants are applied to the soil or used in storehouses.
5. *Solutions and ultra low volume solutions.* These chemicals are completely dissolved in water.
   b. *Dry formulations.* The common dry formulations include the following:
   1. *Baits.* The active ingredient is mixed with food or feed. Baits are commonly used in the storehouse or to trap rodents and other mammals in the field.
   2. *Dusts.* The active ingredient is carried in fine talc, clay, or some other material. Dusts are prone to drift (blown by wind).
   3. *Granules.* Granules are formulations that are in the form of granular particles. Herbicides, nematicides, and pesticides used in managing soil pests are often formulated as granules.
   4. *Wettable powders.* These are formulations in the form of fine powders that require mixing with water before application.

Adjuvants

Pesticide formulations may include compounds that enhance the biological activity. These compounds are called activator *adjuvants* and include **surfactants**, vegetable oils, crop oils, and crop oil concentrate. These additives improve the emulsifying, dispersing, spreading, wetting, and other surface modifying properties of liquids. Sometimes, certain compounds called *spray modifiers* are added to the spray solution for various purposes during field application (e.g., drift control).

Surfactants. Substances that can modify the nature of surfaces (expecially reduction in surface tension).

General Classification of Herbicides

Herbicides are commonly classified by selectivity, mode of action, timing or application, and chemistry (Table 4). *Selective herbicides* (narrow spectrum) and kill only certain plant species. Commonly, there are broadleaf and narrowleaf (grass) herbicides. *Nonselective herbicides* are broad action (broad spectrum) and kill indiscriminately, killing both grasses and broadleaf plants (e.g., Roundup®). They are best applied where all plants are not desirable, as is the case around railway tracks.

Herbicides may also kill by *contact* or *translocation* through the plant (systemic). Some herbicides are designed to be applied before sowing crop seed (called *preplant herbicides*), before weeds or crop seedlings emerge (called **preemergence herbicides**), or after the crop has established (called **postemergence herbicides**). Most herbicides in use are organic-based. They include organic arsenicals and phenoxy herbicides, the latter group being hormonal in action (e.g., 2,4-D).

Preemergence herbicides. Herbicides applied before weeds or crop seedlings emerge.

Postemergence herbicides. Herbicides applied to control weeds after crop establishment.

Herbicide Mode of Action Groups

Herbicides have been designed to interfere with various physiological pathways and growth processes. The major modes of action of herbicide groups are as follows:

1. *Contact herbicides.* This group of herbicides kills plant tissue upon contact. Hence, they are applied directly to the target plants. Examples include diquat and paraquat. They are translocated from the point of contact to the point of action.
2. *Growth regulators.* Some herbicides are growth regulators and sometimes are used in research studies in appropriate doses to perform need functions (e.g., 2,4-D is used in tissue culture experiments). When absorbed, these herbicides disrupt plant growth. Examples are phenoxy acids (e.g., 2,4-D), benzoic acids (e.g., dicamba), and pyridines (e.g., picloram). Growth regulators are mainly effective on dicot plants, in which they cause malformation of the leaves and stems.

Table 4 A Classification of Herbicides

Based on Selectivity
1. Selective herbicides
2. Non-selective herbicides

Based on Site of Action
1. Contact herbicides
2. Translocated herbicides

Based on Timing of Application
1. Preplant
2. Preemergence
3. postemergence

Based on Chemistry of Active Ingredient
1. Inorganic herbicides
2. Organic herbicides
    a. Organic arsenical
    b. Phenoxy herbicides
    c. Diphenyl ethers
    d. Substituted amide
    e. Substituted ureas
    f. Carbamates
    g. Triazines
    h. Aliphatic acids
    i. Arylaliphatic acid
    j. Substituted nitrites
    k. Bipyridyliums

---

3. *Photosynthetic inhibitors.* This group of herbicides interferes with the function of the photosystems (PS) of the electron transport system in photosynthesis. Inhibitors of PS I are contact herbicides (e.g., diquat and paraquat). The treated weeds become chlorotic and necrotic. Herbicides that inhibit PS II site A include the triazines (e.g., atrazine) and triazinones (e.g., metbuzin). Others affect the PS II site B (e.g., phenylureas, such as diuron, and nitriles, such as bromoxynil).
4. *Pigment inhibitors.* Pigment inhibitors block the formation of carotene in chloroplasts, causing the leaves to bleach and consequently to be unable to perform photosynthetic functions. Examples include triazoles (e.g., amitrole) and pyridazinones (e.g., norplurazon).
5. *Meristematic inhibitors.* Meristems are the growing points in the plants. When these are destroyed, plants exhibit various malformations of the growing points. Some herbicides are applied to the soil for various reasons (e.g., they are sensitive to light). Dinitroanilines (e.g., trifluralin) are such herbicides. They inhibit root growth and development. Similarly, amides (e.g., alachlor, acetachlor) and carbamothioates (e.g., EPTC) are applied to the soil. They cause malformations in the shoots.
6. *Enzyme pathway inhibitors.* These herbicides block key steps in the metabolic pathways in plants by targeting specific enzymes. Examples include acetyl CoA carboxylase (ACCase) inhibitors (e.g., sethoxydim) and acetolactate synthase inhibitors, of which there are sulfonylureas (e.g., chlorimuron), imidazolinones (e.g., imazethapyr and imazaquin), and sulfonamides (e.g., flumetsulam). There are

also inhibitors of 5-enolpyruvylshikimate-3-phosphate (ESPS) (e.g., glyphosate), glutamine synthetase inhibitors (e.g., glufosinate), and protoporphyrinogen oxidase inhibitors (e.g., lactofen and fomesafen). These inhibitors cause a wide variety of symptoms (e.g., stunting, chlorosis, necrosis, death, purpling or reddening of plant parts) in treated plants, depending on the species.

Pesticide Toxicity

Pesticides are designed to kill pests; thus, users must handle them with great caution. They are assigned a *hazard rating,* which is a function of toxicity and exposure. **Toxicity** is a measure of the degree to which a chemical is poisonous to an organism. Toxicity depends on several factors. A pesticide that is toxic as a concentrate may not be as hazardous as a granule. Further, a pesticide of low toxicity may become very hazardous when used at a high concentration. The frequency of use and the experience of the operator may increase or decrease the hazard level. Toxicity is normally measured by the **lethal dose (LD$_{50}$)** of the chemical. The LD$_{50}$ is the milligrams of a toxicant per kilogram of body weight of an organism that is capable of killing 50% of the organisms under the test conditions. The higher the LD$_{50}$, the less poisonous or toxic the chemical (Table 5). The active ingredient may be an inorganic compound, a natural organic compound, or a synthetic compound.

Toxicity. A measure of the degree to which a chemical is poisonous to an organism.

Lethal dose (LD$_{50}$). A measure of toxicity that indicates the milligrams of a toxicant per kilogram of body weight of an organism that is capable of killing 50% of the organism under test conditions.

Active Ingredient. The ingredient in a pesticide that determines its effectiveness.

Choosing and Using Pesticides Safely

There are certain general steps that may be followed by a crop producer in the decision-making process of pest management (Figure 4).

1. *Detection.* The problem (pest) must first be detected. This may be by visual observation or other tests. Early detection is the key to success in pest control.

Table 5 LD$_{50}$ Values of Selected Pesticides

Pesticide	LD$_{50}$
Fungicides	
Captan	9,000–15,000
Maneb	6,750–7,500
Thiram	780
Zineb	8,000
PCNB	1,500–2,000
Insecticides	
Carbaryl	500–850
Dursban	97–279
Malathion	1,000–1,375
Pyrethrum	820–1,870
Rotenone	50–75
Herbicides	
DCPA	3,000
EPCT	1,600
Simazine	5,000
Oxyzalin	10,000

Source: Extracted (and modified) from extension bulletin B-751, Farm Science Series, Michigan State University, University Cooperative Extension Service.

FIGURE 4 Pest management involves a number of steps, starting with detection through choice and application of a desirable method. Record keeping is an integral part of a good and effective pest management program.

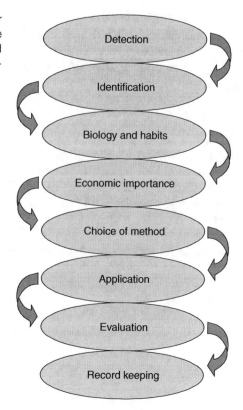

2. *Identification.* After observing a problem, the producer must make a positive identification of the insect or pathogen. This may be done with the help of an expert from, for example, the Cooperative Extension Service.

3. *Biology and habits.* As indicated previously, an organism has a lifecycle with stages in which it is destructive to plants. There are also stages in the lifecycle in which the pest is most vulnerable. It is important to know the feeding habit of the pest (nocturnal, piercing, chewing, etc.) For example, once the European corn borer has penetrated the stalk of the plant, it is ineffective to spray against it.

4. *Economic importance.* It is important to know the economic injury the pest can cause to crop production. If the threshold population does not occur, it may not be economical to implement pest control measures.

5. *Choice of method of control.* The method that is most effective, most economical, safest (least toxic), and easiest to apply, with minimal environmental consequences, should be selected. Persistent herbicides control weeds for a long time. Atrazine is widely used because it is effective and relatively inexpensive.

6. *Application.* When using a chemical, the best formulation, correct rate, proper equipment, best environmental conditions, and timeliness of application are critical considerations for success.

7. *Evaluation.* The producer should evaluate the effectiveness of an application to determine if there is a need to repeat the application. If repeat application is needed, there may be a need to modify the rates, timing, or some other aspect of the application.

8. *Record keeping.* It is important to keep good records of all pesticide applications. This will provide records for computing production costs and other future needs.

Pesticide label: read it

A pesticide label displays certain specific pieces of information for the effective and safe use of the pesticide. The key pieces of information are

1. Name of product (includes trademark name and chemical name)
2. Company name, address, and logo (where applicable)
3. Type of pesticide (e.g., fungicide or insecticide)
4. Product chemical analysis [active ingredient(s), proportions of component compounds, product common name, chemical name(s) of ingredient(s), formulation]
5. Target pest(s)
6. Directions for proper and effective use, plus any restrictions
7. Hazard statements (appear as *caution, warning, danger* messages)
8. Storage and disposal directions
9. Government administrative stipulations (e.g., EPA approval and number)
10. Net content

Of the names of the product, the chemical name is most unwieldy and technical—for example,

Common name: Cyanazine

Chemical name: 2-((4-chloro-6-(ethylamino)-s-triazin-2-yl)amino)-2-methylpropionitrile

Trade name: Bladex® 4L (the "4" indicates that the concentration of the active ingredient is 4%; the "L" indicates the formulation is liquid)

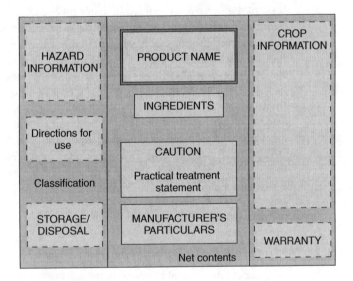

Pesticides are designed to kill and should therefore be handled very carefully all the time. The following are some measures to be observed for the safe application of pesticides.

1. Select the correct pesticide for the job; choose the safer alternative all the time.
2. Purchase only the quantity needed for a job to avoid the need to store leftovers.
3. Read the label on the container and follow directions carefully.
4. Wear protective gear.
5. Do not eat while handling chemicals.
6. Apply under the best environmental conditions.
7. Keep the pesticide out of the reach of children and pets.

8. Apply with care and caution.
9. Know what to do in case of an accident.
10. Clean the applicator after application.
11. Store the pesticide properly, if needed.
12. Be careful about applying near the time of crop harvest.

Methods of Application of Pesticides

In terms of the target to which the pesticide is applied, pesticides may be applied in the following general ways:

1. *Foliar application.* The pesticide is directed at the leaf so that it penetrates the plant through pores (stomata) directly into the plant system. Foliar application is effective against fungal diseases that attack the leaf tissue.
2. *Soil treatment.* In soil treatment, the pesticide is applied to the soil, not the plant directly. Plants absorb the poison through their roots during the process of extraction of water and nutrients. Formulations used for soil application are usually granules. Soil treatments may be fumigants (e.g., chloropicrin), non-fumigant fungicides (e.g., PCNB), or non-fumigant nematicides (e.g., carbofuran).
3. *Seed treatment.* Seed treatment usually takes the form of coating the seed with a pesticide prior to planting. This is sometimes called *seed dressing* and is commonly used for the control of fungal diseases. Seed treatment may be either contact (e.g., captan, thiram) or systemic (e.g., metalaxyl). The protection of contact treatment lasts through the period shortly after emergence of the seedling.
4. *Fumigation.* Fumigation involves using gases and is best done in an enclosed environment. Nematodes and soil fungal pathogens such as *Pythium* may be managed by using soil fumigants. Soil fumigants include chloropicrin and dichloropropene. They work best in moist and loose soil at temperatures between 50° and 75°F. Wet soil impedes diffusion. Dry soil encourages loss. Movement is also impeded by soil compaction and cold soil temperature.

The most common method of pesticide application in the United States is ground application (Figure 5).

Methods of Herbicide Application

In terms of the methods of placement, herbicides may be applied in one of several ways, taking into account the location, the nature of the weed problem, the formulation, equipment, and other factors. Granules are suitable for *broadcast application.* When narrow strips of weeds are to be controlled, *band application* is suitable. Single plants may break through cracks in concrete walkways, or weeds may be located in hard-to-reach areas. These weeds are controlled by *spot application* or treatment.

The following are general guidelines for effective weed control:

1. Identify the weed species correctly.
2. Assess the level of weed infestation.
3. Select the appropriate herbicide for the weed species present.
4. Apply at the correct time (e.g., preemergence, postemergence).
5. Apply at the correct rate (prepare correctly and use well-calibrated equipment).
6. Treat the area adequately.

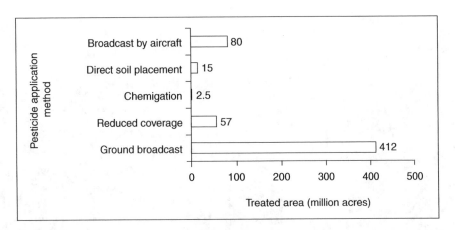

FIGURE 5 Ground broadcast is the most common method of pesticide application, accounting for 412 million acres of treated cropland in the 1994 to 1995 cropping season. Corn and soybeans received the most broadcast application. A total of 356 million acres (representing 87% of the total treated area) were treated by ground broadcast application. Chemigation is not a widely used method of pesticide application. (Source: USDA)

7. Consider the weather factors (no rain in forecast, no strong winds).
8. Consider the age of the weed plants (younger plants are easier to control).
9. Consider the ground cover and soil type (organic soils and clay soils absorb pesticides).

Role of Plant Growth Stage and Stress on Herbicide Efficacy

Weeds are best controlled when they are young. They are more responsive to herbicide treatment at a tender stage than when they are grown. At a more advanced age, weeds require more of the herbicide (especially if a contact herbicide) to control them. A more serious problem, however, is that generally a crop is more likely to be injured when herbicides are applied when the plants are bigger. Weed control is more effective when herbicides are applied to actively growing plants. Weeds are less responsive under stress (e.g., drought). On the other hand, it appears that crop plants are more susceptible to herbicide injury when under stress (e.g., drought, disease, nutritional).

Factors Affecting Pollution of Surface Water and Groundwater

Pollution of surface water and groundwater by agrochemicals is affected by factors such as soil CEC, depth of water table, erosion, precipitation leaching, soil texture, plant residue on the soil surface, and rate and timing of application of chemicals. A high CEC indicates the presence of a large amount of soil colloids (e.g., clay, organic matter). The pollutants in the soil solution can be temporarily removed by CEC. Pollutants will have a higher water table sooner than a lower water table. High rainfall promotes high surface runoff and erosion into surface water. Plant residue on the soil surface can slow soil erosion and surface runoff. Coarse-textured soils allow quicker water infiltration and thereby reduce surface runoff that carries pollutants into surface water. Applying agrochemicals at rates higher than recommended, or when the pest pressure is low, leaves excess chemicals to be washed into the soil and surface water. Rainfall after an application of pesticide will wash more of the chemicals into the soil than when there is a dry period after application.

FIGURE 6 Application of pesticides in the field requires the use of various kinds of equipment, depending on the acreage to be treated, type of crop, type of chemical to be applied, and the economic situation of the producer. The major methods of pesticide application are ground broadcast, reduced coverage, chemigation, direct soil placement, and aircraft.

11.6 PESTICIDE APPLICATION EQUIPMENT

Application equipment may be designed for small areas or large ones. Some field applicators are shown in Figure 6. Consult the Internet reference provided at the end of the chapter for more examples.

11.7 PESTICIDE INJURY TO CROPS

The goal of pesticide application is to kill the target pest without injuring the crop. However, crop plants may be injured as a result of the operator's inexperience or carelessness but also as a result of the weather conditions at the time of application, the genotype, the characteristics of the chemicals, and the method of application.

1. *Genotype sensitivity.* Certain plants are naturally sensitive to certain chemicals. For example, certain plants are intolerant of fluoride in domestic water and are injured when domestic water is used for irrigation. Plant sensitivity may also manifest at only a certain stage of the lifecycle. For example, some herbicides (e.g., Accent) must be applied before corn plants reach 20 inches tall.
2. *Weather factors.* Pesticides (especially sprays and dusts) are best applied when the air is relatively still, in order to reduce the chance of drift that can damage unintended targets. However, an intended target may be damaged under proper weather conditions. For example, rainfall following an application of preemergence herbicide may cause the chemical to move down to reach the crop seed and possibly injure it.
3. *Residual effect (persistence).* Generally, herbicides that persist longer in the soil are more effective in controlling weeds. However, the residual effect of an herbicide applied to a previous crop may injure the germinating seedlings of the current crop (e.g., Scepter applied to soybean may injure corn in a rotation). Persistence of herbicides in the soil is favored by cool temperatures and a dry environment. Herbicides used in crop rotation should be applied with care, making sure to select with the crop sequence in mind.

4. *Pesticide formulation.* Pesticides may be formulated in various forms (e.g., granules, dust, liquid). Some formulations are safer to handle and are less injurious in certain situations.

5. *Rate of application.* Producers should pay attention to the recommended rates of application of herbicides for effective, safe, and economic application. A higher than normal rate will increase the persistence of the herbicide in the soil and will have a higher chance of crop injury.

6. *Method of application.* Herbicides such as Roundup® may be safely applied as a preplant without injury to crop plants. It may be used in the lawn while the turfgrass is dormant. Some herbicides are more injurious to crop plants when applied as granules to the soil than when applied as foliar sprays and vice versa.

7. *Pesticide interaction.* Applying different pesticides together may result in severe crop injury if the pesticides are incompatible (e.g., applying Asure II and Blazer together is injurious to soybean). Accidental mixtures or contamination may happen when equipment is not properly cleaned between applications.

11.8 FACTORS AFFECTING PERSISTENCE OF SOIL-RESIDUAL HERBICIDES

Herbicides that are persistent in the soil are desirable for their long action. However, the residual effect may have potential adverse effect in a crop rotation system. Factors that influence herbicide persistence in the soil and its effect on plants include the following:

1. *Soil moisture.* High soil moisture promotes leaching of herbicides and other soil water-soluble nutrients. Further, it also enhances the rate of biological degradation of herbicides. Consequently, the persistence of herbicides in the soil is less in wetter soils than in dry soils.

2. *Soil temperature.* Temperature accelerates the microbial degradation of soil organic matter, a material that binds and holds herbicides in the soil. Further, the herbicides themselves are prone to more rapid decomposition under high temperatures. Hence, herbicides will persist longer in the soil under cool soil temperatures.

3. *Soil pH.* Soil pH may increase or decrease soil herbicide persistence. Herbicides belonging to the classes of triazines and sulfonylureas tend to persist longer in alkaline soils, whereas clomazone persists longer at acidic pH of 5.9 or less.

4. *Soil microbes.* Soil microbes may directly decompose the herbicide or decompose soil organic matter that has high affinity for some herbicides. Microbial activity is enhanced by warm temperatures.

5. *Rate of application.* Pesticides applied at higher rates persist longer in the soil than those applied at lower rates. It is important to apply herbicides at recommended rates.

6. *Timing of application.* Late application of a herbicide as a result of late planting of the crop means that the gap between the current crop and the next crop in the rotation will be shorter. The persistent herbicide is more likely to be present in the soil at a higher concentration at the time of seeding the next crop.

7. *Type of crop cultivar.* Crop species differ in sensitivity to residual herbicides. Similarly, cultivars of the same crop differ in their sensitivity to residual herbicides in the soil. The producer should be aware of crop and cultivar sensitivity and develop the appropriate crop sequence in the rotation cycle, as well as the proper choice of herbicides to apply. Oat is intolerant of residual atrazine. Similarly, metribuz (Sencor) is injurious to some wheat and barley cultivars.

The producer should consult the manufacturer's instructions for application of herbicides in order to make the correct decisions. The length of delay in the planting date of the next crop following an application of a herbicide depends on the crop and the herbicide. For example, when Raptor (an imidazolinone) is used on soybean, a 3-month delay of seeding is recommended for wheat following soybean in the rotation, a 4-month delay for barley or rye, and a 9-month delay for corn or tobacco.

12: INTEGRATED PEST MANAGEMENT

Integrated pest management (IPM).
A pest management strategy that combines the principles of other pest managmenet systems, but with reduced emphasis on the use of chemicals, to reduce pest populations below levels that can cause economic loss.

Pests may be managed by an interdisciplinary approach. **Integrated pest management (IPM)** is a strategy of pest management whose goal is not eradication but, rather, to keep pest population below that which can cause economic loss to crop production. This is accomplished by an interdisciplinary approach (Figure 7). The principles of ecology underlie the philosophy of IPM. Several definitions of IPM are in use. The National Coalition on IPM defines IPM as a sustainable approach to managing pests by combining biological, cultural, physical, legislative, and chemical tools in a way that minimizes economic, health, and environment risks. It is implemented not in isolation but as one of the components of the total crop production system, which integrates physical, biological, and management factors for successful crop production. Pesticide use is reduced to the barest minimum and is not a first but a last resort. An insect trap used to trap boll weevils in cotton fields is shown in Figure 8. IPM programs strive to achieve safe (to user and environment) and economic management of agricultural pests.

Biological pest management and natural resources conservation are promoted by this method of pest management.

12.1 THE UNDERLYING PRINCIPLES OF IPM

The principles underlying IPM may be summarized as follows:

1. *Ecological bases.* IPM considers the agroecosystem as the management unit in crop production. Producers are manipulators of the agroecosystem. Because a

FIGURE 7 Integrated pest management employs an interdisciplinary approach to pest management. The goal is not eradication but, rather, to keep pest population at or below a threshold above which it causes economic loss. It combines all the five main methods of pest management: legislative, cultural, physical, biological, and chemical.

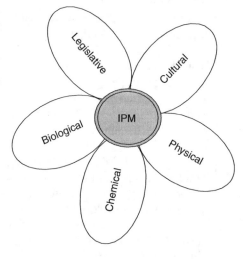

FIGURE 8 An IPM insect trap in use on a cotton farm to trap boll weevils.

management action implemented by the producer may yield an unpredicted adverse effect, IPM embraces a holistic approach to pest management, responding to a pest situation through a broad, interdisciplinary approach.

2. *Threshold natural population.* In proper balance, a pest can be present in the agroecosystem at a level that can be tolerated without economic loss. In chemical pest control, as previously indicated, the producer should not spray at the first sight of a pest. There is a pest population threshold beyond which economic injury is imminent. The economic threshold is the pest population level at which an appropriate pest management intervention must be implemented to prevent the pest from reaching the economic injury level. Hence, IPM embraces the fact that there is a natural control mechanism in the ecosystem that can regulate pest populations and keep them below the injury threshold.

3. *Pest suppression, not pest eradication.* All organisms have natural enemies in the ecosystem. Completely eradicating one organism may cause shifts in the balance of the ecosystem such that new pests arise. The concept of a "refuge" for susceptible pests, as promoted in the use of genetically modified crop varieties in production, creates a "buffer system" that maintains a low level of the pest and reduces the chance that pest resistance will occur.

12.2 JUSTIFICATION OF IPM

A unilateral approach to pest control involving pesticides has limitations because an agroecological system deals with a complex and dynamic biological system. Sooner or later, target pests develop resistance to pesticides, requiring more potent pesticides to be developed. Pesticides disrupt the natural mechanisms of control in the ecosystem and are environmentally intrusive, endangering humans, livestock, and wildlife. Disrupting natural systems encourages pest outbreaks. IPM optimizes pest control in an economically and ecologically prudent manner.

Steps in an IPM program are

1. Identify pests and beneficial organisms.
2. Know the biology of the pest and how the environment influences it.
3. Determine the tolerable pest population threshold.
4. If economic injury is possible, select the best method of pest management.
5. Select a pest control management method that will destroy pests without harming beneficial organisms. Consider cultural methods first—for example, using resistant cultivars, altering planting time, and providing supplemental nutrition.
6. Develop a pest monitoring schedule.
7. Evaluate the pest management method and make appropriate adjustments.

13: PESTICIDES IN OUR ENVIRONMENT

How do pesticides impact the environment? Pesticides contribute to environmental pollution. Improper use of pesticides adversely impacts non-target organisms, groundwater, and food safety. Pesticides are classified among many other substances called toxic chemicals (e.g., polychlorinated biphenyls [PCDs], heavy metals, and oils). Pesticides kill pests that reduce crop yield. However, their effects frequently linger in the environment and threaten human and animal life through contamination of groundwater, food, and feeds. It is estimated that agriculture accounts for approximately 70% of all pesticides used in the United States. Further, only about 5% of the pesticides are estimated to leach into groundwater. Unfortunately, this is enough to endanger human health and other life on earth. The Environmental Protection Agency (EPA) and the Food and Drug Administration (FDA) are federal agencies in the United States that set safe standards for the use of pesticides and monitor their presence in the food chain and the general environment.

The goal of industry and regulatory agencies is to produce that elusive or safe pesticide. The properties of such an ideal pesticide are

1. *Short-lived (non-persistent) in the environment.* A safe pesticide should be able to destroy the target pest within a short period (1 to 2 weeks) and dissipate rapidly. This reduces the chance of its entering and thriving in the food chain.
2. *Effective and safe to operators.* Pesticides are harmful to operators; thus, the pesticide should be readily amenable to safe application. If accidentally spilled or touched, it should be easy to wash away.
3. *Not carcinogenic, mutagenic, or teratogenic.* It is difficult to determine this attribute, which is often the source of much debate and discussion. There has been a shift from the use of persistent organochlorides such as DDT to organophosphates that are less persistent in the environment.

Minimizing Spray Drift

Pesticides are targeted at crop plants, weeds, or the soil, depending on the chemistry and other properties. Application of pesticides should be made under favorable environmental conditions, using appropriate and properly calibrated equipment, as well as according to the guidelines to apply it at the proper rate. The movement away of spray droplets from the intended target is called *spray drift*. Sometimes, a high vapor pesticide is converted to gas during application (called *spray volatilization*), polluting the air in the process. These two major sources of environmental pollution from pesticide application are enhanced by various sprayer characteristics and weather conditions. Spray drift is increased under windy conditions. Certain sprayer additives (called drift control agents) may be included in the tank mixture to reduce spray drift. Drift is higher when the spray volume is low (i.e., smaller droplets) and when high pressure is applied. Off-site drift is increased when the sprayer nozzle is raised high above the target. High wind speed and high temperature tend to increase drift.

14: Pesticide Use in U.S. Crop Production

How important is pesticide use in U.S. crop production? What types of pesticides are most commonly used? In 1996, the USDA estimated that agricultural pesticides cost U.S. producers a total of about $7.5 billion, of which two-thirds consisted of the cost of herbicides (Figure 9). Further, agricultural production and storage use accounted for 75% of all pesticides used in the United States. The cost of pesticides constitutes about 4% of total production expenses.

The application of synthetic pesticides to major crops (corn, wheat, cotton, soybean, fall potato, vegetables, citrus, apples, and other fruits) first peaked in 1982. The conventional way of measuring pesticide use is the amount in pounds of active ingredient. In 1964, pesticides used amounted to 215 billion pounds, while in 1982, producers used a total of 572 billion pounds of pesticides. The 1995 total used was 565 billion pounds. This increase was due to an increase in planted acreage. Application rates during this period were also higher. As commodity prices fell after 1982 and large amounts of farmland were idled, pesticide use also dropped. Most of the pesticide use was accounted for by corn production, being more than double that used in the production of any other U.S. crop (Table 6 and Figure 10). Further, fall potato production received the most intensive pesticide use on a per acre basis.

The most widely used microbial pesticide in 1997 was the Bt spray (Figure 11). Herbicides are the largest pesticide class and accounted for 57% of pounds of active ingredients in 1995. The most commonly used active ingredients of herbicides are atrazine, 2,4-D, and glyphosate (Figure 12). Atrazine is used to control weeds in corn and sorghum. It is very persistent in the soil. Trifluralin is most commonly used in cotton, soybean, and vegetable weed management programs. However, with the advent of imazethapyr and other imidazalinone and sulfonylurea herbicides, the use of trifluralin in especially soybean production has declined.

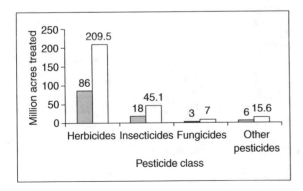

FIGURE 9 Crop producers in the United States use large amounts of pesticides, especially herbicides. The figure shows application of pesticides to 244 million acres of corn, soybeans, wheat, cotton, potatoes, fruits, and vegetables in 1997. (Source: USDA)

Table 6 Amount of Pesticide Applied and Acres Treated in U.S. Production of Major Crops

Crop	Active Ingredient (Million Pounds)	Acres Planted (Millions)
Corn	201	64
Potatoes	87	1
Cotton	84	17
Soybeans	69	61
Other vegetables	67	3
Citrus and apples	36	3
Wheat	21	49

Source: USDA, ERS 1995 estimates.

FIGURE 10 Most of the pesticides used on crops in 1997 were applied to corn. Corn and soybeans accounted for most of the herbicides used. Cotton was the largest user of insecticides, accounting for 32% of the total quantity of insecticides. Pesticides used on potatoes were mostly fumigants and vine killers. (Source: USDA)

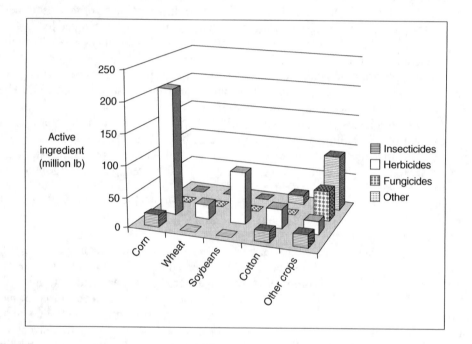

FIGURE 11 The most widely used microbial pesticide in 1997 was the Bt (*Bacillus thuringiensis*) spray. It is used to treat the Colorado potato beetle, cotton budworm, and several other fruit and vegetable crop pests. In 1997, it was used to a lesser extent (4%) on field crops and mostly on vegetables (16%) and fruits (11%). (Source: USDA)

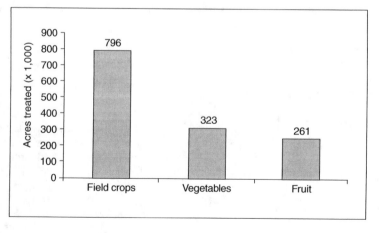

Insecticides made up 13% of the total quantity of pesticides used in crop production in the United States in 1995. The most preferred active ingredients were chlorpyrifos, methyl parathion, and terbufos, accounting for 43% of pesticides used on the five major field crops (Figure 12). Chlorpyrifos was the most widely used insecticide in corn fields to combat rootworm larvae, cutworms, and Russian wheat aphid, while methyl parathion was used to manage boll weevils and other cotton insects. The most common insect pests targeted for management in crop production were the cotton boll weevil and bollworm (Figure 13).

Fungicides are less used in crop production. They are used to manage pests in vegetable production and potato production. In 1995, 44.6 million pounds of fungicides were used in crop production in the United States. Fumigants are also used to manage soil pathogens and other organisms.

The use of pesticides in crop production is affected by factors including pesticide prices, federal programs, pesticide legislation, pesticide resistance, pesticide registrations, and development of alternative pest management strategies. Pesticide prices are not a major factor affecting pesticide use, since price changes have generally not been dramatic in recent times. Federal programs such as those that encourage land idling tend to reduce use of pesticides. Also, federal legislation through the Environmental Protection Agency (EPA) and laws such as the Clean Air Act of 1970 and Clean Water Act of 1992 tend to decrease the use of pesticides. Various states have various laws regulating the use of pesticides. Further, pesticide manufacturers are compelled to spend more in developing more environmentally safe pesticides, thus driving costs up. The Food Quality Protection Act of 1996 requires that approved pesticides be periodically reevaluated for safety. Those found to have potential safety concerns are withdrawn from use. For example, the use of propargite on fruits such as apples, peaches, and plums was banned, due to the concern about

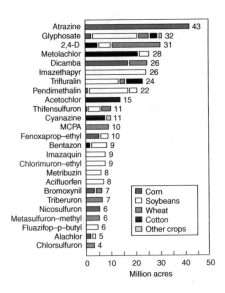
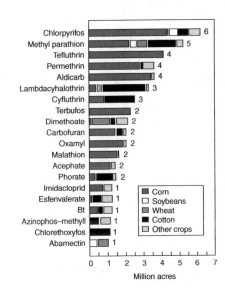

FIGURE 12 Atrazine was the most common herbicide ingredient applied to crops in 1999. It was used almost exclusively on corn and grain sorghum. Glyphosate was the second most widely used herbicide ingredient. It was used commonly in orchards and vineyards as well as in no-till systems in corn, wheat, and soybeans. Chlorpyrifos was the leading insecticide ingredient applied to crops. Chlorpyrifos and methyl parathion were the two most widely used insecticide ingredients. They are both organophosphates. Most of the insecticides used were restricted use and applied only by licensed applicators. (Source: USDA)

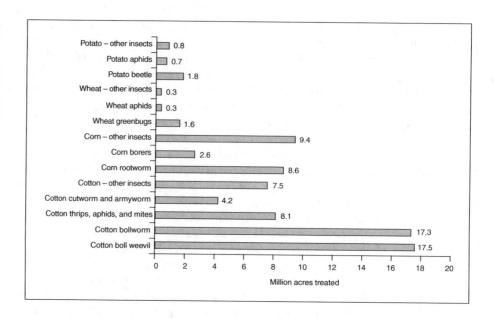

FIGURE 13 The most common insect pests targeted for management in crop production in 1994 and 1995 were the cotton boll weevil, bollworm, and corn rootworm. About 17% of all treated acreage was targeted for cotton bollworm or cotton boll weevil. (Source: USDA)

residues that posed potential hazards to infants. The continual use of pesticides has produced pests that are resistant to certain products. For example, weeds resistant to triazine herbicides (atrazine, cyanizine, and simazine) have been reported. To reduce the incidence of pesticide resistance, using lower doses of pesticides is recommended, along with alternating the use of pesticide families. When new and more effective pesticides are produced to replace less efficient ones, there is a reduction in the use of pesticides. For example, Imazethapyr, introduced in 1989, has become the most preferred herbicide in soybean weed management because it is used in lesser concentration than others such as trifluralin. Similarly, the introduction of transgenic corn and cotton seeds (Bt corn and cotton and other crops) has reduced the need for pesticides in the production of these crops.

SUMMARY

1. Yield losses from biological sources occurs at various stages in plant development.
2. Biotic factors that cause yield reduction are of both plant and animal origin. The five categories are disease-causing organisms, weeds, insect pests, non-insect invertebrate, or vertebrate pests.
3. The four disease-causing organisms are viruses, bacteria, fungi, and mycoplasma-like organisms.
4. Some microorganisms are beneficial—for example, certain fungi (mushroom) and bacteria *(Rhizobia)*.
5. In order for disease to occur, there must be a pathogen (causal organism), susceptible host (plant), and favorable environment.
6. A disease cycle consists of inoculation, penetration, infection, dissemination, and overwintering or oversummering.
7. Plants have physical and chemical means of defense against diseases.
8. True resistance to disease is genetically controlled.
9. Insect pests cause a variety of damage to crops in the field and storage house.
10. Weeds are important pests in crop production.
11. The four basic strategies of pest management in an agroecosystem are exclusion, eradication, protection, and resistance.

12. It is better to prevent a pest attack than to control it, since the latter is usually expensive.
13. Pest management strategies should be implemented only when economic injury is imminent.
14. The methods of pest management are biological, cultural, legislative, physical, and chemical.
15. Biological pest management is the oldest method of pest management and is based on the rationale that every organism has its natural enemies.
16. Cultural methods of pest management involve the manipulation of the crop production environment and production practices to control pest populations.
17. Legislative pest management (or quarantine) is the use of laws to control the movement of plant materials across specified borders.
18. Physical pest management involves the physical removal of pests or the use of agents to suppress them.
19. Chemical methods of pest management use pesticides that may be natural or synthetic, as well as organic or inorganic.
20. Pesticides are common in modern crop production. They have an adverse environmental impact.
21. Pesticides should be used judiciously and with caution.
22. Integrated pest management is an interdisciplinary approach to pest management whereby all methods are utilized strategically. Chemicals are especially used only as a last resort, and then very cautiously.

REFERENCES AND SUGGESTED READING

Agrios, G. N. 1988. *Plant pathology.* 3d ed. New York: Academic Press.

Bohmont, B. L. 1997. *The standard pesticide user's guide.* 4th ed. Englewood Cliffs, NJ: Prentice Hall.

Duke, S. O., ed. 1986. *Weed physiology,* vols. 1 and 2. Boca Raton, FL: CRC Press.

Economic Research Service/USDA. 1997. *Agricultural resources and environmental indicators, 1996–97.* Agricultural handbook No. 712. Washington DC: USDA.

Elzinga, R. J. 1987. *Fundamentals of entomology.* 3d ed. Englewood Cliffs, NJ: Prentice Hall.

Klingman, G. C., F. M. Ashton, and L. J. Noordhoff. 1982. *Weed science: Principles and practices.* 2d ed. New York: Wiley.

Lucas, G. B., C. L. Campbell, and L. T. Lucas.1985. *Introduction to plant diseases.* Westport, CT: AVI.

Powers, E. R., and R. McSorley. 2000. *Ecological principles of agriculture.* Albany, NY: Delmar.

SELECTED INTERNET SITES FOR FURTHER REVIEW

http://www.ipm.ucdavis.edu/PMG/crops-agriculture.html

Pests of agricultural crops, floriculture, and turfgrass; their management guides; great photos of insects, mites, nematodes, and diseases.

http://www.ipm.ucdavis.edu/

Discussion of IPM; photos, methods of management, etc.

http://www./ipm.ucdavis.edu/PMG/WEEDS/california_arrowhead.html

Weed identification; photos.

http://www.farmphoto.com/album2/html/noframe/fld00068.asp

IPM photos.

http://www.farmequip.com/cihfield.jpg

Photos of various farm equipment.

OUTCOMES ASSESSMENT

PART A

Answer the following questions true or false.

1. T F Viruses are obligate parasites.
2. T F Fungi cause most of the infectious diseases of importance in crop production.
3. T F Mushroom is a fungus.
4. T F In insects with no metamorphosis, the young look like small versions of adults.
5. T F The degree of pathogenicity of a pathogen is called its toxicity.
6. T F A pesticide used to control fungi is called a miticide.
7. T F The relative capacity of a substance to be poisonous to a living organism is called its lethal dose.
8. T F The higher the LD_{50} of a pesticide, the more toxic or poisonous it is.
9. T F Pesticides may be formulated as "dusts."
10. T F The use of traps is an example of a cultural method of pest management.
11. T F Aerosols are best used in open air situations.
12. T F Organochlorines are more biodegradable than organophosphates.
13. T F Most herbicides in use are organic-based.

PART B

Answer the following questions.

1. Diseases are caused by organisms called _____.

2. List the categories of microorganisms that cause diseases.

3. The capability of a pathogen to cause disease is called its _____.

4. Give the steps in a disease cycle.

5. What is complete metamorphosis in the lifecycle of insects?

6. Give four of the important insect orders in crop production.

7. Classify weeds according to lifecycle.

8. Give the four basic strategies of pest control.

9. What is economic injury?

10. The method of using laws to manage pests is called _____.

11. What is crop rotation?

12. Give the corresponding names of pesticides used to manage each of the following pests in crop production: rodents, fungi, nematodes, insects.

13. Aviacides are pesticides used to manage _____.

14. What is the toxicity of a pesticide?

15. Give three specific methods of pesticide application.

16. Discuss the classification of herbicides according to (a) mode of action, (b) timing of application, and (c) selectivity.

17. The compound responsible for the killing action of a pesticide is called the _____.

18. What does the acronym IPM stand for?

PART C

Write a brief essay on each of the following topics.

1. Discuss the disease triangle.

2. Discuss the infection stage in a disease cycle.

3. Discuss vertical resistance.

4. Discuss horizontal resistance.

5. Describe the genetic basis of disease incidence in plants.

6. Describe how pathogens affect crop productivity.

7. Discuss the preventive strategies in pest management.

8. Discuss the biological method of pest management.

9. Discuss a specific method of cultural pest management.

10. Discuss the lethal dose of a pesticide.

11. Describe the safe use of pesticides in crop production.

12. Discuss the strategy of integrated pest management.

13. Discuss the impact of pesticides on the environment.

14. Discuss the factors affecting herbicide effectiveness.

PART D

Discuss or explain each of the following topics in detail.

1. Why are viral infections not controlled by pesticides?

2. Discuss the trends in the use of pesticides in crop production (emphasize active ingredients).

3. Discuss the issue of resistance of pests to pesticides.

4. Predict and discuss the status of pesticides in crop production in the next decade.

5. Can modern agricultural production be totally pesticide-free?

Organic Crop Production

Purpose

The purpose of this chapter is to discuss the principles and practices of organic crop production.

Expected Outcomes

After studying this chapter, the student should be able to:

1. Distinguish between organic farming and conventional farming.
2. Discuss the principles of organic farming.
3. Describe the standards for organic crop production.
4. Discuss the importance of organic crop production in U.S. agriculture.

Key Terms

Compost   Farmyard manure   Organic farming

To the Student

Modern crop production depends heavily on agrochemicals to protect plants and to increase soil fertility. Excess agrochemicals find their way into the general environment, where they pollute groundwater. Pesticides enter the food chain through animals feeding on contaminated plants and the use of toxic products to protect food crops in the field and the storehouse. Increasingly, the public is demanding a cleaner environment and a safer food chain. There is a demand for food produced without the use of agrochemicals. This may be likened to a return to the second era of agriculture, the era of resource conservation and regeneration. Organic agriculture is an approach to production in which the producer relies on ecosystem management rather than external inputs. As you study this

From Chapter 12 of *Principles of Crop Production: Theory, Techniques, and Technology*, Second Edition, George Acquaah.
Copyright © 2005 by Pearson Education, Inc. Published by Pearson Prentice Hall. All rights reserved.

chapter, visualize the farm as a giant organism comprised of biotic components (animals and plants) and abiotic components (soil, environment) that are managed or manipulated by humans (farmers) in an economically sustainable and environmentally sound fashion.

1: What is Organic Farming?

1.1 DEFINITION OF ORGANIC FARMING

The word *organic* has become part of the vocabulary of participants in the food marketplace. However, it appears the word is interpreted a little differently by different sectors of the food marketplace. To the consumer, a product labeled *organic* means it was produced by methods that exclude agrochemicals. To the crop producer, it means the crop was produced by following the guidelines set forth by certifying agencies and using practices based on ecological principles.

Organic farming. The system of agricultural production in which synthetic agricultural inputs are excluded.

The Organic Producers Association of Manitoba Cooperative Ltd. defines organic products as those raised, grown, stored, and/or processed without the use of synthetically produced chemicals or fertilizers, herbicides, fungicides, or any other pesticides, growth hormones, or growth regulators. A simple definition of **organic farming** is difficult to arrive at, because organic farming systems are very complex. The National Organic Standards Board of the USDA defines organic agriculture as "an ecological production management system that promotes and enhances biodiversity, biological cycles, and soil biological activity. It is based on minimal use of off-farm inputs and on management practices that restore, maintain, and enhance ecological harmony. 'Organic' is a labeling term that denotes products produced under the authority of the Organic Foods Production Act. The principal guidelines for organic production are to use materials and practices that enhance the ecological whole. Organic agricultural practices cannot ensure that products are completely free of food residues; organic growing methods are used to minimize pollution from air, soil, and water. Organic food handlers, processors, and retailers adhere to standards that maintain the integrity of organic agriculture products. The primary goal of organic agriculture is to optimize the health and productivity of interdependent communities of soil life, plants, animals, and people."

The Consumer and Corporate Affairs Canada defines organic farming this way: "Organic farming seeks to create ecosystems that achieve sustainable productivity and provide weed and pest control through a diverse mix of mutually-dependent life forms, through recycling of plant and animal residues, and through crop selection and rotation, water management, tillage, and cultivation. Soil fertility is maintained and enhanced by a system which optimizes soil biological activity as the means to provide nutrients for plant and animal life as well as to conserve soil resources."

1.2 "ORGANIC" VERSUS "NATURAL"

Various terms are used to varying extents in the food marketplace to draw attention to the manner in which the product was developed. Newer terms include *eco* or *green* labeling as well as *natural*. Some consumers tend to use the terms *organic* and *natural* synonymously, but this is not correct. Natural foods are generally products that do not contain any "artificial" (without natural counterparts) additives. The U.S. Food Safety and Inspection Service defines natural as a product that contains no artificial ingredients and is no more than minimally processed in accordance with the rules of the agency. *Minimal processes* is interpreted to mean activities that are ordinarily undertaken in a household kitchen (e.g., washing, peeling of fruits, homogenizing of milk, freezing, canning, bottling, grinding of nuts, baking of bread, aging of meats). Just because a product is labeled *natural* does not mean it is *organic*. It does not guarantee synthetic inputs were not used in its production.

1.3   GOALS OF ORGANIC FARMING

The International Federation of Organic Agricultural Movements (IFOAM) summarizes the principles and practices of organic farming in its standards manual as follows:

1. To produce food of high nutritional quality in sufficient quantity
2. To work with natural systems rather than seeking to dominate them
3. To encourage and enhance biological cycles within the farming system, involving microorganisms, soil flora and fauna, plants, and animals
4. To maintain and increase the long-term fertility of soils
5. To use, as far as possible, renewable resources in locally organized agricultural systems
6. To work as much as possible within a closed system with regard to organic matter and nutrient elements
7. To give all livestock conditions of life that allow them to perform all aspects of their innate behavior
8. To avoid all forms of pollution that may result from agricultural techniques
9. To maintain the genetic diversity of the agricultural system and its surroundings, including the protection of plant and wildlife habitats
10. To allow agricultural producers an adequate return and satisfaction from their work, including a safe working environment
11. To consider the wider social and ecological impact of the farming system

2:   PRINCIPLES OF ORGANIC FARMING SYSTEMS

Organic farming is an agricultural production system based on ecological principles. Producers strive to incorporate laws of natural ecosystems into the choice of production practices to use in their enterprises. Generally, organic farming is a farming approach that aims to create an integrated, humane, and environmentally and economically sustainable agricultural production system. In such systems, maximum reliance is placed on locally or farm-derived renewable resources and the management of self-regulating ecological and biological processes and interactions in agricultural production. As previously discussed under the topic "models of agriculture," organic farming is a sustainable model in which producers conduct their activities in harmony with nature (i.e., working with nature rather than controlling or subjugating it). The organic farm is viewed in this regard as an organism in which all its constituent parts (soil, nutrients, water, organic matter, microbes, animals, plants) together with humans (as manipulators) interact to create a holistic, coherent, and stable whole.

The functions of an organic farm within an ecological framework may be summed up by three basic ecological principles—interdependency, diversity, and recycling:

1. *Interdependency.* An ecosystem is a complex entity that consists of mutually dependent life forms that also interact with abiotic systems. The ecological balance can be upset by changing one of its components. For example, overfertilization may cause soluble nitrates to leach into groundwater, and phosphates into streams and lakes, causing eutrophication to occur.

2. *Diversity.* An ecosystem thrives on diversity in life forms, which work to establish the checks and balances that are necessary to suppress the outbreak of pest species (each has natural enemies). Organic crop production mimics such diversity by adopting practices that include the production of different crops on the farm.

3. *Recycling.* Natural ecosystems maintain various nutrient cycles (nitrogen, phosphorus, sulfur, carbon). Green plants (primary producers) harvest solar energy and convert it into photosynthates for use by consumers. These nutrients are returned to the soil upon decomposition. Organic producers exploit nutrient cycling systems to reduce the need for infusion of soil amendments in production.

These three principles will be discussed further in the chapter to describe specific practices employed in the production of crops in an organic farming system.

3: ADOPTION OF CERTIFIED ORGANIC FARMING

The worldwide adoption of organic products is increasing. In 2000, there were an estimated 600 certified organic programs in 70 countries. In the United Kingdom, it is estimated that the market for organic products is growing at the rate of over 20% annually. Germany is one of the largest producers and consumers of organic products in the world. The United States is ranked fourth in land area managed under organic farming systems, behind Australia (with 19 million acres), Argentina (6.9 million acres), and Italy (2.6 million acres). In terms of the percentage of total farmland under organic farming, the United States is not among the top 10% in the world. The leaders in 2002 were Switzerland (9%), Australia (8.64%), Italy (6.7%), Sweden (5.2%), Czech Republic (3.86%) and United Kingdom (3.31%).

In the United States, 2.3 million acres were devoted to organic production, representing 0.3 percent of total cropland and pastures in 2001. Of this, 1.3 million acres were certified organic farming cropland and 1.0 million acres as pasture and rangeland. All states, except Mississippi and Delaware, had some certified cropland. The top states in certified organic cropland in 2001 were Minnesota, Wisconsin, Iowa, Montana, Colorado, Idaho, South Dakota, and Michigan (Figure 1). In terms of pasture and rangeland, the top states in 2001 were Colorado (514,000 acres), Texas (221,000 acres), and Montana (137,000 acres). Organic acreage declined overall in Georgia, Louisiana, South Carolina, Indiana, West Virginia, Florida, and Idaho between 1997 and 2001. The Southeast generally has less certified organic farmland than any other state in the United States. Some of this decline was due to severe drought (e.g., in Idaho) or decertification of crops (e.g., St. John's wort in Florida and Idaho).

4: CROPS IN ORGANIC CULTURE

It is typical for certified organic growers to produce several crops (diversity principle) because of the use of crop rotations and green manures as essential practices in organic production. The major grain crops grown in the United States include wheat, corn, rice, oats, and barley. A total of 457,415 acres were cropped in 42 states in 2001, North Dakota leading with 64,000 acres. Of the total U.S. acreage, 194,000 acres were devoted to

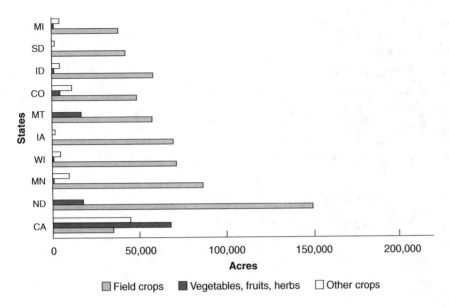

FIGURE 1 Top states in certified organic production in the United States in 2001. Vegetables are the most important organic crop in California, whereas other states produce organic field crops. (Source: USDA)

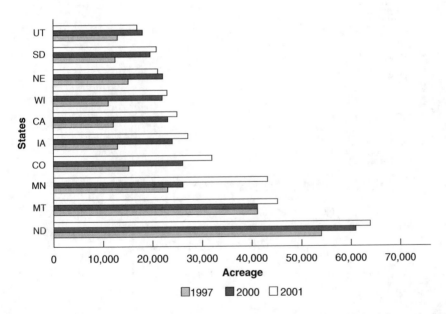

FIGURE 2 Organic crop acreage in the top 10 production states in the United States in 2001. North Dakota leads in organic crop acreage. (Source: USDA)

wheat, 93,000 acres to corn, and 30,000 acres each to oats and barley. About 31,800 acres were under rice production in 2001. Montana had the most wheat acreage, while Minnesota had the most corn and rye acreage (Figure 2).

Organic soybean was produced in 32 states on 174,400 acres in 2001. This represented a 28% increase from the previous year (Figure 3). It was determined that certified organic soybean growers received two times the conventional price for their

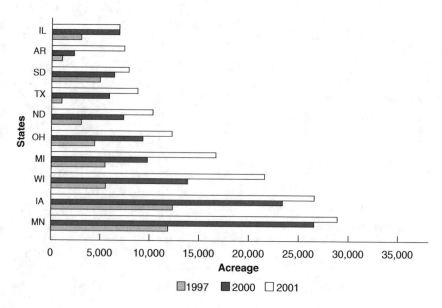

FIGURE 3 Top 10 organic soybean production states in 2001. (Source: USDA)

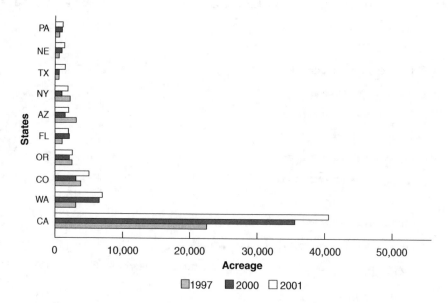

FIGURE 4 California is the biggest producer of organic vegetables in the United States. (Source: USDA)

product. Other legumes organically produced include dry beans, lentils, and peas. Twenty-one states produced organic flax and sunflower on 44,000 acres in 2001.

Many farms produce organic hay and silage. In 2001, 40 states produced 253,600 acres of hay and silage, the leading states being Idaho, Wisconsin, New York, North Dakota, and Iowa. States experiencing dramatic increases in production between 2000 and 2001 were New York (35%), Minnesota (43%), and South Dakota (45%). California is the biggest producer of both conventional (57%) and certified organic vegetables (Figure 4).

5: ORGANIC FARMING PRACTICES

Organic crop producers adopt a variety of practices to eliminate the need for agrochemicals and to conserve soil physical and chemical properties. These practices will only be briefly presented here. The needs of crops in organic production are identical to those of conventional production systems (e.g., temperature adaptation, sunlight), disease-free environment, weed-free environment). The difference lies in how the needs are met. The two areas of need that are supplied in different ways are soil fertility and plant protection (weeds, diseases, insects). In these two areas of need, certified organic production forbids the use of synthetic chemicals. The four categories of practices adopted by organic crop producers are as follows.

5.1 PRACTICES FOR INCREASING SOIL FERTILITY

The ecological principle applied here is nutrient cycling. Plant materials are incorporated into the soil to be decomposed to release nutrients into the soil. As previously indicated, organic farming typically grows different crops. This has the advantage of exploiting soil nutrients at different levels in the soil. The different species have diverse needs of soil nutrients and feed at different levels in the soil. Some crops (e.g., legumes) are capable of biological nitrogen fixation and hence enhance soil fertility when they are harvested. Some practices (use of catch crops) prevent soil nutrients from been leached out of the soil during the period when the field is not in an economic crop. The key practices that enhance soil nutritional status in organic crop farming are

- **a.** Green manuring/cover crops—this is the most common method of fertilizing in organic crop production in the United States.
- **b.** Use of organic manures—animal byproducts (e.g., farmyard manure)
- **c.** Crop rotation involving legumes for biological nitrogen fixation
- **d.** Catch crops—to absorb nutrients that otherwise would be lost in off-season
- **e.** Fallow—resting the land to accumulate soil moisture needed for the critical soil solution

Some organic producers sometimes apply aglime to correct soil pH to make nutrients more available.

A key to nutrient cycling is maintaining a biologically active soil that provides microbes for mineralization of organic matter. It is also important to know what crops remove nutrients the most (e.g., grasses extract potassium vigorously) and how to minimize losses while maximizing returns. Losses can be minimized by promoting natural recycling processes (e.g., nitrogen cycle) and biological nitrogen fixation. The availability of nutrients to plants depends on the rate at which nutrients are cycled by these biological processes.

To ensure that the soil remains biologically active, new sources of organic matter must be added at regular intervals. The rate of organic matter decomposition depends on its C:N ratio. Green manuring is used by organic farmers to provide nitrogen to the soil. They are generally readily degradable if plowed under at the appropriate age (i.e., when the plants are young and green). Crop residue from harvesting crops can also be incorporated into the soil. Green manure crops contribute little to soil organic matter due to their rapid rate of decomposition. However, crop residues that add to soil organic matter content decompose slowly. Farmyard manure is more effective at increasing soil organic matter than green manures. Organic farmers should know these characteristics of crop residues and green manure in order to make the most use of the nutrients by planting at the appropriate times. When leguminous crops are used as green manures, they contribute to soil nitrogen through symbiotic nitrogen fixation. Symbiotic nitrogen fixation is a primary source of nitrogen in organic farming.

The major sources of organic matter for organic farming are compost, farmyard manure, slurry, and liquid manures.

Compost

Compost. A mixture of organic residues and soil that has been piled, moistened, and allowed to decompose biologically.

Composting is often considered the essential practice in organic farming. **Compost** is desirable because the decay process is optimized to produce a product that is stable and comparable to what would occur in an undisturbed ecosystem. Farmyard manure is more useful after being composted to a more stabilized product. Composting involves piling suitable materials in a compost heap. The materials are placed in layers. Compostable materials should have a C:N ratio of between 25:1 and 35:1. If the ratio is too narrow, there will be insufficient carbon for microbes. On the other hand, a wide range (e.g., as in straw with 80–100:1) will have low nitrogen. Materials include **farmyard manure**, fallen leaves, grass, and straw from small grains. The material should have good moisture content (55 to 70%). The compost heap should be watered if it is too dry. The third critical requirement is that the heap be adequately aerated. The compost pile may be layered out in windrows to improve aeration.

The compost site should be within or close to the farm to facilitate transport of the bulky product to the field. A permanent concrete base may be constructed for composting windrows. This base prevents nutrient losses into the ground. The compost heap is covered with plastic and left to decompose. It takes 4 to 6 months for compost to become mature, or ripe, for use. During this time, the compost heap undergoes changes in pH and temperature. The mature compost is slightly acidic in reaction. High temperatures develop in the compost heap, reaching about 70°C. This high temperature helps kill weed seeds and disease pathogens. Further, pesticide residues are decomposed in the heap. The compost heap may be inverted after several months.

Farmyard manure. Organic wastes collected from livestock barns for use as organic fertilizer.

Farmyard (barnyard) Manure

Farmyard manure may be applied fresh or partially rotted, the latter being preferred. To minimize leaching losses and environmental pollution, farmyard manure should be applied in the late winter or early spring. It should be applied in thin layers by using spreaders. It is then harrowed into the topsoil. The producer should allow at least 6 weeks after application of farmyard manure before cropping the land, to allow time for the manure to be properly incorporated into the soil.

Slurry and Liquid Manures

Slurry and liquid manures are stored in containers such as tanks and lagoons. These materials are difficult to manage and expensive to store. The source of slurry and liquid manures are livestock operations where the animal waste accumulates in that form. Above-ground storage in tanks is environmentally safer and preferred to ground storage in lagoons. Slurry may be aerated to reduce odors caused by anaerobic decomposition of the materials that produce noxious chemical compounds (e.g., butyric acid and ammonia). Aeration is, however, expensive. Slurry and liquid manures are spread by tankers or by injectors, the latter technique being more effective for reducing losses from volatilization.

5.2   PRACTICES FOR DISEASES AND INSECT PEST CONTROL

The applicable ecological principle is diversity (to avoid disease buildup). The key practices for plant protection are

a. Crop rotation—this is the most common practice for pest control in organic production
b. Biological pest control—deployment of beneficial organisms (e.g., Bt)
c. The use of disease/insect resistant cultivars—this is also widely used
d. Sanitation—burying and burning of diseased plants to avoid the spread of disease

In this approach, the producer seeks to enhance the activities of natural enemies (beneficials) of crop plants. Beneficials include lacewings, spiders, aphids, and parasitic fungi. Enhancing biological diversity over time (e.g., using crop rotation, manipulating planting and harvesting dates, and discontinuing monocultures) and diversity in space (using varietal mixtures) is effective for pest management. Biological diversity helps prevent insect pest outbreaks through a variety of mechanisms such as interference with colonization, repelling, trapping, and increasing the population of beneficials. Trap crops and green manures are techniques that can be used to alter the behavior of pests.

Green manuring has been used to manage cyst nematodes using sugar beet, rape, and brassicas. Species such as corn, peas, beans, and clovers deter the beet cyst nematode. Wheat and oats act as hosts for cereal cyst nematodes, while potatoes and tomatoes act as hosts for potato cyst.

When peanut is intercropped with corn, the corn borer *(Ostrinia furnaculus)* is controlled, while intercropping corn with beans regulates leaf hoppers *(Empoasca kraemeri)*, leaf beetle *(Diabrotica balteata)*, and fall army worm *(Spodoptera fragiperda)*.

5.3   PRACTICES USED FOR WEED CONTROL

To control weeds, the applicable ecological principle is diversity in plant species and population density. Planting at an appropriate time provides a rapid ground cover to suppress weeds. The key practices adopted include the following:

a. Use of cover crops—control weeds, protect soil during fallow, improve soil organic matter
b. Cultivation—mechanical tillage to destroy weeds
c. Mulching—to suppress weeds
d. Crop rotation—to break weed cycle and suppress
e. Crop density—to suppress weeds by shading them out

Weed management is one of the major challenges of organic farming. Weed problems can be successfully managed without the use of herbicides, by adopting

1. Appropriate husbandry practices
2. Biological weed management
3. Direct mechanical and physical intervention

Weed species, like other plants, differ in preference for soil factors—physical and chemical. Some species (e.g., horsetail) prefer well-drained sandy or loamy soils, whereas others, such as field bindweed, prefer well-lit, heavy soils that are fertile. Some species are adapted to dry soils, while others prefer soils with good moisture. Drainage of soils can be used to manage horsetail and rushes that prefer good moisture. Liming of acidic soils or increasing soil acidity by applying sulfur can be used to manage pH-sensitive species.

Crop rotation may also be used to manage weeds. Crop species have weed complements. Thus, alternating between contrasting types (e.g., between annuals and perennials, or between autumn crops and spring-germinating crops) helps prevent certain weed species from becoming dominant in the field. Cultivation of the soil buries seeds and kills them, while other seeds are brought to the soil surface where they germinate. Through proper timing between seedbed preparation and cultivation activities, reserves in weed seed bank can be diminished. A "false seedbed" may be created for seeds to germinate, then subsequently harrowed prior to planting.

Another practice in weed management in organic farming is to give the crop a competitive edge over weeds by early planting and quick establishment. Techniques to accomplish this include pre-germination of seeds and transplanting, as well as seeding for high plant density. These practices help in certain cases to establish a ground cover that shades out weeds. Broadleaf species more effectively smother weeds than narrowleaf species (e.g., cereals). The spread of weeds may be reduced by using clean, weed-free seed, cleaning equipment after use, and using manures after they have been composted to kill weed seeds.

Weeds may also be managed by biological pest management techniques. Weeds are commonly controlled by direct mechanical intervention through mechanical cultivation, using various implements such as hoes and harrows. Harrowing should be done carefully to avoid damaging plants. It should be done after the three-leaf stage. Harrowing is not effective against well-established weeds. As a last resort, some producers use flame weeding to control weeds. The technique involves exposing weeds to flame temperatures in excess of 90 to 100°C to dehydrate and kill weeds.

5.4 PRACTICES FOR CONSERVING SOIL AND ITS PROPERTIES

To preserve soil structure and nutrients, the ecological principle of nutrient cycling and soil conservation principles to prevent soil loss are applied. The key practices applied include

a. Use of cover crops—to control weeds, protect soil during fallow, improve organic matter when plowed under
b. Use of catch crops—to absorb nutrients that could be lost to leaching in off-season
c. Use of conservation practices—to protect soil from erosion

6: CERTIFICATION AND STANDARDS

Products marketed as "certified organic" command premium prices. To reduce consumer fraud, certification and standards were developed for the organic farming industry in the early 1970s by private and nonprofit organizations. State certification was undertaken by several states in the 1980s. The federal Organic Foods Production Act was passed by Congress in 1990 to provide nationwide standards for the industry.

In 2000–2001, a total of 14 state and 39 private organizations provided certification services to organic producers, some of the oldest being the California Certified Organic Farmers, the Northeast Organic Farmers Association of Vermont, and the Maine Organic Farmers and Gardeners Association.

The U.S. Congress passed the Organic Foods Production Act (OFPA) of 1990 to establish national standards for organically produced commodities in order to facilitate the domestic marketing of such products and to assure consumers that these products conform to uniform standards. This legislation is implemented by the USDA's National Organic Program, which was authorized under the OFPA.

The USDA proposed new rules for organic farming and handlers on March 7, 2000:

1. Land would have no prohibited substances applied to it for at least 3 years before the harvest of an organic crop.
2. Crop rotation would be implemented.
3. Use of genetic engineering (included in excluded methods), irradiation, and sewage sludge would be prohibited.
4. Soil fertility and crop nutrients would be managed through tillage practices, supplemented with animal and crop waste materials and allowed synthetic materials.
5. Preference would be given to use of organic seeds and other planting stock, but a farmer could use non-organic seeds and planting stock under certain specified conditions.
6. Crop pests, weeds, and diseases would be controlled primarily through non-chemical management practices, including physical, mechanical, and biological controls; when these practices were not sufficient, a biological, a botanical, or an allowed synthetic chemical substance could be used.

The USDA introduced the Final Rule on October 21, 2002, to require all organic certifiers to be accredited under the USDA's national organic standards. All producers selling more than $5,000 a year must comply by seeking certification by the state or a private agency. The program established the following:

1. National production and handling standards for organically produced products, including a national list of substances that can and cannot be used
2. A national-level accreditation program for state and private organizations, which must be accredited as certifying agents under the USDA national standards for organic certifiers
3. Requirements for labeling products as organic and containing organic ingredients
4. Rules for the importation of organic agricultural products from foreign programs
5. Civil penalties for violations of these regulations

The USDA's requirements are the minimum; additional labeling of organic products is permissible by the certifying agencies. Certain synthetic substances such as insecticidal soaps and horticultural oils are permitted in organic farming as a last resort. However, genetically engineered products and irradiation are not permitted. Any use of materials to control pests must be documented.

7: Markets and Marketing

In 2001, the U.S. organic sales totaled $9 billion to $9.5 billion, up from $7.8 billion, and only $1 billion in 1990. The major world markets are the United States, Japan, Denmark, France, Germany, the Netherlands, Sweden, Switzerland, and the United Kingdom, together receiving $21 billion in sales. Organic products were once rich people's products, but they are gradually becoming mainstream products, sold in a variety of venues—farmers' markets, natural foods supermarkets, club stores, and conventional supermarkets. In 2000, about 49% of all organic products were sold in conventional supermarkets versus 48% in natural food stores.

About 80% of producers in the United States market mainly by wholesale. The prices of organic products are significantly higher than those for conventional products.

In 1999, organic corn sold for about $5.20 per bushel, while soybean sold for $11 to $22 per bushel, depending on the variety. The price premiums were more than 50% for corn, soybean, wheat, and oats between 1993 and 1999. Fresh produce is the top-selling organic category, followed by non-dairy beverages, bread grains, and packaged food. Organic food sales account for 1 to 2% of the total food sales in the United States and other countries. In terms of field crops, organic soyfoods (from soybean) are among the major organic products on the market.

The organic market is largely underdeveloped but is rapidly expanding. It is driven by the fact that more consumers are seeking what they perceive to be healthful and safe foods that are produced in an environmentally responsible manner. In the United States, research conducted in the mid-1990s indicated that about 25% of all adults make purchasing decisions that are influenced by their social and environmental values.

It is projected that organic foods will constitute about 10% of the total retail food market by 2008 in the United States, up from its current proportion of 3 to 5%. Although consumers are willing to pay premium prices for certified organic products, they also demand the quality of conventional products (e.g., appearance, size, etc.).

8: BASIC CONVENTIONAL FARMING VERSUS BASIC ORGANIC FARMING

Basic conventional farming and basic organic farming systems have many things in common. The key areas in which they differ are in practices that require the use of agrochemicals. Most agrochemicals are prohibited in organic farming. Some practices, though applicable to both systems, are standard or dominant to one system and optional or less important in the other. The similarities and differences between the two systems are summarized in Table 1.

9: CONSTRAINTS ON ORGANIC FARMING TECHNOLOGY

Though more energy-efficient than conventional production technology, organic farming has constraints:

1. *High labor input.* Labor input in organic farming is substantially higher than in conventional farming.
2. *Limitation to supply of organic fertilizer.* Organic farmers may utilize green manuring, composting, and other strategies to provide fertility in crop production. However, in order to utilize farmyard manure, slurry, and liquid manures economically, the farm should be located near sources of supply of these bulky manures (i.e., near livestock farms).
3. *Difficulty with certification standards.* There has been a general lack of uniform and nationally enforced standards for defining the term *organic*. The proposed standards by the USDA would help to resolve this constraint.
4. *Other constraints include markets, credit, and lack of research.* These constraints will be resolved with increased acceptability of organic products.

Table 1 Key Comparisons Between Organic and Conventional Crop Production

Factors	Organic Production	Conventional Production
Cultivars used	Conventional cultivars only	Conventional cultivars Transgenic cultivars
Certification	Required for production	Not required
Fertilizers	Organic sources Cover crops	Organic sources Cover crops In-organic sources

Pest control	Crop rotation
	Use of resistant cultivars
	  (conventional only)
	Biological pest control
	Cultural control
	Limited use of chemicals
		Crop rotation
		Use of resistant cultivars (conventional
		  and genetically modified)
		Biological pest control
		Cultural control
		Liberal use of pesticides

Weed control	Mechanical tillage Mulching Crop rotation	Mechanical tillage Mulching Crop rotation Use of herbicides
Environmental impact	Limited	Extensive pollution may occur
Marketing	Special label used	Labels not required
Principles	Sustainable production Ecological basis	Not sustainable

SUMMARY

1. Organic farming is a production practice that avoids or largely excludes the use of synthetically compounded agrochemicals in agricultural production.
2. Organic farming is known by various synonymous names such as alternative farming, regenerative farming, and sustainable agriculture.
3. Organic farming depends on site-specific natural resources and those developed on-site through techniques such as green manuring and composting.
4. In organic farming, the crop producer manages self-regulating ecological and biological processes for sustainable and economic production of crops and products.
5. The soil is cultivated to a shallow depth with light implements, mixing the residue with the topsoil. This promotes water infiltration and prevents soil erosion.
6. A key goal of organic farming is to operate the farm as a closed system as much as possible.
7. Nutrient cycling is a key source of fertility for crop production. It is therefore critical to maintain soil health and thereby promote biological activity in the soil atmosphere.
8. Biological nitrogen fixation is important in organic farming.
9. The major sources of organic matter for organic farming are compost, farmyard manure, slurry, and liquid manures.

10. Crop rotation is used to create biodiversity on the farm as a means of establishing equilibrium in the agroecosystem.
11. Diseases and pests in organic farming are managed by means of biological management techniques such as use of beneficials, crop rotation, and disease-resistant cultivars.
12. With organic farming, cultural practices such as drainage are used to control certain weeds and diseases and pests.
13. The USDA has proposed nationwide rules for organic farming and handling activities.

REFERENCES AND SUGGESTED READING

Kitto, D. 1988. *Composting: The organic, natural way.* New York: Sterling.

Lampkin, N. 1990. *Organic farming.* Cambridge, UK: Farming Press.

Poincelot, R. P. 1972. *The biochemistry and methodology of composting.* Connecticut Agricultural Experimental Station Bulletin 727.

SELECTED INTERNET SITES FOR FURTHER REVIEW

http://www.ofrf.org/about_organic/index.html

Organic Farming Research Foundation site; various related topics; good links.

http://www.ers.usda.gov/whatsnew/issues/organic/

Issues of organic farming; crop acreages from states in the United States; certification information; links.

OUTCOMES ASSESSMENT

PART A

Answer the following questions true or false.

1. T F Organic farmers do not use any synthetic fertilizers.
2. T F Farmyard manure is more stabilized after composting.
3. T F Organic farming is not sustainable.
4. T F Roundup® herbicide can be used in organic farming.
5. T F Vegetables are the most commonly produced crops in organic farming.

PART B

Answer the following questions.

1. Give the two specific reasons organic farming is attractive to some producers.

_____

_____

2. What act was passed in 1990 by the U.S. Congress to regulate organic farming?

   _____

3. Give four field crops that are grown by organic farmers in the United States.

   _____

4. Give 5 of the top 10 states that are leading producers of organic crops.

   _____

5. Give two specific constraints on organic farming.

   _____

   _____

PART C

Discuss or explain the following topics in detail.

1. Define the term *organic farming*.
2. Briefly discuss the role of nutrient cycling in organic farming.
3. Briefly describe how weeds are managed in organic farming.
4. Discuss the role of crop rotation in organic farming.
5. Explain why organic farmers adopt shallow tillage.

PART D

Discuss or explain the following topics in detail.

1. Organic farming is sustainable crop production. Discuss.
2. Organic crop production is on the rise in the United States. Discuss.

Harvesting and Storage of Crops

PURPOSE

This chapter is devoted to the discussion of the importance of harvesting a crop (grain or forage) at the appropriate time, and presenting the produce in the best quality to the consumer. The importance of storage of produce is also discussed.

EXPECTED OUTCOMES

After studying this chapter, the student should be able to:

1. Distinguish between physiological maturity and harvest maturity.
2. Describe the methods of harvesting field crops.
3. Discuss the nature of spoilage and the role of microbes in spoilage.
4. Describe the types of grain storage.
5. Describe the methods of drying grain in storage.
6. Describe the methods of silage preparation.

KEY TERMS

Bin burn	Curing	Silage (ensilage)
Combines (combine harvesters)	Harvest maturity	Straw
	Physiological maturity	Windrowing (raking)

TO THE STUDENT

The time of harvesting a crop product has implications in its yield, use, quality, and storage. Delaying harvesting or harvesting prematurely often adversely affects product quality. Premature harvesting is desirable for certain products for certain markets. As plant

From Chapter 17 of *Principles of Crop Production: Theory, Techniques, and Technology*, Second Edition, George Acquaah.
Copyright © 2005 by Pearson Education, Inc. Published by Pearson Prentice Hall. All rights reserved.

cells mature, the cell wall often becomes lignified. As a result, products that are preferred juicy and succulent may become fibrous and tough. Sugar may be converted to starch, reducing the sweetness of some products. The processing (e.g., milling) of cereal grains is impeded if the crop is not at the proper stage of maturity and moisture content. If the crop is left in the field for too long after maturity, it becomes predisposed to pest attack and deterioration from the vagaries of the weather. Premature harvesting may mean improper filling of the seed or grain, leading to reduced yield and quality of product. If poor-quality produce is placed into storage, poorer-quality produce will come out of storage. It should be clear by now that timeliness of crop harvesting is of the essence. As you study this chapter, pay attention to the factors affecting crop harvesting and how producers manage them for better product quality and yield.

1: TIME TO HARVEST

How important is the harvesting operation in the profitability of a crop production enterprise? Harvesting is literally "reaping what you sow." The potential yield expectation from a production operation depends on several factors. For a set of production conditions (cultivar, production inputs, weather factors, husbandry practices, etc.), a certain potential yield is expected of a crop. In order to obtain this potential yield or harvest, the crop must be harvested at the right time (when the economic product is at its optimal quantity and quality), and by the right method (to minimize harvest losses), and stored in the right way (to minimize post harvest losses).

What is the best time to harvest a crop? What factors influence the decision to harvest a crop? Generally, crops are harvested when they are said to be "mature." The concept of crop maturity is discussed in this section. The best time to harvest a crop depends on a number of factors, including the economic part (product), utilization of the product, and postharvest storage.

1. *The economic part.* The economic part or product of the crop plant can be the root, leaves, stem, grain, or other parts. These plant parts have different times when it is best to harvest them. At certain times in the plant lifecycle, there is partitioning of dry matter to various parts of the plant. Repartitioning of assimilates occurs under certain conditions. Translocation of the stored food from the plant part of economic importance to parts of no economic use will reduce the yield of the desired products. Crops should be harvested when the desired product is at peak quality and quantity.

2. *Utilization.* The economic product may come from the same part of the plant but, on one occasion, it may be desirable to harvest it fresh, while on another it may be best to harvest it dry. For example, corn may be harvested fresh or dry, depending on the intended use. The purpose of growing the crop determines when it is best to harvest it in order to have the highest quality and quantity of the desired plant product. For example, alfalfa may be grown for forage or for seed, while corn may be grown for silage or grain.

3. *Storage method.* Harvested products often require some form of storage at the site of production while awaiting shipment to the market. The product may deteriorate in storage if harvested at an improper moisture content. Cold storage is required for grain with high moisture content. Many grain producers have supplementary drying facilities for drying the harvested product to a "safe" moisture content for storage.

1.1 CROP MATURITY AND THE TIME TO HARVEST

What is crop maturity? There are several operational and technical categories of crop maturity used by scientists and crop producers. The common ones are physiological maturity, harvest maturity, and storage maturity.

Physiological Maturity

Scientists define **physiological maturity** as the stage of development in the lifecycle of the plant when the plant reaches maximum dry weight. At this stage, increasing production inputs does not produce any gains in yield. In grain crops, there is cessation in growth and grain filling at this stage. The grains at this stage have about 40% moisture content and are of *hard dough* consistency. Since grain ripening within a head and among different heads on the plant does not occur at a uniform rate, growth may continue in certain species until the moisture content is less than the average of 40%. If grain is harvested prior to its physiological maturity, it has low dry matter and lower quality (low starch content), and it shrivels upon drying. Producers of various crops use specific indicators of maturity. In corn, for example, the development of a *black layer* at the base of the kernel signifies the onset of physiological maturity.

Physiological maturity. The stage of development of the product at which maximum dry weight has been attained by the plant and consequently no gains in product yield can occur with increased production inputs.

Harvest Maturity

Harvest maturity for a crop is when the product of interest is at peak quality and quantity (i.e., maximum yield). Crop producers normally determine when harvesting a crop will produce the highest yield of the product of interest by using certain indicators acquired through experience or knowledge of the crop. In certain grains, harvesting is done at 25 to 35% moisture. Mechanized harvesting may result in considerable losses unless the crop is at the appropriate maturity. In some cases, this means the grain should ripen to moisture content of about 15 to 18%. Corn can be shelled at 27% moisture content but then must be dried to 13 to 14% moisture before safe storage. Soybean, on the other hand, must dry in the field to at least 16 to 18% moisture content before it can be successfully harvested.

Harvest maturity. The stage of harvesting a product to obtain peak quality and quantity, as determined by the producer.

When crop plants are grown for forage and pasture, the best time to harvest them is when the crop has attained the maximum vegetative yield, coupled with high quality (high protein and digestibility). In cases where multiple harvests will be made during the year, another factor to consider is a healthy and well-maintained stand after each harvest. The stage of maturity for cutting grain crops for silage is variable among species. It is best to cut barley or wheat in the milk stage, whereas sorghum is cut in the medium to hard dough stage.

Storage Maturity

In production systems where postharvest drying is not available, the crop is harvested at a stage when it can be directly hauled into storage. For grains, this means allowing ripening (desiccation) to occur to less than 14% moisture content.

What may happen if a crop is not harvested on time? Sometimes, inclement weather, equipment failure, or other eventualities delay harvesting of field crops. Crops may be harvested prematurely or when overmatured, each with consequences:

1. *Crop yield reduction.* Harvesting early means seed development and filling is curtailed prematurely. The attainable dry matter will not be realized, leading to lower yield. Delayed harvesting may cause lodging or crinkling of the stem and shattering of seeds. These events lead to increased harvest losses from mechanization.

2. *Grain quality reduction.* Prematurely harvested grains are shriveled and have low starch content. Delayed harvesting in the field causes field weathering of grains, leading to reduced germinability and storability. Delayed harvesting may cause certain products to be fibrous and undesirable.

3. *Loss of value.* Weathered grain (sun-bleached) attracts low prices. It is generally rated low on the quality grading scale. In certain species, precocious germination may occur, leading to loss in yield and quality and hence market value.

2: METHODS OF HARVESTING

There are two basic ways in which field crops are harvested: by grazing animals and by humans.

1. *Grazing animals.* Pasture is field that is seeded to forage species for livestock to graze or browse. Animals can also graze or browse plants on the range. Producers of cereal crops, such as wheat, may allow livestock to graze the crop for a period during the growing season.

2. *Humans.* There are two ways in which humans harvest crop products—through either manual harvesting or mechanized harvesting.

2.1 MANUAL HARVESTING

Manual harvesting is routine in most developing countries and in small operations. In the United States, certain crops are harvested manually for highest quality and premium prices (e.g., delicate vegetables fruits). Certain crops are handpicked using no tools. For small grains, hand-harvesting tools include the scythe, sickle, and cutlass. Manual harvesting is tedious and labor intensive.

2.2 MECHANIZED HARVESTING

Curing. The preparation of harvested products for handling and storage that involves drying.

Machines used for mechanized harvesting may be placed into several operational categories according to how they are used. How crop plants are harvested depends on several factors, including the economic part of the plant, the harvest maturity, and the field **curing** required. Certain field crops require a period in the field, after harvesting, in order for the product to cure to attain a certain quality.

In one category of harvesting, the whole plant is cut at or near the ground level, before the economic part is retrieved immediately or at a later date (e.g., in soybean harvesting). In another situation, the plant is left standing, while only the economic part is removed (as in picking cotton or corn).

In another categorization, mechanized harvesting may be grouped into *one-step* and *multi-step*. In the one-step operation, harvesting the economic product is obtained in a state that can be placed directly into storage (e.g., in harvesting grain crops such as corn and wheat). Several operations are conducted in one pass of the machine (combination harvesting or combine harvesting). In multi-step harvesting, the economic part may be harvested along with other plant parts and left in the field for a period of curing or drying (e.g., alfalfa). The material is later collected and further processed for storage.

FIGURE 1 Combines facilitate grain harvesting. They vary in size and design, and some can be adapted for harvesting more than one kind of crop.

Combine Harvesting

Combines (or **combine harvesters**) are routinely used to harvest field crops (e.g., soybeans, small grains, beans, dry peas). The combine is a complex machine that is capable of performing multiple harvesting operations (Figure 1). As the name implies, this machine combines several operations (harvesting and threshing) in one pass over the field. Originally designed for small grains, the combine is now widely used for other crops, including corn and soybean.

> **Combines (combine harvesters).** Machines that are capable of multiple operations, usually harvesting, shelling, and cleaning.

Cutting and Gathering   The front end of a combine is fitted with *cutter bars* or sickles that can be set to different heights. Once cut, the plant material is gathered and conveyed into the *threshing chamber.* Grain loss can occur with improper height of cutters. If cutters are set too high, some low-located pods (e.g., in beans) may be left unharvested. Similarly, if set too low, the cutter may slice some soil, thereby introducing foreign matter into the harvested crop material. Grain loss can also result from using dull sickles that may not cut certain plants or may violently agitate the plant to cause shattering of grain. Harvest losses also depend on the speed of the combine. The operator should be sure to operate the combine at appropriate settings and speed. Front-end harvest losses are due primarily to these factors, as well as improper ground and reel speeds.

Threshing   In the *threshing chamber,* a cylinder rotates to thresh the crop. For best results, the cylinder should be operated at an appropriate speed and spacing (clearance). If the rotating cylinder space is set too wide, incomplete threshing will occur. On the other hand, if the space is too narrow, the grain may be physically damaged (chipped or cracked). Similar damage and losses are also attributable to combine cylinder speed—a slow speed causing incomplete threshing, a fast speed causing physical damage.

Cleaning   The grain falls through *sieves* of appropriate sizes to clean out foreign material such as gravel. Losses occur also at the threshing and cleaning stages, caused by improper fan speeds and sieve settings.

Separating   The chaff (glumes, lemma, palea) and straw (stem and leaves) are shaken out of the combine onto the ground.

Handling   The clean grain is transported into the holding tank by means of augers and elevators. Grain is stored temporarily in this tank until emptied into a truck for hauling to the grain storage barn.

Windrowing

Windrowing (raking).
A method of multi-stage harvesting in which the crop is cut, gathered, and left in the field for a period to undergo additional ripening, before being picked up for threshing.

Windrowing (or **raking**) is the method of harvesting whereby the crop is cut and gathered by an implement called a *windrower* (Figure 2). The material gathered is left in piles in rows in the field. The harvest is left for a period before it is gathered for further processing. Windrowing may be appropriate when producing crops that ripen unevenly. Leaving harvested materials in the field for a period brings about the desired uniformity in ripening of the product. The rows of harvested material are picked up for threshing. Sometimes, when early harvesting is desired, the crop is windrowed. Windrowing is also

(a)

(b)

(c)

(d)

FIGURE 2   Haymaking involves the slashing and raking of the material after it has dried in the field. Windrowing equipment is used for gathering the hay for baling. Haymaking equipment includes (a) disk mower/condition, (b) swather, (c) rake, and (d) round baler.

used when harvesting occurs under heavy weed infestation. Windrowing is applicable to forage species such as alfalfa, small grains (e.g., barley and oats), legumes (e.g., peas and beans), and commercial crops (e.g., flax). It is used to sun-cure hay to facilitate baling.

Picking Machines

Pickers are used to remove only the economic part of the plant that is located on an aerial part. There are pickers for crops such as corn and cotton.

2.3   HARVESTING IS A "THRASHY" OPERATION

After the economic part of the crop is harvested, a variety of vegetative material is left over in the field. The material depends on the type of crop. Three types of remnants are straw, stover, and stubble.

Straw

Whether harvesting is done by completely cutting the plant and separating the economic part, or by picking only the economic part from the plant, some plant material remains on the field after the operation. **Straw** is the term used for all the dried fine stems and other plant parts left after the seed has been threshed at harvest maturity. The remnant plant material may be baled for later use. Straw may be used as mulch. It can also be plowed under to improve the soil's physical qualities. Straw from leguminous species (e.g., cow pea and soybean) is of high nutritional and soil amendment value. The carbon:nitrogen (C:N) ratio of straw is very high. Due to this characteristic, the use of straw as a soil amendment should be accompanied by nitrogen fertilization in order to avoid yield depression. When bacteria are decomposing straw, they mine the native nitrogen in the soil during the process. The nitrogen level in the soil returns to normal when mineralization occurs. Straw is also useful as bedding material in animal barns.

Straw. The remnant material after the economic part has been removed, consisting of finer stemmed grasses and legumes.

Stover (Stalks)

Stover is the stalks of corn or sorghum plants that remain after the ear or head is picked or removed.

Stubble

Stubble refers to both straw and stubble, especially those that remain rooted in the soil after harvesting. Stubble may be used as mulch (stubble mulch).

3: HASTENING HARVEST MATURITY AND FACILITATING HARVESTING

Sometimes, it is desirable to hasten the time of crop harvesting. After a grain crop reaches physiological maturity, any delay in harvesting may cause deterioration in quality and yield reduction. A number of direct and indirect methods may be adopted by crop producers to hasten the time of crop harvesting.

3.1 DIRECT METHODS

Defoliation and Desiccation

Once a plant has attained physiological maturity, it cannot accumulate any more dry matter. Leaving it in the field longer predisposes it to weathering. Sometimes, inclement weather threatens the quality of the harvest, thereby compelling the producer to make adjustments in the harvesting schedule. Such adjustments include "inducing" early harvest maturity by applying a *defoliant* or *desiccant*. A defoliant causes leaf-drop, while a desiccant causes the plant to dry out in the field and die. In cotton production, green leaves tend to stain the fibers. Defoliation of cotton prior to mechanized harvesting reduces not only the amount of undesirable plant debris in the harvested fiber but also the chance of tainting it with plant pigments. In haymaking, a chemical treatment (e.g., with Endothal) hastens drying of the plant material in the field.

Topping

Topping is the preharvest reduction of vegetative material (mainly leaves). This slows photosynthetic activity and hastens drying of the economic part (e.g., pods).

3.2 INDIRECT METHODS

Generally, crops are harvested when the conditions of the economic product are such that the product can be stored for a reasonable period of time without deterioration. However, if the producer has a facility for drying, the crop may be harvested sooner than normal harvest maturity, then dried to storable moisture content at a later date.

4: STORING GRAIN

Some type of storage is usually an integral part of a crop production enterprise. Harvested grain needs some type of on-farm storage after harvesting, unless the product is to be shipped immediately to the user or market. The duration of storage may be a few days, weeks, or even years. Some producers deliberately hold their grain in hope of higher prices in the future.

There are four general ways in which seed can be stored for varying lengths of time. The method chosen depends on the duration over which it is desired for seed to maintain its quality, among other factors. Seed quality cannot be improved during storage, since quality declines with time.

4.1 CONDITIONED STORAGE

Seeds are maintained in a dry and cool environment. For most grain crops such as corn, wheat, and barley, seed moisture at storage should be about 12 to 13% and the temperature 20°C (68°F) or less. These conditions can hold seed quality for about 1 year. Many commercial seed companies operate such a facility.

4.2 CRYOGENIC STORAGE

Cryogenic storage of seed is used when seed needs to be stored for a very long period. Such seeds are held in liquid nitrogen at −196°C (−295°F). The practical use of this method of storage is limited by the small size of the cryogenic tank. It is widely used by germplasm banks for long-term storage.

4.3   HERMETIC STORAGE

Seeds under this type of storage are sealed in moisture-resistant containers. Metal containers are used when very long storage periods are desired. Before the container is sealed, the ambient air inside may be replaced with an inert gas (e.g., argon or nitrogen) for best results.

4.4   CONTAINERIZED SEED STORAGE

In containerized seed storage, seeds (usually high-value germplasm) are maintained in specially constructed rooms, equipped with dehumidifiers and other environmental control systems. Sometimes, a desiccant is used to control the level of humidity of the environment.

Grain may be stored in large amounts, unpacked, or in *grain bins* or *grain elevators*.

Grain Bin Storage

On a large commercial scale, grain is usually stored in bulk in bins of different sizes and materials (Figure 3). The bin may be made of concrete, steel, or wood. It may be airtight or ventilated. Airtight storage reduces respiration and subsequent spoilage resulting from the absence of oxygen. However, cold air from the atmosphere can cause moisture accumulation in the top layer of the grain in airtight storage. This moisture results from condensation of warm air rising from the bottom of the bin. The use of ventilation (e.g., using a fan) circulates air through the grain and prevents temperature rise and heat buildup.

Grain Elevators

In large grain-producing areas, a number of large silo-type bins are constructed together to create what is called a *grain elevator* (Figure 4). These structures are usually constructed at railroad sidings or waterfronts in order to facilitate grain transportation. The storage bins are loaded in various ways, including the use of elevators, pneumatic systems, and conveyor belts.

FIGURE 3 Storage may be provided on the farm or away from the farm. Storage bins differ in structure and material, common materials being metal and concrete.

FIGURE 4 Grain elevators are large storage facilities that are often constructed near major transportation routes. (Source: USDA)

5: THE GOALS OF GRAIN STORAGE

Grain products coming out of storage should be of good quality. The goal of storage is to preserve product quality and quantity (prevent losses) to meet the demands of the end users. The end results depend significantly on the condition of the product prior to storage. A high-quality product from storage should have certain characteristics:

1. *The product should have high purity.* Before storage, the seed should be cleaned to remove contaminating seed (admixture) such as weeds, other crop seeds, and chaff. In practice, mechanical harvesting unavoidably includes some impurity in the form of weed seeds, other crop seeds, plant debris, and even soil. The quantity and the type or source affect the usefulness of the harvest. The presence of toxic crop seeds such as castorbean (*Ricinus communis* L.) and weed seeds such as crotalaria (*Crotalaria spectabilis* Roth) and jimsonweed (*Datura stramonium* L.) makes the seed unsafe for food or feed.

2. *It should be in good physical condition (shape, size, color).* There should be no shrinkage, distortion, discoloration, or heat damage. Improper temperature can cause shrinkage, while mold infestation can produce discoloration of grain. Discoloration or dullness in color and shriveling reduce the eye-appeal. For certain crops, artificial drying produces less attractive product than natural drying.

3. *There should be minimal mechanical damage (breakage, cracks, and splits).* Mechanical harvesting may cause subtle internal injuries to the seed, thus accelerating its deterioration in storage. More visible damage includes split seeds and chipped, cracked, or broken seed. Soundness (lack of mechanical damage) of seed is a quality index of paramount importance in seed evaluation.

4. *The seed should have high viability.* This is critical when stored grain is intended for use as planting seed. For most uses, stored grain does not need to remain viable. However, low viability indicates problems in storage (e.g., improper temperature or moisture content) that may lead to spoilage caused by microbial invasion.

5. *There should be no damage from insects (holes, devoured contents).* Insect damage is common when grain is stored in large quantities. Storehouse insect

damage includes loss of harvested produce weight caused by feeding on cotyledons or endosperm, excreta, dead insect parts, loss of nutrients, and others. Insect damage can reduce grain quality and income to the producer or processor.

6. *There should be no molds or disease infection.* Drying to safe moisture content prior to storage reduces the incidence of molds and the growth of other pathogens. Whereas mold damage in storage is practically impossible to eliminate, it can be prevented from increasing. Mold infestation reduces seed viability while discoloring seed and creating a foul odor. Molds may also cause toxic substances to develop in the product, making it unsafe for food or feed.

7. *There should be no contamination from rodent droppings.* Storage facilities attract rodents. Mechanical traps and baits should be used to trap and destroy these pests.

8. *There should be no pesticide residue.* Sometimes, it is necessary to manage storage pests by using chemicals. The choice of pesticides should be made carefully to avoid tainting the stored product.

9. *There should be no toxic microbial metabolites.* Toxic metabolites are released as a result of mold infestation and the presence of insects under high moisture conditions in storage.

10. *There should be no loss of flavor.* Off flavor may be caused by bin burn (and charring from excessive heat buildup in storage), fermentation, and other factors. Stored bulk grain develops considerable heat, resulting from the use of hexose sugars by microbes according to the following reaction: $C_6H_{12}O_6 + O_2 \rightarrow 6CO_2 + 6H_2O$ + heat. Improper drying (high moisture content) predisposes stored grain to heat damage. The affected grain has darkened pericarp or seed coat. Wheat is very heat-sensitive and can be damaged in storage to the extent of not being fit for flour production. Heat damage also makes grain brittle and more predisposed to further mechanical damage during handling. Grain also loses viability. In order to be usable for certain products, the grain chemical characteristics are critical. Sometimes, protein and starch deteriorate in storage.

11. *There should be no foul odor.* Spoilage caused by high moisture and disease infection produces odor in the grain.

12. *There should be adequate moisture in the product.* Depending on the storage environment, stored grain may lose or gain moisture. It is important to store produce at a moisture content that will prevent fungal growth and molding. Grains from different parts of the plant may have different moisture percentages at harvest. When grains are dried artificially, it is often difficult if not impossible to have uniform drying. Sometimes, certain producers deliberately mix different lots of grain in an attempt to achieve certain desired average moisture content. This method is not recommended from the standpoint of moisture content. The maximum moisture content allowed is set by industry in order to have a standard for fair trade. For soybean, for example, the maximum percentage of moisture allowed for U.S. grades 1, 2, and 3 are 13, 14, and 16%, respectively.

6: DRYING GRAIN FOR STORAGE

Grain must be dried to a safe moisture content before storage. Drying is necessary after harvesting because certain grains, such as corn, are difficult to dry in the field to desired moisture before harvesting. In rice, the grain can be safely combine-harvested if moisture is high; otherwise, checked kernels will occur during milling. Grain can be dried in three ways: natural air-drying; drying with forced, unheated air; and drying with heated air.

6.1 NATURAL AIR-DRYING

Natural air-drying is accomplished by exposing the grain to the heat of the sun and gentle breeze. It is an inexpensive way of drying grain, especially in arid and semiarid regions where there is abundant sunshine and dry winds. Grain harvested in humid seasons usually has excess moisture and requires drying prior to storage.

Cereal crops may be harvested and bundled into shocks and left to stand in the field to dry. In certain cultures, the bundled material is hung to dry on fences or a line. Damp grain may be spread on a mat, concrete floor, or tray to a shallow depth for drying in the sun. During the night, the grain is covered to avoid reabsorption of moisture in the cool of the night. The grain or produce is stirred often by raking and mixing to bring the lower layer up for more exposure to the sun. Grain at about 18% moisture content can be air-dried to about 14% in about 3 weeks.

Grain in storage can be dried by ventilation through perforations in the walls or floor of the bin. Some bins have perforated tubes or screen flues inserted through holes in the sides and across the bin at certain intervals. Drying grain this way is effective when the moisture at harvest is not very different (less than 2%) from the ideal storage moisture. The disadvantage of ventilated bins with cowls (either wind pressure or exhaust wind types) is that the stored grain absorbs moisture during damp periods, unless there is a way to close these vents.

6.2 DRYING WITH FORCED, UNHEATED AIR

Binned grain may be mechanically dried by forcing unheated air through the grain. The bin may have perforated ducts or false floors. A fan is used to draw air (about 1 to 6 cubic feet per minute per bushel of grain). The humidity of the air should be below 70%. This level of humidity usually occurs from the late morning (10 A.M.) to late afternoon (about 6 P.M.). If drier grain (less than 13% moisture) is needed, the air humidity should be lower than 60%. To be efficient, the grain to be dried this way should be clean and free from debris that impedes air flow through the mass of grain.

6.3 DRYING WITH HEATED AIR

Drying grain in storage with heated air is more rapid and dependable than the other methods but is also more expensive. Heaters that burn natural gas or petroleum fuels are frequently used for drying grain. They are more efficient in drying grain during the summer months than in winter. Since these heaters are capable of delivering heat at high temperatures, it is very important for the producer to know the end use of the product in storage in order to dry at the appropriate temperature. Temperatures in excess of 130°F (54.4°C) destroy the grain quality of wheat, corn, and sorghum. The starch is damaged to the extent that starch separation is low. Grain for feed can tolerate higher temperatures, but the protein digestibility can be severely impaired.

Construction designs differ, but commercial dryer design is usually the column design, in which grain is moved downward slowly through perforated columns. Hot-air fans force heated air into chambers between the columns as the grain slowly streams down the columns. Column-type dryers are also used on farms.

7: Temperature and Moisture Effects on Stored Grain

Notwithstanding the storage facility, two factors are critical to the retention of grain quality for a long period of time: the temperature and moisture content of grain. Seeds in a single head do not ripen uniformly but over a period of about 3 to 10 days. At this stage, the average moisture content of the seed is about 25 to 30%. This moisture is too high for bin storage. For storage in winter, the grain moisture should be more than 14% in most cases. In the Coastal Plains and Gulf Coast, a lower moisture content of 11 to 12% is recommended. Lower percent of moisture (1% lower on the average) is required in the summer months. If storage will be in cribs, where natural drying can occur in fall and spring, ear corn can be stored at 20 to 21% or less moisture content in winter. The appropriate crib size should be used. Larger cribs (10 feet) are recommended for drier regions, while smaller cribs (3 to 6 feet) are used in cool and humid areas.

A combination of high moisture (13% or greater) and high temperature (70°F, or 21.1°C) promotes infestation by microorganisms and insects that leads to spoilage. Under such conditions, the grain respires, producing heat, carbon dioxide, and water. This additional water further increases grain moisture content. The organisms that are introduced into the storage facility from the field or the air include bacteria and fungi, especially *Aspergillus* spp. (e.g, *A. glaucus, A. flavus,* and *A. candidus*) and *Penicillium, Helminthosporium,* and *Fusarium.* These organisms create moldiness in stored grain. Some, like the *A. flavus,* produce deadly toxins (e.g., the mycotoxin *aflatoxin* in grains such as corn and crops such as peanuts).

The respiratory activities of the organism raise the heat in the grain bin, sometimes to 90° to 160°F. The intense heat is responsible for the browning of grain (called **bin burn**) and even a charred appearance and off-taste. At temperatures above 130°F (54.4°C), heat sterilization occurs in the bin, killing insects and inactivating microbes.

Under conditions of high moisture (greater than 14%) and low oxygen, fermentation occurs in the bin. This is more of a problem when deep bins (such as those used in terminal elevators) are used for grain storage. It is important to aerate these bins to avoid condensation of moisture. This happens by convectional current (warm air at the bottom of the bin rising through the grain and being replaced by cold air). The rising warm air may condense near the top of the bin where the cool grain is. To avoid this condition, an exhaust fan is installed to draw up the warm air at the bottom of the bin through a metal pipe. This pipe has perforations near the bottom and is installed in the center of the bin to draw up the warm air at the bottom of the bin.

Bin burn. The brown discoloration of grain in storage caused by intense heat generated from the respiration of organisms in the enclosed storage bin.

8: Storage Pests

How does stored grain lose quality? A variety of pests cause grain spoilage in storage. Spoilage of grain takes several forms: mold growth, decrease or loss of viability, increase in moisture content of grain, change in color or discoloration of grain (bin burn), change in chemical content (carbohydrates, protein, fats), decay, and direct insect damage. If the bin is not protected adequately, rodent attack can become a big problem. The taste of grain may change to become sour and the grain may develop an odor as a result of fermentation. The grain can also be lost through eating by rodents and insects (Figure 5).

FIGURE 5 Storage pest: grain weevil. (Source: USDA)

In certain grains, such as wheat that is cultivated principally for flour, the characteristic elastic properties caused by the protein gluten is lost, reduced, or completely destroyed by pests eating it. Such grain is no longer fit for making bread flour.

The most common storage pests that damage stored grain include the rice weevil *(Sitophilus oryzae)*, granary weevil *(Sitophilus granarius)*, *Angoumois* grain moth *(Sitotroga cerealella)*, Australian wheat weevil *(Rhizopertha dominica)*, and the lesser grain borer found in elevators. Others are *Ploidia interpunctella*, which damages corn in particular; cadelle *(Tenebroides mauritanicus)*; khapra beetle *(Trogoderma granarium)*; saw-tooth grain beetle *(Oryzaephilus surinamensis)*; and confused flour beetle *(Tribolium confusum)*.

Saprophytic fungi (feed on dead tissue) are the most important microbes in quality deterioration of stored grain. Molds are more important than yeast, the latter requiring high humidity of at least 88% (not usually present in storehouses) to develop.

Fungi may infect grain in the field, the major species being *Alternaria, Cladosporium, Helminthosporium,* and *Fusarium.* Their role in quality deterioration in storage is minimal. Storage fungi of importance are *Aspergillus, Penicillium,* and to a lesser extent *Sporendonema.* Fungal growth in storage is influenced by seed moisture content, relative humidity of the storage environment, temperature, air quality (O_2/CO_2), and duration of storage. These factors interact. Moisture, especially interseed moisture, is the most critical in seed quality deterioration during storage. Equilibrium relative humidity of 65% or less is considered safe for long-term (6 months) storage. The seed moisture content and storage area environment should equilibrate at about 65%. Longer storage should be at a lower temperature and seed moisture content.

9: STORING FRESH OR UNPROCESSED PRODUCE

Dry products, such as nuts and grains, store for long periods of time in dry environments. Fruits and vegetables have a much shorter shelf life, unless preservation measures are taken to prolong it. The storage conditions (especially temperature, humidity, and light) and the kind of crop (regarding quality characteristics and condition at time of storage) affect the duration of storage the crop can withstand before deteriorating. Even under the best conditions, poor quality of produce at the time of storing will cause rapid deterioration. The general goals of storage are to slow the rate of respiration occurring in living tissues (which also slows the rate of microbial activity) and to conserve moisture in the tissues (to prevent excessive dehydration). These goals are accomplished by providing the appropriate temperature (usually cool to cold), maintaining good levels of oxygen and carbon dioxide, and controlling humidity. Bruised products respire at a higher rate than intact ones. Further, the areas around the wounds become discolored. Certain crops have inherent genetic capacity for prolonged storage. Those with dormancy mechanisms have a reduced respiration rate in storage.

As a general rule, cool season crops are stored at low temperatures (32° to 50°F), whereas warm season crops are stored at warmer temperatures (50° to 54°F). However, sweet corn, a warm season crop, should not be stored at warm temperatures that cause the conversion of sugar into starch, an event that reduces the sweetness of the corn. Instead, sweet corn that is not going to be used soon after harvesting should be placed in cool storage. Fresh fruits and vegetables should be stored at high relative humidity to keep their succulence and general quality. Crops such as lettuce and spinach require higher relative humidity (90 to 95%) than crops such as garlic and dry onion (70 to 75%). Storage should take place in darkness or in subdued light. Light may cause produce such as potato tubers to green (from the development of chlorophyll). There are two general methods for storing unprocessed produce: the low-temperature method and the low-moisture method.

9.1 LOW-TEMPERATURE METHOD

Fresh products retain the capacity for certain physiological activities, such as respiration. Because respiration is accompanied by the evolution of heat, ventilation in storage is critical for fresh produce to avoid excessive heat buildup to cause rotting. The respiration rate of crops such as spinach is very high. At a given temperature, strawberries can respire about six times as much as lemons. Temperature is known to affect the rate of respiration, lower temperatures slowing down all biochemical and enzymatic reactions. Temperate or cool season crops generally tolerate lower temperatures than do tropical crops that are readily injured by cold.

Whether at home or in a commercial setting, the *mechanical refrigerator* is the workhorse for cooling. Refrigerated trucks and containers are used to transport fresh horticultural produce over long distances. For produce and products, such as cut flowers, strawberries, and lettuce that should be stored dry (no contact with moisture), a *forced-air cooler* system is used to pass cooled air through a stack of the produce in a cold room. Some commercial growers use *vacuum cooling* for the direct field packing of leafy crops. *Package icing* involves the use of slush ice. In the fall, vegetable produce may be stored outside in earthen mounds or trenches.

The rate of respiration is affected by the concentration of carbon dioxide and oxygen in the environment. Where carbon dioxide levels are very high (low oxygen), respiration slows down. The normal levels of oxygen and carbon dioxide in the air are 21% and 0.03%, respectively, nitrogen being 78%. In an airtight room full of fresh fruits, such as apples, the oxygen soon gets used up in respiration and is replaced by the byproduct of respiration (carbon dioxide). After a period of time in storage, the carbon dioxide level reaches about 21% (the previous level of oxygen). At this stage, the fruits respire anaerobically (fermentation), a process that produces alcohol. This is undesirable; hence, growers should ventilate such a storage room before anaerobic respiration sets in. It has been determined that, when the carbon dioxide level is raised, fruits can be stored at high temperatures of 37° to 45°F instead of the low 30° to 32°F.

The gaseous environment during storage can also be enriched with a variety of volatile organic compounds in order to influence ripening. One of the most common is ethylene, which is used to commercially ripen bananas. Certain fruits produce ethylene naturally as they ripen. Since the gas is harmful to cut flowers, fruits (e.g., apples) should not be stored in the same room with cut flowers. The storage environment should be maintained at an appropriate humidity level in order to avoid excessive moisture loss from fresh produce. High humidity predisposes stored produce to decay. A relative humidity of 90 to 95% is appropriate for most fruits, including apples, bananas, pears, and pineapples. In the case of leafy vegetables that are prone to wilting, high relative humidity (RH) of 95 to 100% is recommended. Examples of such crops are lettuce, broccoli, celery, and root crops such as carrots and turnips. On the other hand, vegetables such as garlic, dry onions, and pumpkins store better at 75 to 85% RH. It is important to maintain good ventilation when manipulating RH to avoid condensation and the accumulation of undesirable gases.

9.2 LOW MOISTURE METHOD

Many crops, including grapes, plums, dates, figs, and apples, may be preserved for long periods of time by drying. *Solar dehydration* is a relatively inexpensive method for drying in areas where a long dry and reliable sunny period occurs. The produce is spread in appropriate containers and exposed to open, dry, warm air. For more rapid dehydration of large quantities of produce, the *forced hot air* method, which involves air heated to 140° to 158°F is used. This method removes water by dehydration. However, water may be removed by *sublimation* or ice at temperatures below freezing point by using the *freeze-drying* method. This method is expensive, but the product quality is restored by rehydration to the level of the quality of products stored by freezing. As occurs in cold storage, the oxygen concentration of the storehouse may be reduced by increasing the carbon dioxide concentration. Fresh produce stored in reduced oxygen environments respire slowly and thus deteriorate slowly.

The succulence of fresh produce depends on how well it retains its moisture content. A high relative humidity reduces the rate of water loss from plant tissue; however, in the presence of high temperature, the combination might encourage the growth and spread of disease-causing organisms. The provision of ventilation in a storage room ensures that condensation of moisture does not occur, while harmful gases do not build up in the room.

Rodents are usually controlled by using mechanical traps and baits. Insect pests are commonly managed by the use of fumigants. To reduce pests and diseases, the grain should be dried to the appropriate moisture content prior to storing. The storehouse should be adequately ventilated. Storage insects are more prevalent in certain parts of the United States than others. Storage insects are more difficult to control in the southern states.

10: MECHANICALLY HARVESTED FORAGE

Livestock producers grow forage crops in the field to be grazed by livestock. Sometimes, they graze animals on native (or wild) pasture. Green pastures are not available year-round to livestock producers because of seasonal factors and the vagaries of the weather. Forage species grow slowly or become dormant in winter, or they may not be accessible to livestock (e.g., because of rainfall). Most forage species are productive for 7 months. Hence, additional feed is needed for 3 to 4 months. Livestock producers must have feed year-round for their animals. Some forage crop is hence mechanically harvested and stored in various forms for use during the off-season.

Mechanically harvested forage costs about twice as much as grazed forage. It is costly in terms of labor, machinery, and time. Consequently, the first choice of forage managers is to extend the growing season—for example, by planting mixtures of forage species or by overseeding a winter annual on fields that have dormant warm season species.

There are two main products of mechanically harvested forage—hay and **silage** (or **ensilage**). A third product, *haylage,* is considered to be a cross between hay and silage. There is also *green chop,* or *soilage,* fresh forage harvested each day for livestock feeding.

Silage (ensilage).
Forage that is chemically changed and preserved in succulent condition by fermentation.

10.1 MAKING HAY

Hay is herbage of grasses or other fine-stemmed plants that are harvested and cured for forage. It is the most durable of the harvested forages, keeping its quality for a long time in storage. Hay is made literally "while the sun shines" and under aerobic conditions.

Wild hay is harvested from mature species that grow in the wild. Crop species can be deliberately planted in pure stands or mixtures and harvested as hay. The most widely used hay crops are alfalfa (pure and mixtures), clover and timothy grass (or other grass) mixtures, wild hay, grain hay, and lezpedeza. Others are tall fescue, bromegrass, sudangrass, sweet clover, and vetch. Just like grain crops, the quality of hay depends on the stage of maturity of the plant material.

Hay production in 2001 totaled 157 million tons harvested from 63.5 million acres, with an average yield of 2.47 tons/acre. Texas led the United States in total production of all hay (accounting for 10.8 million tons), followed by South Dakota, California, and Kansas, in order of decreasing production. Alfalfa hay production in 2001 totaled 80.3 million tons, harvested from 23.8 million acres and averaging 3.37 tons/acre. The production of all other hay totaled 76.4 million tons.

Stage of Development of Plant Material

Young, immature plant material may yield low dry matter but is high in nutritional quality and palatability. Crops for hay are cut at certain intervals. This can be labor-intensive and time-consuming. However, delay in cutting plants can result in an increase in plant fiber content (lignin increases), resulting in decreased nutritional quality. Grasses for hay are best cut between early bloom and full bloom, while sweet clover is best cut when in the bud stage. Cereal crops may be grown for hay. They are most desirable when cut at the soft- to medium-dough stage of grain development. Since hay crops are cut several times during the growing season, it is critical that each cut does not endanger regrowth for the next round of cutting. Improper cutting can reduce plant vigor, reducing the yield of subsequent cuts. For example, alfalfa is more nutritious when cut prior to bloom. However, cutting in the bud stage reduces plant vigor more than when cutting is delayed until full bloom. The nutritional quality of hay changes as the plant matures (Table 1). In alfalfa, for example, prebloom crude protein is about 22%, while seed storage protein is about 14%. Conversely, prebloom crude fiber is about 25%, while seed-stage level is about 37%. The trend is the same in grasses.

Curing

Hay is commonly cut by a tractor mower, windrower, or mower-crusher-windrower and left in the field to cure in the sun (sun-cured hay). To hasten the curing process and minimize losses, hay crushers or conditioners may be used to crush the herbage between rolls. The goal of curing is to dry the crop to 25% moisture or less. The drying process should occur such that the herbage retains its nutrients and good green color. In the event of rain during the curing process, the hay may be stirred using a machine called a *tedder.* Rapid drying reduces field-curing losses such as leaf loss, dry matter loss, loss of nutrients, spoilage, reduced palatability, and loss of color. Leaf loss is very serious, since leaves contain most of the nutrients (proteins, vitamins, calcium, and others).

Table 1 The Effect of Stage of Maturity on Chemical Composition of Hay

Hay Crop and Selected Stages of Maturity	Chemical Composition (%)				
	Ash	Crude Protein	Crude Fiber	Nitrogen Free Extract	Ether Extract (Fat)
Legume (Alfalfa)					
Prebloom	11.24	21.98	25.13	38.72	2.93
Half bloom	10.69	18.84	28.12	39.45	2.90
Full bloom	9.36	18.13	30.82	38.70	2.99
Seed stage	7.33	14.06	36.61	39.61	2.39
Grass (Timothy)					
No head showing	8.41	10.18	26.31	50.49	4.61
Beginning to head	7.61	8.02	31.15	49.14	4.07
Full bloom	6.10	5.90	33.74	51.89	2.38
Seed (dough stage)	5.38	5.06	30.21	56.48	2.87
Seed (mature)	5.23	5.12	31.07	55.87	2.72

Source: Extracted from *Principles of field crop production.* 2nd ed. NY. Macmillan.

Hay may be artificially cured. This method has reduced losses, compared with sun-curing. The hay is first left to dry to about 35 to 40% moisture, then dried artificially in the storage structure. Unheated air is forced through the hay using blowers. Drying may also be accomplished by using heated air.

Certain losses accompany field-curing of hay. These losses can be minimized with rapid curing. There are nutrient losses from loss of leaves (they contain most of the plant's protein, vitamins, phosphorus, and calcium). In alfalfa, leaf loss may be about 6 to 9% of total weight. There is also 10 to 25% loss of dry matter. Oxidation causes carotene to decompose immediately.

Dehydrated Hay

Hay dehydration is an expensive process. Chopped hay is placed into a rotary drum drier at 760° to 815°C (1,400° to 1,500°F). The product from this process is of high quality.

Raking (Windrowing)

The third activity in hay harvesting is raking. When hay is mowed in strips (called *swaths*), a side delivery rake or a buncher attached to the mower may be used to windrow the herbage.

Processing (Packaging)

After curing, the hay is packaged for storage. Hay may be processed in one of several ways:

1. *Baled hay.* Baling is the most common packaging for cured hay. It is done by using a *field baler.* This implement gathers the windrowed hay, compresses it, and rolls it into a cylinder (called *rolled bale* or *round bale*). The bale is tied with twine or wrapped with plastic (Figure 6). Some round bales may weigh up to 2,500 lb (1,135 kg). Baling equipment may also be designed to produce square-shaped bales *(square bales)* (Figure 7). Square bales weigh up to 80 lb (36 kg). Some of the modern square bales weigh 400 kg or more.

FIGURE 6 Round bales may be unwrapped or wrapped in plastic, the latter being a newer method that preserves the quality of the hay for a longer period.

FIGURE 7 Square bales vary in size, but they are much easier to handle by one person.

2. *Stacked hay.* Before baling was introduced, hay was simply stacked in piles, using a hay stacker. A stack may be as heavy as 6 tons. Instead of baling, hay may be compressed and stacked. Hay may also be stored loose in the loft or mow of the barn.

3. *Chopped hay.* Hay may be chopped into small pieces by a field forage harvester and blown into a trailer. This may be dehydrated and then pelleted or pressed into wafers of 12 to 16% moisture content. Chopped-hay production can be completely mechanized.

10.2 MAKING SILAGE

As previously mentioned, silage is a forage crop preserved in succulent condition by the process of fermentation (i.e., under anaerobic conditions). In what fundamental ways is haying different from ensiling? Silage is made under anaerobic conditions. To prepare silage, green forage is chopped and stored in a silo. If silage is properly prepared and stored, nutritive losses are minimal.

Storage Containers

Bunker silos are generally less expensive to construct. Trench silos are suited to semiarid and arid regions because of both low cost and less interference from rain during filling or emptying of the containers. Trench and bunker silos are amenable to automatic feeding by means of movable feeding racks at the end. The animals reach through the rack for the feed and move it forward as the feed is consumed. Automatic unloaders may be used to unload tower silos.

Silage may be stored in one of six containers:

1. *Bunker silos.* Bunker silos are erected above the ground with concrete or wood.
2. *Trench silos.* Trench silos are constructed such that the container top is level with the ground level.
3. *Stack silos.* Stack silos entail piling up the silage in stacks on the ground and covering the stacks with sheets of plastic.
4. *Tower silos.* Tower silos are circular structures with vertical walls reaching about 60 feet (18.2 meters) high and 30 feet (9.1 meters) in diameter.
5. *Plastic sacks.* Silage may be stored in commercially prepared sacks such as AGBAG®.
6. *Pit silos.* These are like giant cisterns located in the ground.

Crops Used for Silage

Corn silage production in 2001 was estimated at 102.4 million tons, harvested from 6.2 million acres, with an average yield of 10.6 tons/acres. Sorghum silage production was estimated at 3.7 million tons.

Corn and sorghum are the two principal silage crops. Alfalfa is used significantly in certain regions (e.g., Midwest). However, any carbohydrate-rich crop (i.e., more than two parts of carbohydrate to protein) may be used. Corn is the crop of choice for silage. It yields the best product when ensiled when the grain is in the dough stage. There is a loss of dry matter when more mature corn is used. Under drought conditions, sorghum is preferred over corn as a silage crop. For sorghum silage, it is best to harvest at a later maturity (stiff dough stage) than corn. The product at this stage is less palatable to animals.

Other silage crops include forage grasses (e.g., timothy) and legumes (e.g., alfalfa, clover, vetch, and soybean). Alfalfa is comparable to corn in palatability when used for silage. Sugar beet and certain wild plants are also usable. Silage prepared from coarse materials such as stems of corn and sorghum after harvesting is called *stalkage.*

Advantages of Silage

Crops used for silage can be harvested even under wet conditions, since no drying is required. Silage making is a means of preserving succulent roughage for winter feedings as well as saving forages that otherwise would be wasted, damaged, or completely lost. Whereas ensiling is relatively more expensive than haying, silage has the advantage of preserving a greater proportion of the nutritive value of the green plant.

10.3 MAKING SILAGE BY FERMENTATION

Silage is formed under anaerobic conditions. The silage crop is chopped and stored in a tight silo at 60 to 70% moisture content. The plant material is packed into silos. It may be necessary and desirable to trample by feet or with a tractor. The trench silo is more durable in dry regions.

After closing the silo, the microorganisms respire aerobically during the first few hours (3 to 5 hours). This activity increases the carbon dioxide concentration in the chamber to about 70% (the remainder is mainly nitrogen). This condition favors the rapid growth and multiplication of lactic acid-forming bacteria, reaching millions per gram of silage.

The bacteria convert glucose in the plant tissue to alcohol and then to mostly lactic acid (and others such as acetic and succinic acids, in minute quantities, temperature reaching 60°C, or 140°F). This occurs in about 3 to 4 days. Corn and sorghum content are easily fermented, producing acidity in the process. Due to low content of basic elements, the pH of the environment reaches about 4 or lower. Legume species produce high pH due to their low soluble carbohydrate content and high calcium content. The most desirable pH for silage is 4.6. Poor-quality silage contains significant amounts of other acids (e.g., butyric acid, acetic acid, succinic acid, and ammonia). The odor of poor-quality silage comes from these additional chemicals, especially butyric acid and ammonia. Further, proteins and amino nitrogen are broken down to ammonia forms. These forms are less digestible and, coupled with the odor, make poor-quality silage less palatable.

Leaf color changes slightly during fermentation, even though the carotene content is relatively unchanged. Ensiling is completed in about 12 days. The finished product, if properly done, has a pleasant odor and a sour taste.

Certain energy and material losses occur during the fermentation process. There is a loss of energy as glucose is changed to lactic acid and then to butyric acid. There is also a loss of dry matter (5 to 20%) through gases and seepage. Exposure to air (through cracks in the container) can result in spoilage.

10.4 CAUSES OF POOR-QUALITY SILAGE

The principal causes of poor-quality silage are improper anaerobic conditions, poor-quality crop material, and improper moisture content.

Improper Anaerobic Conditions

Good-quality silage has an alcoholic odor and sour taste. Poor-quality silage, on the other hand, has a strong odor caused by high concentration of ammonia, hydrogen sulfide, and butyric acid. The two key organic acids associated with silage production are butyric acid and lactic acid. Glucose is converted to lactic acid, which in turn is converted to butyric acid. The amount of lactic acid increases rapidly as fermentation progresses, producing good-quality silage. However, under unfavorable conditions, lactic acid is rapidly converted to butyric acid. The high amount of butyric acid (and the low amount of lactic acid) is the key factor in the poor quality of silage.

Poor-Quality Crop Material

Garbage in, garbage out! Ensiling, contrary to popular misconception, does not improve the nutritional quality of the product. If the plant material is not at the proper stage of maturity, the product will be of low quality. From a nutritional standpoint, it is critical that the total digestible nutrients (i.e., protein content, fiber content, and dry matter content) be optimal in the plant material at harvest. Poor-quality material may also be due to the presence of foreign matter.

The science of ensiling

Fermentation is the key biochemical process in ensiling. The task of the silage producer is to manage fermentation by providing optimal conditions for this anaerobic process to occur. The ensiling process is not identical for all crop species, even though the principles are the same. For best results, the producer should be familiar with the fine details regarding optimum conditions for the crop species of interest. Changes that occur in conditions during the ensiling process involve moisture, temperature, and air composition. There are five basic phases of ensiling:

Phase 1: Loading the silo (aerobic phase). The plant material is chopped and placed in the silo. It is important to load quickly, distribute evenly, and pack tightly to reduce air damage. Plant cells continue to respire while bacteria use up the oxygen to digest the carbohydrates in the plant material. With time, the oxygen concentration drops while carbon dioxide concentration increases. There is a dramatic rise in temperature in the silo. Too high a rise in temperature (above 100°F) may cause decomposition of silage and a poor-quality product.

Phase 2: Acetic acid production (anaerobic phase). All the oxygen is used and plant cells die. Digestion of fermentable carbohydrates continues. Organic acids, primarily acetic acid, are produced, resulting in the lowering of pH from 6.0 to 4.2.

Phase 3: Lactic acid formation. This phase starts on the third day. Acetic acid production declines while lactobacillus bacteria multiply rapidly, causing the production of lactic acid.

Phase 4: Lactic acid formation continues. Lactic acid production continues for about 2 more weeks. The temperature gradually drops to the 80s; pH drops to 3.8 as a result of organic acid produced. At this acidity, bacterial digestion of fermentable carbohydrates ceases.

Phase 5: Steady phase. The pH holds steady and the acids in the system prevent further breakdown of carbohydrates in the silage. At proper storage conditions, the silage will be preserved by the organic acids generated for a long period.

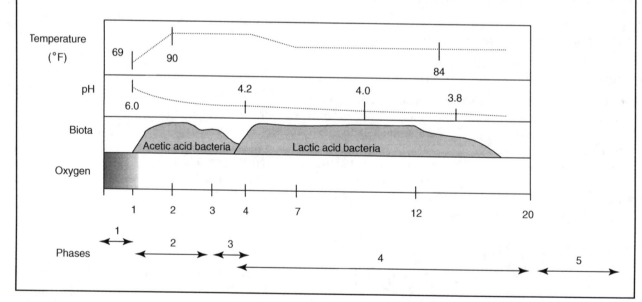

Improper Moisture Content

The moisture content of beginning plant materials should be 60 to 70%. Materials with high moisture (above 70%) have low carbohydrate content and may not attain the desired anaerobic environment needed for fermentation. Undesirable organic acids may form under such conditions. Further, the desirable low pH (3.6 to 4.6) may not occur. However, when the moisture content of the material is low (below 60%), anaerobic conditions may not develop at all (unless the material is stored in an airtight container). This situation may cause molds to grow, leading to poor-quality silage.

10.5 ENHANCING SILAGE QUALITY

The quality of silage produced may be enhanced by several means:

1. Use finely chopped (0.25 to 0.50 inches, or 0.63 to 1.27 centimeters) plant material and compact it very well in the silo to eliminate air for high anaerobic conditions to occur.
2. Include silage additives such as phosphoric or hydrochloric acids to lower the pH of the environment to the optimal level.
3. Increase the carbohydrate content of the silage material by adding ground grains and molasses.
4. Decrease the moisture in the silage material, if necessary, by using partially withered (60 to 70% moisture content) grasses and legumes instead of using all fresh materials.

10.6 HAYLAGE

Hay is dried to a low moisture content (about 10%), whereas silage retains a high moisture content (70 to 80%). Haylage is forage that has been cut and rapidly dried to about 40 to 60% moisture content. It is sometimes described as specialized forage for horses. Because hay has a low moisture content, mold spores easily become air-borne and may cause an allergic respiratory disease, called chronic obstructive pulmonary disease (commonly called broken wind, dust cough, or dust allergy), that is prevalent in the horse industry. Once affected, a horse never recovers and requires special care to manage the problem. Haylage reduces this disease incidence.

Haylage is semiwilted forage that has been allowed to dry for 1 or 2 days, then compressed and packed into heat-sealed bags (layers of stretch film). Hence, it is sometimes called *round bale silage*. The forage then undergoes rapid fermentation, producing a final pH of 5–5.5. The curing period is less than that of silage production. The moisture at baling is critical (50 to 60%); if it is too high, the feed quality will be reduced. However, lower moisture reduces fermentation and increases mold production. An inoculant (e.g., *Lactobacillus plantarum* MTDT) may be added to control yeast and molds and to improve the efficiency of fermentation to lactic acid and dry matter recovery.

10.7 SOILAGE (GREEN CHOP)

Sometimes, livestock cannot get to the pasture to graze the forage. The forage may then be harvested fresh each day and taken to the animals. There is no curing or wet preservation involved. Feeding by green chop is a laborious practice. Drought-damaged corn may be used for animal feed. However, because corn is heavily fertilized with nitrogen, the shoot often contains high quantities of nitrates. When such material is used for silage, some of the nitrates are neutralized. However, using drought-stricken corn for green chop can be very hazardous to livestock, even more so when the chopped material sits in the feed bunks or feed wagons in the heat for a long time. This condition causes nitrates to be converted to nitrites, which are about 10 times more toxic to animals than nitrates are.

SUMMARY

1. Potential crop yield depends on the cultivar, production inputs and practices, weather factors, and the methods of harvesting and storage.
2. The best time of harvesting depends on the economic part of the plant, utilization, and the method of storage.
3. Improper timing of harvesting causes yield reduction, reduction in product quality, and loss of economic value.
4. Field crops can be harvested by humans using manual or mechanical methods or by animals (grazing or browsing).
5. Harvest time may be hastened by methods such as defoliation, dessication, and topping.
6. To prevent spoilage in storage, the grain should be in proper condition prior to being placed in storage (e.g., right moisture content of material). The storage conditions should be appropriate (temperature and moisture).
7. Saprophytic fungi are the most important microbes in quality deterioration of stored grain.
8. The quality of hay depends on the stage of maturity of the plant material and the curing process.
9. Corn and sorghum are the two most common silage crops.
10. Some crops are difficult to dry to desirable moisture content in the field and thus require additional drying in storage.
11. Silage making is an anaerobic process. Too high or too low moisture content of materials causes improper anaerobic environment, leading to poor-quality silage.

REFERENCES AND SUGGESTED READING

Anderson, K. B. *Grain producer marketing alternatives.* Stillwater, Oklahoma State University, Current Report, CR-480.

Burton, W. G. 1982. *Postharvest physiology of food crops.* London: Longman.

Hall, C. W., ed. 1980. *Drying and storage of agricultural crops.* Westport, CT: AVI.

Horrocks, R. D., and J. F. Vallentine. 1999. *Harvested forages.* Academic Press.

Richardson, C. W., and L. Rommann. *Harvesting and ensiling silage crops.* Oklahoma State University Stillwater, Extension Facts, No. 2039.

Tilley, D. S., and K. B. Anderson. *Wheat producer's marketing objectives and plans.* Oklahoma State University Stillwater, Extension Facts, No. 472.

SELECTED INTERNET SITES FOR FURTHER REVIEW

http://www.farmphoto.com/album2/html/noframe/fld00102.asp

Silos and storage bins.

http://www.farmphoto.com/album2/html/noframe/fld00099.asp

Hay balers.

http://www.farmphoto.com/album2/html/noframe/fld00114.asp

Forage; baling of hay.

http://www.encarta.msn.com/find/MediaMax.asp?pg=3&ti=761558496&idx=
461516721

Harvesting wheat.

http://www.encarta.msn.com/find/MediaMax.asp?pg=3&ti=761558496&idx=
461568310

Combine harvesting of corn.

http://www.encarta.msn.com/find/MediaMax.asp?pg=3&ti=761558496&idx=
46156518

Baling hay (round bales).

http://www.das.psu.edu/dcn/catforg/396/phases.html

Discussion of silage making.

OUTCOMES ASSESSMENT

PART A

Answer the following questions true or false.

1. T F The stage of development in the lifecycle of a plant when the plant reaches maximum dry weight is called physiological maturity.
2. T F The remains of corn or sorghum plants in the field after the ear or head is removed are called the stover.
3. T F Curing hay increases its succulence.
4. T F Excessive drying of grain in the field causes bin burn.
5. T F Seeds in a single head of grain ripen uniformly.

PART B

Answer the following questions.

1. Define physiological maturity.

2. The best time to harvest a crop depends on three main factors. Name them.

3. What is stover?

4. Give four of the major microbes involved in deterioration of grain in storage.

5. Give four of the major storage insect pests.

6. What is bin burn?

7. The method of harvesting whereby the crop is cut, gathered, and left in piles in rows in the field is called _____.

PART C

Write a brief essay on the following topics.

1. Discuss the role of weather factors in grain harvesting.

2. Discuss the methods of mechanical harvesting of field crops.

3. Discuss the consequences of improper timing of crop harvesting.

4. Discuss harvest maturity of field crops.

5. Discuss the desired quality of a grain product.

6. Describe how microbes cause deterioration of grain in storage.

7. Describe the process of curing of hay.

8. Describe the making of silage by fermentation.

9. Discuss the factors that affect longevity of stored grain.

PART D

Discuss or explain the following topics in detail:

1. How important is mechanized harvesting to modern crop production?

2. A high-quality grain product from storage should have certain characteristics. Discuss these characteristics.

3. Distinguish between the methods of storing dry grain and storing fresh produce.

Crop Improvement

PURPOSE

This chapter is devoted to discussing the genetic basis of crop improvement and the methods employed by plant breeders in the development of new crop cultivars.

EXPECTED OUTCOMES

After studying this chapter, the student should be able to:

1. Discuss basic Mendelian concepts.
2. Discuss the principles of plant breeding.
3. Describe the steps in plant breeding.
4. Discuss the various breeding systems.
5. Discuss the strategies for increased crop productivity (breeding objectives).
6. Discuss the role of biotechnology in crop improvement.

KEY TERMS

Allele	Genotype	Phenotype
Biotechnology	Harvest index	Recombinant DNA
Cross-pollination	Heritability	Self-pollination
Gene	Heterosis	Transgenic plant

TO THE STUDENT

Plant breeders genetically manipulate crop plants for high productivity. They manipulate plants based on their understanding and application of various basic sciences, especially genetics, the science of heredity. They are more concerned about the heritable aspects of crop productivity. A plant cannot be forced to produce a product for which it has no

From Chapter 5 of *Principles of Crop Production: Theory, Techniques, and Technology*, Second Edition, George Acquaah.
Copyright © 2005 by Pearson Education, Inc. Published by Pearson Prentice Hall. All rights reserved.

genes. Genes are not expressed in a vacuum but in an environment. Organisms can express their genetic potential only to the extent permitted by their environment. Therefore, a high-yielding cultivar is only as good as its cultural environment. That is, in order for a crop to yield highly, it must be provided adequate nutrients, moisture, and other essential growth factors. Some of the specific goals of plant genetic manipulation are to:

1. Improve the yield of a desired plant product (e.g., grain, oil)
2. Improve the quality of a desirable product (e.g., protein quality)
3. Adapt a crop to different climatic areas
4. Change the morphology of a plant (e.g., change a climber to a bush cultivar)
5. Protect plants from diseases and pests

Crop improvement is an art and a science. As the years go by, it is increasingly becoming science-based. In this chapter, both the traditional and cutting-edge plant breeding methodologies are discussed. The topics discussed include a review of pertinent genetic principles, conventional plant breeding methodologies, common plant breeding objectives, and the role of biotechnology in plant improvement.

1: THE SCIENCE OF GENETICS

1.1 GENES CONTROL THE EXPRESSION OF HERITABLE TRAITS

Gene. The basic unit of heredity comprised of base pairs in the DNA and functioning to determine the synthesis of a particular polypeptide.

Allele. One of two or more alternate forms of a gene.

The science of genetics is critical to understanding and conducting plant breeding. Gregor Mendel first discovered that plant traits, or characteristics, are passed from parents to offspring according to certain predictable patterns. He discovered that traits are controlled by hereditary factors called **genes**. The alternative expressions of a gene are called **alleles**. A pair of such alleles resides at a location on a chromosome and interacts to produce the observed trait. For example, Mendel observed that the gene for flower color in the pea plant (*Pisum*) had two alleles, one that determined purple color and the other white. When two plants with these contrasting expressions of this trait were crossed, the offspring had purple flowers. When two of the offspring with purple flowers were crossed (selfed), he observed both purple- and white-flowered plants in the progeny. These outcomes were explained by the genetic analysis in Figure 1. Purple flower is controlled by a dominant allele that suppresses the expression of the white flower allele (the recessive allele) in the first cross product or *first filial generation* (F_1). Upon selfing of two F_1s, the two alleles reappeared in the F_2. Mendel formulated two laws to explain these events:

1. *Mendel's law I (the law of segregation).* This law states that the pair of alleles of a gene separate (segregate) independently during gamete formation such that only one form of each pair ends up in each gamete (egg or pollen grain).
2. *Mendel's law II (the law of independent assortment).* This law states that pairs of alleles of a gene controlling different traits separate independently of each other during gamete formation and combine randomly to form zygotes.

The pattern is the same for cases involving more than one gene (*monohybrid cross*), only more complex. Try genetic analysis involving two genes (*dihybrid cross*) and then three genes (*trihybrid cross*). A plant breeder needs to know the inheritance of a trait before he or she can develop appropriate strategies to manipulate it. Breeding methods for traits controlled by dominant genes differ from those used for traits controlled by recessive genes.

(a)

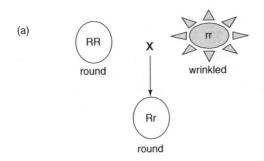

(b)

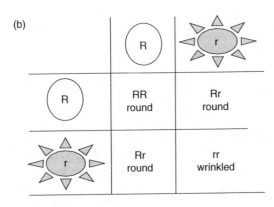

FIGURE 1 Mendel's laws: (a) dominance and recessiveness and (b) segregation in a monohybrid cross with dominance. The expression of the recessive allele is suppressed in the F₁ but is expressed in the F₂.

FIGURE 1 Mendel's laws: (a) dominance and recessiveness and (b) segregation in a monohybrid cross with dominance. The expression of the recessive allele is suppressed in the F_1 but is expressed in the F_2.

Landmark genetic-based impact on crop production

Domestication of plants (the invention of agriculture in 10,000 B.C.) was accompanied by thousands of years of primitive and slow efforts at improving crop productivity. Farmers learned through experience and trial-and-error to identify and select better-performing plants with greater adaptation to the cultural environment. The quality and quantity of agricultural products gradually increased over long periods of time.

The first significant and dramatic change in the performance of crop plants came in the 1860s, when Gregor Mendel discovered the laws of inheritance. With a better understanding of plant genetics, scientists were equipped to manipulate plants with more purposefulness and greater success. Plant breeding became more of a science than an art. Plant breeding is viewed as the "old biotech." Crop plant products increased in quality. Further, crop productivity also increased. The most dramatic change in crop productivity came with the development of *hybrids*. Exploiting the phenomenon of hybrid vigor, hybrids outyield their counterparts. These hybrids were first developed in cereal grains. Using the hybrid technology, the next major impact of genetics on crop productivity came with the Green Revolution of the 1960s. Short-stalked corn, rice, and wheat cultivars that were environmentally responsive (adapted to high-input agriculture) revolutionized crop production in the tropics. Hybrids have been developed for many crops including non-cereal plants.

The next most significant leap in crop productivity was brought about by the introduction of molecular techniques into plant breeding in the 1980s. Molecular plant breeding technology was able to circumvent some of the limitations of conventional breeding. Genes can now be transferred across literally all natural biological barriers, since deoxyribonucleic acid (DNA) is universal. New plant types equipped to exploit the production environment and resist diseases and insect pests have been produced. The "old" and "new" biotechnologies work together.

1.2 ONE OR A FEW GENES CONTROL SOME TRAITS; SEVERAL TO MANY GENES CONTROL OTHERS

Plant breeders need to have an idea about the number (few or many) of genes that control a trait. Traits controlled by one or a few genes are classified as *qualitative traits* or simply *inherited traits,* while traits controlled by many genes are called *quantitative traits* or *polygenic traits.* In the F_2, qualitative traits can be categorized into non-overlapping groups (e.g., white vs. purple flowers, green vs. yellow cotyledons) by counting. Quantitative traits (or metrical traits), on the other hand, are measured or weighed. Many traits of agronomic importance, such as yield, are quantitative traits. They are influenced by the environment to a greater extent than are qualitative traits. That is, changing the growth environment (through irrigation, fertilization, or temperature control) can change the degree of expression in production.

1.3 CERTAIN GENES MAY INTERFERE WITH THE EXPRESSION OF OTHER GENES

Can scientists always predict the exact outcome of a cross between two parents of known genotypes? There are certain occasions on which the outcomes of a cross cannot be predicted. In the expression of a trait that is controlled by several genes, the phenomenon of *epistasis* may cause one gene to mask the expression of another. When this occurs, the expected Mendelian ratios in the F_2 are not observed (i.e., *non-Mendelian inheritance*). For example, instead of 9:3:3:1, various outcomes such as 15:1 or 9:7 may be observed. Another factor that causes this deviation from expected ratios is *genetic linkage,* the physical association of adjacent genes on a chromosome that prevents independent assortment. It is desirable for certain genes to be linked. However, in certain situations a desirable gene is linked with an undesirable one. This presents a problem for breeders when they attempt to enhance the desirable trait. The process of *crossing over* that occurs during *meiosis* (the process by which gametes, or sex cells, are formed) breaks linkage naturally.

1.4 GENES INTERACT WITH THE ENVIRONMENT TO PRODUCE A VISIBLE TRAIT

Genotype. The genetic constitution of a cell or an organism.

Phenotype. The appearance of an organism as a result of the combined influence of its genetic constitution and environmental factors.

The genetic makeup (the sum total of all the genes in a cell) of an individual constitutes an individual's **genotype** (or *genome*). For academic purposes, genes are represented by letters, an uppercase for a dominant allele and a lowercase for a recessive allele (e.g., GG, Gg, gg). When the pair of alleles is identical (GG), the location *(locus)* of the gene is said to be *homozygous;* otherwise it is *heterozygous* (Gg). The observed trait is called a **phenotype.** A homozygous locus and a heterozygous locus have the same phenotype if the locus is under dominance gene action. The environment and modifier genes may also alter the manifestation of a genotype.

1.5 DNA IS THE GENETIC MATERIAL

The hereditary material DNA occurs in chromosomes. Is the DNA the sole hereditary material for all organisms? (A few organisms such as certain viruses have RNA and no DNA.) DNA consists of four *nitrogenous bases* (adenine, thymine, cytosine, and guanine, which are represented as A, T, C, and G, respectively), a *sugar* (deoxyribose), and a *phosphate.* When these three components link up, they form a *nucleotide,* the unit of

Mitosis: Producing cells for growth and development

Mitosis is a process by which the nucleus of a cell divides after the chromosomes have doubled. This division results in two daughter nuclei that are identical to the nucleus of the parent. Mitosis is the foundation for growth and development of eukaryotes. A multicellular organism begins life as a *zygote*, the product of the fusion of an egg and sperm. Genetically, the zygote is a diploid (two sets of chromosomes). Mitotic division results in identical cells that later may differentiate into complex structures in the plant. Increase in size of the plant is largely due to an increase in the number of cells resulting from mitosis. When plants become injured, damaged tissue is repaired by producing new cells through mitosis.

Mitosis usually consists of two kinds of division: *nuclear* (or *karyokinesis*) and *cytoplasmic (cytokinesis)*. The latter sometimes fails to occur. The sum of the phases of growth of an individual cell is called the *cell cycle*. Upon proper stimulation, the cells proceed to interphase (S). The S stage is where DNA synthesis begins in preparation for chromosome replication. It is followed by the G2 phase, in which DNA synthesis stops. Mitosis follows G2 and occurs in five stages: prophase, prometaphase, metaphase, anaphase, and telophase.

The cell cycle is under genetic control. A gene called *cdc2* (cell division cycle 2) that codes for the enzyme cdc kinase is essential for the entry of a cell into mitosis. Another gene, P.53, is responsible for arresting the cell cycle in the G1 stage.

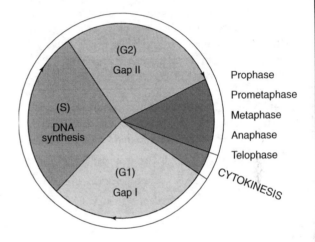

A summary of the cell cycle.

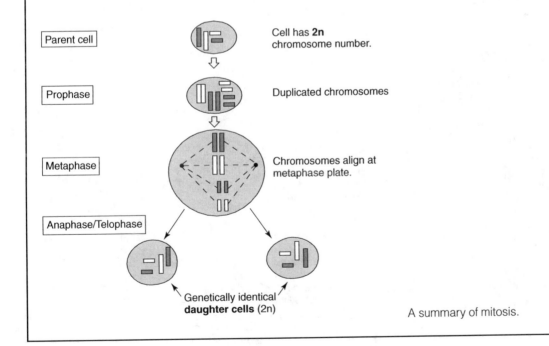

A summary of mitosis.

Meiosis: Producing sex cells and generating biological variation

Meiosis, unlike mitosis, occurs only in sexually reproducing organisms. It involves two successive nuclear divisions, after which the resulting daughter nuclei have reduced amounts of genetic material and are unidentical to the parent nuclei. The resulting cells have half the chromosomes (haploid number) of the parent nucleus. This is the process by which gametes (egg and pollen) or spores are formed. The parental diploid number is restored following fertilization, the process that unites haploid cells. Meiosis ensures genetic variation among members of a species by shuffling the parental chromosomes, and by the process of crossing over (exchange of parts of chromosomes between nonhomologous, or unidentical, chromosomes). This is followed by the independent assortment of chromosomes into gametes, thereby creating biological variation.

The process of meiosis is more involved than mitosis. Just like mitosis, it is preceded by DNA synthesis. The first nuclear division (meiosis I) is described as re-

ductional because the homologous chromosomes separate. The homologous chromosomes pair, or synapse (called *synapsis*), forming a structure called a *bivalent*. Bivalent chromosomes replicate to produce a tetrad of four chromatids. Prophase I in meiosis has five stages. During diplonema, non-sister chromatids exchange parts (*crossing over*) at one or a few areas where they intertwine. These regions are called *chiasmata* (singular, *chiasma*). At the end of meiosis I, the two homologs separate into two dyads of two chromosomes each, still joined at the centromere.

In meiosis II, the division is equational, each dyad separating into two *monads* of one chromosome each. Monads that were involved in crossing over are called *recombinant chromosomes* (have undergone genetic recombination to mix maternal and paternal genetic information). After telophase II, four unidentical gametes are produced.

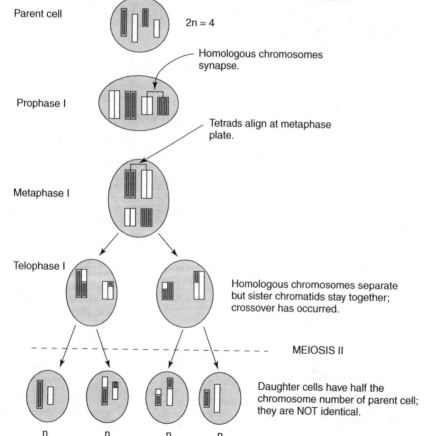

MEIOSIS I

A summary of meiosis

Parent cell — 2n = 4

Homologous chromosomes synapse.

Prophase I

Tetrads align at metaphase plate.

Metaphase I

Telophase I — Homologous chromosomes separate but sister chromatids stay together; crossover has occurred.

MEIOSIS II

Daughter cells have half the chromosome number of parent cell; they are NOT identical.

n   n   n   n

DNA (Figure 2). Numerous nucleotides join to form a chain called a *polynucleotide chain*. A DNA molecule consists of two polynucleotide chains that are linked in predetermined fashion by hydrogen bonds. In the bonding of the two chains, C always bonds with G, and A always with T. The two strands are complementary.

The message of the polynucleotide chain occurs in a *genetic code*. This code is a *triplet code* (three nucleotides), also called a *codon*, that codes for a specific amino acid. Amino acids then join in various fashions to create long chains called *polypeptide chains*. These chains combine in various ways to form protein. Each gene codes for one polypeptide chain.

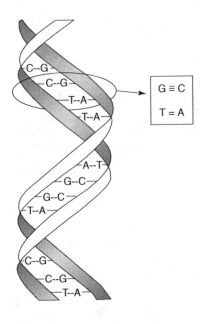

FIGURE 2 Structure of a DNA molecule. The double helical structure of the DNA molecule consists of a sugar-phosphate backbone connected by nitrogenous bases that pair in predictable and restrictive pattern.

Central dogma of molecular biology

Genetic information flow occurs in a certain fashion. The genetic message naturally flows in one direction, from DNA to proteins and not the reverse. This is called the *central dogma of molecular biology*. Because of advances in science, the reverse process is now routinely accomplished in the laboratory. Given a protein product, scientists can synthesize the corresponding DNA, called a *complementary DNA* or *cDNA*.

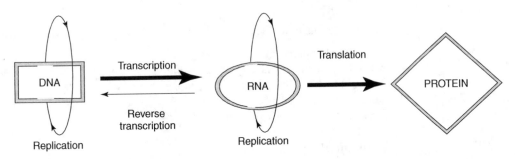

The central dogma of molecular biology describes the path of genetic information travel as normally from DNA to protein.

2: PLANT BREEDERS GENETICALLY MANIPULATE PLANTS TO PRODUCE NEW TRAITS

2.1 PLANT BREEDERS ARE GUIDED BY GENETIC PRINCIPLES IN THEIR WORK

Plant breeders are not able to genetically manipulate every trait. Therefore, it is important for them to determine whether or not a trait can be genetically manipulated before embarking on an improvement program. An underlying concept in making this decision is embodied in the following equation:

$$P = G + E$$

where P = phenotype, G = genotype, and E = environment. Simply stated, what is seen is a product of the interaction of the genotype with its environment. To change the phenotype, the genes that code for the trait may be changed (e.g., through crossing), the environment may be changed, or both factors may be changed. Changing the environment is done through agronomic practices (e.g., irrigation, fertilization, and pest control). Changing the genotype is permanent; changing the environment is only temporary, meaning that the conditions must always be reintroduced for the trait to be expressed.

Heritability. The degree of phenotypic expression of a trait that is under genetic control.

Another concept of importance to plant breeders is **heritability.** This is especially important when considering the improvement of a quantitative trait. Heritability is the degree of phenotypic expression of a trait that is under genetic control. Mathematically, it is expressed by the following equation:

$$H = Vg/Vp$$

where Vg = genetic variance and Vp = phenotypic variance. In this form, the formula estimates *heritability in the broad sense.* The values of this estimate range between 0.0 and 1.0 (or 0.0 and 100%). If the estimate of heritability is high, it indicates that the success of manipulating for improving a trait through breeding is likely. Otherwise, the trait may be enhanced through improving the cultural environment during crop production. In reality, both genotype and environment are important in production. A genotype is only as good as the environment in which it grows. High-yielding cultivars require good environment to attain their potential yield capacity.

2.2 CONVENTIONAL PLANT BREEDING FOLLOWS CERTAIN BASIC STEPS

How is plant breeding done? The general steps in a plant breeding program are as follows:

1. Determine the breeding objective(s).
2. Assemble genetic variability (or heritable variation).
3. Recombine the variation (cross, hybridize).
4. Select desirable recombinants.
5. Evaluate the selections.

Breeding Objectives

A breeding program is initiated for a specific purpose or objective. This may be yield increase, disease resistance, improved quality (e.g., high oil or protein content), and others as determined by the breeder. The method used for breeding depends on the objective (the trait to be manipulated and the direction of manipulation). A breeding objective may arise from the need of producers. For example, producers may desire a cultivar that does not shatter if harvesting time is delayed. They may desire disease resistance in an adapted cultivar or improvement in the architecture of the plant to adapt it to mechanized cultivation. Consumers may also dictate breeding objectives. If the end users of a crop product prefer a certain quality (e.g., sweeter taste, smaller size, high starch content), they will influence the breeding program in that direction. Plant breeders may also initiate objectives on their own. They may survey the producers and users to find problems that they encounter and then develop breeding programs to solve them. Selected objectives are discussed in detail later in this chapter.

Heritable Variation

Is all variation heritable? No, some variation is caused by differences in the environment. Without heritable variation, it is not possible to conduct a breeding program—that is, to genetically manipulate plants. If a breeder desires to increase the protein content of an existing cultivar, somewhere there must exist a genotype with high protein. Otherwise, such a trait must be induced, if possible, by mutation. Variation used in plant breeding can be obtained from many sources:

1. *Adapted cultivars.* These may be old and "retired," or "heirloom," cultivars, landraces (unimproved local variety), or even current cultivars in use. The advantage of using adapted material is that the new cultivar that is bred is already adapted to the environment and can be released to farmers much sooner.
2. *Recombinants.* New combinations or recombinants can be generated through recombination that occurs when genetically unidentical plants are crossed.
3. *Breeder seed.* When plant breeders conduct breeding programs, the newly created genotypes that do not make it to the farmer as cultivars may nonetheless have certain desirable qualities. These breeding materials are kept and may be incorporated into future breeding programs as needed.
4. *Plant introductions.* New plant types may be imported from other regions of the world. To aid researchers, certain facilities throughout the world are devoted to the collection and maintenance of plant variation. Plant breeders may request specific kinds of variation from such collections (called *germplasm banks*).
5. *Wild plants.* Cultivated plants have wild ancestors, or progenitors. These are excellent sources of genes for incorporating into breeding programs.
6. *Mutation.* Mutation is the ultimate source of variation. When all else fails, the breeder may attempt to induce the desired trait by subjecting plant materials to agents of mutation, or *mutagens*.

Recombination

The conventional way of creating variation is through hybridization, or crossing of two different plants. The effect of this action is the reorganization of the genotypes of the two plants into a new genetic matrix to create new recombinants. The ease of crossing varies from one species to another. In species where plants utilize pollen from the same plant, the breeder usually has a more difficult time with crossing. The flower of one plant must be designated as male and the other as female. The female flower is usually rid of all male organs by the often tedious process of *emasculation*. However, plants that are naturally cross-pollinated, and thus utilize pollen from other sources, do not need emasculation. The breeder simply plants the parents next to each other for pollen transfer to occur naturally by agents such as wind and insects.

It is critical that a cross be authenticated before it is used to continue a breeding program. A tag is often used, at a minimum, to identify the emasculated flower that becomes artificially pollinated. The seed from the putative cross can be further evaluated when the F_1 seed is planted, provided a genetic marker is incorporated in the breeding program. A *genetic marker* is a trait that is readily identified or assayed and is linked to another trait the breeder seeks to improve. When the marker is observed, the other trait, which is usually difficult to observe or evaluate, is assumed to be present.

Selection

After crossing, the breeding program proceeds with a series of selections (genetic discrimination) of desirable recombinants. The way selection is conducted depends on the method of breeding.

Evaluation

The evaluation phase of plant breeding entails testing a number of genotypes over several locations and years, in comparison with existing commercial varieties. The most desirable and superior performing genotype is then released as a new variety following existing protocol, and increased for distribution to farmers.

2.3 CONVENTIONAL PLANT BREEDING HAS CERTAIN LIMITATIONS

Conventional breeding is beset by the following weaknesses:

1. *Long duration.* The breeding program lasts for several to many years in some cases.
2. *Limited to crossing within species.* To hybridize, the parents must be compatible and belong to the same species (occasionally, crosses between different species is possible though problematic).
3. *Lower selection efficiency.* The methods used to sort among the enormous variations generated from a cross is not precise. This is the reason that markers are used to improve breeding efficiency.
4. *Large segregating population.* In order to have a high chance of identifying the recombinant of interest, plant breeders usually plant large numbers of plants in the segregating population (e.g., F_2). This requires large amounts of space and thus increases breeding expense.

3: METHODS OF BREEDING DEPEND ON THE BREEDING SYSTEM OF THE PLANTS

3.1 SOME PLANTS ARE PREDOMINANTLY SELF-POLLINATED, WHILE OTHERS ARE PREDOMINANTLY CROSS-POLLINATED SPECIES

Self-Pollination

Self-pollination. The transfer of pollen from the anthers of a plant to stigmas of flowers of the same plant "or a plant of the same genotype."

Self-pollination, or *autogamy* is the mating system in which pollen grains are transferred from the anther of one flower to the stigma of the same flower or that of another flower on the same plant. Progeny from such mating are said to be naturally inbred and are more uniform genetically and phenotypically. *Cleistogamy* (self-pollination that occurs in a flower before the bud opens) is a mechanism enforcing self-pollination. Examples of crop plants that are normally self-pollinated are presented in Table 1. Self-pollinated crops may experience some natural cross-pollination, normally less than 5%.

Cross–Pollination

Cross-pollination, or *allogamy,* is the sexual production in which a stigma may receive pollen (more than 40%) from sources other than the flower itself. Such species are prone to adverse consequences of loss of vigor (inbreeding depression) when they are artificially crossed. Like self-pollinated crop plants, certain natural mechanisms enforce cross-pollination. Dioecy (the occurrence of male and female plants in one species) and *self-incompatibility* (lack of self-fruitfulness) encourage cross-pollination. Examples of crops with normally predominant cross-pollination are given in Table 2.

Cross-pollination. The transfer of pollen from the anthers of one flower of a plant to the stigma of a flower of a different plant.

Table 1 Selected Predominantly Self-Pollinated Species	
Barley	*Hordeum vulgare*
Clover	*Trifolium* spp.
Common bean	*Phaseolus vulgaris*
Cotton	*Gossypium* spp.
Cowpea	*Vigna unguiculata*
Flax	*Linum usitatissimum*
Oat	*Avena sativa*
Pea	*Pisum sativum*
Peanut	*Arachis hypogea*
Rice	*Oryza sativa*
Sorghum	*Sorghum bicolor*
Soybean	*Glycine max*
Tobacco	*Nicotiana tabacum*
Tomato	*Lycopersicon esculentum*
Wheat	*Triticum aestivum*

Table 2 Selected Predominantly Cross-Fertilized Species	
Alfalfa	*Medicago sativa*
Buckwheat	*Fagopyrum esculentum*
Cassava	*Manihot esculentum*
Coconut	*Cocos nucifera*
Cucumber	*Cucumis sativa*
Corn	*Zea mays*
Fescue	*Festuca* spp.
Onion	*Allium cepa*
Potato	*Solanum tuberosum*
Pumpkin	*Cucurbita* spp.
Rye	*Secale cereale*
Sugar beet	*Beta vulgaris*
Sunflower	*Helianthus annus*
Sweet potato	*Ipomea batatas*

3.2   COMMON PLANT BREEDING METHODS

1. *Breeding methods for self-pollinated species.* The common methods of breeding self-pollinated species (Table 3) include mass selection (Figure 3), pedigree selection (Figure 4), and backcross (Figure 5).
2. *Breeding methods for cross-pollinated species.* Mass selection is applicable to cross-pollinated species. A very widely used method of improving cross-pollinated species, also used for self-pollinated species to a lesser extent (because of practical reasons), is *hybrid breeding* (Table 4).

Table 3   Selected Methods of Plant Breeding

Key Concepts in Mass Selection (See Figure 3)

1. Mass selection is the oldest of all breeding methods.
2. It is an easy and rapid method of breeding; it can be done by growers themselves.
3. It improves the population rather than creating a cultivar from a single plant.
4. It is based on visual selection (phenotypic-based) of the desired trait; hence, heritability is important. Success is limited if heritability is low.
5. It is applicable to both self- and cross-pollinated species.
6. It is suitable for breeding for horizontal resistance to diseases.
7. The product is heterogeneous.
8. Since selection is based on phenotype, the breeder should ensure that selection environment is homogeneous.

Key Concepts in Pedigree Selection (See Figure 4)

1. It is an extension of the pure-line breeding method.
2. It is started by crossing parents of a known genotype.
3. Record keeping is the key activity for maintaining an accurate record of relationship (pedigree).
4. Success depends on operator's skill and ability to identify desirable individuals.
5. Method is long if only one growing season per year is available.
6. Products have high genetic purity.
7. Suitable for breeding for vertical resistance to disease.

Key Concepts in Backcross (See Figure 5)

1. It is a conservative method of breeding; no recombination is allowed to occur to create new recombination of traits.
2. It is used for improving an existing highly desirable cultivar that is deficient in one or a few genes (e.g., lack of resistance to a particular disease).
3. It is effective for transferring qualitative trait genes.
4. It is easier for transferring monogenic dominant allele.
5. The outcome is predictable from the beginning.
6. The derived cultivar is like its progenitor plus the transferred trait.
7. It is suitable for introgression through wide crosses.
8. It may be combined with other breeding methods for specific purposes.

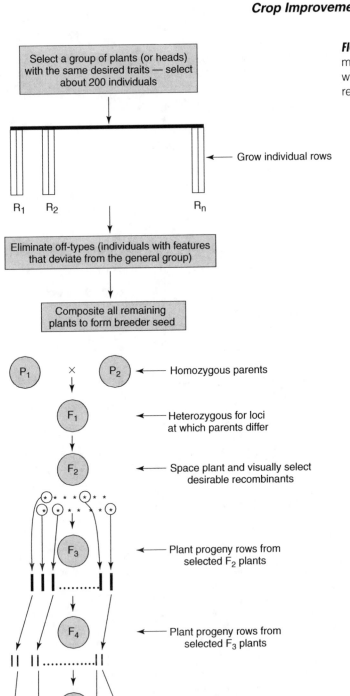

Select a group of plants (or heads) with the same desired traits — select about 200 individuals

Grow individual rows

R₁ R₂ Rₙ

Eliminate off-types (individuals with features that deviate from the general group)

Composite all remaining plants to form breeder seed

FIGURE 3 A summary of the mass selection breeding method. Mass selection is an "inclusive" strategy whereby only the atypical materials are discarded. The result is a product of a wide genetic base.

P_1 × P_2 ← Homozygous parents

F_1 ← Heterozygous for loci at which parents differ

F_2 ← Space plant and visually select desirable recombinants

F_3 ← Plant progeny rows from selected F_2 plants

F_4 ← Plant progeny rows from selected F_3 plants

F_5 ← Plant family rows from selected F_4 plants

F_6 ← Conduct preliminary yield trials

F_7 ← Conduct replicated trials, followed by location trials, certification, release in F_8-F_{12}

FIGURE 4 A summary of the pedigree breeding method. This method starts with a cross that is followed through the breeding program by maintaining records of lineage. This way, the breeder can always go back to reconstitute a particular cultivar. It is an "exclusive" method in which desirable recombinants are retained while all others are discarded.

FIGURE 5 A summary of the backcross method of breeding. This is a conser-vative method of breeding in which genetic recombination that produces genetic variability is prevented. The genotype of the original recipient parent is kept intact while incorporating only the donor gene.

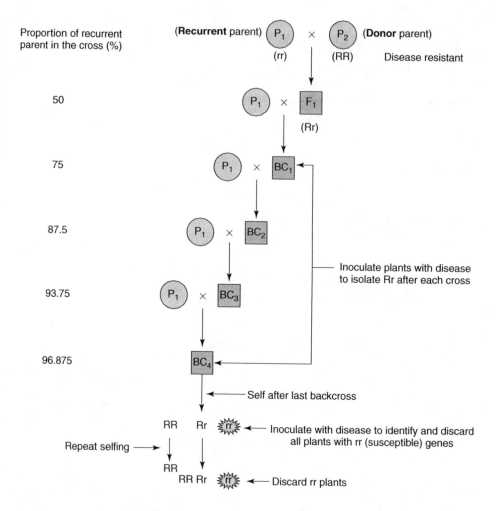

Proportion of recurrent parent in the cross (%)

(Recurrent parent) P_1 × P_2 **(Donor** parent)
(rr)   (RR)   Disease resistant

50   P_1 × F_1 (Rr)

75   P_1 × BC_1

87.5 P_1 × BC_2

Inoculate plants with disease to isolate Rr after each cross

93.75 P_1 × BC_3

96.875 BC_4

Self after last backcross

RR   Rr   rr ← Inoculate with disease to identify and discard all plants with rr (susceptible) genes

Repeat selfing → RR

RR Rr   rr ← Discard rr plants

Table 4 Breeding Hybrid Corn: Key Concepts

1. A hybrid is the progeny of a cross between two parents.
2. It depends on the phenomenon of **heterosis** (hybrid vigor) for success.
3. Commercial hybrid production requires the use of inbred lines (because they reproduce true to type and allow hybrids to be produced consistently year after year).
4. There are three basic types of crosses: single cross (A × B); double cross [(A × B) × (C × D)]; triple cross [(A × B) × C]. There are variations of these types.
5. The basic steps in hybrid productions are (a) development of inbred lines, (b) identification of compatible inbreds (combining ability for productivity), and (c) production of commercial seed by crossing and increasing seed from compatible inbred.
6. To cross, one inbred line is designated as male and the other as female (by emasculation—removing male parts of flower before self-fertilization).
7. Emasculation is tedious; hence, hybrids are easier to produce in a crop in which it can be done easily or avoided altogether.
8. To avoid emasculation, a cytoplasmic-genetic male sterility system is used in crops such as corn.

Heterosis. The increased vigor, growth, size, yield, or function of a hybrid progeny over the parents that results from crossing genetically unlike organisms.

4: COMMON PLANT BREEDING OBJECTIVES

Plant breeding is conducted to improve a variety of aspects of plants that eventually make for increased productivity and quality of product.

4.1 CROP YIELD IS OFTEN THE ULTIMATE GOAL OF CROP IMPROVEMENT

Yield is a product of the interaction of numerous physiological and biochemical plant processes. Breeding for higher yields requires understanding plant physiology, genetics, and agronomy, among other factors. In addition, the plant breeder has to be able to develop a model of that ideal genotype suited to a specified production environment.

Photosynthesis is the basis of crop yield through the production of dry matter. In order to increase crop productivity, the photosynthetic rate needs to be increased. Identifying or producing genotypes with improved morphology and functioning of the photosynthetic apparatus may accomplish this. Further, the dry matter produced should be partitioned or directed to organs of economic importance. This may be accomplished through the manipulation of the growth functions of these organs and the interaction between them.

4.2 BREEDING STRATEGIES FOR INCREASED CROP PRODUCTIVITY

There are several strategies for increased crop productivity, including improving photosynthetic efficiency, breeding for photosensitivity, determinate stem habit, dwarf stature, early maturity, yield stability, and improved harvest index.

Improving Photosynthetic Efficiency

Photosynthetic efficiency of a plant may be improved by improving light interception and leaf orientation, among other factors.

Light Interception   Photosynthetic efficiency is the primary component of dry matter productivity. It depends on several factors. Canopy light interception is the most important of these factors. Photosynthetic rates (crop growth rate) are higher in genotypes with more erect leaves, lower extinction coefficients, and therefore higher critical leaf area indices. Genetic control of short, stiff, upright leaf habit in rice has been studied. In order for a crop to realize maximum yield, leaf area should expand to reach its optimum rapidly. Further, the leaves should remain photoactive for a long period and during senescence be able to supply assimilates to the reproductive and/or storage organs.

Leaf Orientation (Angle)   Open crop canopy enhances the penetration of light into the crop canopy. Erect leaves (smaller leaf angle) are effective in increasing photosynthetic efficiency in small grains. These plants are planted at high densities for significant yield advantage.

Other Strategies   Scientists have studied the genetics of stomatal frequency and conductance and found high stomatal frequency to be associated with high photosynthetic rates.

Production of hybrids

A hybrid is the product of a cross between two parents that differ in one or more inherited traits (i.e., the parents are not identical). Hybrid breeding is often used to breed cross-pollinated species (even though it can be applied to self-pollinated species, but with less ease). Hybrid production exploits the phenomenon of heterosis. The following conditions are necessary to increase the chance of success of a hybridization program:

1. *Heterosis*. The parents must be compatible enough (high combining ability) to manifest a high degree of heterosis in the offspring.
2. *Elimination of fertile pollen from the female parent*. The female parent should not contribute any pollen to the progeny, only the egg. There should be a practical and inexpensive way of excluding the female pollen from the cross.
3. *Adequate pollination and fertility restoration*. The pollen source should supply adequate pollen to pollinate all plants in the breeding program.
4. *Availability and maintenance of parents*. Parents used in hybrid programs are inbred lines. There should be a system in the breeding program to maintain the parental lines in good condition.
5. *Efficient pollen transport*. Hand pollination is laborious, slow, and expensive. Commercial hybrid production should utilize economical pollen distribution—e.g., by wind or insects.
6. *High economic return*. Hybrid seed production is expensive and hence uneconomical to use in plants with low economic return.

Types of hybrids

There are three basic types of hybrids: single cross, double cross, and three-way cross. A single cross is the most common hybrid produced. Its products have the highest heterosis but are less uniform.

Eliminating emasculation

In corn the female plant is detasseled. The silk is covered with a paper bag to eliminate any stray female pollen until it is time to be pollinated with the desired sources of pollen. This process is slow and tedious. To circumvent this, the female is rendered male sterile through deliberate introduction of sterility genes into the plant. The system of male sterility commonly used is *cytoplasmic male sterility*. A comparison of the two methodologies is shown in the figure on the following page for a single cross and a double cross. The inbred male-sterile lines (female) are called A lines while the maintainer lines are called B lines. The fertility restorer lines are called R lines.

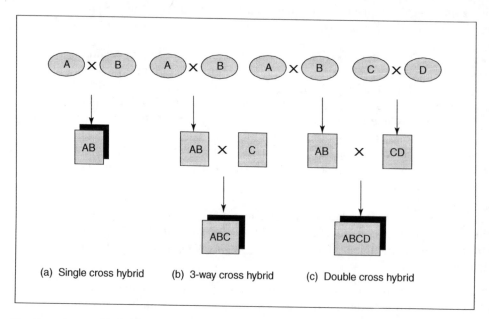

(a) Single cross hybrid   (b) 3-way cross hybrid   (c) Double cross hybrid

The three types of hybrids: single, three-way cross, and double cross.

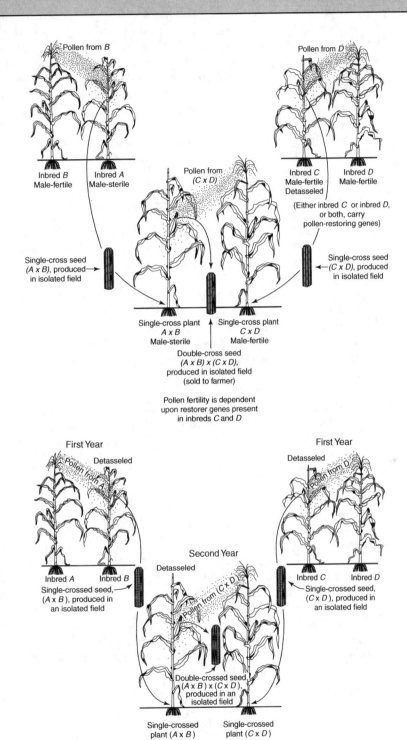

Older methods of conventional breeding of hybrid corn required emasculation or detasseling.

(Source: USDA)

Breeding for Photoinsensitivity

Plants may be categorized as short-day, long-day, or day-neutral. The daylength requirement of plants may limit their adaptation. Day-insensitive plants flower under both long-day and short-day conditions. Seed stocks of such new cultivars can be increased very rapidly. Major world cereal crops (wheat, rice, corn) have wide adaptation because of the development of photoinsensitive cultivars. Photo sensitivity is under genetic control, being single recessive or double recessive in rice. Similar genetic control is reported in other species. In soybean, photoinsensitivity is dominant over photosensitivity.

Both conventional breeding and mutation breeding have produced day-neutral genotypes. Day-neutral cultivars have been bred in cowpea, *Phaseolus* bean, potato, cotton, and pigeon pea.

Breeding for Determinate Stem Habit

Determinacy is a trait that may occur naturally or can be induced. Among other traits, determinate genotypes are short stemmed, and they have fewer and thicker internodes. These plants are less prone to lodging, have a shorter life cycle, and have early pod set. They have high harvest index and are amenable to mechanization. These genotypes in which vegetative growth becomes attenuated at some point in time have been shown to increase yield in certain species. This trait has been most widely studied in soybean. Determinacy is controlled by a single gene, dt_1, and indeterminacy, Dt_1. Semideterminacy was found to be controlled by a single dominant gene, Dt_2. Further, dt_1 is epistatic to Dt_2 or dt_2. Determinate cultivars require less space and can be planted at high density to increase yield.

In terms of grain yield, climbing, or pole, cultivars tend to yield higher than determinate, or bush, cultivars. This deficit is compensated for, however, by planting bush cultivars in higher densities. A recessive gene controls determinate stem habit in *P. vulgaris.*

Breeding for Dwarf Stature

Dwarf genes were pivotal in the success of the Green Revolution. The Norin 10 dwarf genes (Rht_1, Rht_2) used to improve Mexican wheat by Norman Borlaug in 1954 revolutionized tropical agriculture. These vegetative growth reducing genes produced high harvest index and increased grain yield. The Norin 10 genetic system consists of two partially recessive independent genes that act additively together. Duplicate recessive genes control dwarfness in pigeon pea, while additive and non-additive gene action for height has been recorded in peas. Dwarf genomes have been developed in rice using nonconventional methods such as tissue culture and mutation breeding.

Dwarf cultivars are more responsive to fertilization without lodging and have high grain yield. The root system of dwarf cultivars of wheat were generally deeper penetrating than the non-dwarf cultivars. This is advantageous when water and nutrients are limiting in production. Dwarf cultivars have better partitioning of assimilates to the developing ear. This results in higher grain yields.

Breeding for Early Maturity

Photoinsensitivity is desirable for wide adaptation. Coupled with early maturity, crop producers are able to produce multiple crops per growing season. It also enables crops to be produced in regions where the growing season is short (e.g., arid regions). Early-maturing crops yield lower than late-maturing ones, but their smaller plant size enables the producer to compensate for low yield by adopting high plant populations.

Early-maturing crop plants have shorter vegetative and reproductive phases and hence reduced dry matter accumulation. The challenge in breeding early-maturing and high-yielding cultivars is to reduce the vegetative phase while protracting the grain or seed filling period for maximum partitioning of dry matter into economic parts.

Several genes control earliness. These genes may have dominant, additive x additive, or epistatic effects. In wheat, earliness was found to be partially dominant over lateness and of high narrow sense heritability. Early flowering in rice is dominant to late. Flowering duration in cotton is controlled by additive gene action. However, some dominance gene action has also been reported. Induced mutagenesis (mutation breeding) has been employed to develop early-maturing mutants in barley, maize, rice, cotton, and other species.

Improving Harvest Index

All yield is biological, but not all yield is economic. **Harvest index** is the ratio of economic yield to total plant biological yield. It is believed that low grain yield in legumes is attributable primarily to low harvest index. Harvest index is highly correlated with grain yield. Cultivars with high harvest index are found to be more efficient in converting plant growth nutrients into grain production. A high harvest index is a good indication of yield stability. It is less variable under changes of environment than biological or grain yield. There is significant genetic variability in high harvest index in different varieties of most crop plants. Highest harvest index values for cereal range between 0.50 and 0.60.

Harvest index. The proportion of the crop that is of economic importance.

High harvest index is partially dominant over low harvest index. Breeders have several strategies for increasing harvest index. Reducing vegetativeness by, for example, reducing plant height (dwarfing) has increased harvest index. Dwarf rice cultivars, for example, generally have higher harvest index than tall ones. To be economic, high harvest index should be accompanied by early maturity. This decrease in crop duration, however, should affect only the vegetative phase of plant development.

Other plant architectural traits that should complement high harvest index are determinacy, suppressed tillering, and branching (uniculm). Further, with the reduced stature of plants, producers can increase yield by increasing plant population density.

Achieving Yield Stability

Yield stability is a key breeding objective. However, it is difficult to achieve. It is the attribute of a crop to maintain its yield over changing environments. This attribute is especially important in production regions where the growth environment is variable and capital for providing supplemental inputs is limited. For a cultivar to be successful in production, it should perform predictably across the range of environments in which it will be produced. That is, it should have minimum genotype x environment interaction.

Yield stability is achieved through three general categories of mechanisms—*genetic heterogeneity, yield component compensation,* and *tolerance to environmental stresses.* A crop cultivar that has genetic heterogeneity (mixture of genotypes) has insurance against changing environments. Yield buffering of multiple cross (double, three-way crosses) genotypes tends to make them more stable than single cross genotypes.

The phenomenon of yield compensation enables one yield component to make up for the reduction in the expression of another. Crop yield is affected by biotic and abiotic factors. The effect of stress depends on the stage of development of the plant.

Breeding for Yield per se

Breeding for yield per se is a daunting task. This is because yield is a genetically complex trait that is quantitatively controlled. It has low heritability. Yield is a product of the interaction among numerous physiological and biochemical processes.

Since yield is a quantitative trait, plant breeders employ quantitative genetics in selecting appropriate parents for crossing. Molecular markers have been developed to tag quantitative trait loci (QTLs) to facilitate breeding of complex traits.

Some breeders attempt to improve yield by targeting certain yield components or physiological processes. These components (e.g., seed weight, number of seeds per pod) tend to be more heritable than yield per se. Various genetic analyses are available for use in predicting the performance of a parent in a cross. One of the oldest and widely used is the Jink's *diallel analysis,* which evaluates parental lines crossed in all possible combinations. This method enables plant breeders to identify parents most likely to produce the highest-yielding segregates.

Finlay-Wilkinson's strategy of breeding for yield per se focuses on selecting for increased adaptability. Good yielders perform well over a wide range of environments.

Breeding for Improved Product Quality

There are numerous quality factors in crop production; some of them are chemical, while others are physical. One nutritional component of importance in food crops is proteins. Proteins may be classified according to their solubilities in various solvents as follows:

1. *Albumins*—proteins that are soluble in salt-free water
2. *Globulins*—proteins that are insoluble in salt-free water but are soluble in dilute neutral salt solutions
3. *Prolamins*—proteins that are soluble in 60 to 80% ethyl alcohol or dilute alkali but not in the solvents mentioned in 1 or in 2
4. *Glutelins*—proteins that are soluble in dilute alkali or acid

Albumins and globulins are involved in regulatory processes, enzymatic reactions, nutrient reserves, and other roles. Prolamins *(zein)* are the nutritionally least useful of the four categories of proteins. They lack lysine and tryptophan. The *opaque*-2 and *floury*-2 genes have the effect of reducing the prolamin protein and increasing albumins and globulins.

Plant breeders breed for quality of the economic product. The goal in this objective differs according to the end use of the product. For food, nutritional quality includes protein content and protein quality. A success story in this regard is the breeding of the *high-lysine corn* that specifically improved the content of the amino acid lysine. Quality improvements may focus on taste, flavor, quantity of a nutritional factor, shape of fruits, and others. For industrial products such as cotton, quality may mean fiber length, strength, color, or some other factor. One of the outstanding modern day successes in breeding product quality is the development of the *Flavr Savr* tomato that has prolonged the shelf-life of vine-ripened tomatoes.

Breeding for Disease Resistance

The biological environment of crop plants includes pathogens that cause yield-reducing diseases. Under pathogenic attack, plants may resist or tolerate the pathogen or, if susceptible, may die. There is a genetic basis of host-pathogen relationship. The genetic basis for disease resistance is described by the *gene-for-gene concept.* For each gene that confers resistance in the plant (host), there is a corresponding gene that confers virulence

Table 5 The Genetics of Disease Resistance in Plants: The Gene-for-Gene Concept

Virulent or Avirulent Genes in the Pathogen	Resistance or Susceptibility Genes in the Plant	
	R (Resistant) Dominant	r (Susceptible) Recessive
A (avirulent) Dominant	AR (−)	Ar (+)
A (virulent) Recessive	aR (+)	ar (+)

Note: Where − is incompatible (resistant) reaction (no infection) and + is compatible (susceptible) reaction (infection develops). AR is resistant because the plant (host) has a certain gene for resistance (R) against which the pathogen has no specific virulent (A) gene. This does not mean other virulent genes do not occur. Ar is susceptible due to lack of genes for resistance in the host and hence susceptible to other virulent genes from the pathogen. The aR host has the resistance gene but the pathogen has a virulent gene that can attack it; ar is susceptible because the plant is susceptible and the pathogen is virulent.

Table 6 Genetics of Disease Resistance in Plants: A Case of Multiple Genes

		[Resistance (R) or Susceptibility (r) Genes in Plants]			
		R_2R_2	R_1r_2	r_1R_2	r_1r_2
[Virulence (a) or avirulence (A) in the pathogen]	A_1A_2	−	−	−	+
	A_1a_2	−	−	+	+
	a_1A_2	−	+	−	+
	a_1a_2	−	+	+	+

in the pathogen, and vice versa (Table 5). *Virulence* is the capacity of the pathogen to overcome the influence of a resistant gene in the host. *Avirulence* is the inability of the pathogen to infect the host. This relationship is very specific. A fungal pathogen has a range of different types (called *physiological races*) that differ in their capacities to overcome the resistance in the host. Unless a race of a pathogen carries all the virulent genes corresponding to the number of resistance genes in the host, it will be unable to attack the host (Table 6). A challenge to plant breeding against fungal diseases is the problem that arises because some pathogens may mutate rapidly to produce the appropriate virulent genes to overcome the resistance in plants. Plant breeders thus have to breed new cultivars regularly using new sources of resistance to the pathogen. Sometimes, they incorporate multiple genes for resistance to pathogens in one cultivar, in order to delay the breakdown by virulent genes.

Breeding for Resistance to Insect Pests

The genetic basis of insect resistance is similar to that of fungal diseases. Plant breeders employ one of three strategies in breeding against insect attack. One strategy involves improving the mechanical or physical resistance to insect access to plant tissue through the strengthening or creation of barriers to feeding by sucking or chewing insects. The epidermal layers of leaves or stems are thickened or strengthened through breeding. Another strategy is to introduce genes in the plant that modify the plant's metabolism to produce toxins *(antibiosis)* that injure insects upon feeding on the plant. The third approach is to modify plant morphology or palatability such that insects avoid the plant. Pubescence on the plant interferes with oviposition in insects.

Breeding for Lodging Resistance

Lodging is the tendency for the stem of a plant to incline. The bending may occur at the base of the stem or the roots (especially in cereals), or the stem may break. Lodging may occur at any stage during plant development. The effect of lodging depends on the stage in which it occurs. Recovery from lodging may be possible if it occurs early in development.
Lodging is caused by several factors:

1. Stem or stalk decay caused by disease which, in turn, is caused by fungi such as *Gibberella* spp
2. Attack from insect pests such as stalk borer, rootworm, and cutworm
3. Weather conditions, including strong wind, excessive rain, hail, and other storms, cause stems to bend or break
4. Cultural damage from improper use of machinery that causes plants to be injured; planting at high density causes etiolation or spindly growth and weak stems; further, overfertilization causes excessive vegetative growth, which results in top-heavy plants that are easily toppled or bent by winds
5. Genetic susceptibility of certain plants
6. Heavy bearing or yielding, which causes plants to become top-heavy

Harvest Losses   Lodging may cause yield reduction due to reduction in net assimilation rate from reduced interception of light and absorption of nutrients and water. Apical dominance may be destroyed, leading to increased tillering and branching. The additional vegetative growth is wasteful if it does not contribute to harvestable yield. Severe lodging causes the grain to be too close to the ground such that the combine is unable to harvest it.

Reduced Quality of Product   In severely lodged plants, the ears, pods, or heads may come into contact with the soil and cause pathogenic infection. Dry seed may sprout in the pod. Deterioration reduces product quality and the harvestable quantity.

Reduction of lodging can be reduced through the following actions:

1. Space plants properly (proper density) to avoid etiolation.
2. Fertilize plants at appropriate rates and good nutritional balance for proper growth.
3. Use lodging-resistant cultivars for planting.
4. Harvest on time to avoid stalk rot that occurs—for example, in mature corn.
5. Spray against insect pests and diseases.
6. Use dwarf cultivars.

Field crops in which lodging is a problem include small grains, corn, soybean, and sorghum. To breed for lodging resistance, breeders seek to improve plant architecture by improving the culm strength (stiff, sturdy stalks) and reducing plant stature (dwarfing). Resistance to insects and diseases that weaken the stalk and roots is also a goal in breeding against lodging. A major accomplishment in this regard is the discovery and use of the *Bt* gene, developed by Monsanto Company, which protects plants that have the gene (e.g., *Bt* corn and cotton) from insects that contribute to lodging.

Breeding for Shattering Resistance

Shattering is the discharge and loss of seeds from pods or heads prior to harvest. Plants such as soybean and small grain are prone to shattering. A delay in harvesting by a few days can result in significant yield loss. Shattering resistance is a quantitative trait. Cultivars that are resistant to shattering have been developed for major field crops.

Breeding for Heat and Drought Resistance

Moisture stress and excessive heat occur in regions of high temperature and low rainfall. These conditions, coupled with strong winds, cause accelerated desiccation of plant tissue. Respiration also occurs at a higher rate than photosynthesis. Consequently, yield is drastically reduced. The effect on yield depends upon the stage in the growth cycle at which drought occurs. Heat stress is most devastating to crop productivity when it occurs during the flowering period. At this stage, pollen viability, stigma receptivity, and seed formation are reduced by excessive heat.

There are two basic mechanisms for drought resistance in plants. The plant may avoid *(avoidance mechanism)* or tolerate *(tolerance mechanism)* it. Genotypes with deep root systems can exploit moisture from a lower depth in the soil and thereby avoid moisture stress. Some species have avoidance mechanisms such as leaf rolling under moisture stress, the effect being a reduction in transpiration loss. Plant breeders sometimes breed early maturity in genotypes for use in drought-prone areas. This technique allows the genotypes to flower before severe heat stress sets in.

Breeding for Winter Hardiness

Winter hardiness is important in regions where winters are severe. Under such weather conditions, plant tissues may freeze or plants may heave (uplift).

5: Biotechnology Exceeds Conventional Breeding Methods

Biotechnology offers new avenues for manipulating plants beyond the capabilities of conventional breeding methods. Conventional plant breeding involves manipulating plants at the whole plant level. The breeder manipulates plants on the basis of phenotype. A plant with purple flowers is assumed to have genes for purple flower. Further, crossing is limited to parents that are compatible by way of pollination.

Molecular plant breeding involves the manipulation of plants at the cellular and subcellular levels. The DNA is manipulated directly, using the methodologies of biotechnology. **Biotechnology** is a collection of tools based on a living system used to manipulate organisms or use them to make products. Conventional plant breeding is thus considered to be biotechnology.

One of the tools of biotechnology is **recombinant DNA** technology (or *genetic engineering*), whereby a piece of DNA can be taken from any organism and transferred into another. The DNA of all organisms obeys the same laws (i.e., DNA is universal). Through advances in science, plant breeders are able to circumvent a major limitation in conventional plant breeding—that is, genes do not have to be mixed—by recombination through meiosis.

When the segment of the polynucleotide chain corresponding to the gene of interest has been identified, it is chemically snipped out using an enzyme called *restriction endonuclease*. The isolated piece of DNA is unable to function independently. It is inserted

Biotechnology. A collection of tools used to manipulate organisms or use them to make products.

Recombinant DNA. The biotechnology whereby genes can be mixed across biological barriers.

Recombinant DNA technology: Crossing natural borders to create new variants

Perhaps the most prominent of the biotechnologies is the recombinant DNA (rDNA) technology. Also called *gene cloning* or *molecular cloning*, rDNA involves a number of research protocols employed to transfer DNA from one organism to another. The key activities in rDNA research are as follows: (a) the DNA to be transferred is identified in the donor and cleaved; (b) the target DNA is inserted into a carrier that will deliver it into the DNA of the host; (c) the target DNA is transferred into and maintained in a host cell until the next step; (d) the host cell with the foreign DNA is selected from among numerous others without the foreign gene; and (e) depending upon the goal of the research, the incorporated target DNA can be manipulated to be expressed in the host cell.

Upon identification, the target gene is enzymatically cleaved by using *restriction endonucleases* (bacterial enzymes). These enzymes cleave DNA upon recognizing enzyme-specific base sequences (called

recognition sequences) that are typically a few base pairs long (e.g., 4, 6, or 8). The cleaved piece of DNA is inserted into a carrier molecule called a *cloning vector*. A common cloning vector is a bacterial *plasmid*, a circular DNA molecule that is self-replicating and double-stranded. Plasmid cloning vectors are engineered to have recognition sites embedded in genes for resistance to antibiotics. These are used in a selection scheme to help identify and select cells that have incorporated the target gene. The plasmid is cleaved with the same restriction enzyme used to cleave the target DNA. The recombinant plasmid (containing the target DNA) is inserted into a bacterium by a process called *transformation*. The bacteria are transformed using a laboratory technique called *electroporation*, which involves incorporation of the plasmids in an electric field. Once inside the bacterial host, it can be maintained and replicated clonally.

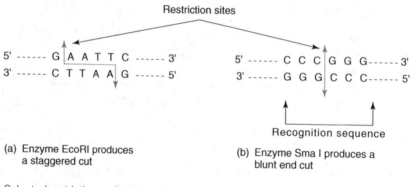

(a) Enzyme EcoRI produces a staggered cut

(b) Enzyme Sma I produces a blunt end cut

Selected restriction endonucleases and their characteristics.

Transgenic plant. A plant whose genotype consists of introduced foreign DNA from an unrelated source.

into a carrier molecule capable of replication called a *cloning vector*. This molecule, a circular DNA called a *plasmid*, is found in bacteria. The recombinant plasmid (plasmid with the alien piece of DNA) is reinserted into a bacterium. The bacterium is then said to be *transformed*.

The next stage is to transfer the cloned gene into a plant. Cloned genes are transferred into plants in a variety of ways. The tumor-forming bacterium *Agrobacterium tumifaciens* is used as carrier of the recombinant plasmid. This bacterium is then introduced into plant cells in tissue culture. Some plant cells incorporate the recombinant plasmid and become transformed. They then individually develop into plants with foreign DNA in their genome and are called **transgenic plants**.

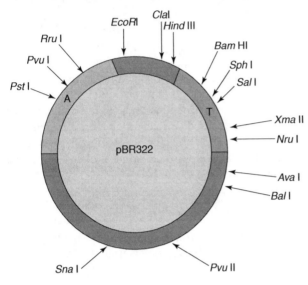

A restriction map of a plasmid.

After transformation, the successful cells are selected by a two-step process. For example, if the *pBR322 cloning vector* is used along with the *Bam*HI restriction enzyme, the *Bam*HI gene is incapacitated as a result of the insertion of the target gene. The transformation mixture is plated onto a medium containing the antibiotic ampicillin. Bacterial cells with intact pBR322 or recombinant pBR322 will grow; all nontransformed cells will not. The purpose of the second selection step is to distinguish between the two

cell types that grow. Cells from colonies in the first selection step are transferred to a tetracycline-agar plate. Cells with intact pBR322 will grow; transformed cells whose tetracycline resistance gene has been disrupted by the insertion of the target gene will not grow. The corresponding colonies on the first plate carrying the pBR322-cloned DNA constructs are identified and maintained in cultures.

The cloned target gene is transferred into plant host cells in a variety of ways. The "tumor-inducing" (Ti) plasmid found in most strains of the soil bacterium *Agrobacterium tumifaciens* is used as a vector to carry target genes into plants. The Ti plasmid used is incapacitated to be ineffective in causing tumors. Upon inserting the target gene into the Ti plasmid, the bacteria are attached to plant cells for the bacteria to enter through wounds to naturally enter the cell's genome. Target genes can also be transferred by physical methods. A physical DNA delivery system for plants is the *microprojectile bombardment* (or *particle bombardment* or *biolistics*). Gold or tungsten spherical particles of about 1 to 4 mm diameter are coated with DNA and accelerated in an apparatus called a *particle gun* or *gene gun*, using gunpowder or compressed gas, into plant tissue.

After integrating the foreign DNA into the plant genomic DNA, the transformed cells are identified with the aid of selectable markers and genes whose proteins produce a readily detectable response to a specific assay. These are called *reporter genes*. The transformed cells are cultured and nurtured into plants, and the plants are called *transgenic plants*.

5.1 BIOTECHNOLOGY IS USED TO SOLVE A VARIETY OF PROBLEMS IN CROP PRODUCTION

There are some general ways in which biotechnology is used in agriculture to benefit society:

1. Biopharming
2. In vitro techniques
   - Micropropagation
   - Somatic cell genetics
   - Transgenic plants

3. Artificial seed production
4. Diagnostics and control of diseases and pests
5. Remediation
6. Biofertilization and phytostimulation

Biopharming

Biopharming uses plants (and other organisms) to develop and produce pharmaceuticals for humans. Using transgenic animals to produce proteins and other chemicals for humans is well advanced. Successes include the production of human serum albumin (used to treat emergency blood losses and chronic blood deficiency), factor VIII (required by the body to repair injuries of blood vessels), and human growth hormone. These are produced in goat milk. The use of plants in this regard is in its infancy. Plants under consideration include tobacco, banana, and potato.

Micropropagation

Micropropagation is the propagation of plants in *tissue culture* (nurturing of plant parts in vitro, sometimes to produce full plants). This technology is used in a variety of ways. The advantages of this technology include the following:

1. Quick way to generate new plants
2. Large-scale production of new genotypes
3. Requires only a small amount of plant tissue
4. Raising pathogen-free materials from diseased plants

Micropropagation is conducted in a sterile environment. The tissue used to start the process may be obtained from any part of the plant, such as the leaf, stem, pollen, or root. The starting material is called the *explant*. It is surface-sterilized and placed on a sterile nutrient medium consisting of macronutrients and micronutrients, sugar, vitamins, and growth regulators. A common recipe for a medium is the Murashige and Skoog (MS) medium. The explant changes into an amorphous, undifferentiated mass of tissue called a *callus*. The growth regulators can be manipulated to induce rooting and other vegetative growth into a full plant.

Sometimes, the growth medium is manipulated by scientists to induce mutations through the inclusion of mutagens (mutation-inducing substances). This procedure is called *somatic cell selection*. Heritable variability can, however, arise spontaneously in tissue culture without any intervention by researchers and is called *somaclonal variation*. Some of these variants have agronomic value and have been used by plant breeders for crop improvement.

Disease-free propagules can be obtained from plants infected by systemic pathogens. The older cells have the systemic pathogen (virus or bacterium), but the meristematic tissue is usually free of such pathogens. Scientists are able to carefully extract the disease-free material and culture it in tissue culture. This is a way of purifying an infected parental stock.

In crop improvement, plant breeders cross genetically divergent plants to produce new recombinants. This is usually successful if the parents derive from the same species. Sometimes, plant breeders find it necessary to cross parents from different species, a procedure that is frequently problematic. The hybrid embryo often fails to develop properly. Plant breeders then remove the immature embryo and culture it in tissue culture, a technique called *embryo rescue.*

Somatic Cell Genetics

In addition to propagating plant materials directly in tissue culture, scientists are able to propagate haploid plants from microspores (e.g., pollen grains). Haploid cells can then be hybridized (called *somatic hybridization*) by the process of *protoplast fusion*. The process enables crossing for introgression of agronomically useful traits across genetic barriers.

Transgenic Plants

The genetic engineering of crop plants has revolutionized crop improvement by allowing gene transfer across genetic crossing barriers. This substantially improves the results of the techniques of embryo rescue of offspring from interspecific crosses and cell fusion techniques. This novel technique, in theory, does not only allow gene transfer but allows the plant breeder to select the organ in which to express the gene, as well as the strength of expression. Major accomplishments in transgenic plants include those described in Table 7.

Synthetic Seeds

Plant in vitro techniques can be used to induce a high rate of *somatic embryogenesis* (the development of embryos in tissue culture). These structures are then encapsulated in biodegradable protective coating to produce *synthetic seeds,* or *artificial seeds,* for propagation. This coating may be fortified with fertilizers, pesticides, or some other seed dressing. Artificial seeds provide a way of propagating plants clonally.

Diagnostic Tools and Control of Plant Pests

Numerous biotech diagnostic tools have been developed for early monitoring and detection of plant diseases, pests, and chemical residue in the environment. These include nucleic acid probes, dot-blot hybridization, monoclonal antibodies, and enzyme-linked immunosorbent assay (ELISA).

Inorganic pesticides damage the environment. Biopesticides are safer to humans and the environment and are more pest-specific. Microbial sprays in use include the *Bacillus thuringiensis* spray for controlling cutworms, corn borers, and cabbage worm, among others, and the aerial application of spores of the fungus *Collectotrichum gloesporides* for controlling northern jointvetch in rice fields. Biocontrol is employed in the postharvest control

Table 7 Examples of Plants Genetically Engineered for Specific Traits

Species	Traits Incorporated
Corn	*Bt* gene for resistance to European corn borer; herbicide resistance (Roundup® ready)
Cotton	*Bt* gene as in corn
Rice	Provitamin A (Golden rice)
Tomato	*Flavrsvr* (for delayed postharvest spoilage)
Canola	Lue-enkephalin (a mammalian neuropeptide)
Sweet potato	Protein quality gene
Sugar beet	Herbicide resistance (phosphinoticin or Basta®)
Arabidospsis	Polyhydroxybutyrate (biodegradable plastic)

This list is designed only to sample the immense variation in the use of plant biotechnology to solve various problems. Numerous species have been transformed and successfully regenerated to express a wide variety of genes.

Are bioengineered foods safe?

Biotechnology is embroiled in a great deal of controversy. Because biotechnology is truly ubiquitous in its impact, the debate involves the news media, consumers, politicians, government officials, business executives, and scientists, to name a few. Much of the controversy is because the field of biotechnology is developing rather rapidly, and our knowledge about it is incomplete and fragmentary. Such gaps in our knowledge often trigger fears and fuel public apprehension about scientific innovation. The capacity of molecular biotechnologists to transfer genetic material across natural boundaries, especially, is at the heart of the current ethical controversy over the development and application of biotechnology.

Ethics, to a great extent, is concerned with procedures or rules society employs to convert value and value-free knowledge into prescriptions as to "what ought or ought not to be done." Traditionally, many scientists have tended to view ethical issues and questions as matters beyond the realm of objective investigation or research. They generate information that contributes to knowledge that is value-free with respect to the characteristics of conditions, situations, things, and acts. Biotechnology has realized and anticipated beneficial impacts on various aspects of society, but it also has anticipated adverse impacts, both of which need to be addressed objectively. Ethical issues are wide-ranging.

Are bioengineered foods the "silver bullet" they are touted to be, or the "frankenfoods" they are being projected to be by some? In 1999, about 50% of the American soybean crop carried an herbicide-resistant gene, while about 25% of the corn crop was Bt corn (i.e., corn carrying the insect resistance gene from the bacterium *Bacillus thurigiensis [Bt]*). There are other major crops that have been bioengineered for a variety of purposes, so how is bioengineering of food different from conventional plant breeding? Simply, biotechnology provides more precision and control over what new characteristics are introduced into plants. Instead of reorganizing the entire genomes of two parents in a new genetic matrix, resulting in the inheritance of a combination of genes from the two parents in the offspring, biotechnology enables scientists to insert one or more specific genes of interest into the recipient parent.

The obvious question is do the introduced genes or their protein products have any adverse effects on consumers? Since the genetic code is universal, the foreign DNA per se does not have any ill effects on humans. However, it is known that insertion of foreign DNA in genomes can cause defective growth and alter levels of plant compounds. For this reason, breeders conduct extensive research and product testing prior to releasing new cultivars. The protein products are virtually identical to nontoxic enzymes already present in the plant and are present in very low levels that can be easily digested. What about the alleged possibility of allergies? Certain products are known to cause allergies (e.g., eggs, fish, cow's milk, shellfish, tree nuts, wheat, and legumes). Biotechnology products are not inherently different from their conventional counterparts, and no research data are available to show that biotechnology foods have allergens.

Another source of apprehension from the public is about the inadvertent introduction of antibiotic resistance into the environment as a product of the actual research methodology. Certain molecular biotechnology techniques utilize antibiotic resistance marker genes. This is suspected by some to be a source of transfer of health risk, as this could increase the antibiotic resistance of bacteria already in the system. To preclude such a possibility, the Food and Drug Administration (FDA) has advised biotech companies involved in food development to refrain from using clinically important antibiotics in their marker selection procedures. The FDA, the Environmental Protection Agency (EPA), and the United States Department of Agriculture (USDA) are the three federal agencies that monitor and regulate bioengineered foods for safety. This includes labeling of foods and monitoring of environmental impact. Foods containing bioengineered products for industrial purposes, such as canola oil with altered fatty acid composition, are required to be labeled appropriately.

The making of a miracle grain: The story of the "Golden rice"

What do you get when you cross a bacterium with a daffodil and then with rice? A few years ago, such a question would have been considered a riddle. Nowadays, thanks to modern biotechnology, science solves such riddles with relative ease.

Thanks to a scientist with a passion to help the poor and malnourished, today the world has a miracle grain that has the potential to make more than just a dent in the worldwide efforts at attaining food security and fighting malnutrition. Professor Ingo Potrykus of the Swiss Federal Institute of Technology in Zurich is responsible for this wonder product, called "Golden rice," which is fast becoming a "postercrop" for what is good about biotechnology, in the face of all the bad press the technology has been receiving.

The successful creation of Golden rice was not a solo effort by Potrykus. In 1990, Gary Toenniessen, the director of food security for the Rockefeller Foundation, identified the specific problem for Potrykus. Toenniessen recommended the use of the more sophisticated tools of genetic engineering in addressing the lack of beta-carotene in the grain of rice, a crop that is a staple worldwide. Potrykus hooked up with Peter Beyer of the University of Freiburg, an expert on the beta-carotene pathway in daffodils. With $100,000 seed money from the Rockefeller Foundation, the duo embarked on what turned out to be a seven-year journey and a $2.6 million tab, with contributions from the Swiss government and the European Union. With 100% noncommercial support, the scientists hoped that they could give the product away without any consequence.

The feat was accomplished by following the steps described in the figure. In all, three organisms unrelated to rice were involved in creating the new rice: daffodils and the bacterium *Erwinia uredovora* provided the genes that encode beta-carotene, while the crown gall bacterium (*Agrobacterium tumifaciens*) provided the plasmids that served as gene couriers into rice tissue.

Potrykus and Beyer wanted to give away their Golden rice free of charge, but one of the genes they used had been patented by a biotech company, AstraZeneca of London. Needless to say, a commercial company is in business to make money. After some negotiations in which AstraZeneca received exclusive commercial marketing rights for Golden rice, the company decided to support the scientists' cause and work toward making the seeds available free of charge to farmers in the poor regions of the world.

The dream of two scientists may have come true in the end, but the manner in which it ended was not anticipated. Anti-biotechnology activists and critics saw the transaction between the scientists and a big biotech company as a pact with the devil and as more ammunition for their campaign against genetically modified foods. This notwithstanding, the world should be thankful that, because of Golden rice, millions of children potentially would not have to suffer from vitamin A deficiency and be predisposed to blindness. However, the finished product is still years away from the plates of the targetted consumers.

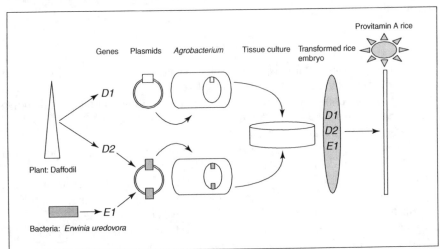

Golden rice was created with genes for beta-carotene from daffodils and the bacterium *Erwinia uredovora*. These were transferred into the embryo of rice by the method of *Agrobacterium* mediated transformation.

of spoilage in horticultural fruits such as citrus and apples. A suspension of the bacterium *Bacillus subtilis* is used to delay brown rot caused by the fungus *Monilinia fruticola.*

Researchers have moved a step further by developing transgenic plants that express endotoxins. Proteins such as protease inhibitors, alpha-amylase, and lectins from *Bacillus* spp. have been shown to have potent insecticidal activity. Plants resistant to certain herbicides such as glyphosate (in corn, soybean, cotton), 2,4-D (in cotton, tobacco), Atrazine (in tobacco), and Dalapon (in tobacco) have been developed.

Phytoremediation

Certain plants have the capacity to absorb heavy metals and salts and are used to clean up sites that need detoxification or desalinization.

Bioremediation

Bioremediation is the removal of toxic pollutants from both terrestrial and aquatic ecosystems using microbes. Like phytoremediation, microbes are used for cleaning sites that have been contaminated by chemicals such as oil. Fungi are used to degrade pollutants such as PCB, TNT, and DDT. These substances are anthropogenic (human-made) and recalcitrant in the soil.

Biofertilization and Phytostimulation

Many microorganisms, in association with plant roots, are able to produce compounds that stimulate plant growth and productivity. Microbes fix nitrogen for plant use by one of several processes. *Rhizobia,* by living in the roots of legumes, undertake biological nitrogen fixation in a symbiotic relationship. Biological nitrogen fixation is responsible for over 60% of soil nitrogen used in crop production. This host-specific process involves the development of root swelling called *nodules. R. leguminosarium* bv. *viciae* nodulates pea, while the bv. *trifolii* nodulates clover. Soybean is nodulated by *Bradyrhizobium* (previously called *R. japonicum*). Biological nitrogen fixation occurs in non-leguminous trees involving bacteria of the genus *Azospirillum.* These bacteria in the rhizosphere affect the development and function of grass and legume. They help to improve mineral uptake (especially NO_3^-, PO_3^{3-}, and K^+) and water uptake. *Azospirillum* promotes root hair formation in the roots of seedlings.

Mycorrhizae (fungi-plant root association) increases the effective root surface area and thereby aids in nutrient uptake.

SUMMARY

1. Plant breeders manipulate plants for high productivity.
2. Plant breeding is based on the principles of genetics.
3. Some traits are controlled by one or a few genes (qualitative traits), while others are controlled by several to many genes (quantitative traits).
4. Plant breeding depends on heritable variation for success.
5. The methods used in breeding depend on the breeding system of the plant—self-pollination or cross-pollination.
6. Crop productivity may be improved by adopting a variety of strategies—such as improving photosynthetic efficiency, breeding dwarf stature, breeding early maturity, breeding for yield stability, and improving harvest index.
7. Breeding may be done by conventional methods or by using genetic engineering. The two are used in a complementary fashion.
8. Genetic engineering allows plant breeders to transfer genes across genetic barriers.

REFERENCES AND SUGGESTED READING

Acquaah, G. 2002. *Horticulture: Principles and practices.* 2nd ed. Upper Saddle River, NJ: Prentice Hall.

Klug, W. S., and M. R. Cummings. 1996. *Essentials of genetics.* Englewood Cliffs, NJ: Prentice Hall.

Nash, J. M. 2000. Grains of hope. *Time.* 31 July, 39–43.

Poehlman, J. M. 1995. *Breeding field crops.* 4th ed. Westport, CT: AVI.

Simmonds, N. W. 1979. *Principles of crop improvement.* New York: Wiley.

Wallace, R. A. 1997. *Biology: The world of life.* 7th ed. New York: Benjamin/Cummings.

SELECTED INTERNET SITES FOR FURTHER REVIEW

http://www.aba.asn.au/

A discussion of general biotechnology.

OUTCOMES ASSESSMENT

PART A

Answer the following questions true or false.

1. T F   Plant traits are controlled by hereditary factors called genes.
2. T F   One or a few genes control quantitative traits.
3. T F   In dioecy, male and female plants occur in one species.
4. T F   All yield is biological, but not all yield is economic.
5. T F   Traits with low heritabilities are best improved by agronomic strategies.
6. T F   DNA is universal.

PART B

Answer the following questions.

1. Give the chemical composition of DNA.

2. Give four specific breeding objectives in crop improvement.

3. _____ is the ultimate source of biological variation.

4. What is heterosis?

   _____

5. Define biotechnology.

   _____

6. What is a transgenic plant?

   _____

7. What is the central dogma of molecular biology?

   _____

PART C

Write a brief essay on each of the following topics.

1. Discuss the concept of heritability in plant improvement.
2. Discuss the sources of variation for crop improvement.
3. Describe how hybrids are developed.
4. Describe how breeding for dwarf stature improves crop productivity.
5. Discuss the importance of yield stability in crop productivity.
6. Discuss the importance of shattering resistance in crop productivity.
7. Discuss the importance of micropropagation in crop production.
8. Discuss the landmark genetic-based impact on crop production.
9. Describe how transgenic plants are developed.

PART D

Discuss or explain the following topics in detail.

1. Do you think the general public should have a direct say in how scientists produce new crop cultivars for the market?
2. Can crop performance (yield) be increased indefinitely through genetic manipulation?
3. In the use of technology, does the end justify the means?
4. In biotechnology and crop production, is the best yet to come?
5. How has crop improvement (plant breeding) impacted crop production?
6. In what specific way would you like to see genetics (crop improvement) used in crop production?

Appendix: Metric Conversion Chart

INTO METRIC			OUT OF METRIC		
If You Know:	Multiply By:	To Get:	If You Know:	Multiply By:	To Get:
Length					
inches	2.54	centimeters	millimeters	0.04	inches
feet	30	centimeters	centimeters	0.4	inches
feet	0.303	meters	meters	3.3	feet
yards	0.91	meters	kilometers	0.62	miles
miles	1.6	kilometers			
Area					
sq. inches	6.5	sq. centimeters	sq. centimeters	0.16	sq. inches
sq. feet	0.09	sq. meters	sq. meters	1.2	sq. yards
sq. yards	0.8	sq. meters	sq. kilometers	0.4	sq. miles
sq. miles	2.6	sq. kilometers	hectares	2.47	acres
acres	0.4	hectares			

From *Small Fruit Crop Management,* Gene J. Galletta and David G. Himelrick. Copyright © 1990 by Prentice-Hall, Inc., a Pearson Education Company. All rights reserved.

INTO METRIC			OUT OF METRIC		
If You Know:	Multiply By:	To Get:	If You Know:	Multiply By:	To Get:
Mass (weight)					
Ounces	28	grams	grams	0.035	ounces
pounds	0.45	kilograms	kilograms	2.2	pounds
short ton	0.9	metric tons	metric tons	1.1	short tons
Volume					
teaspoons	5	milliliters	milliliters	0.03	fluid ounces
tablespoons	15	milliliters	liters	2.1	pints
fluid ounces	30	milliliters	liters	1.06	quarts
cups	0.24	liters	liters	0.26	gallons
pints	0.47	liters	cubic meters	35	cubic feet
quarts	0.95	liters	cubic meters	1.3	cubic yards
gallons	3.8	liters			
cubic feet	0.03	cubic meters			
cubic yards	0.76	cubic meters			
Pressure					
lb/in^2	0.069	bars	bars	14.5	lbs/in^2
atmospheres	1.013	bars	bars	0.987	atmospheres
atmospheres	1.033	kg/cm^2	kg/cm^2	0.968	atmospheres
lb/in^2	0.07	kg/cm^2	kg/cm^2	14.22	lbs/in^2
Rates					
lb/acre	1.12	kg/hectare	kg/hectare	0.892	lbs/acre
tons/acre	2.24	metric tons/hectare	metric tons/hectare	0.446	tons/acre
gal/acre	9.354	liters/hectare	liters/hectare	0.107	gal/acre
Temperature					

$$°F = (°C \times 1.8) + 32 \qquad\qquad °C = 0.555 \times (°F - 32)$$

Appendix: Metric Conversion Chart